PHILOSOPHY FOR THE FUTURE

THE MACMILLAN COMPANY
NEW YORK · BOSTON · CHICAGO
DALLAS · ATLANTA · SAN FRANCISCO

MACMILLAN AND CO., LIMITED
LONDON · BOMBAY · CALCUTTA
MADRAS · MELBOURNE

THE MACMILLAN COMPANY
OF CANADA, LIMITED
TORONTO

PHILOSOPHY
FOR
THE FUTURE

The Quest of Modern Materialism

EDITED BY

Roy Wood Sellars
V. J. McGill
Marvin Farber

NEW YORK
THE MACMILLAN COMPANY
1949

The Editors thank the following publishers for permission to quote from their publications:

Appleton-Century-Crofts, Inc., for an excerpt from Ralph Linton, *The Study of Man*, New York, 1936.

Cambridge University Press, for a passage from Bertrand Russell, *A Critical Exposition of the Philosophy of Leibniz*, London, 1900.

Columbia University Press, for excerpts from Abram Kardiner, *The Individual and His Society*, New York, 1939.

Victor Gollancz Ltd., for a passage from A. J. Ayer, *Language, Truth and Logic*, London, 1936.

Harcourt, Brace and Co., Inc., for a quotation from Rudolf Carnap, *The Logical Syntax of Language*, New York, 1937.

International Journal of Psychoanalysis, for an excerpt from Ernest Jones, "A Valedictory Address," Vol. 27, 1946.

International Publishers, for excerpts from F. Engels, *Herr Eugen Dühring's Revolution in Science*, New York, 1939; F. Engels, *Dialectics of Nature*, New York, 1940; and Marx and Engels, *Correspondence 1846-1895*, New York, 1934.

Liveright Publishing Corp., for excerpts from A. R. Luria, *The Nature of Human Conflicts*, New York, 1932.

Longmans, Green & Co., Inc., for an excerpt from Mortimer Adler, *What Man Has Made of Man*, New York, 1937, copyright, 1937, by Mortimer J. Adler; and one from T. V. Moore, "Human and Animal Intelligence," in *Scientific Aspects of the Race Problem*, New York, 1941, copyright, 1941, by Longmans, Green & Co., Inc.

Methuen & Co., Ltd., for a passage from R. R. Marett, *Psychology and Folklore*, London, 1920.

New Republic, for a passage from Paul Radin, "The Mind of Primitive Man," Vol. XCVIII, April 19, 1939.

Oxford University Press, Inc., for passages from B. Malinowski, *The Foundations of Faith and Morals*, London, 1936; and from Paul Sweezy, *The Theory of Capitalist Development*, New York, 1942, copyright, 1942, by Oxford University Press, Inc.

Routledge and Kegan Paul Ltd., for passages from Karl Mannheim, *Ideology and Utopia*, London, 1936; and from Rudolf Carnap, *Philosophy of Logical Syntax*, London, 1935.

Psychiatry, for a passage from Judd Marmor, "The Role of Instinct in Human Behavior," Vol. 5, 1942, pp. 515–516.

The Psychoanalytic Review, for an excerpt from Otto Fenichel, "Psychological Remarks on Fromm's book, *Escape from Freedom*," Vol. 31, 1940, pp. 138–140.

Psychological Review and the American Psychological Association, Inc., for an excerpt from E. G. Boring, "The Use of Operational Definitions in Science," Vol. LII, 1945, Lancaster, Pa.

Simon and Schuster, Inc., for a passage from Bertrand Russell, *A History of Western European Philosophy*, New York, 1945, copyright, 1945, by Bertrand Russell.

Watts & Co., for an excerpt from B. Farrington, *Head and Hand in Ancient Greece*, London, 1947.

Yale University Press, for an excerpt from A. G. Keller in *Studies in the Science of Society* (George P. Murdock, ed.), New Haven, 1937.

PRINTED IN THE UNITED STATES OF AMERICA

First Printing

FOREWORD

THE growth of science and technology, the advance of medicine, universal education, and general enlightenment have greatly increased the valid authority of science. Any number of social questions which were once the exclusive prerogative of religion and conventional morality are now recognized as falling within the sphere of the social sciences. Sex and family relations are examples. Virtue and wickedness have largely given way to personality adjustment and maladjustment; and crime is traced in considerable measure to social causes. The schoolboy is no longer beaten as inherently bad or lazy because he neglects his studies. Nutritional, medical, personality factors are, instead, investigated, and the home life and associates of the boy are searched for contributing causes. In this shift from moral condemnation to technical remedies, we see the concurrent rise of science and humaneness. This kind of progress has resulted in an increasingly materialist outlook. But, as we shall see, it is a more subtle and adequate kind of materialism.

The purpose of this cooperative book in which scientists and philosophers collaborate is, quite simply, the exploration and reformulation of materialism.

Although anticipated by the Milesians and Heraclitus of Ephesus, the first clear-cut materialists of ancient Greece were Leucippus, Democritus, and Epicurus. A passage from Lucretius' poem "On the Nature of Things" will show the searching insights of these ancient thinkers:

But nature 'twas
Urged men to utter various sounds of tongue,
And need and use did mould the names of things,
About in same wise as the lack-speech years
Compel young children unto gesturings,
Making them point with finger here and there
At what's before them.*

* William Ellery Leonard's translation, Everyman's Library.

The early Greeks wrote the first chapter of materialism, but many more are still to be added.

In this volume we are concerned mainly with modern materialism. Scientists have joined philosophers to examine the issues with as much light and as little heat as possible. Modern materialism, as we understand it, asserts the following: The inorganic pattern of matter is prior to living, minded and purposive organisms, which arise gradually and only as a result of a complex evolutionary development. With the advent of organic life, new, biological laws begin to operate. The principles of physics and chemistry necessarily apply, but are not by themselves sufficient to the biological level. Thus mechanism or the theory that physicochemical explanation is adequate to all levels, is emphatically rejected. If a thing can be explained by physics and chemistry, however, it must be so explained, and there is no justification for adverting to any other level of the organization of matter. The inorganic and organic constitute distinctive levels, which can be referred to as lower and higher, in the sense that organic material systems are more highly organized and more complex, exhibiting new behavior traits. There are also many subsidiary levels, gradients, and resonances within the inorganic and organic. Within the organic, for example, we have cell, tissue, organ, organ system, organism, and population. Each level except the first contains all lower levels within it. For example, the tissue contains cells, which in turn have chemical components. The cell within a tissue, however, does not behave just as it does outside the tissue. Chemistry within the cell, too, is altered by the envelope which contains it. The one-floor plan of the classical biological mechanism is thus superseded by a modern structure displaying many diverse stories. The top stories, however, are always supported by the lower floors; and all floors must rest upon the ground floor studied by physics and chemistry. The diverse stories, the modern materialist insists, can be easily confirmed by scientific methods. Organized matter reveals integrative levels of organization characterized by distinctive laws.

As to the nature of matter, the materialist as a philosopher has nothing factual to add to the account of the scientists, although scientists may sometimes use "matter" in a limited sense (interpreting light, for example, as matter if it is corpuscular, but not if it is of wave form). The materialist holds that philosophers cannot improve upon the descriptive concepts of matter supplied by the working scientists of his time. He accepts what the physicist, chemist, biologist, histologist, etc. say as the best approximation at any given time. But he should be able to add considerable epistemological clarification along with semantic and categorial analysis. History shows this is also needed.

The theory of integrative levels turns its back upon any crude mechanism, much as recent science is doing, but also guards against new and subtle forms of Vitalism. In conformity with the findings of the biological sciences, purpose, intention, plan are confined to the top reaches of the phylogenetic scale. General teleology is therefore excluded. The modern materialist forgoes the comfort, unless it be in poetic reverie, of imagining that the order of nature is attuned to his purposes, or endowed with sensitivity and beneficence. Such longings have yielded myths in all ages, but are scarcely appropriate for a scientific era like our own. The materialist makes himself at home in the world, not by investing Nature with purpose, but by transforming it to meet his needs. The vast strides already accomplished by science in controlling and utilizing and molding nature are an earnest of the advances to be worked for and achieved in the future. Modern materialism is thus marked by an effective, working optimism.

Modern materialism is hospitable to every effective method of the sciences, and excludes no procedure which is likely to yield understanding or prediction. It characteristically emphasizes explanation in terms of causal and genetic relations, in contrast to idealism, which makes the relations of ideas primary, and explains the course of the world in terms of abstractions. While insisting on the indispensability of highly specialized, detached studies of various subject matters, the modern materialist recognizes the equal importance of integrating special departmental studies into a comprehensive world view. He thus emphasizes, in contrast to many other philosophical tendencies, the interrelatedness of things. Materialism does not doubt the possibility of satisfying man's need for a comprehensive picture of the universe, and asserts the capacity of scientific methods eventually to cope with basic human problems. It therefore combats agnosticism, skepticism, and all irrational confessions of defeat.

Thought and symbolism have a strategic role in the material world at the human level, but always in close connection with brain events and brain traces. No mental process occurs without its appropriate neural patterns. In the behavior of the organism, the psychic and biological are fused. The movement of an animal is not merely transposition in space but also movement to escape, for example, or movement for food. Movement is psychobiological. There are not two processes that satisfy basic needs and desires—one mental, the other physical—but rather one psychobiological process. The study of behavior is the only scientific approach to the understanding of mind; but this does not rule out hypotheses as to the contents of other minds, that is, reconstructions of mental states of others, on the basis of behavior. Language is here of primary import. Introspection is, of course, a valid method, but the final test of it is behavioral. Obviously excluded by our position are dualisms, parallelisms, and simple or reductionist identity views of mental and bodily processes.

The psychobiological individual must be understood in his development and relations. Personality is conditioned by society and can only be comprehended in its historical context. The alleged conflict between the individual and society as such is artificial, for a human being is highly socialized. Conflicts which arise are concrete and historical. In accounting for the development of societies and their members, increasing importance has been assigned to economic factors, such as natural resources, technology, and ownership relationships; but it is necessary to recognize likewise the interweaving of other factors, such as education, art, and morals. The latter themselves, however, are not independent of economic conditions. To be rejected, in our view, are historical idealism, extreme economic determinism, and romantic pluralism, that is, the view that no systematic empirical account of history is possible.

The advance of science, technology, industrial organization, and rationality opens up the opportunity of a far fuller servicing of human needs than has ever been possible before. It is the socio-economic organization of men which lags behind, and prevents the full realization of human values inherent in our industrial and scientific efficiency.

Because modern materialism recognizes that cultural values must, in general, wait upon the servicing of vital needs, it favors forms of social organization which release the productive forces of the economy, so that men, living in some leisure and dignity, can express their genius, their intellectual and artistic bent. It demands a society which organizes full production for the maximum benefit of all its members. There is no evidence meanwhile that, with security and basic needs supplied, man will not make good use of his additional leisure and abundance, realizing indefinite potentialities.

Like naturalism, modern materialism is opposed to any other criterion of human value and policy than human needs and aspirations. It combats all forms of authoritarianism in morals and arts, opposes reduction of ethics to mere formalism, and rejects the appeal to any supposed extranatural source of experience. With the removal of a supernatural perspective, man must stand consciously on his own feet. Let him rise to his full stature and dignity.

The term "naturalism" has been defined by R. B. Perry as "the philosophical generalization of the sciences," and it has been determined with respect both to the content and to the method of the sciences. Unfortunately, the historical forms of naturalism have often been distinguished by their readiness to compromise, or cautiously to set limits to the use of scientific method. Thus, the naturalism of Spencer was tempered by his agnosticism; and the same may be said of Huxley. Added to this fact is the further circumstance that the evolutionary movement eventuated in what may be called a "pseudo-evolutionary" social philosophy, often referred to as "social Darwinism," in which there was a dangerous confusion of biological and social concepts. It is a notorious fact that writers such as Pearson and Kidd extolled or apologized for social conflicts in the name of biological values. The general term "naturalist" has been applied not only to such types, but also to the pantheistic Haeckel, to some emergent evolutionists with their natural piety and theistic acknowledgments, and to the contemporary group influenced by Dewey. In the recent volume *Naturalism and the Human Spirit* (edited by Y. H. Krikorian) the reader is informed that "contemporary naturalism recognizes much more clearly than did the tradition from which it stems that its distinction from other philosophical positions lies in the postulates and procedures which it criticizes and rejects rather than in any positive tenets of its own about the cosmos."

This passage will serve clearly to distinguish current naturalism from the frank materialism described above. Whereas this type of naturalism is reluctant to commit itself to a positive theory of the world, materialism endeavors to set forth a synoptic view of man and the universe implicit in the sciences at their present stage of development.

Realism, the view that matter is independent of cognition, is essential to materialism. The Realists, both the New and the Critical, did yeoman service against persisting forms of idealism. In so far as the New Realists were faithful to their realism, and did not resolve matter into sense-data or so-called neutral stuff, their thesis resembles a main tenet of materialism. On the whole critical realism is closer to materialism. Both schools, however, were myopic, restricting their interest to a few epistemological and metaphysical questions, whereas the gamut of materialist theory goes far beyond.

Just as realism and naturalism have taken many forms, there are also varieties of materialism. A number of these are listed in the fairly classical summaries of materialism in English, American, German, and French dictionaries and encyclopedias. There is *cosmological* and *ontological materialism,* whose dominant motive is a comprehensive world-scheme. There is *medical materialism,* directed by the bias of physicians in favor of physiological causes for disease. There is *scientific materialism,* expressive of the methodology of science and opposed to dualistic vitalism. And there is *historical materialism,* begun as a protest against the speculative and idealistic approach to history. It held that economic and class relations were the main, though not the only, determinants of social development. And in all this we must be on guard against emotional transfers, such as moral materialism, and question-begging assumptions.

Materialism has had a long history, reflecting scientific climates and clashing cultural currents. Hobbes turned materialism to defense of secular power against the claims of the Church, and to the undermining of superstition. The spirit of the Enlightenment continues in the writings of Diderot, La Mettrie, Holbach, and Cabanis. The ideas of peace, progress, indefinite perfectibility and equality were impressed upon men's minds. Physiological interest grew. The brain came in for ever more consideration as something of its powers was guessed. In literature, this mode of thought maintained itself with Stendhal beyond the romantic reaction, to Balzac and Zola. The next wave of materialism appeared in Germany, largely as a challenge to speculative idealism. Here Feuerbach played a crucial part in a transition from Hegelian idealism to the dialectical materialism of Marx and Engels. Parallel to this development was the popular materialistic literature of Vogt, Moleschott, and Büchner. Despite crudities and confusions, they were instrumental for a short period in disseminating materialistic ideas and perspectives. Dialectical materialism, on the other hand, has continued its development, and today exerts enormous influence. It is a matter of regret to the Editors that an article on this subject could not be obtained in time.

Almost simultaneously with the understanding of social development came the theory of organic evolution. Now, for the first time, massive evidence was given for the view already suggested by ancient materialists, that man is inseparable from nature, and is the product of a long and continuous development from simpler forms of life.

"Materialism" has been used as a term of opprobrium for so long that numerous scholars who might well identify themselves with it, at least as a broad tendency, have chosen to use other names, and have carefully justified that action by repudiating "crude" forms of materialism in the past. But is it more justifiable to renounce "materialism" because of its crude and partially antiquated beginnings than to repudiate science because so many epochmaking changes in concepts and methods have come only in recent decades? The use of a particular term is not important in itself. The avoidance of a term or designation may, however, be important. It would not take long for a truly critical naturalism to become an object of condemnation in fideistic and conservative quarters, just as forthright materialism is today. The broad, programmatic, and self-corrective character of modern materialism makes unreserved endorsement possible to scholars who wish to preserve their birthright of independence, and the ideal of following wherever the facts may lead, in all fields of inquiry.

In this Foreword, we must limit ourselves to indicating the questions to be taken up in the chapters that follow. An effort has been made to integrate science and philosophy in a cooperative and supplementary fashion. In the first part will come relevant historical surveys. In the second, scientists and philosophers delineate different stories of the architectonic of nature. The third part is devoted to a critical study of diverging philosophical positions, such as subjectivism, pragmatism, positivism, and Neo-Thomism. The stress throughout is upon understanding rather than polemic. It is the feeling of those taking part that the possibilities of a critical modern materialism should be explored.

The vast accumulation of our knowledge of the world, the effective conquest of nature which has transformed the conditions of life, has obliged us all to take stock. In the long run, is it not better to face realities, as the psychologists are constantly telling us? In any case, we are offering analyses, facts and theories for what they are worth. We ask only that they be pondered and, if the spirit moves, that they be discussed.

The Editors are grateful to scientists and philosophers who have made this cooperative volume possible. Individual writers are not responsible for the views expressed by others. Such differences of opinion as exist among them are of a kind to be expected in a growing philosophical movement. Philosophy for the future cannot be confined, any more than advancing science, within set limits. It is an enduring quest, and we believe that such a recurrent and perennial philosophy as materialism deserves a more systematic and penetrating study than it has received, up to now, at the hands of scientists and philosophers.

ROY WOOD SELLARS
V. J. MCGILL
MARVIN FARBER

CONTENTS

DEMOCRITUS, PLATO, AND EPICURUS

by

BENJAMIN FARRINGTON

Benjamin Farrington, now Professor of Classics at University College, Swansea, was educated at Cork and Dublin and has been Professor of Classics also at Capetown. He is general editor of the Past and Present series of studies in the history of civilization. His own writings include *Science in Antiquity* (1936), *Science and Politics in the Ancient World* (1939), *Greek Science: Its Meaning for Us* (1944).

The universe is not to be narrowed down to the limits of the understanding, which has been men's practice up to now, but the understanding must be stretched and enlarged to take in the image of the universe as it is discovered.

—Francis Bacon, *Parasceve* (Aphorism iv)

FRANCIS BACON gave his *Novum Organum* the subtitle *Aphorisms concerning the Understanding of Nature and Man's Dominion over it.* His fundamental contention was that man's dominion over nature was the proof of his understanding of it. In this identification of theory and practice, or, as he called it, knowledge and power, lay the profound originality of his book. Generations of academic philosophers have insisted on treating the book as a contribution to logic and have often wondered in what precisely his contribution consists. But the book was more than a contribution to logic, it was a contribution to practice. The Encyclopedists in France and the founders of the Royal Society in England were in no doubt as to the importance of his contribution to life.

Bacon asserted the identity of knowledge and power. On the basis of this identification he uttered his famous condemnation of the works of Plato and Aristotle, those light planks, as he called them, which had floated down to us on the tide of antiquity while the weightier matter of the pre-Socratics had gone to the bottom. There was much in the history of Greek science that was unknown to Bacon. In particular he was ignorant of the researches of the later Aristotle and his successors in the headship of the Lyceum, as well as of the achievements of the early period of the Museum. If he had understood this period he could not have limited the fruitful years of Greek science to the two hundred years from Thales to Democritus. Nevertheless there was an essential justice in his judgment which is recognized by his materialist successors.

The Baconian judgment of the unique importance of the pre-Socratics and their special relation to the birth of modern science was reasserted by the founders of Marxism. In the Introduction to his *Dialectics of Nature,* for instance, Engels wrote:

> We have once again returned to the point of view of the great founders of Greek philosophy, the view that the whole of nature, from the smallest element to the greatest, from grains of sand to suns, from Protista to men, has its existence in eternal coming into being and passing away, in ceaseless flux, in unresting motion and change, only with the essential difference that what for the Greeks was a brilliant intuition, is in our case the result of strictly scientific research in accordance with experience, and hence also it emerges in a much more definite and clear form.

For the pre-Socratic tradition as it culminated in Democritus, Wisdom meant the knowledge of the laws of change in the material universe. For Plato, Wisdom was knowledge of suprasensible realities lifted far above the material world of change. Henry Macran, that brilliant but unproductive Hegelian, in the Introduction to his translation of Hegel's *Logic of World and Idea,* wrote:

> Plato may justly be called the founder of idealism in the sense that he was the first to draw asunder into explicit and emphatic contrast the truths or eternal universalities—which he called ideas—on the one hand, and on the other hand, the phenomena or transitory facts of existence; for it is on this contrast that idealism rests.

This is well said. It is indeed true that idealism rests on making and maintaining an unbridgeable contrast between the universal and the particular. But this is not the whole truth nor the whole mischief. Idealism rests also on the earlier and more fundamental premise, and error, that truth is wholly a matter of contemplation, not of practice.

For Bacon, the founder of British materialism, as for his Marxist successors, theory is part of practice. It rises out of practice and must be proved in practice. We fall into idealism when we abstract it from practice and deify it as an eternal verity.

The nature of this preliminary step from fruitful practice to barren idealism was analyzed by Hegel. The last great idealist, after whom no progress is possible except the transition to materialism, discussed the different consciousness of the Lord and Serf (or Master and Slave, for he had the ancient as well as the medieval world in mind) in his *Phenomenology of the Mind.* The relation of the Lord to the Thing, he said, is indirect, through the Serf. Having thrust the working Serf between himself and the Thing, the Lord has to deal only with that side of the object which has been worked on by the Serf, that is, with the tame side, which he can fully enjoy. The untamed side is left to the Serf to work on.

The position of the Lord is precisely that of the Platonic philosopher. The material basis of the philosopher's life was to be secured by the slave or serf labor controlled by a slave overseer. Only thus could the leisure be secured for a life of contemplation, the precondition for the attainment of truth. But such a life presents the philosopher with a sort of predigested world. All he needs to know about things is their logical aspect. He fails, however, to realize that it is an historical accident which puts him in this privileged position. There is no gain without loss. The leisure-class philosopher has time for some hard thinking, and his hard thinking has been necessary to the progress of truth. But he is unaware how the range of his contemplation has been restricted and the product of his thinking distorted.

Hegel employed a class principle, drawn from the changing structure of society, in his analysis of the development of different types of consciousness. The class analysis of the formation of consciousness is firmly embedded in Hegelianism. No doubt it was owing to their profound initiation into this philosophy that the youthful Marx and Engels exploited this method so brilliantly. In their *German Ideology,* which they left to the gnawing criticism of the mice, but which the mice happily spared for the instruction of our generation, they wrote:

Division of labor only becomes truly such from the moment when a division of material and mental labor appears. From this moment onwards consciousness *can* really flatter itself that it is something other than consciousness of existing practice, that it is *really* conceiving something without conceiving something *real;* from now on consciousness is in a position to emancipate itself from the world and to proceed to the formation of "pure" theory, theology, philosophy, ethics, etc.

Among the Greeks this emancipation of thought from the world of practice reached its consummation in Plato.

Prior to the fifth century not the contrast but the unity of thought and deed is uppermost. In the epic and lyric knowledge is practical; to know is to know how; wisdom is skill in action and therefore power to act. Heracleitus, the first of the philosophers to turn to this theme, assumes as a matter of course that *logos* and *sophiē* carry the double reference of true word (and thought) and right deed.[1]

As with Heraclitus so with Democritus. For though the flight from the world which was to give us Plato was already foreshadowed, Democritus was free of it. Wisdom for him still meant understanding of the order of nature. He did not admit the existence of the supernatural. When he spoke of the soul it implied no dualism of soul and body. Soul and body were both atomic structures dependent on each other for their existence. Art (technē) was power to control nature resulting from the Wisdom which understands the order of nature.

In this materialistic system it was natural that the mode of explanation should be genetic. Genetic analysis is the hallmark of materialism, ancient and modern. Marx and Engels, in the work to which we have already referred, remark: "When we conceive things as they really are and happened, every profound philosophical problem is resolved quite simply into an empirical fact." Thus the idealist seeks the definition of man *per genus et differentiam.* He is the rational animal, or the religious animal, or the laughing animal, what you will. Marx and Engels offer a genetic explanation: "Men begin to distinguish themselves from animals as soon as they begin to *produce* their means of subsistence."

The genetic mode of explanation as employed by Democritus may be illustrated by his account of the origin of human society, speech, and techniques. "The first men lived a random life like wild animals.

going out to pasture independently of one another. When individuals became the prey of carnivorous beasts expediency taught them to co-operate. This brought about recognition of their common human form and the need for communication. From their confused utterance speech developed when they slowly agreed on the meanings to be attached to sounds. None of the conveniences of life had yet been invented. Lacking clothing, shelter, fire, cultivated foods, and even the idea of making a store of wild fruits, men suffered and died, till necessity fostered the invention of the arts. Necessity was the teacher, but she found an apt pupil in man, with his hands, speech, and mother-wit." [2]

In the wreck of our Greek heritage the loss of the works of Democritus is the heaviest item. The Academy, which existed for nine hundred years, preserved all the published works of Plato. No similar fortune defended the writings of the man whom Plato is said to have hated so heartily that he never mentions him, though he challenged all his main positions. For Plato, Wisdom meant a knowledge not of nature, but of the supernature constituted by the ideas. When he spoke of the soul it implied a sharp dualism with the body. The soul was immortal and had acquired its knowledge of reality before its birth into this world and union with the body. As for art—that power to control nature, the slow acquisition of which by man Democritus regarded as identical with his self-differention from the animals—it was relegated by Plato to a kind of limbo. It belonged to the sphere of opinion, the bastard knowledge of the slave, not the truth of the philosopher.

The mode of explanation appropriate to this view of reality was not the genetic one, which is immersed in time, but the pure logic of the eternal verities. Wisdom was not an end product of an historical process but an eternal premise, the connection of which with time was an insoluble mystery. To take a particular example: While Democritus tried to deduce from observation the historical conditions under which language gradually arose, treating it as a product of society, an imperfect invention of average men, Plato regarded language as created once for all by a language-legislator, who submitted it to the approval of a metaphysician whose business it was to guarantee the fitness of words to the expression of the corresponding ideas. This entirely unhistorical conception makes of language a creation of pure reason, constitutes man (or, at least, the philosophic freeman) the rational animal by definition, and authorizes him to find the ultimate truth of reality in words rather than in things.[3]

Both in ancient and in modern times Platonic idealism has been an obstacle to progress. The purpose of Bacon—"the real progenitor of English materialism," as Marx called him—was to clear the decks for the application of science to industry and the radical transformation of the conditions of human life. He was an enemy of the whole age-long movement which reduced science to contemplation. Hence his reversion to the pre-Socratic position. He was not profoundly interested in the eternal verities, protesting that Truth was the product of Time, not Wit. He understood the social conditioning of men's minds. He said that there were times unfavorable for the discovery of truth, and that the formation of the minds of individual men was the work of circumstance. He regarded the separation of the mind from things as the insuperable obstacle in the way of progress in science, denouncing the false opinion "that the dignity of the human mind is imparted by long and close intercourse with particulars, subject to sense and bound in matter." He laughed at the folly of looking for truth in words rather than in things. He protested that skepticism as to man's ability to understand the laws of nature not only hindered the acquisition of contemplative truth, but "cut the sinews of industry."[4] Finally, in adopting every one of these positions he made it sufficiently clear that he was combating the authority of Plato, though he sought not to prejudice the acceptance of his message by continual and open conflict with such an exalted name.[5]

If this was the position of Bacon with regard to Platonism in the seventeenth century of our era, what, we may well ask, was the situation of Greek philosophers of the immediately following generations? First, we may consider the absolutely fundamental question raised by the contradiction between Platonic skepticism and the needs of practical life. If true knowledge of the phenomenal world is not to be had, how are the processes of industry possible? Unless philosophy were to become mere speculation, a retreat from such skepticism was necessary; and even the aristocratic Lyceum retreated from it when Aristotle so transformed the theory of ideas as to make the ideas capable of yielding knowledge about the phenomenal world.[6]

But for a philosophy with a vast popular appeal like that of Epicurus the Platonic skepticism was quite inadmissible. In Epicureanism the revolt from such skepticism was fundamental, and its connection with the claims of practical life explicit. Epicurus felt that even Democritus was not sound on this point, and the absolute trustworthiness of sensation is the basis of his whole system. The connection of this teaching with practical life is revealed in the title of the work of Colotes: "That even life itself is impossible, if we adhere to the opinions of other philosophers." Colotes was one of the favorite friends and disciples of Epicurus and was certainly expressing his views. This rejection of the Platonic skepticism was equally essential for the other great popular philosophy of the time, Stoicism. Accordingly we find the Stoic in Cicero protesting: "If you steal from us perception, how will you distinguish the man who knows an art from him who does not? . . . What result can possibly be produced by the aid of art, unless he who is to practice the art has perceived a number of facts?" [7] This is the fundamental criticism of Platonic skepticism, disposing of it not by logic but by appeal to practice, and revealing it as the illusion of a privileged class which does not realize that life itself would cease if society accepted the philosopher's view.

Bacon protested not only against the skepticism of the Academy. He complained also that Plato corrupted natural philosophy by superstition.[8] The same complaint was made in antiquity. Epicurus was the bitter opponent of the astral theology of Plato. This has not always been recognized. In my *Science and Politics in the Ancient World* (1939) I took it for granted without elaborate argument that the polemic of Epicurus was directed against Plato. "Epicurus," I wrote, "was fighting for two causes to which Plato was relentlessly opposed, the Ionian scientific tradition and the spread of popular enlightenment. Plato was in a quite peculiar sense the object of his attack." There was a certain originality in the assumption of this position at the time. The idea was foreign to our greatest authority on the subject in the English-speaking world. In his *Epicurus* (1926) Cyril Bailey had consistently interpreted the polemic of Epicurus against false astronomical beliefs as an attack on popular superstition. In his *Greek Atomists and Epicurus* (1928) he had written: "Although in Epicurus there are traces of the influence of Aristotle and a keen critic has even seen an approach to the doctrines of Plato, there is never a word of polemic against either." Authority seemed against me, nor had I seen Bignone's

L'Aristotele Perduto (1936) till my own book was in the hands of the printers.

Bignone, in the more than one thousand pages of his very remarkable book, defines more accurately, more fully, and more learnedly than I could, the relation of Epicurus to Platonism. He regards Epicurus as a continuator of the philosophy of Democritus and the old Ionians who was engaged, as I also said, in bringing materialism up to date to meet the criticism of the Socratic schools. But he rightly points out, what I had completely missed, that the passionate polemic of Epicurus was directed first against the lost writings of the youthful Platonizing Aristotle, then against various disciples of Aristotle and the Academy, and of course finally against their common master, Plato. This, though a rectification, is of course a confirmation of my view. The point is important. It is unlikely that the philosophy of Epicurus will ever again be described without recognition of the fact that, in one aspect, it is a sustained polemic against Platonism. It is gratifying to note that the recent book of the brilliant French scholar Festugière (*Epicure et ses Dieux,* 1946) fully accepts this point of view.

The astral theology expounded by Plato in the tenth book of his *Laws* bears an equivocal character. It is established by argument but imposed by law. If you resist the force of the argument the penal code is there to effect conviction. Is it science or legislation? The question forces itself on the modern reader. We may be sure it did so also upon the ancient. In his *Letter to Pythocles* (par. 86), protesting against a false mode of interpreting celestial phenomena, Epicurus writes: "It is impermissible to conduct the inquiry into nature by empty assumptions and *acts of legislation.*" Bignone and I have independently seen in this passage an allusion to the title of the *Laws* and to the equivocal character of the astral theology set forth therein.[9] It is, in fact, a shrewd thrust neatly exposing the political character of Plato's astronomical science.

The exposure of the political function of the new religion founded by Plato on the supposed (or alleged) motions of the heavenly bodies is uppermost in the Epicurean polemic. In Athens a public service imposed upon an individual was called a "liturgy." Epicurus makes this word carry the burden of his attack. The vice of the false astronomy he detests is that it imposes "liturgies" on the gods.[10] He condemns it, not simply because his gods had no share in running the world, but because it involved them in the religion of fear, which it was his special task to oppose. Festugière puts the point thus:

> The Epicurean doctrine of *ataraxy* . . . came into open conflict with these novel Platonic dogmas. For, if one makes of the celestial movements the image of Necessity herself, and if one attributes this Necessity to the will of the gods, the consequence follows that all events here below are ordered by the command of the gods. And, since these events are for the most part painful, one is forced to suppose that the gods pursue us with their hatred, a hatred that one cannot turn aside and that will never cease. It is to immortalize the regime of fear. There is no more pernicious error.

Lucretius put the same point in the famous lines:

> O genus infelix humanum, talia divis
> Cum tribuit facta atque iras adiunxit acerbas! [11]

The protest is not merely against burdening the divine nature with the task of administering the activities of the heavenly bodies. The special bitterness of the protest is directed against attributing the regular phenomena of the heavens, which excite such awe in men's minds, to *angry* gods, thus summoning the most recent achievements of mathematical astronomy to the aid of the worst aspect of ancient superstition.

We must now return to the Platonic skepticism as to the possibility of a science of nature. We have seen that this arose out of the separation of the consciousness of the philosopher from the business of the production of material life. We have also seen that the difficulties caused by this skepticism were promptly felt. Aristotle, with his comment, "The whole *enquiry* into nature is abolished," [12] had expressed the inconvenience of the idealist position from the point of view of the disinterested researcher into nature. The Stoics and Epicureans had to go beyond this aristocratic objection. They voiced the more practical objection that the *arts of life* were abolished.

The difference in character of the two protests is instructive. Aristotle in the *Metaphysics* safeguarded his scientific interests; but he betrayed his relative indifference to the claims of the productive arts by his remark: "the comforts and refinements of life had been sufficiently provided for [this among the poverty-stricken Greeks!] before the quest for Wisdom [that is the kind of science he was interested in] began." [13] Thus his quarrel with Platonic skepticism was half-hearted.

As for any serious revolt on Aristotle's part against the politico-religious function of Plato's astral theology, that did not exist. In the lost *De Philosophia* he developed a dual physics, which served him also at later periods of his life. This dual physics was materialist for the earthy creation and spiritualist for the planets and the stars.[14] In other words, he was a materialist in so far as it did not threaten the astral theology which was now beginning to be universally recognized as the best religion yet invented. The candid historian has not always been able to approve his compromise. "Aristotle," said Rosmini, "exerted himself to compose a philosophical polytheism and flattered himself that he had risen far above the prejudices of the vulgar. But all that he had done was to deny to the divinity the forms of men and animals and bestow upon it that of the stars." [15]

Far different was the position of the Epicureans and the Stoics. It has been a tradition of scholarship to regard the later enmity between the Garden and Porch as characteristic also of their beginnings. This is not so. As popular philosophies they were united in their opposition to the aristocratic Academy and Lyceum. During the lifetime of Epicurus and Zeno and their immediate disciples there was no controversy between Epicureans and Stoics, but both were united in opposition to the Academy and the Lyceum. Nothing could be more natural. Both the schools were materialist. Both were fighting skepticism with regard to sense evidence in the interests of practical life, and both were enemies of that aristocratic and disinterested scientific speculation which characterized the Academy and the Lyceum.

It might indeed be said that it was not till they had won their victory against the idealist schools that the Garden and the Porch had occasion to quarrel among themselves. Then the Stoic adherence to astrology put a widening gap betwen them and fitted Stoicism in its turn to become the patron of an astral state religion. Nilsson is probably right in his view that it was cooperation between astrology and Stoic philosophy that created the Solar theory which towards the end of antiquity became a religion of the Empire.[16] This long process could only excite the increasing hostility of the followers of Epicurus.

The Epicureans were the most consistent champions of materialism in antiquity. They were the most determined enemies of the supernatural. They best kept alive the conviction of the possibility of a true science of nature. They did most to keep alive an understanding of the achievement of the pre-Socratics. They were the surest guardians of the view that man had made himself by his conquest of nature, and that his civilization was to be understood as a human experiment. But it would be a mistake to suppose that they had any hope of a radical betterment of the material lot of man on earth by an organized attack on nature. Ancient society was already in decline, and the ambition of Epicurus was to ease the lot of the individual. He rid his followers of the fear of the supernatural, taught them a rational pursuit of pleasure, and instructed them to look to friendship as the chief security in life. The gods he made were in his own image. "Gods who did no wrong. Gods who were not wicked . . . Gods without hatred and without ill-will. Such was the gospel Epicurus brought the world." [17] Gods also who had no power to affect nature. And in this too they were like their maker. For the evidence is that Epicurus was a simple-lifer, who would cheerfully have reduced life to the level of a picnic. Detesting the injustices of society, he sought only not to have part in them. Centuries were to pass, bringing with them the disappearance of slavery, before a Bacon could preach materialism the burning heart of which was the power of man to transform radically his material conditions of life; and still more centuries before a Marx could reveal the dialectical connection between the conquest of the material environment and the destruction of class society. Meanwhile, so long as class society survives, we shall have our idealists with us. They are its product as well as its defenders.

References

[1] Gregory Vlastos, "Ethics and Physics in Democritus," *Philosophical Review*, Jan., 1946, p. 60 n.

[2] That Democritus adopted the genetic mode of explanation is known. The example given above is from Diodorus Siculus I, chaps. vii and viii, and its ascription to Democritus, though highly probable, is not certain. See Gregory Vlastos in *American Journal of Philology*, Vol. LXVII, No. 1, pp. 51–59, for the latest discussion.

[3] Lucretius (V, 1041 ff.), with obvious reference to this passage of the *Cratylus*, scouts the idea of a language-legislator.

[4] Such opinions are to be found everywhere in Bacon, but see especially *Novum Organum* I, lxxi, lxxviii, xlii, lxxxv; *De Aug.* VI, i.

[5] He let himself go only once, in the *Temporis Partus Maximus* (c. 1608),

where he apostrophized Plato thus: "When you falsely said truth is the native inhabitant of the human mind and not an immigrant from outside, when you turned our minds from the study of things themselves, to which they can never be sufficiently applied, and taught them to wallow among their own confused idols under the name of contemplation, then you dealt us a mortal blow. It was no less a crime to deify this folly and presume to bolster up your worthless thoughts by religion." Bacon knew this for a half-truth. But it *is* half the truth.

[6] Aristotle's realization that the theory of ideas makes all inquiry into nature impossible is openly expressed in *Meta* I, p. 992b, 7–9.

[7] Academica II, 22. It is the merit of Bignone in his *L'Aristotele Perduto* to have emphasized this point. See especially Vol. I, p. 9.

[8] *Novum Organum* I, xv.

[9] Bignone, *L'Aristotele Perduto*, Vol. II, p. 386. Farrington, "Epicurus and the Laws of Plato," *Proceedings* of the Classical Association, vol. XXXVI (May, 1939).

[10] Three times he makes this point (*Letter to Herodotus,* par. 76; *Letter to Pythocles,* pars. 97, 113).

[11] O hapless race of men, when it ascribed these doings (i.e., the celestial phenomena) to the gods and joined therewith bitter wrath. *De Rerum Natura* V, 1194 f.

[12] *Metaphysics* A, 992 b.

[13] *Ibid.,* 982 b.

[14] The phrase is from Bignone, *op. cit.,* II, 388.

[15] Quoted from Bignone, *op. cit.,* II, 387.

[16] *The Rise of Astrology in the Hellenistic Age* (Historical Notes and Papers, No. 18, Observatory of Lund, Sweden, 1943).

[17] Festugière, *Epicure et ses Dieux,* p. 102.

HOBBES AND ENGLISH POLITICAL THOUGHT

by

CHRISTOPHER HILL

Christopher Hill (M.A., Oxford) is fellow and tutor in Modern History, Balliol College, Oxford, and University Lecturer in Modern History. His main publications are: *The English Revolution, 1640* (1940); *Two Commonwealths* (under pseudonym K. E. Holme, 1945); *Lenin and the Russian Revolution* (1947). Soon to be published is a volume illustrating social aspects of the English Revolution.

THOMAS HOBBES was born in 1588 and lived till 1679. His life thus extends from the defeat of the Spanish Armada to the beginning of the Popish Plot; from the year in which the independence of Protestant England was first ensured to the period when a threat to restore Catholicism in England was less a political reality than the stunt of a parliamentary party. In the middle of Hobbes's life occurred the decisive event of modern British history—the revolution of 1640–1649. In this revolution political power passed from the crown and the House of Lords, representing the state church and the great landed magnates, to the merchants and gentry, the class represented in the House of Commons. The defeat of the Armada in the year of Hobbes's birth, the supreme achievement of the Tudor monarchy, had made the survival of absolute monarchy in England impossible. Those classes which had profited by the Tudor internal peace and by Tudor foreign policy—the merchants, enclosing gentry, and industrialists—had henceforth nothing to fear from foreign invaders. The only obstacle to their continued expansion was internal—

a fiscal system designed in feudal times to run England as a private estate of the king's. This system had been rendered obsolete by the sixteenth century rise in prices resulting from the influx of American silver into Europe, and by the growing complexity of administration which was itself a reflection of England's economic expansion. But if the financial system of the country was to be reorganized those who were to pay the taxes wanted to have a greater say in the government.

Over this the clash came. The crown clung to its ancient privileges, the House of Commons put forward new demands. The whole complex of quarrels grew up—quarrels over foreign policy, over control of the church, over control of the economic life of the country. But the real issue, as Hobbes was one of the first to see, was one of political power, of sovereignty: who was to have the decisive word in governing the country? The king, backed by the state church and most of the lords, asserted the rights of the old system; the House of Commons, representing the new go-ahead classes, began to claim supreme power. The issue was fought out in the Civil War, and Parliament won. After 1646 the revolution went—from the point of view of those who started it—dangerously far to the left; and finally in 1660 fear of the democratic left brought the solid mass of the bourgeoisie and gentry to compromise with their defeated enemies. Charles II, the bishops, the House of Lords were restored—to guarantee the new social order. For whatever the trimmings, the reality of power was henceforth in the hands of the gentry and the bourgeoisie. Charles II, prudent man, realized this when he said he didn't want to go on his travels again; James II, less prudent, traveled. The year 1688 finally formulated and consolidated the compromise settlement of 1660, legitimized the union of merchants and landed aristocracy which produced the eighteenth century Whig oligarchy.

That was the world in which Hobbes lived. His main ideas had taken form before 1640; but they had been shaped by the intellectual forces of his world. The revolution which took place in England between 1640 and 1649 was only one manifestation of a process which had been taking place all over Europe, and which includes the German Reformation, the rise of Calvinism, and the Revolt of the Netherlands. In the world of thought Reformation—not directly, and not in accordance with the desires of the early Reformers—had led to a great intellectual liberation. The assertion of human dignity implicit in

Luther's "priesthood of all believers," the translation of the Bible into vernaculars, the endless discussion of fundamental philosophical problems, had ultimately produced a quite new rationalism, a reliance on the human intellect as such, rather than on authority, whether of Pope or Scriptures, King or common-law precedent. The new bourgeoisie was shaking itself free from the traditional fetters which had bound feudal society down in a hierarchy of principalities and powers. Modern science was also emerging to meet the needs of the new productive forces: this is the age in which Copernicus and Galileo are making discoveries which the Inquisition cannot suppress, starting ideas which will overthrow Aristotle and the schoolmen.

In England the intellectual process is summed up and synthesized in Bacon, the father of the inductive method, of scientific experiment, of empiricism. Bacon had a robust optimism, an infinite confidence in the power of human reason if freely and honestly applied. He was also a utilitarian, believing that man's reason should be applied to the problems of life on earth, rather than to the more abstruse speculations of theology. Science was necessary to give man power; to command nature, he said, we must first obey her; and to obey we must understand.

Hobbes at one period—we do not know exactly when—worked in close collaboration with Bacon and acted as his amanuensis.

What then was Hobbes's position in society, in the old world whose institutions were breaking down and the new world which was forming itself in man's consciousness? Like so much else in that age of revolutionary transition, Hobbes's very social position was ambiguous, facing both ways.

His father was a country vicar, and by all accounts not a very learned one. But he died while Hobbes was still young, and the boy was brought up by his uncle, a glover of Malmesbury. His mother was of yeoman stock. They managed to send him to Oxford. From there he passed in 1608 into the service of the great family of the Cavendishes, as tutor to the future Earl of Devonshire. With brief interruptions he remained in the service of this family until 1640, when he fled to Paris and the Cavendishes began to gather an army for Charles I. In Paris, he was for a time tutor to Prince Charles.

In 1653, after his return to England, Hobbes resumed his service with the Cavendish family, though this did not prevent Cromwell offering him official employment.

The contradiction is apparent. Hobbes, the small bourgeois, the clever boy making good at Oxford, is taken into the service of one of the most conservative of the great feudal families, which still ruled large tracts of the economically backward north of England. When Hobbes takes his noble pupils on the grand tour of Europe he meets the most progressive intellects of his time—Galileo, Descartes, Gassendi. He comes home to discuss their ideas with the Duke of Newcastle.

Hobbes's station in the world thus rendered him conscious of conflict, of the rifts in society which were plunging it into a civil war that would be fatal to his position as a hanger-on of the old order. In *Behemoth* he gives a convincing class analysis of the causes of the civil war. In the *De Cive* and *The Leviathan* his object is to prevent that class conflict (or any other conflict) ever taking the extreme form of civil war. Hobbes's theory of sovereignty dates from the actual period of armed conflict in England between the social classes.

So Hobbes, suspended between two worlds, is equally critical of both. His environment and mode of life may have affected the objectives he set himself and the practical conclusions he reached; but none can deny the revolutionariness of his method, of his criticism, the boldness of his rejections. Even his reasons for not being a bourgeois-revolutionary themselves have far-reaching implications: for his critical-skeptical approach cut right through the religious smoke screen behind which the seventeenth century bourgeoisie advanced on power.

What then was the Hobbesian revolution?

Hobbes found official political thought dominated by the idea that government was to be obeyed because ordained of God; and he substituted the theory that the state was instituted by man for his own convenience, and that it should be obeyed because the consequences of disobedience can be demonstrated to be more disagreeable than obedience, in almost all cases. That is to say, expediency, not morality, is for Hobbes the motive for political obedience.

Hobbes found opposition thinking dominated by the idea that government should not be obeyed when it conflicted with divine law, natural law, natural rights; and he showed that natural law, morality, and rights in society are derived from the state, and that it is nonsense to speak of "natural rights" antecedent to the state, just as it is impossible to obtain agreement among men on what constitutes divine, natural, or fundamental law except in so far as these have been defined by the sovereign. That is to say, he made power, not right, the key question in politics.

Finally, Hobbes abandoned the old games of text swapping and precedent hunting for logical argument. That is to say, he made reason, not authority, the arbiter in politics. Paradoxically, it is the absolutist Hobbes who demonstrated that the state exists for man, that it is the product of human reason, and therefore that political theory is a rational science.

Despite his practical conclusions, then, the whole essence of Hobbes's approach to politics, his mental atmosphere and presuppositions, are bourgeois. He postulates a society in which traditional static hierarchical feudal relations have broken down. In the feudal state the important questions had been those of personal status and privilege: the relation of lord to serf, of gild member to purchaser, of cleric to layman. But by the seventeenth century society has dissolved into its component parts, who face one another not as members of estates or corporations but as egoistic individuals. This new individualism is reflected in religion: Hobbes's view of human nature is that of Calvinism or Jansenism; he has as little use as Calvin for the hierarchy of saints, the mediating priesthood, the round of formal "works" by which the medieval Catholic hoped to save his soul. Hobbes sees society as a collection of atoms, in which the important relations are contractual, such as those between employer and workman, the Nonconformist and the minister whom he selects: the emphasis is on the individual, not on the social group. Hobbes's natural man is an individualist, like Robinson Crusoe or Adam Smith's economic man. Like Descartes, Hobbes believes he can generalize about the passions of all men by examining his own. His state is a mechanical contrivance, set up by contract. The contract idea which he adopts was almost the private property of the Puritan and revolutionary opposition, whether we consider the *Vindiciae contra Tyrannos,* which was the Bible of the Dutch revolutionaries and the French Huguenots, or the Solemn League and Covenant which bound together the Scottish and English opponents of Charles I.

Hobbes postulates the complete equality of natural man in "the faculties of body and mind." "The inequality that now is, has bin introduced by the Lawes civill."[1] "Good Counsell comes not by Lot, nor by Inheritance; and therefore there is no more reason to expect good Advice from the rich, or noble, in matter of State, than in delineating the dimensions of a fortresse." So the sovereign will give the hereditary aristocracy "no further honour, than adhaereth naturally to their abilities."[2] No egalitarian democrat could go further. How right Clarendon was to upbraid Hobbes for "his extreme malignity to the Nobility, by whose bread he hath bin alwaies sustain'd." The noble lord correctly pointed out that the Levelers concurred with Hobbes's view "that no man may have priviledges of that kind by his birth or descent."[3]

Man in the state of nature, for Hobbes, is an abstraction from the competitive world he saw about him. Human nature is bourgeois nature: the fittest survive. Indeed, he goes out of his way to tell us that his state of nature is a logical abstraction rather than a piece of historical description.[4] Natural man is bourgeois man with the policeman removed. Hobbes is consciously talking to a bourgeois audience. The main objections which he makes to his state of nature are such as would occur to and appeal to the commercial classes: "There is no place for Industry; because the fruit thereof is uncertain: and consequently no Culture of the Earth, no Navigation, nor use of the commodities that may be imported by Sea; no commodious Building; no Instruments of moving, and removing such things as require much force; no Knowledge of the face of the Earth; no account of Time; no Arts; no Letters; no Society."[5] The setting up of the sovereign state is the only escape from the natural state of war.[6]

Man escapes from the state of nature by his own efforts, by self-help based on the use of reason. The laws of nature are "precepts or general rules, found out by reason," and they lead to the elevation of the sovereign to save men from the state of war which is at once the state of nature and the condition of "feudal anarchy." "To seek peace and ensue it" is for Hobbes the first law of nature, the clue to all success in politics; and peace, internal order, and security are the first necessities of existence for the commercial and industrial classes. It had been the function of the Tudor monarchy to provide this peace and order in England against "feudal anarchy"; and in so far as the Tudors gave internal peace and order, and security from external attack, they had been supported by the commercial classes. A great deal of Hobbes's theory, in fact, looks back to the Tudor age, in which he was brought up, and which was the golden age alike for the small bourgeoisie and for the landowning aristocracy adapting itself to capitalism.

The overriding problem of seventeenth century politics, which Hobbes was shrewd enough to see absolutely clearly, was, Who was to interpret conflicting customs—king or parliament, Lords or Commons? A new social order had grown up, with some support from the Tudors in its early stages, without any fundamental modification of the laws and institutions of the country. As a result of the largely rural nature of English capitalism, the House of Commons had come by 1640 to represent mainly the merchants and progressive landowners. As the crown, in its financial extremity, became less able to respect the rights of property so the House of Commons resurrected the claims to power of fifteenth century Parliaments, through which big feudal lords had dominated the state directly. There were therefore conflicting precedents, with which the conflicting claims could be supported. Most students of politics devoted themselves to antiquarian research to find arguments for their own side, or to the hopeless task of discovering which side was "right." Hobbes brushed all these cobwebs aside, and showed that such questions were not decided by "right" but by power; what mattered was not arguments, but who was to decide between them. Custom, precedents, admittedly could produce contradictory conclusions: very well, then, the only important question was, Who was to interpret conflicting customs? This is the historical point of Hobbes's theory of sovereignty.

Hobbes agrees with almost all contemporary political theorists in seeing the rise of private property from a previously existing state of primitive communism as the cause and justification of the state. "For before constitution of Soveraign Power . . . all men had right to all things; which necessarily causeth Warre: and therefore this Proprietie, being necessary to Peace, and depending on Soveraign Power, is the Act of that Power, in order to the publique peace." [7] As property is inherited, and we may not go behind possession (sanctified by the sovereign) to question *right,* so sovereignty itself passes by inheritance, and we have no right to question the arrangements made by our ancestors. Sovereignty and property stand or fall together, are maintained by the same laws of inheritance.

Here again Hobbes is transitional, and this part of his argument seems the weakest in the light of later and more sophisticated contractual theories. But we must remember when and for whom Hobbes wrote. His combination of contract and inheritance reflects the position of the landowner, for whom an unchallengeable succession of property is the important thing. It is only after the victory of the bourgeoisie that even land loses its feudal status and becomes a commodity, which can be bought, sold, and devised, and is secured by contract. This development is reflected in political theory by the transition from divine hereditary right to Locke's contractually limited monarchy. Hobbes is defending an intervening stage of absolutism, and his arguments are addressed to the contractualists, to those, like Selden, who held that "a King is a thing men have made for their own sakes, for quietness' sake." [8] There is already nothing divine about the sovereign's right: that is why Hobbes was so unpopular with the high-flying Church of England men.

Hobbes is also a spokesman of the new attitude towards poverty in capitalist society. The idea that poverty was a holy state had long been abandoned. Opinion was now shifting away from the sixteenth century view that the new social problems of pauperism should be dealt with by Christian charity. That solution had been sufficient for the occasional victims of misfortune in the more static feudal society: it could not cope with the mass unemployment created by early capitalism and enclosure of arable lands for sheep farming. Hobbes saw that pauperism on the new scale was a problem for the state. "And whereas many men, by accident unevitable, become unable to maintain themselves by their labour; they ought not to be left to the Charity of private persons; but to be provided for, (as far-forth as the necessities of Nature require,) by the Lawes of the Common-wealth." But even this subsistence minimum must not be rashly distributed. "For such as have strong bodies, the case is otherwise: they are to be forced to work; and to avoyd the excuse of not finding employment, there ought to be such Lawes, as may encourage all manner of Arts: as Navigation, Agriculture, Fishing, and all manner of Manifacture that requires labour." Emigration is also a remedy for unemployment. And with Malthus and all clear-sighted investigators of the structure and implications of capitalism, Hobbes concludes: "And when all the world is overcharged with Inhabitants, then the last remedy of all is Warre;

which provideth for every man, by Victory, or Death."[9] The function of the state in a competitive world, as Hobbes sees it, is the mercantilist one of building up power for wealth and wealth for power, and building up power and wealth for ultimate war, the final arbiter of wealth and power in the new world.

One final point about the contract. "Whatsoever is not Unjust, is Just," says Hobbes. "And the definition of INJUSTICE, is no other than the *not Performance of Covenant.*"[10] Justice is the keeping of contracts: no more. One consequence of this will be clear to anyone who is acquainted with the social problems of sixteenth and seventeenth century England. The burning question of the day was the position of the small proprietor, the copyholder or cottager, whose holding was frequently an obstacle to consolidation of estates, enclosure, racking of rents, and all the familiar methods by which one section of the gentry was enriching itself and sharing in the commercial and industrial boom of the century before 1640. The attack on the security of tenure of these small men, the mere idea that customary rents could be raised and that peasants unable to pay might be evicted, had seemed in the sixteenth century a grave moral crime, a breach with all that was right and proper, a gross violation of equity even when the letter of the law was observed. For most copyholders and cottagers held by customary right, at customary rents, not automatically enforceable at common law. There was no contractual basis for their claims. The aim of the improving landlord was to replace copyholds by leaseholds, copyholds for lives by copyholds for a fixed term of years; to substitute precise, limited, and determinable contracts for the indeterminate, traditional, customary rights of the medieval peasantry; to pass from status to contract. It had been a moral as well as an economic revolution, an intrusion of the alien standards of the market into a sphere hitherto unaffected by them.

By the middle of the seventeenth century, no doubt, the new morality of competition was becoming generally accepted. The last attempt to legislate against depopulating enclosures was defeated in Parliament in 1656. But the peasants' struggle for stable copyholds still went on, supported by the Leveler movement just before the publication of *The Leviathan.* The last pamphlets against enclosure were published in the fifties. At least the new standards were regarded as a lapse from the old, a concession to the wicked covetousness of fallen man. But now here was Hobbes making contract the basis of morality! Justice is the keeping of covenants: no contract, no injustice. This was as complete a breach with traditional Catholic morality as with the feudal hierarchial state. The bourgeois free-contract state received its ideological foundation: and already the expropriated and starving laborer is coming to bargain with an employer whose ability to wait until the workman accepts his terms is fortified by the rewards of past waiting. Nowhere is the fundamentally bourgeois nature of Hobbes's approach to the state and to morality more apparent than in this, the foundation of both.

It should be noted, moreover, that though the basis is *contractual*, force is needed too to maintain contracts. (This again exactly reflects the contradictions of capitalist society.) Contracts are free, but must be maintained by force against the unfortunate. As that good Hobbist, Commissary-General Ireton, put it four years before the publication of *The Leviathan*: "Any man that makes a bargaine, and does finde afterwards 'tis for the worse, yett is bound to stand to itt." "They were couzen'd," replied the Leveler Wildman, "as wee are like to be." [11]

The bourgeois characteristics of Hobbes's thought come out perhaps most clearly in his attitude to the Roman Church, and to magical elements in religion altogether. The point of the attack on the Kingdom of Darkness in Part IV of *The Leviathan* is that Hobbes is defending the negative achievements of the Reformation, its break with priestcraft, its denial of the need for a hierarchy to mediate between man and God.

In the first three decades of the seventeenth century, in opposition to pressure from the Puritanism of the revolutionary class, the Church of England under Lancelot Andrewes and Laud had reverted to a kind of social papistry. With no desire to return to the papal allegiance, they wished to elevate the dignity of the priest as maker of magic, to distinguish him from the mass of the congregation, to emphasize the formal and symbolic aspects of worship (prayer and the sacraments) as against the rational (preaching). "There should be more praying, and less preaching," said Hobbes's patron, the Duke of Newcastle; "for much preaching breeds faction, but much praying causes devotion." [12] Hobbes had no love for Puritanism, for he held that the logical conclusion of its belief in the rights of the individual conscience was complete anarchy; but he was far too imbued with the new science to have any truck with the neo-papist movement. In Part IV of *The Leviathan* he is attacking "ghost" ideas, in Ibsen's sense of the world; clearing away impediments to rational thought. He openly contrasts religion with science. He mercilessly attacks superstition and belief in magic, for the specific reason that they are the means by which priests establish their authority over the people. "Who will not obey a Priest, that can make God, rather than his Soveraign; nay than God himselfe? Or who, that is in fear of Ghosts, will not bear great respect to those that can make Holy Water, that drives them from him?" [13] Claims to inspiration may be a cheat; and at best fear of hell and hopes of heaven are unsatisfactory as motives for political action.[14]

Hence Hobbes's Erastianism, which is as great as that of the majority of the House of Commons in 1640. The state must wield the vast power over men's minds which religion still possesses, just because of the infinite possibilities of disagreement and dispute which there would otherwise be. For "the most frequent praetext of Sedition, and Civill Warre, in Christian Common-wealths hath a long time proceeded from a difficulty, not yet sufficiently resolved, of obeying at once, both God, and Man, then when their Commandements, are one contrary to the other." [15] It is in fact the question of sovereignty. Who is to decide? In the last resort, Hobbes thinks this is a question of power. The quarrel between the Puritans and Laud was only in appearance over doctrinal niceties, the position of the communion table, the priestly vestments. In fact two philosophies of life were in conflict, two social orders: the medieval, the Catholic, the hierarchic, the feudal; and the modern, the Protestant-rationalist, the individualist, the bourgeois.

Yet whilst attacking the priesthood Hobbes has a clear perception of the uses of religion for keeping the vulgar in order. The ancient Romans "obtayned in order to their end, (which was the peace of the Commonwealth,) that the common people in their misfortunes, laying the fault on neglect, or errour in their Ceremonies, or on their own disobedience to the lawes, were the less apt to mutiny against their Governors. And being entertained with the pomp, and pastime of Festivalls, and publike Games, made in honour of the Gods, needed nothing else but bread, to keep them from discontent, murmuring, and commotion against the state." [16]

Hobbes's definition of religion sufficiently indicates his view of its purpose, and his own complete Erastianism: *"Feare* of power invisible, feigned by the mind, or imagined from tales publiquely allowed, RELIGION; not allowed, SUPERSTITION. And [with a blatantly cynical nod to the decencies] when the power imagined, is truly such as we imagine, TRUE RELIGION." Religion, in fact, is an instrument of government. "In all things not contrary to the Morall Law, (that is to say, to the Law of Nature,) all Subjects are bound to obey that for divine Law, which is declared to be so, by the Lawes of the Common-wealth." "An opinion publiquely appointed to bee taught, cannot be Haeresie; nor the Soveraign Princes that authorize them, Haeretiques." [17] The calmness with which Hobbes describes on paper and rationalizes the practice of all governments in his day takes one's breath away. He alone had the courage to justify the *cujus regio ejus religio* principles on which every government acted.

It is not surprising, therefore, that the great enemy for Hobbes is the claim to inspiration, to direct revelation, to be able to work miracles. Here he is attacking the sectaries on the left as well as the papists on the right; and in the process his rigorous logic undermines the whole Christian position. "To say God hath spoken to him in a Dream, is no more thaen to say he dreamed that God spake to him . . . So that though God Almighty can speak to a man, by Dreams, Visions, Voice, and Inspiration; yet he obliges no man to beleeve he hath so done to him that pretends it; who (being a man) may erre, and (which is more) may lie." "All the Miracle consisteth in this, that the Enchanter has deceived a man; which is no Miracle, but a very easie matter to doe . . . For two men conspiring, one to seem lame, the other to cure him with a charme, will deceive many: but many conspiring, one to seem lame, another so to cure him, and all the rest to bear witnesse; will deceive many more." Hobbes denies possession by devils, even in those cases where the devil was cast out by Christ. He also denies the existence of a local hell or everlasting torment.[19]

It is quite clear, in fact, that Hobbes does not really believe in Christianity, in any normal sense of the word "belief," and merely accepts it as the creed authorized in the state in which he lived.[20] "It was . . . almost impossible for man without the special assistance of God, to avoid both rocks of atheism and superstition." [21] God saves the situation by direct revelation; but we have already seen how dubious Hobbes is about claims to revelation as such. He is no Pascal, using skepticism to build up a firmer faith; he uses the existence of faith to inculcate skepticism. "Shall whole Nations," he asks, "be brought to *acquiesce* in the great Mysteries of Christian Religion, which are above Reason; and millions of men be made believe, that the same Body may be in innumerable places, at one and the same time, which is against Reason," and shall it be impossible to educate them into the more sensible principles of the Leviathan? [22]

Hobbes sneers at arguments based only on biblical texts. Those who employ them "by casting atomes of Scripture, as dust before men's eyes, make every thing more obscure than it is; an ordinary artifice of those that seek not the truth, but their own advantage." [23] He develops his own case by logic and rational demonstration first, then proceeds to bolster it up by texts, "with submission nevertheless both in this, and in all questions, whereof the determination dependeth on the Scriptures, to the interpretation of the Bible authorized by the Common-wealth, whose Subject I am." [24] Individual interpretation of the scriptures, carried to its logical conclusion, means as many truths and schemes of salvation as there are citizens: Hobbes wants uniformity in the interest of stability. But his method again diminishes respect for the sacred books. He himself indulges in some daring historical criticism of the attributions of authorship of books of the Bible.[25]

Rather unexpectedly, though less so if we consider the social roots of his theories rather than the form those theories took, Hobbes approves of Independency so long as it does not degenerate into sectarian anarchy.[26] But that is really only a measure of his indifference, of his approval of the independent separation of politics from theology, of the tendency of Independency to approach deism and rationalism. For though Hobbes is prepared through indifference to defend political intolerance, still tolerance—at least of opinions not translated into actions—is more natural to him. "But what reason is there for it?" he asks of persecution. "Is it because such opinions are contrary to true Religion? that cannot be, if they be true. Let therefore the truth be first examined by competent Judges, or confuted by them that pretend to know the contrary." [27] Here again Hobbes links up with the skeptical or deist aristocrats of the Restoration period, with the whole drift of political thought to the sort of practical toleration *de covenance* realized after 1688, in which considerations of expediency and the welfare of trade played a far greater role than the passion for liberty of a Milton. "Forasmuch as some ease to scrupulous consciences in the exercise of religion may be an effectual means to unite their Majesties' protestant subjects in interest and affection . . ." ran the preamble to the Toleration Act of 1689, frankly. This is how Hobbes put it: "There is another Errour in their Civill Philosophy . . . to extend the power of the Law, which is the Rule of Actions onely, to the very Thoughts, and Consciences of men, by Examination, and *Inquisition* of what they hold, notwithstanding the Conformity of their Speech and Actions: By which, men are either punished for answering the truth of their thoughts, or constrained to answer an untruth for fear of punishment."[28] It is not the noblest strain in which to plead liberty of conscience, but it has proved perhaps the most acceptable political argument; and it is one for which the author of *The Leviathan* has received insufficient credit.

The scientific spirit of Hobbes is most clearly shown in the structure of *The Leviathan* itself. Dr. Strauss has argued that all Hobbes's fundamental ideas existed before he became acquainted with the scientific ideas of his contemporaries, that the scientific method is imposed on Hobbes's material and does not grow out of it.[29] Even if true, this does not affect my main contention—that *both* Hobbes's philosophy *and* the scientific method grew out of one and the same social environment, and so naturally could be fused. I do not think Dr. Strauss is altogether convincing when he argues that the scientific method *conflicts* in any way with what Hobbes is trying to say: certainly Hobbes thought he was establishing "the science of justice," lack of which had brought about the civil war.[30] The style and form of *The Leviathan* were undoubtedly influenced by the new sciences: that is why the book is so important in the history of English prose. Its construction is beautifully logical. Once we have started, it is almost impossible to break the chain of Hobbes's argument without going back to the beginning. He is self-consciously rigorous in his use of words. All his terms are defined in Book I, and a close attention to those definitions disposes of some of the alleged contradictions in the later chapters. For "when men register their thoughts wrong, by the inconstancy of the signification of their words . . . they register for their conceptions, that which they never conceived; and so deceive themselves." [31]

Hobbes tries to reduce the rational process to calculation. "For REASON, in this sense, is nothing but *Reckoning* (that is, Adding and Subtracting) of the Consequences of generall names agreed upon, for the *marking* and *signifying* of our thoughts." [32] This is a kind of Benthamite calculus, borrowed from the countinghouse and the merchant's ledger: as bourgeois as Benjamin Franklin.

Together with this goes a denial of all metaphysical absolutes. Hobbes's corroding skepticism worked a revolution of destruction in the world of thought parallel to that which was taking place in institutions and social standards. Hobbes has no use at all for conventional moral noises. "For one man calleth *Wisdome,* what another calleth *feare*; and one cruelty, what *another justice* . . . And therefore such names can never be the true grounds of any ratiocination." Standards are entirely relative, except for Leviathan's absolutes. "Whatsoever is the object of any mans Appetite or Desire; that is it, which he for his part calleth Good." [33] And this moves over to politics. "The doctrine of Right and Wrong, is perpetually disputed, both by the Pen and the Sword: Whereas the doctrine of Lines, and Figures, is not so; because men care not, in that subject what be truth, as a thing that crosses no mans ambition, profit or lust. For I doubt not, but if it had been a thing contrary to any mans right of dominion, or to the interest of men that have domination, *That the three Angles of a Triangle, should be equall to two Angles of a Square;* that doctrine should have been, if not disputed, yet by the burning of all books of Geometry, suppressed, as farre as he whom it concerned was able." The laws of nature, therefore, are precepts or general rules, found out by knowing the consequences, by bookkeeping, by counting the cost.[34] They have no transcendental moral binding force; only a man would be irrational, unaware of his own best interests if he did not observe them, just as a merchant would be a fool if, having once learned to keep accounts, he let his affairs get into confusion by failing to keep them.

There are various hints which suggest that Hobbes would agree with Rousseau in holding that no true commonwealth, in his sense of the term, has ever yet existed: that he was legislating for the future. In the chapter "Of Dominion Paternall, and Despoticall," he wrote: "The greatest objection is, that of the Practise; when men ask, where.

and when, such Power has by Subjects been acknowledged. But one may ask them again, when or where has there been a Kingdome long free from Sedition and Civill Warre . . . For though in all places of the world, men should lay the foundation of their houses on the sand, it could not thence be inferred, that so it ought to be."[35] "So, long time after men have begun to constitute Commonwealths, imperfect, and apt to relapse into disorder, there may, Principles of Reason be found out, by industrious meditation, to make their constitutions (excepting by externall violence) everlasting. And such are those which I have in this discourse set forth."[36]

Hobbes knows that a new world has come into existence, to which the standards of the old feudal order will no longer apply. He may not have been a practical revolutionary himself; his theory has kinks and idiosyncrasies, hangovers of the past and criticisms of the present which can be explained by his own peculiar station in society; but all the assumptions of his approach to politics are new, radical, and bourgeois—though stripped of the religious swaddling clothes in which bourgeois revolutionary thought was still clothed. Rousseau had only to insist that sovereignty must and could lie in the people alone, in order to convert Hobbes's political philosophy into a revolutionary creed that would overthrow the thrones of Europe.

Combined with this scientific spirit we find in Hobbes what was its almost invariable accompaniment in the seventeenth century—materialism. This is flatly stated in chapter I, "Of Sense": "The cause of Sense, is the Externall Body, or Object." It is only "not knowing what Imagination, or the Senses are" that allows some schoolmen to say "that Imaginations rise of themselves, and have no cause; . . . that Good thoughts are blown (inspired) into a man, by God."[37] "A wooden top that is lashed by the boys, and runs about sometimes to one wall, sometimes to another, sometimes hitting men on the shins, if it were sensible of its own motions would think it proceeded from its own will, unless it felt what lashed it. And is a man any wiser, when he . . . seeth not what are the lashings that cause his will?"[38] "The words *In-powred vertue, In-blown vertue,* are as absurd and insignificant, as a *round quadrangle.*"[39] This is politics of course: "For who will endeavour to obey the Laws, if he expect Obedience to be Powred or Blown into him?"[40] Hobbes regards no philosophical question as academic, but sees that the most apparently abstract theories lead to practical conclusions. He attacks idealism as such. "The causes of this difference of Witts, are in the Passions; and the difference of Passions, proceedeth partly from the different Constitution of the body, and partly from different Education." He expresses his disbelief in an eternal soul which can exist separately from the body; and so denies dualism.[41]

Hobbes has also a fascinatingly historical sense, the product no doubt of his early preoccupation with historical studies. He is aware of the social, the materialist origin of ideas: "Leasure is the mother of Philosophy; and Common-wealth, the mother of *Peace,* and *Leasure*: Where first were great and flourishing *Cities,* there was first the study of *Philosophy.*"[42] He makes an extremely shrewd criticism of the quality of scholastic thought when he points out that much of it cannot be translated "into any of the moderne tongues, so as to make the same intelligible; or into any tolerable Latine, such as they were acquainted withall, that lived when the Latine tongue was Vulgar."[43] That shows a real appreciation of the connection between living thought and living language, an awareness of the social nature of language and thought.

Hobbes turns to history, as Bacon did, for the application.[44] A striking feature of his thought, linking it again with Bacon and the best of seventeenth century science, is its domination by the idea of motion, change, development. Like a modern biologist, he asserts, "The constitution of a mans Body, is in continual mutation." "Life it selfe is but Motion." "Felicity is a continuall progresse of the desire, from one object to another; the attaining of the former, being still but the way to the later."[45] "The knowledge of the nature of motion," he says, is "the gate of natural philosophy universal," which Galileo opened.[46]

This motion, as is clear from the passages last quoted, is conceived as a dialectical process. So too is thought. "When in the mind of man, Appetites, and Aversions, Hopes, and Feares, concerning one and the same thing, arise alternately; and divers good and evill consequences of the doing, or omitting the thing propounded, come successively into our thoughts; so that sometimes we have an Appetite to it; sometimes an Aversion from it; sometimes Hope to be able to do it; sometimes Despaire, or Feare to attempt it; the whole summe of Desires, Aversions, Hopes and Feares, continued till the thing be either done, or thought impossible, is that we call DELIBERATION." "As the whole chain of Appetites alternate, in the question of Good, or Bad, is called *Deliberation;* so the whole chain of Opinions alternate, in the question of True, or False, is called DOUBT. No Discourse whatsoever, can End in absolute knowledge of Fact, past, or to come." [47]

Important though theory always is for Hobbes, it is always closely associated with practice, to which it leads and without which it is sterile. But rational theory may always come up against the irrational in practice. Hobbes has an overwhelming sense of the obstructive power of vested interests to dangerous truths. In his final apologetic conclusion he is anxious to show that "there is nothing in this whole Discourse . . . contrary either to the Word of God, or to good Manners; or to the disturbance of the Publique Tranquility;" and that it will in fact encourage men to obey and to pay taxes willingly. And here Hobbes sums up all the bitterness of his cynicism, all the penetration of his social analysis, and all his confidence in the ultimate trimph of rational science: "For such Truth, as opposeth no mans profit, nor pleasure, is to all men welcome." [48]

After the Restoration, Macauley said, Hobbism "became an almost essential part of the fine gentleman." For in 1660 the monarchy and the House of Lords had been restored as guarantees of the new social order against the threat from the left. The returned aristocracy had lost all faith in its own ideology, and was not captivated by that of the victorious bourgeoisie. (The ideology and ideologists of revolutionary Puritanism, in fact, were hastily shed by the respectable sections of the bourgeoisie of the Restoration.) Skepticism prevailed among the restored feudalists, busily adapting themselves to bourgeois society. The intellectual history of England in the second half of the seventeenth century is the history of the dialectical interaction of the materialist theory of the court aristocrats with the religious ideologists of the moving classes of the revolution—the progressive small gentry, yeomen, small industrialists. In the 1640's and 1650's Puritanism in the hands of the lower orders was slowly working its way to a rationalism which was also egalitarian (Fox, Winstanley) and so frightened off the propertied classes, who saw the need for restoring ecclesiastical discipline and the hierarchy to control the thought of the lower orders. As the century wore on, the aristocracy came to repent of their Hobbist atheistic materialism, of the skepticism of the Restoration dramatists; they began to see the need to bring back God into science: hence the turn to "rational Christianity," deism, tolerance. The two great enemies were atheism and "enthusiasm." So we get Milton arduously working his way *through* Puritanism to a position similar to that from which, in a very different social environment, Falkland and Chillenden had started; and we find Locke synthesizing Bacon and Hobbes, Milton and Cudworth, science and religion; and leaving out everything that had made religion exciting, much that had made science politically dangerous. The materialism of Bacon and Hobbes was discarded, and with it their confident and exclusive reliance on the scientific method for the progress of human thought. Science was necessary to the economic advance of the bourgeois social order, religion to its political stability. So religion and science were reconciled by limiting the sphere of each.[49] Locke's synthesis performed a social function invaluable for his class. But it was woefully incomplete, for it left out the dialectical element of thought which the Puritan revolutionaries and the early scientists had grasped. It was the dogma of a static civilization.

One aspect of Hobbism came back into its own with Bentham and the utilitarians, themselves the product of the industrial advance of eighteenth century England. Materialism came back to England by way of the French Encyclopedists. At the same time the revolutionary-democratic ideas of the Levelers were revived by the theory and practice of the American and French revolutions, and began to take the new form of socialism. All these ideas, which we can trace back to Hobbes, were caught up by Marx and Engels and synthesized with a life-giving dose of dialectics to form the new revolutionary body of ideas which today we call Marxism.

References

[1] *The Leviathan,* pp. 63, 79.

[2] *Ibid.,* pp. 187–188.

[3] Clarendon, *A brief view and survey of the dangerous and pernicious errors to Church and State in Mr. Hobbes's book, entitled Leviathan,* pp. 181–182.

[4] *The Leviathan,* p. 65.

[5] *The Leviathan,* pp. 64–65. Cf. p. 89.

[6] It leads, of course, to wars between states; but the state of nature is worse than the condition of warfare between nations, which may indeed be profitable to the bourgeoisie: "But because they uphold thereby, the Industry of their Subjects;

there does not follow from it, that misery, which accompanies the Liberty of particular men" (*ibid.*, p. 65).

[7] *Ibid.*, p. 93. For primitive communism, see *English Works,* Vol. II, p. vi.

[8] John Selden, *Table Talk* (1847 ed.), p. 97.

[9] *The Leviathan,* p. 185.

[10] *Ibid.*, p. 74.

[11] *Clarke Papers* (Ed. C. H. Firth, 1891–1901), Vol. II, p. 404.

[12] Duchess of Newcastle, *Lives of William Cavendish, Duke of Newcastle, and His Wife, Margaret,* ed. C. H. Firth, p. 124.

[13] *The Leviathan,* p. 369.

[14] *Ibid.*, p. 76.

[15] *Ibid.*, p. 319.

[16] *Ibid.*, pp. 59–60.

[17] *Ibid.*, pp. 26, 153, 316.

[18] *Ibid.*, pp. 200, 238–239.

[19] *Ibid.*, pp. 351, 244, 342.

[20] *Ibid.*, p. 241.

[21] *English Works,* Vol. II, p. 227.

[22] *The Leviathan,* p. 180.

[23] *Ibid.*, p. 329.

[24] *Ibid.*, p. 241.

[25] *Ibid.*, pp. 204–205.

[26] *Ibid.*, p. 380.

[27] *Ibid.*, p. 376.

[28] *Ibid.*, p. 374.

[29] Leo Strauss, *The Political Philosophy of Hobbes,* passim.

[30] *English Works,* Vol. VI, p. 363.

[31] *The Leviathan,* p. 13. Cf. pp. 15, 20, 21, 369.

[32] *Ibid.*, p. 18.

[33] *Ibid.*, pp. 18, 24.

[34] *Ibid.*, pp. 18, 52–53, 66.

[35] *Ibid.*, pp. 109–110. Cf. p. 93. Clarendon takes this up, naturally enough: "He will introduce a Government of his own devising" (*A brief view . . .*, pp. 46–47).

[36] *The Leviathan,* p. 179.

[37] *Ibid.*, pp. 3, 8.

[38] *Works,* Vol. V, p. 55.

[39] *The Leviathan,* p. 17.

[40] *Ibid.*, p. 369.

[41] *Ibid.*, pp. 35, 337–338.

[42] *Ibid.*, p. 364.

[43] *Ibid.*, p. 40.

[44] Leo Strauss, *op. cit.*, p. 89.

[45] *The Leviathan,* pp. 24, 30, 49.

[46] *De Corpore,* Dedication.

[47] *The Leviathan,* pp. 28, 30.

[48] *Ibid.*, pp. 391–392.

[49] Cf. Maurice Cornforth, *Science Versus Idealism,* pp. 37–40. Already Hobbes had marked a decline as well as an advance on Bacon. As Marx put it: "Materialism becomes one-sided. Hobbes is the man who systematizes Baconism materialism. Knowledge based upon the senses loses its poetic blossom, it passes into the abstract experience of the mathematician . . . Materialism takes to misanthropy." (Quoted by Engels, *Socialism, Utopian and Scientific,* p. xi.) This misanthropy is reflected in Hobbes's reactionary political position, as contrasted, say, with a revolutionary religious philosopher like Milton. Consideration of this fact may help to explain why, in the next century, a radical like Blake proclaimed himself a Berkeleian, whilst the Tory Dr. Johnson refuted idealism. Materialism, so long as it is mechanical, cannot be isolated as the only progressive strand in thought. Until materialism becomes dialectical it cannot be revolutionary in the political sense.

REMARKS ON THE MATERIALISM OF THE EIGHTEENTH CENTURY

by

H. J. POS

Hendrik Josephus Pos has been Professor of Philosophy at the University of Amsterdam since 1932 and is a member of the Royal Dutch Academy of Arts and Sciences. His publications include *Zur Logik der Sprachwissenschaft* (1922) ; articles concerning philosophy of language in the *Philosophischer Anreizer, Recherches philosophiques,* and the *Proceedings* of the 2nd, 3rd, and 4th International Congresses of Philosophy. Editor of a book about anti-Semitism (1938), and editor in chief of *Algemein Nederlands Tydschrift von Wysbegeerte* (Netherlands General Journal of Philosophy).

(Translated from the French by Henry F. Mins)

THE first representative of materialism in European philosophy was Democritus, who stands at the end of a current of thought coming down from Thales of Miletus. These thinkers were all materialists, in the sense that they considered the reality of the cosmos as autonomous and objectively given. To say that the cosmos is made up of the element of moisture or of air is to consider it and its fullness as materially based on a datum which is itself material. The meaning to be given here to the notion of matter is that of something which is hard, which exists outside us and independently of us, and which is active. By the hardness of matter we mean the resistance it offers to the senses ; by its activity, the fact that all matter affects other matter. The materialistic naturalists of the pre-Socratic period saw no reason why matter should not comprise all reality, including living beings and, in particular, man. They inclined the more readily to this view because they drew no sharp distinction between inert and living matter. The same Thales who proclaimed moisture as the principle of the cosmos seems also to have said that "everything is full of souls." There is nothing spiritualist about this, for the ancients considered the soul as a thing which was material, in a secondary way: the souls which live in the land of the dead are like images, without force, regretting the complete existence they had on earth. Democritus' materialism, more developed and epistemologically more sophisticated, denotes as ἐτεῇ, real, the existence of atoms. Sense phenomena derive from this reality, but it remains unperceived by the senses. This is the objectivity of the atoms. The point of the materialistic philosophy is to recall to us what is objective even if phenomenologically, in immediate consciousness, we can not always maintain awareness of this objectivity. We cannot, because the life of the organism does not let us think of it all the time, and because the senses present matter to us in the light which corresponds to their own function. Here arises the problem of the duality between the truth, which is identical with objective reality, and the appearances to which the living being's consciousness is subjected. If matter, or the indestructible energy which is everywhere, is the objective reality, why is this truth hidden? And why is it that, even after having rediscovered it, consciousness finds itself unable to persist in it uninterruptedly? Or again, is not so-called objective reality a creation of the spirit, whose limitations appear in the difficulties just mentioned?

Materialism will always have this attractive side, that it takes for its starting point a substratum continuous for all phenomena. Even when it does not specify the precise nature of the matter which underlies whatever takes place, it has the great merit of giving unity to all that is real, and thereby avoiding the impasses of dualism. Its task is, if not to reduce every phenomenon to matter, at least to exhibit its fundamental relation to the universal substratum. This task will have a critical and a positive aspect.

Critically, it will consist in restraining the inclination of thought to isolate the spiritual and the ideal from the real, and in showing that the links of the chain are never broken. All spirituality is a liberation, but one whose conditions can be traced all the way into the biological sphere. Spirituality always entails a subjective interpretation of itself, comparable to the sort of subjective interpretation of colors which imagines itself to be objective. In this case, it is materialism which embodies the objectivist point of view, by stressing the real ground of every spiritualist position. It may be subjectively more satisfying to distinguish many realms of reality, each independent of the others; objectively, however, we are compelled to ask how, in this hierarchy, each stage rests on the preceding one, and to what degree it is prepared for by it. If spiritualism and idealism fix their eyes on high and look down on phenomena, materialism will be diligent to the contrary, refusing except under direct compulsion to accept any structure transcending the structure that is given. Obviously, certain fundamental distinctions resist all attempts at reduction, e.g., the distinction between dead and organized matter, and in particular that between the animal and the human kingdoms. Here materialism has the positive task of showing how the higher structure could emerge from the lower without having been previously implicit in it. Materialism thus conceived is not a conception of universal reality, but a method of inquiry which proceeds from the simpler to the more complex. It is in accordance with this method not to set qualitative, impassable boundaries between structures, but to suppose that the qualitative differences have had quantitative origins, which have accumulated. If accumulations everywhere give rise to changes in quality, then this correlation is to be accepted as a universal experience, and furnishes a link between the world of matter and that of life and spirit, one which is opposed to any deep-reaching dualism.

The materialist criticism, based on the durable element in reality, will reject metaphysical notions of an after-life, along with the deduction of the world from a first cause. In so doing it will bring out the fact that the value of the spiritual side of our nature does not imply its unlimited duration, and that reality loses none of its mystery when we presuppose another reality behind it. But it is no longer transcendental realities that this criticism will have to oppose primarily. In the eighteenth century this was to be sure the principal theme of the discussion between spritualism and materialism. Today the dispute has moved to other ground; it is no longer the beyond which is in question, but the autonomy of the spiritual or ideal domain. The transcendental dualism of other days has been replaced by an equally rigorous immanent dualism which gives the old transcendentalism a new form in terms of a radical separation between the realm of the ideal and that of the real. This duality is accompanied by a moral doctrine which, with Kant, makes a distinction between actions motivated by "desire" and those inspired by "the moral law."

German philosophy presents many variations on this idealism, all of them looking down from above on the real as something of an inferior species compared to the ideal. This idealism always tends to speak of the "merely real," to make it appear that the ideal transcends it in value. It maintains that the moral act has no connection with impulse and desire, and that the cognitive act is independent of the play of sensations and associations. It likes to speak of eternal truth, effecting a radical separation between it and its provisional content, but attributing eternity to the very formula in which it is embodied at the present moment. Idealism thereby runs the risk of impeding the progress of science. It engages in semantic analysis of what is meant by a science in general, abstracting from the part played by the real, which is grasped by knowledge.

The French materialism of the eighteenth century owed much to its English predecessors. Francis Bacon's empiricism was all but materialistic, and the doctrine of Thomas Hobbes was so completely. It is true that Newton and Boyle founded the mechanism of the universe on the divine will, but their contributions to science were purely mechanist in tendency. If the French mind, which was originally inclined to skepticism, began to embrace materialism after the death of Louis XIV, this was largely in order to have it as an ally against dogma. La Mettrie, who was a materialist 100 per cent, called himself a Pyrrhonian, and considered Montaigne the first Frenchman who dared to think. Voltaire, we recall, introduced Newton's celestial mechanics into France. Newton had reconciled mechanism and Providence, and Voltaire followed his lead. Nevertheless the continuation of Newtonian ideas in France culminated in Laplace, for whom the origin of the world required no creator. If Voltaire attacked the Church, it was not in order to prove that God does not exist, but to argue in favor of the natural light of reason which enables us to know Him. He therefore strongly opposed materialism, whose chief representatives were La Mettrie and Holbach.

Julien Offray de La Mettrie was born at Saint-Malo in 1709. He took up medicine, and went to Leyden to study under Boerhaave, who had got the reputation of atheism for his Spinozistic sympathies. A severe attack of fever gave La Mettrie the opportunity to observe the influence of the circulation on thought, observations which he utilized in his *Histoire naturelle de l'âme*. The fundamental idea of the book is the unity of body and soul. Anyone who wishes to study the soul should commence by studying the body, of which the soul is the form, as all matter has form. The senses are our guide in respect to knowledge. Since matter is inert of itself, and the living body is matter in movement, the soul is the principle of movement. But movement can no more be separated from matter than can form. A *primum movens* outside matter is meaningless. Matter itself is form, movement, and sensation. Starting from the substantial forms of scholasticism, La Mettrie arrived at the thesis that whatever is capable of sensation is material. Likewise, the *Histoire naturelle de l'âme* uses the philosophizing of the ancients as a starting point from which to go on to show to what extent they can be dispensed with.

In a second work, *L'Homme machine* (1748), the tone is more direct and positive. Descartes is criticized for his radical dualism; Leibniz "spiritualized matter instead of materializing the soul." Experience and observation should be our only guides. Only doctors, who have observed the soul in its greatness and its misery, have the right to discuss it. The great system-making minds have all neglected experience; they have failed to consider that it is the temperament (which is determined by physical causes) that determines the characters and acts of men. Food and drink imperiously sway man's moral side. It is a prejudice to think that man is radically distinct from the animals. It is by intelligence, which is linked to language, that he has achieved his superiority. La Mettrie declare that he does not wish to take part in the discussion as to the existence of God and the life after death, but he lets his actual opinion show through. He sees Descartes's greatness in his mechanical explanation of the living body.

La Mettrie's theories were not designed to gain him the support of most of his contemporaries. Moreover, the frivolity shown in some of his writings furnished a pretext for rejecting the totality of his thought indiscriminately. His *Discours sur le bonheur* is frankly hedonist. The most elevated spiritual joys are necessarily corporeal in nature, but are preferable to sensual pleasures, which are short-lived. It is true that La Mettrie was no saint; but he had the courage not to hide what he was, and thereby rose above all hypocrisy. And philosophy is indebted to him for that keen sense of observation which so greatly helped in eliminating prejudices and opening the way to a richer and more precise knowledge of man's nature, whose duality reduces to two aspects, basically linked.

The works of Baron d'Holbach differ from those of La Mettrie by their systematic structure. His principal work, *Système de la nature, ou des lois du monde physique et du monde moral,* appeared in 1770, in London. Lagrange, the great mathematician, and Diderot contributed to it. In 1772 the author published a popular résumé, entitled *Le Bon sens, ou idées naturelles opposées aux idées surnaturelles,* in which the sovereignty of the people and their right to revolution are openly defended. Nature is the only real being; anything else, said to be correlative to it, is imagination only. The human mind has become what it is only because of the satisfaction which it gives the instincts in their struggle with the environment. Movement dominates everything; it is the cause of our sensations and knowledge, even up to its most abstract forms. There is continuous interaction among the three kingdoms of nature. The tendency to self-conservation is in everything; in physics it is called inertia, and in morals self-love. Holbach criticized the notions of order and disorder, applied by the mind to nature, as purely anthropocentric. What we call an anomaly is produced by the same necessity which gives rise to the normal. The beautiful and the ugly are of human origin. While La Mettrie liked to describe himself as a disciple of Descartes, Holbach accused Descartes of having been the first to make a radical dichotomy between the body and the soul, instead of concluding that matter is capable of feeling and thinking. In matters of ethics, Holbach followed La Mettrie closely, but was free from his frivolity. For him too, it was medicine that must solve the problems of morality. His idea that the criminal is a sick man is in profound agreement with this conception. Ethics and politics have everything to learn from the materialist conception of man. He attacks the idea of God in all its forms. Religion is responsible for the great corruption of man, even in its deistic and pantheistic forms. An extensive analysis shows that the proofs of the existence of God are untenable. Even Spinozism, which for a long time counted as equivalent to materialism, is condemned. Morality is absolutely independent of religion, which has made no contribution whatever to uplifting the human race. In this judgment, clearly, our philosopher shows an absolute lack of the historical sense. Religion certainly did contribute to the education of Europe after the fall of ancient civilization; what happened was that the dogmatic envelope which protected moral values cracked at a certain time, after it had performed its service.

This lack of the historical sense prevented eighteenth century materialism from seeing an ally in religion rather than an adversary. If it had been more open to the spiritual history of humanity, it would have been able to justify dogma for its pragmatic value instead of rejecting it as immoral and absurd. It would have recognized that an altruistic enthusiasm, even when accompanied by supernatural imagery, bears within it an unquestionable moral value. On this point the critcism of religion in Kant was much more prudent. It can be said that Kant was the first to give a pragmatic interpretation of religion, and was thus prevented from seeing in it only a pretense or an absurdity.

The materialism of the eighteenth century thus has its historical limitations: it is too static to be able to explain the traditional spirituality against which it reacts, and too theoretical to admit the pragmatic value of a supernatural inspiration in so far as the latter proves rich in consequences for human life. Its function in the eighteenth century was primarily that of being in opposition, and as a result it was sometimes led into an overnegative dogmatism. Nevertheless, its attitude yields certain principles which make materialism, if not a basis, at least an essential aspect of every rational method of philosophizing. A first principle, it seems to us, which holds good for all rational thought, is that of the subsistence of a world which does not depend on any conscious activity but to a certain extent determines consciousness. This world is an ensemble of elements, inanimate and animate, whose essential character is to act on one another. There is no need to make pronouncements as to the structure of the substratum which underlies all the phenomena of the world. It is not the atom nor the cell that assures reality to the substratum, which consists in this very coherence of which we have been speaking. The fundamental category is not matter, but the real. But any aspect of it, even the most ideal, is not wholly independent of this coherence in which all elements interpenetrate.

The reality of history and of psychological and social phenomena, while presenting particular aspects in relation to matter, are also integrated in the cosmos. The dualism of body and mind fails to recognize that there is a continual transition from one aspect into the other. The supreme value which human life attributes to the spiritual side should not cause us to forget that everything is connected, and that nothing has an autonomous existence.

It is inevitable that the real should divide into forms, and that in this process entities should appear which are very distant from the primordially real. Here the method of "materialism" shows its value, recalling to us that there is no life without matter and no spirit without life, and reducing the higher levels to lower, as far as possible, without denying or falsifying their hierarchy. If therefore we reject the dogmatic position held by the materialism of old, we assign it a permanent critical function which consists in reducing another dogmatism which tends to isolate spiritual phenomena from material and biological reality, and thus destroys the unity of the real. This criticism is not unaware that life evolves upward; but it keeps in mind that all is linked, and that, if a superior order is not caused by what underlies it, it is still conditioned thereby.

HEGEL, MARX, AND ENGELS

by

AUGUSTE

CORNU

Auguste Cornu (docteur de droit and docteur es lettres, University of Paris) is Professor of German Literature at the Lycée Buffon, Paris. He is the author of *Karl Marx, l'homme et l'œuvre* (1934), *Moses Hess et la gauche Hégélienne* (1934), *Karl Marx et la révolution de 1848* (1948), and is a contributor to *Pensée, Europe,* and *A la Lumière du Marxisme.*

(Translated from the French by Henry F. Mins)

THE OBJECT of this essay is to fix the role and the essential contributions of Hegel, Marx, and Engels in the evolution of modern thought, taking it in its connections with economic and social evolution.

At first the movement of modern thought followed the development of the rising class, the bourgeoisie, and in this phase reached its highest point in materialist rationalism and in Hegel. Thereafter, it was taken up by the new rising class, the proletariat, and in Marxism attained a conception of the world which was adapted to a new mode of economic and social organization.

It took form under the influence of the great discoveries of the fifteenth century, which infinitely expanded the world's boundaries and provoked a rapid growth of needs and the consequent development of a new economic system based on a greater freedom of production and circulation of wealth. This system caused at once a profound change in men's way of life and a progressive transformation of the static conception of the world into a dynamic conception which was dominated, like the system itself, by the notions of liberty, movement, and progress.

This thought, which at the outset found its expression in the two great movements of spiritual liberation, the Renaissance and the Reformation, took its first major form in rationalism, which adds the notion of progress to the idea of liberty, and, after Renaissance and Reformation, marked a second stage in the adaptation of the general conception of the world to the new way of life. Rationalism, the philosophy of the rising bourgeoisie, rejected the notion of an immutable and eternal preestablished order, and supported the revolutionary action of the bourgeoiesie in maintaining the necessity of transforming the world to give it a rational character and content. Rationalism tended to evolve from spiritualism to materialism, thereby expressing the growing importance of concrete material reality in human life, as a result of the unceasing development of production.

Despite its tendency to unite spiritual reality more closely to material reality, rationalism did not succeed in solving the essential problem of the integration of man into his natural and social milieu—a problem raised by the very development of production. For, being a reflection of bourgeois society, it came up against the fundamental contradiction, inherent in the capitalist system, between an increasingly collective mode of production, which brings men closer and closer together in their economic and social activity, and an individualist mode of appropriation based on private property and the quest for profit, which isolates men and sets them, as individuals, against society. Rationalism is led to conceive of man as an individual opposed to his social milieu and cannot therefore arrive at a conception of the world as an organic whole; it remains essentially dualistic and allows the traditional opposition to subsist between spirit and matter, between man and nature.

Yet the very development of the new system of production, which integrates man more and more deeply in the external world, brings about the need to go beyond this dualism and arrive at an organic conception of the world. However, all the attempts made by bourgeois thought in this direction failed by virtue of the fact that in defending the principle of private property and thus putting itself on the plane of the contradiction which the capitalist system gives rise to, it could abolish this contradiction only in a utopian manner, by an illusory surmounting of individualism and the integration of man in an imaginary milieu.

After Rousseau, who integrated man into an idealized nature and a utopian society, and Kant, who gave this integration a formal character, reducing it to the *a priori* forms imposed by the mind on the external world, German idealist philosophy, whose greatest figure was Hegel, strove to pass beyond rationalist dualism to an organic conception of the world. It was inspired by Goethe who, after Spinoza's fashion, considered mind and matter as two manifestations of the divine, different in their forms but similar in essence, and held that man should plunge into nature in order to participate in the universal life which animates the world (Faust).

German idealist philosophy added to this idea of an organic union of man and the external world the notion of development and progress, which it applied to the totality of beings and things; it thus attained a new conception of the world, which was no longer considered as an ensemble of things ruled from without and functioning as a mechanism, but as the expression of a single life animating all beings, as an immense organism developing itself under the action of internal laws and forces.

Inasmuch as life cannot be conceived otherwise than in its unity and development, this philosophy was of necessity led to reduce spiritual reality and material reality to an organic unity, and to show how this organic totality changes and evolves.

Like rationalism, this philosophy adopted the point of view of bourgeois society and defended its economic and social organization; it was unable to go beyond individualism and bring about the effective integration of man into his natural and social milieu, and could only undertake this integration in an illusory manner, by the reduction of the whole of the real to mind.

Fichte, Schelling, Hegel—the German idealist philosophers—abolished Kant's *Ding-an-sich* which maintained for concrete reality an existence independent of the thinking subject. They reduced all of reality to mind, which, by virtue of its inclusion of concrete reality, became at once subject and object and constituted not only the tool of knowledge but the element which creates and regulates the world.

The real, thus reduced to spiritual activity, was identified with knowledge, in which the subject which knows and the object which is known merge, and whose movement is explained by the autodetermination of the spirit, by the exteriorization of what it potentially contains, by the alienation of its own substance which becomes foreign to it, and which it recovers progressively in becoming aware that it constitutes its essence.

In this conception of evolution as progressive penetration of concrete reality by the spirit, the philosophers were under the inspiration of the French Revolution, which seemed to them to have solved the double problem of the rational changing of the world and the integration of man into his social milieu by going beyond immediate reality and traditional economic and social organization under the action of reason, and by subordinating the individual to the state.

But while the French revolutionaries changed the world effectively, these philosophers, because of Germany's backwardness in economic and social evolution, gave action a theoretical and abstract character, transposing it to the plane of thought. They changed political, economic, and social problems into philosophical problems which they reduced to the central problem of the epoch, the problem of liberty, and proposed to realize the latter by the way of the spirit, convinced that in virtue of the correlation between the development of material reality and that of spiritual reality, it was possible to act on the world and transform it by the unaided power of ideas.

Despite their idealist nature, the systems of these philosophers are distinguished by an ever more marked tendency toward realism, a tendency which led them to ascribe to the world, which was at first considered to be a mere expression of the spirit, an ever more objective and concrete reality.

Fichte, expressing the revolutionary aspirations of his times, put the stress not on the past which has been wiped out, nor on a present which does not change, but on the future. He thereby subordinated to the spirit the external world which should be transformed; he abolished the external world, reducing it to the not-I and making of it the tool of the I, which rises, by a continual surmounting of the not-I which it sets up against itself, to a higher morality and a great autonomy.

Schelling expresses the counterrevolutionary tendencies of the feudal class. He gives the present the task of going back to its source, that is to the past, under the inspiration of the Middle Ages, an epoch of high and strong spirituality, when the Spirit penetrated vitally all the elements of life and the world. In this way he evolves toward a more objective idealism, and, in accord with Spinoza, he assigns Nature an existence distinct from that of the mind, and shows how, by a progressive interpenetration of Spirit and Nature, the world comes in the work of art to a state of complete indifferentiation, where Nature is Spirit and Spirit Nature.

Finally, in Hegel the evolution toward an organic conception of the world, intimately combining the Idea and the concrete reality, man and the external world, is even plainer to be seen. Hegel is the interpreter of the tendencies of a semiconservative bourgeoisie; what he sets himself to justify is not the future nor the past, but the present. Like all doctrinaire conservatives, he stops the evolution of the world at the present moment, to which he gives absolute value as the definitive and perfect result of rational evolution. To this end he strives to give idealism a concrete character. He transposes to the ideological level the ever more powerful action which the development of productive forces enables man to exert on his milieu; and he shows how the spirit integrates itself progressively into the real, which thereby assumes an ever more rational character.

Since he does not succeed, as Marx was later to do, in understanding reality as the object of man's concrete practical activity, and thereby penetrating to the efficient cause of the transformation of the world, he remains essentially idealist in his evolution toward realism, and like Fichte and Schelling considers the real as the object of spiritual activity.

The fundamental problem which then faces him is to show how concrete reality merges in effect with its spiritual representation, and how the development of the spirit not only expresses but determines the evolution of the world. Hegel therefore neglects the contingent, the accidental elements of the real, concentrating on those which express a phase of the spirit and carry out the work of Reason.

Once concrete reality has thus been purged and sublimated to the point of being nothing more than the expression of the spiritual reality, it can be included in the spirit, after which Hegel is enabled to mold as it were the development of the world in the form of the development of the spirit, which is elevated into the creator of the real.[1]

Hegel, unlike Fichte, desired to justify present reality and derived the development of the world not from an absolute will, which no determinate reality can satisfy, but from a reason which is higher than the subjective reason—namely, objective reason, which combines within itself spirit and being.

This objective reason is incarnated in the Absolute Idea, which creates the world by the exteriorization or alienation of its substance, which it then proceeds to resume within itself in stages. The identity of the real and the rational which existed originally in the Absolute Idea is broken by virtue of the exteriorization of its substance in a reality which seems alien to it; but the identity is progressively reestablished by the activity of the spirit, which eliminates the irrational elements from the real and thus leads it to surmount itself constantly, to take a form and a content more and more suited to the reason. This progressive union of the rational and the real, of spirit and being, is realized under the form of concrete ideas which are not a mere representation of beings and things, which man makes for himself, but constitute the reality itself in its essence.

Since the idea is indissolubly attached to the concrete reality, with which it is loaded, so to speak, the movement of the idea does not occur on the plane of pure logic, but is bound up with the general evolution of the world, with the process of history.

This association of logic with history in the development of the spirit gives rise to the particular character of Hegel's doctrine which tends, by the integration of the idea into the real, to eliminate the transcendental conception, which attributes to the spirit a special existence foreign to and distinct from the sensible world. This association also explains Hegel's opposition both to dogmatism (which by separating thought from being renders thought impotent and sterile) and to utopianism (which seeks to subject reality to an arbitrary ideal), as well as to empiricism (which fails to rise above immediate reality and loses itself in the infinite mass of facts, entities and objects, instead of concentrating on the essential part, the spiritual reality).[2]

True reality is linked to the development of the spirit, and is not to be confused with immediate reality. Like spirit, it has a rational character and its movement is in accordance with the principle of a logic adapted to a dynamic conception of the world, dialectics.

As opposed to the ancient logic—which corresponds to a static conception of the world and accordingly considers entities and things in their eternal and immutable aspect, fixing them in their identity by the exclusion of contraries—dialectics is tied up with the very development of entities and things and does not obey the principle of identity, which does not enable us to explain the connections which unite the various elements of the real, and the reasons for their transformations.

Dialectics is founded on the opposite principle, the principle of contradiction; it does not move on a spatial plane of inclusion or exclusion, like the old logic, but on a temporal plane which enables the contradictory elements of the real, instead of merely excluding each other, to imply each other mutually and, by their transformations, to determine the evolution of the world.

The old logic considered contradiction as constituting a defect in things; in dialectics, on the contrary, contradiction appears as the positive and fertile element without which there is no development nor life.[3] For in the world, when considered in its changeableness, contraries unite to form a new and higher reality, the synthesis. The latter does not result from an adjustment or compromise between the contraries, which could only end in a stagnation of the real; it results from a crisis brought about by the accentuation of the contradictions, in whose course the contraries are abolished as such and reabsorbed in a higher unity.[4]

This is the dialectic process in which the contraries change and unite into syntheses within which new contradictions arise, which in turn are reabsorbed in new syntheses; it is in this process that there finds expression the movement of the spirit which, in its movement to go beyond the contradictions which rise continuously, progresses from concept to concept, each of which represents a new level of spiritual reality and of material reality included within it.

Such is the general conception of the world from which Hegel starts, in order to reconstruct and explain the totality of the real reduced to concepts, and to show how in its development it follows a rational course and expresses the movement of the spirit.

After he has, in the *Phänomenologie des Geistes* and the *Logic,* described the somewhat theoretical evolution of the spirit up to the point where it becomes perfect reason and Absolute Idea, he shows how the latter realizes itself in rudimentary fashion in Nature, which appears as its antithesis, and then in a more and more perfect way in history, where it gradually detaches itself from objective reality by considering it as the expression of its own substance. The Absolute Idea reaches its full realization in art, religion, and philosophy, attaining its last stage in the Hegelian philosophy, which encompasses the world as a rational totality in which the identity of the subject and the object, thought and being is realized.

This conception of the dialectic development of the world permitted Hegel to solve the hitherto insoluble problem of the organic union of spirit and matter, of man and the external world, considered in their development. But the solution which he gave this problem took on an illusory character by reason of the fact that in reducing concrete reality to spiritual reality he took away from the world its own nature, and integrated man into an imaginary milieu.

This inability, which he shared with all bourgeois thought, to solve the problem of man's integration into the world, otherwise than on an ideological level, explains the contradictory aspect of his philosophy which, like his entire epoch of transition from a still semifeudal organization to the capitalist system, presents a character of transition and compromise.

From the philosophical point of view, this doctrine constituted a compromise between transcendental idealism, which places the principle and end of entities and things outside themselves, and realism, which is inspired by the idea of immanence and explains their development by their intrinsic nature. Despite the idealism of the doctrine, which reduced the evolution of the world to the movement of concepts, it marked the passage to realism by the integration of the idea in the real. All that was required was to invert the system (as Marx was to do) and subordinate the development of the spirit to the development of economic and social reality in order to arrive at a materialist conception of the world.

From another point of view, this doctrine constituted a compromise between the static and the dynamic conceptions of the world. It was completely imbued with a dynamicism, which expresses the continuous change, the incessant evolution of the world considered in its becoming. But this dynamic quality was not yet fully inherent in the concrete reality, whose development still seemed to be determined by a first principle, the Absolute Idea existing of itself from all eternity. The Absolute Idea is the stable element in the eternal process whose cause and end it is; containing in potentiality all the reality which it creates, it is at the terminus of its development that which it was at the origin. Evolution thus remained illusory, and took the form of an involution, which made this system once more akin to the old static conception of the world.

Finally, in the political field, this compromise between static and dynamic world views was evidenced in the attempt to reconcile a conservative system, which considered the Prussian state and the Christian religion as the perfect and definitive forms of the Absolute Idea, with the dialectic movement of history, which implies a continual change, an unceasing becoming, to which we cannot assign a determinate form as limit and end.

The Revolution of 1830, which destroyed the system of the Holy Alliance and in Germany was marked at once by a rapid economic upswing and by the development of liberalism, was to blow to the surface the inherent contradictions of the Hegelian doctrine, entailing the collapse of the entire system.

Within the Hegelian school itself a division took place between a conservative Right and a revolutionary Left, within which Marx and Engels passed their political apprenticeship. The Hegelian Left, expressing primarily the aspirations of the bourgeoisie, brought about a dissociation and transformation of the Hegelian doctrine in order to adapt it to liberalism.

It rejected the conservative elements of this philosophy and retained only its revolutionary dialectics, forming out of it, in the person of Karl Marx's friend Bruno Bauer, a doctrine of action. Bauer opposed consciousness to substance, making the latter, after the fashion of Fichte's non-ego, the tool which consciousness uses to rise to an ever greater autonomy; he posited in principle consciousness' need to free itself continually from substance, in which it realizes itself and which, by its determinate form, constitutes an obstacle to its development. This liberation is carried out by an incessant criticism of the real which eliminates its irrational elements.[5]

The ideological character of this doctrine, which reduced revolutionary action to a critique of the real, had as its source the fact that the Hegelian Left found no support in the German bourgeoisie, which at that time, like all the European bourgeoisie engaged in a war on two fronts against feudal reaction and the revolutionary proletariat, adopted a policy of the "golden mean." Without this support, the Hegelian Left very soon failed in its liberal activity, and its action rapidly turned into a sterile critique of reality, a mere play of the spirit.

Most of its members evolved with B. Bauer toward individualism and egocentrism, reducing the development of the universal Conscience to that of the Ego. One of them, Max Stirner, drew all the consequences of this tendency toward individualism. He rejected any limitation of the individual's autonomy and recognized only a single reality, the Ego, only a single principle, the cult of the Ego; he made absolute egoism the only motive force of human activity, and ended up in nihilism and anarchism.[6]

At first, Marx and Engels tried, with the Young Hegelians, to adapt the Hegelian doctrine to liberalism and felt that in order to determine the rational course of the world it would suffice to eliminate the irrational elements from the real. But as apart from the other Young Hegelians, Marx, in this point faithful to the basic thought of Hegel, refused to dissociate thought from the real, and rejected the conception of an arbitrary and absolute power of the spirit to transform the world. From the time of his thesis on the *Philosophy of Nature of Democritus and Epicurus* (1841), he showed that philosophy, in contraposing itself to the world by its criticism, changes into a practical activity, which implies its integration into the world and thereby its suppression as abstract principle opposed to the world.[7]

As director of the *Rheinische Zeitung* in 1842, he set about reforming the state (which he with Hegel considered as the regulatory element in society) by a critique of political and juridical institutions. The speedy and total failure of this attempt, signalized by the suppression of the *Rheinische Zeitung,* led him to revise his conception of the state and to study its relations with society.

Along with some members of the Hegelian Left (L. Feuerbach, M. Hess, F. Engels), he turned away from liberalism; he no longer expressed the aspirations of the bourgeoisie but those of the proletariat, and evolved towards communism. In this evolution he, like Hess and Engels, was guided by Feuerbach who drew from a critique of the Christian religion and Hegelian idealism a social doctrine of collectivist nature.

Feuerbach's critique of religion showed that God is the product of man, who projects and alienates in him his own essential qualities, and that as a result of this inversion of subject and attribute the real subject, man, becomes the attribute of God, which he has created. Applying this critique to Hegelian idealism, Feuerbach emphasized that

Hegel, by an analogous inversion of subject and attribute, made the idea the creative subject, and man and the world its product.

To arrive at an exact notion of the relations between God and the world, between the Idea and Being, we must, Feuerbach said, start not from God or the Idea but from concrete and living reality; we must integrate spirit into matter and not matter into spirit, and consider man with his sensibility and needs as the organic expression of that synthesis.[8] His criticism of religion ended up in a social doctrine, in which he showed that religion strips man of his true nature, of his essence, and transfers it to God, and that to restore man's essence to him, his qualities, alienated in God, must be reintegrated in him. The collective being, the species, which constitutes the human essence, and which, if exteriorized in God, is but a transcendental illusion, then becomes a reality for man, who abandons egoism and individualism, and makes the love of humanity the law of his life.[9]

By his inversion of Christianism and idealism, Feuerbach restored their intrinsic reality to the external world and to man; but by his return to mechanist materialism, which subordinates man to the influence of his milieu without considering the action he exerts upon it, Feuerbach's final result was a contemplative and sentimental theory which placed human life outside the social milieu and historical process, a vague collectivism which was a pale reflection of the French socialist doctrines born of a more advanced economic and social development.

This doctrine by its solution, however imperfect, of the problem of man's integration into his natural and social milieu constituted a transition between Hegelianism and Socialism. It opened the way which Moses Hess, Marx, and Engels were to take, to arrive at a new solution of the problem by linking man's integration into the world not to his religious emancipation but to his social emancipation.

Moses Hess gave Feuerbach's extremely vague collectivism a more markedly social character, and showed that the alienation of the human essence in God was the ideological reflection of the alienation which takes place in the capitalist system, where the proletariat exteriorizes its labor power in the commodities it produces, which enslave it by opposing themselves to him in the form of money, capital.

To liberate man from this servitude and enable him to recover his thus alienated essence, Hess said, we must replace the capitalist regime by a communist system; but, being unable to obtain from society itself the sources of its transformation, Hess, like the utopians, transposed the economic and social problems raised by this transformation to a moral plane, and offered as solution the struggle against egoism, and the love of humanity.[10]

For all its defects and inadequacies, this doctrine constituted a transition between Feuerbach's philosophy and French socialism; it was to serve as a guide to Marx and Engels who, starting from an analogous critique of alienation, furnished a new solution to the problem of action and to the social problem. Marx, having been led to review his Hegelian conception of the state and to study the interrelations of state and society, began this revision by a critique of Hegel's *Philosophy of Law,*[11] from which he had drawn the core of his political and social ideas. Now, under Feuerbach's influence, he shows how Hegel reverses the real relations between society and state, making the latter the creator and regulator of society, whereas actually it is but society's instrument. The real state, which is an expression of society, and in which private interest triumphs, is contrasted with the ideal state, a sphere of general interests, created, like God, by the exteriorization in it of the highest social qualities, in which man lives, only in an illusory fashion, a collective life. In order to put an end to this duality between real and ideal states and give the collective life an effective existence, society must be given a collective character.

This criticism of Hegel's *Philosophy of Law* marked the moment at which Marx rejected liberalism by putting the problem of alienation on the political and social plane, but yet found only a vague solution to it, in the form of what he called true democracy.

But after he had taken the content of the ideal state to be the true democracy where there no longer exists any opposition between individual interests and the public interest, he was drawn, by his criticism of bourgeois society conceived as the negation of collective life, to see communism as the solution of the social problem.

He returned to the fundamental idea of his criticism of Hegel's *Philosophy of Law* in his articles in the *Deutsch-Französische Jahrbücher* (1844), where he showed that if we are to do away with the dualism between society and state, which makes man lead the life of an egoistic individual in society while he leads an imaginary collective life in the state, we must integrate the state into society, giving the latter a collective character.[12] This will be the work of a social revolution carried out by the proletariat, which in liberating itself will emancipate all of society, establishing communism.[13]

Marx was now deliberately orienting his thinking toward communism, acting as spokesman for the revolutionary proletariat. He raised the question of alienation, no longer on the plane of undifferentiated humanity, but on the plane of the struggle of classes. Thus he changed the opposition between egoism and altruism, to which Feuerbach and Hess had reduced economic and social contradictions, to a conflict between bourgeoisie and proletariat; he cast social development in the form of dialectics, making the proletariat the antithetic element charged with bringing progress about.

Following a parallel evolution to that of Marx, Engels was then passing, under the influence of Feuerbach and Hess, from liberalism to communism. With Feuerbach and Hess, he considered alienation as the basic phenomenon of present society; but, instead of following them to a utopian plane for the abolition of this alienation, he sought, as Marx did, to find the sources of its elimination in economic and social reality.

In both Engels and Marx, this surmounting of ideology and utopianism was favored by the fact that they had left Germany—Engels to go to England, and Marx to Paris—and thereby took part in the life of two countries which were much more developed economically than Germany; Marx and Engels thus expressed the aspirations of a more powerful proletariat, already possessing a clear class consciousness.

Marx was then justifying communism from a point of view which was essentially philosophical and political. Engels at the same time made use of his study of the contradictions of capitalism—which were especially obvious in England, the most developed capitalist country of the time—to justify communism from an economic and social viewpoint.

In his article "Umrisse zu einer Kritik der Nationalökonomie" [14] in the *Deutsch-Französische Jahrbücher,* Engels showed that the capitalist system did not possess the absolute value assigned to it by the economists of liberalism, and that the economic categories which corresponded to the system—price, competition, profit—had only historic and relative application. His criticism of the capitalist system underlined that its result was to deprive the majority of producers of the fruit of their labor, and thus to reduce them to servitude and poverty. The crises caused by the inherent capitalist unbalance between production and consumption entailed the elimination of the weakest producers, the progressive ruin of the middle class, which was proletarianized, and a constantly increasing concentration of wealth, which finally left only proletarians and big capitalists. This increasing antagonism would cause a social revolution that would abolish private property and competition and inaugurate a communist regime, which would give the economic and social system a human character.

Engels thus reached communism by a route different from that of Marx, that is by a criticism of the capitalist contradictions which enabled him to go beyond utopian socialism and show how the future emerges from the present, adapting the Hegelian dialectic to the development of history thought of from the economic and social viewpoint. Engels made more precise and complete the still theoretical and abstract notion which Marx had of historic evolution and communism.

It was during his stay in Paris in 1844 that Marx came under the influence of the French socialist doctrines and Engels' critique of political economy, and with their aid arrived at a clearer conception of historical evolution and of communism, considering them no longer from a purely philosophical and political viewpoint but also and above all from one which was economic and social.

The merit of the French socialist systems was to give the first positive solution to the problem of the integration of man into the world which bourgeois thinkers had been unable to solve; this they accomplished by showing how it was possible to realize the effective and harmonious integration of man in his natural and social milieu by passing beyond the capitalist contradiction, by conferring on the mode of appropriation the same collective character as the mode of production.

But these systems had been formed at an epoch in which the contradictions of capitalism had not yet become so evident, and in which the proletariat was still only in its inception; hence they transposed economic and social problems to an ideological plane and thus remained utopian. After having criticized the economic and social organization of capitalism, the doctrinaire socialists were unable to go forward and discern in society itself the factors of its transformation; they did not conceive the class struggle as a means of emancipation and put their projected reforms on a rational and moral plane, contrasting present society to an ideal society; they thought it would be enough to convince men of the excellence of this new society to have it realized.

This appeal to reason led them, after denouncing social antagonisms in the critical parts of their works, to take the position of an undifferentiated humanity in their plans for change, and to supplant the notion of class struggle by the notion of a vague antagonism between good and evil, between the just and the unjust, all of which imparted to the solution offered for the social conflicts a character no longer revolutionary but spiritual and moral.

Nevertheless, as the proletariat developed and the contradictions of capitalism became more obvious, these doctrinaires took up a sharper defense of the specific interests of the proletariat, and their ideas came closer and closer to socialism and communism, putting the primary emphasis on the revolutionary role of the class struggle and Marxism, which they announced and heralded.

By applying the Hegelian dialectic to the explanation of social process, Marx had already shown in his articles in the *Deutsch-Französische Jahrbücher* how capitalist society, by reason of the accentuation of the opposition between bourgeoisie and proletariat, had to give birth to a communist society. This communism was still ideological; it acquired a more concrete content from the French socialist doctrines and their analysis of the economic and social contradictions of capitalism; finally, Engels' critique of political economy enabled Marx to pass definitely beyond utopianism by showing him how communist society was engendered by the aggravation of these contradictions; Marx gave communism a scientific character by basing it on the very development of society.

This transition from ideological to scientific communism is the distinguishing mark of the three works preceding the *German Ideology,* in which the main lines of his thought appear as definitively fixed for the first time: *Political Economy and Philosophy* (1844), *The Holy Family* (1845), and the *Theses on Feuerbach* (1845).[15]

Marx still reduced the social question to the problem of alienation, which remained in his view the essential problem; by means of it he solved the problem of action, which enabled him to attain a new conception of historical development and of communism.

He solved these two problems by a parallel critique of Hegelian idealism and Feuerbach's mechanist materialism, a critique inspired by the aspirations of the revolutionary proletariat. In distinction from utopian socialism, he put the problem of suppressing alienation and effectively integrating man in his natural and social milieu not on the theoretical plane but on the practical plane; and he was led thereby to a new conception of action which enabled him to go at once beyond utopian socialism, speculative idealism, and mechanistic materialism, the latter two of which he accused of considering man outside concrete activity taken as practical activity, that is as work. This ignoring of the leading role of practical activity in human life made speculative idealism and mechanistic materialism equally unable to explain the evolution of the world.

Hegelian idealism does stress the capital importance of human activity, pointing out that the world is its product; but since it reduces this activity to spiritual activity and thus suppresses concrete reality as such, it gives an illusory quality both to human life and to the integration of man into the world.[16]

In contrast to idealism, mechanist materialism assigns the object a reality outside thought; but in considering the exterior world as an object of perception and not of action it maintains a passive attitude toward it and therefore ends in a contemplative and deterministic conception of the world, which does not allow it to explain either the effective integration of man into his milieu or his action on the milieu to transform it.[17]

Marx went beyond both speculative idealism and mechanist materialism. He kept the intrinsic reality of the external world and considered it in its transformation by practical activity, work which plays the role of mediator between man and the external world, between spirit and matter, which Hegel attributed to the Idea.

It is by concrete practical activity that man effects his progressive integration into the world which he adapts to his needs. This integration takes place by the exteriorization of man's labor power in the object which he creates and by the appropriation of this object which enables him to recover in it his alienated substance.[18]

In present society this exteriorization becomes an alienation on the part of the most numerous class, the proletariat, which is deprived of the objects it creates and becomes feebler to the very degree that it produces. To do away with this alienation a communist regime must be installed, which will enable all men to fully regain their substance exteriorized in the product of their labor.[19]

By this parallel criticism of idealism and mechanist materialism Marx arrived at a new conception of action. He did not reduce it to a spiritual action nor submit it to a fatalist determinism nor, as the utopians did, put it on the plane of opposition between thought and the real, the ideal and reality; he integrated action into reality.

It is on this new conception of action conceived as concrete practical activity, work, the only conception capable of explaining the effective integration of man into the world, that Marx based his conception of historical and dialectical materialism, the notion that from then on dominated and directed his thought and that of Engels.

He went beyond the problem of alienation, to which he had hitherto reduced the essence of the social question, and subordinated it to the ensemble of human activity, of which it was only one aspect. In the fundamental work which he wrote with Engels, *The German Ideology* (1846), he set himself the task of explaining the grounds of this activity and hence the transformation of society and the flux of history.

Seeking the essential causes and ends of human activity, Marx and Engels found them in the creation of the conditions of material life, in the satisfaction of humanity's primordial needs (food, clothing, shelter) and therefore in the organization of production. This is what gives their basic conception a materialist character.

This materialism is historical; it explains the movement of history essentially by the transformation of the conditions of material life, by the development of the forces of production, and not by an alteration of philosophical, political, or religious conceptions which are but the ideological forms assumed in men's consciousnesses by the real motives of their actions.

And this historical materialism is dialectic; it shows that the movement of history is linked to the development of the relations between the forces of production and the social forces. To determinate productives forces there correspond social relations adapted to the operation of these forces, and every important change in the latter necessarily entails transformation of society. In their continual development the forces of production come up against the organization of society, which evolves more slowly, and sooner or later becomes an obstacle to the operation of these forces, so that it must be replaced by a new and better adapted social organization.

On the political and social level, this opposition between productive forces and social relations is expressed by class struggles, which constitute the motive element in history.[20]

The materialist dialectic conception of history not only furnishes the explanation of economic, political, and social evolution, but enables us as well to explain spiritual evolution. Marx refutes the basic objection of idealism, which asserts that it is impossible to prove that objects distinct from us correspond to the representation which we have of things, and denies too any correlation between material and spiritual evolution. Marx's answer is that man knows the world not as object of pure thought, but as object of his experience, and that the proof of the objective reality and the truth of knowledge is furnished by practical activity.[21]

The idealist conception, which ascribes absolute value and reality to ideas alone, comes from the division of labor, which separates spiritual from material activity, creating a class of thinkers who tend to consider ideas by themselves, apart from the men who conceive them and the circumstances which engender them and alone enable us to understand and explain them.[22]

Marx and Engels thus denied absolute value and reality to ideas, and showed that they develop parallel to men's real mode of life, that juridical, political, philosophical, and religious conceptions are modified as the economic and social organizations change, and that spiritual evolution is thus determined in its main outlines by material evolution.[23]

While thus establishing a correlation between spiritual evolution and economic and social evolution, Marx and Engels did not claim to establish a rigorous parallelism between them, for they do not go forward at the same rhythm. While the transformation of the forces of production is accompanied by a parallel transformation of the social organization, the change takes place in a slower manner in the realm of ideas, whose ties with the mode of production are less direct and immediate.

Moreover, Marx and Engels, while denying ideas a primordial role in historical evolution, nevertheless consider them to be a very important social reality which as such influences the development of history, being able to modify its rhythms and modalities, if not the general course. Marx and Engels, in effect, rejected ideology as the determining factor in historical evolution. They did not make man into a passive tool, the object of a fatalistic determinism; on the contrary, they showed the mounting importance of man's action on his milieu, which he changes more and more deeply, in order to free himself from its grip and adapt it to his needs.[24]

Marx and Engels applied this general conception of historical development to the study of the society of their time, stressing that man's rational alteration of the milieu should at the present time aim essentially at wiping out the contradictions inherent in the capitalist regime and doing away with alienated labor, which is opposed to the integration of man in his natural and social milieu. This abolition cannot take place, as the doctrinaire socialists had already shown, except by the inauguration of a communist system. But unlike the doctrinaires, Marx and Engels did not contrast an ideal to reality, a vision of the future world to bourgeois society, setting up a gap between present and future; instead, they picked out in the present economic and social organization the causes, the tendency, and the manner of its transformation, and showed that the abolition of capitalism will be the work of the economic and social contradictions inherent in this regime, which cannot but engender a social revolution. This, by doing away with alienated labor and transforming the social relations which have been hypostatized as personal relationships, will bring about the harmonious and complete integration of man into his milieu.

Thus with Marx and Engels a great phase of modern thought is completed, that modern thought which is born with capitalism and finds its conclusion in communism. This thought expresses on the ideological plane the successive steps of man's integration into his natural and social milieu, determined by the constant development of the forces of production; it is a thought which leads from a static and dualistic conception, which opposes spirit to matter, man to his milieu, to an organic conception of the world considered in its totality, in which man at last appears fully integrated.

References

[1] Cf. *Wissenschaft der Logik,* Vol. V, p. 26.

[2] Cf. *Philosophie des Rechts* ("Vorrede"), pp. 16, 19; *Encyclopädie,* p. 11.

[3] *Wissenschaft der Logik,* Vol. IV, p. 68.

[4] *Phänomenologie,* pp. 36, 37.

[5] Cf. *Die Posaune des Jüngsten Gerichtes über Hegel den Atheisten und Antichristen,* Leipzig, 1841.

[6] Max Stirner, *Der Einzige und sein Eigentum* (1844).

[7] Cf. Marx-Engels, *Gesamtausgabe,* Vol. I, p. 64 f.

[8] Cf. Feuerbach, *Vorläufige Thesen sur Reform der Philosophie* (1843).

[9] Cf. Feuerbach, *Grundsätze der Philosophie der Zukunft* (1843).

[10] Cf. T. Zlocisti, *M. Hess: Sozialistische Aufsätze* (Berlin, 1921), pp. 37–60 ("Philosophie der Tat"), 60–78 ("Sozialismus und Kommunismus"), 158–187 ("Uber das Geldwesen").

[11] Marx-Engels, *Gesamtausgabe,* Vol. I, pp. 403–553 ("Kritik des Hegelschen Staatsrecht").

[12] *Ibid.,* pp. 576–606 ("Zur Judenfrage").

[13] *Ibid.,* pp. 606–621 ("Zur Kritik der Hegelschen Rechtsphilosophie").

[14] *Ibid.,* II, pp. 379–404.

[15] Cf. *ibid.,* Vol. III, pp. 29–172 ("Oekonomisch-Philosophische Manuscripte aus dem Jahre 1844"), ("Die heilige Familie");Vol. V, pp. 533–535 ("Marx *über Feuerbach"*).

[16] Cf. *ibid.,* Vol. III, pp. 154–156.

[17] Cf. *ibid.,* Vol. V, pp. 533 f. (Theses 1 and 3).

[18] Cf. *ibid.,* Vol. III, pp. 157–163.

[19] Cf. *ibid.,* Vol. III, pp. 82–94, 115–117.

[20] Cf. *ibid.,* Vol. V, pp. 59–65.

[21] *Ibid.,* Vol. V, p. 534 (Thesis 2).

[22] *Ibid.,* Vol. V, pp. 15 f., 21.

[23] Cf. *ibid.,* Vol. V, pp. 26–28, 35 f.

[24] Cf. *ibid.,* Vol. V, pp. 10 f.

SOCIAL PHILOSOPHY AND THE AMERICAN SCENE

by

ROY WOOD SELLARS

Roy Wood Sellars is Professor of Philosophy, University of Michigan. President of the American Philosophical Association (Western Division), 1923. Author of *Critical Realism* (1916), *Evolutionary Naturalism* (1921), *Religion Coming of Age* (1928), *The Philosophy of Physical Realism* (1932). Dr. Sellars has concerned himself largely with crucial points in theory of knowledge and their application in an evolutionary way to the traditional mind-body problem. He welcomes the present exploration of modern materialism since, in his first book, he defended the "new materialism."

IN this concluding chapter of the historical section I wish to introduce into the picture the main themes of the development, on this side of the Atlantic, of that cultural complex called the United States, with its energies, resources, guiding ideas, and operative table of values and institutional traditions. This must needs be done summarily and with an eye to succeeding eras and situations.

It is a truism that, on the contemporary stage of world events, America is no longer the New World of past history and romance but an area of high cultural pressure in the world's climate of opinion. It is very important, therefore, that Americans learn to know themselves and show themselves capable of developing what the French call *irony,* of the gentle and unmalicious kind, to add to their traditional sense of humor. For irony involves perspective and objectivity, an awareness of prepossessions and rationalizations. On the linguistic side, irony is an enemy of stereotypes and emotionally laden abstractions. It is the weapon of realism and sanity. It aids in the search for objectivity. It is in some measure a sign of maturity.

As every one knows, the danger of the present comes from the speed of events. Nations are thrown against one another by what Emerson called the increased *celerity of time* and the shrinking of space. And this reflection was aroused in him by the coming of the railroad age to the America of the stagecoach and the canal. How much more has the tempo of time increased and distance diminished in this day of airplane and rocket! But these are already truisms.

In looking at the American scene, it is wisest to begin with the founding fathers. They will help to give us a frame of reference. The high rational standard which they exhibited, and to which these United States owe so much, was no accident. Washington, Jefferson, Madison, Franklin, Hamilton, Adams, to mention but a few of the outstanding figures, were spiritually representatives and exemplars of the eighteenth century Enlightenment, the Age of Reason, one of the great ages of the world. In religion they were mild deists, disciples of Newton and Locke, believers in law and order in the universe. They eschewed superstition, were skeptical of popular religion, and frowned upon immoderate "enthusiasms." Reason linked with experience was to be the guide in human affairs.

It must not be forgotten that these men were not colonials in the invidious sense of smug Victorian England, but gentlemen of considerable learning, usually well read in the classics of political and moral philosophy and in touch with the latest developments of natural philosophy, as physics was then called. In their libraries were to be found, as a rule, the works of Cicero, Newton, Locke, Hutcheson, Pufendorf, Harrington, and Milton, and, it may be of Beccaria. Franklin was, himself, a recognized contributor to science. Many of the doctors and lawyers of the Middle Atlantic colonies, particularly, were educated at Edinburgh, the home of the Scottish Enlightenment associated with Hume, Brown, and Ferguson. Even Ethan Allen, the Vermont leader, came under the influence of the era through his medical friend and his contacts with English officers, and wrote that rather remarkable book *Reason the Only Oracle of Man.* It was an essentially cosmopolitan period in which nationalism had not yet become extreme. It must be acknowledged that, in many respects, the nineteenth century, because of its turbulence and growing pains, was, by contrast, an era of turmoil and lack of clarity. Industrialism and expansion were goods, but they were undoubtedly purchased at a price.

Let us step backwards in time a moment. It is not as well known as it should be that the New England divines in their heyday had been trained at Cambridge, England, then the center of Cambridge Platonism, the very Platonism discoverable in Milton and Newton. These were not hedge priests but theologians; and, as soon as Newton and Locke came to view, they were read and discussed. Jonathan Edwards knew the *Principia* and the *Essay on the Human Understanding.*

For the time Edwards was the high-water mark in New England thought and the intellectual center shifted to the Middle Atlantic region and to the South. Here there was more heterogeneity and a somewhat less theological set of traditions and impacts. The later stages of the Edinburgh Enlightenment had effect here in law and medicine and a freer field in which to work. Franklin was an institution in himself. With the aid of Jefferson, whose outlook we shall shortly consider, Priestley and Cooper came on the scene. Priestley, Cooper and Rush were pioneers in what would now be called the psychosomatic point of view in considering human beings. Tom Paine, the stormy petrel of common sense, human rights, and reason, moved in the same circle. Not following the sage advice of Poor Richard to the effect that he who spits in the wind spits in his own face, Paine suffered obloquy, because his outspoken deism and rationalism did not please the clergy and he had no secure roots in the soil to which he came so late in life. It must not be forgotten that the Enlightenment was mainly at the top of society and did not have the power to penetrate very deeply to those who had little leisure or learning. Yet it left a residue of ideas in its wake. New England Unitarianism was an aftermath, along with a growth of humanitarianism. But one must not oversimplify. Deism largely died out as America engaged its energies in the new and absorbing job of national life. It had its bitter enemies and, besides, represented an age already passing. It was not until the theory of evolution made its impact in the second half of the nineteenth century that a trend toward naturalism again appeared. In the meantime, America grew westward under the spell of the frontier or began to try out the industrialism of England in the East. Jacksonian democracy was on the horizon. America was lusty, but its energies were not much given to art and science. It was more than ever *a new country*. Yet soon Emerson was to begin his lecture tours over the Middle West. But only the historian can give the full picture of life in the various states.

Having seen the United States launched on its career of nationhood and expansion, let us turn back to Jefferson and the eighteenth century for a more intensive treatment of moral and political ideas. The principles of the Declaration of Independence became a part of American ideology, as can be seen in the case of Lincoln, though the idea of individualistic freedom was, through the pressure of economic pioneering and enterprise, in some measure shoving aside the notion of equality. Equality took the form of legal and electioneering equality combined with what was called equality of opportunity. The table of values could be seen in the working of institutions. Slavery, in itself, had been a continued challenge to what some magnates allowed themselves to call Jefferson's glittering generalities. But America had escaped feudalism; and the common man was not disheartened. Quite the reverse.

For some time in his intellectual maturity, Jefferson had hesitated between overt Epicurean materialism and deism; and had finally swung to deism of a mild Unitarian variety on the basis of the preevolutionary argument from design. His letters make it very clear that he did not like what he called the mysticisms of Plato, "incomprehensible to the human mind" and "foggy." He was in touch with Helvetius and Condorcet. All in all, he was the most philosophically inclined of our American presidents. In him America made fortunate contact with secularism and rationalism. He was the father of the separation of church and state, aided by the variety of denominations. And he had well worked-out schemes for education.

In his letter to William Short he writes: "As you say of yourself, I too am an Epicurean. I consider the genuine (not the imputed) doctrine of Epicurus as containing everything rational in moral philosophy which Greece and Rome have left us. . . . Epictetus and Epicurus give laws for governing ourselves, Jesus, a supplement of the duties and charities we owe to others." Then follows a syllabus of the teachings of Epicurus which begins with the physical and ends with the moral. "Physical,—The universe eternal. Moral,—Happiness the aim of life."

In those days, as Professor Schneider has well pointed out, natural and moral philosophy were essential ingredients of culture rather than things apart. And I find, in Jefferson, ethical insights superior to the assumption of egoistic hedonism which disfigured early utilitarianism and classical economics. A quotation or two must suffice. These are from the letter to Thomas Law:

> Self-interest or rather self-love, or egoism, has been more plausibly substituted as the basis of morality. *But I consider our relations with others as constituting the boundaries of morality.* With ourselves we stand on the ground of identity, not of relation, which last, requiring two subjects, excludes self-love confined to a single one. To ourselves, in strict language, we can owe no duties, obligation requiring also two parties. Self-love, therefore, is no part of morality. Indeed, it is exactly its counterpart. . . . These good acts give us pleasure, but why happens it that they give us pleasure? Because nature has implanted in our breasts a love of others, a sense of duty to them, a moral instinct, in short, which prompts us irresistibly to feel and succor their distresses, and protests against the language of Helvetius.

Much like Aristotle, he speaks of the importance of moral education. The biological nature of man which, in accordance with those days, he calls instinct must be taken in hand and directed. We are more prone today to think in terms of social psychology and socialization. That is, our background is more genetic and evolutionary. But, while more individualistic in his framework, Jefferson had clearly the roots of the matter in his thought.

It will be recalled that Jefferson substituted the term "happiness" in the famous trilogy. Happiness is to be pursued even more than property. This substitution expressed the shift from Locke's jealous concern for absolute "natural rights" against the government, considered as the potential enemy, to a more optimistic perspective. Of course, the fear of the state would long remain, just because it is the center of coercive power. How can it be used and not abused? How can its benevolence be guaranteed? For Jefferson, as for Locke, the last resort is the appeal to revolution. The problem of political philosophy was beginning to shape itself in ethical terms. The good state is that which concerns itself with the general good; does not deviate from this goal even though leaving its attainment to the formation of serviceable institutions which almost run themselves. It was this optimism about natural institutions and methods which was to find expression in laissez-faire economics. The principle of *natural harmony* was to be evoked to support the increasing shift to secular interests. The rationalization of economic individualism was to find expression in the idea of automatic progress. But Jefferson, himself, had his fears of industry and the city. Being a deist, he did not have Adam Smith's confidence in the Guiding Hand.

Now all social scientists at present have an historical sense. They recognize that the rise of the middle class and of economic individualism involved political and economic and moral reinterpretations. But they also see that there is no finality about these emphases and tables of value. The social equilibrium within society is as labile as life itself. It is adjustmental, dynamic. But rational evolution is always better than blocking and revolution. And happy those states in which social forces and social claims—to adapt the terms of Aristotle—can make their adjustments! Americans have learned to think in terms of adjustments by means of the democratic process, much as the British have. But the tempo here has been such that the social picture has a somewhat different configuration. After all, it is continental and federal and diversified geographically and ethnically. Slavery gave it one irrepressible conflict which it was not able to meet by the democratic process. It does not desire another, nor need to have one. But problems do not solve themselves. Are there any criteria to aid solution? To anticipate, we touch here upon the basic problem of the relation of social causation to the functioning of moral principles. Of course, moral principles operate only in moral agents and within a moral order. But this moral order and these moral agents are themselves tied in with the whole social and institutional set-up. Moral progress, I would hold, consists, at one and the same time, in the clarification of absolute moral principles and their interpretation in relation to relevancies and relativities. And, of course, there is no *a priori* guarantee of moral progress. Yet, within a technologically progressive community, there can always be hope for it. There are degrees of freedom with such a society in the relation of means to ends.

In reading books upon American culture and civilization I have always been impressed by the recurrent theme that, in its own context, America reproduced the distortion of natural, moral law into natural, private rights with a minimum of responsibilities so characteristic of the rising middle class in Europe. In other words, that the community and commonwealth tended to be lost sight of in the struggle for place and power. And this reproduction was in a situation from which feudalism was absent. It is usual to say that the individualism of Protestantism and its emphasis upon salvation in another world lost to it this community sense. And there is truth in the indictment. But, of course, there is little use in the pot calling the kettle black, for the other great religious institution remained largely dominated by feudal concepts of an ordered society. And so there was lacking in the nineteenth century any adequate table of moral and humanistic values to set bounds to individualism. The grandson of the Puritans found the fleshpots of Egypt sweet and could rationalize his values in terms of divine approval for the self-made man. Curiously enough, social Darwinism could easily take over, putting the ways of nature in place of the ways of God. And, in the meantime, economic techniques and patterns were undergoing the revolution, after the Civil War rightly called the twin triumph of capitalism and technology.

Now it is my thesis that the founding fathers were far more realistic in their reason than their nineteenth century descendants were in their rationalizations. They were not romantics and saw the current make-up of society pretty clearly. And, on the whole, they were republicans and not advocates of a vaguely defined democracy. In the main, democracy meant for them what it had meant in the classic world, the rule of the many who are poor, the masses. What they lacked was an historical sense, a living awareness of the coming of new social forces and possibilities.

Their outlook is visible in the Constitution and *The Federalist*. Politically, the Constitution was an adventure of an experimental type, though based on colonial experience and thoughtful compromise. Europe soon passed into a period of reaction after the French Revolution; and so Americans were definitely conscious of their advance even after it had ceased to be exceptional. They might be backward and colonially minded as regards art and literature and science but at least they were not ruled by a king. In his early writings Mark Twain exhibits to the full this conviction. But we must not forget the extreme pessimism of his later years. In the Gilded Age something had gone wrong. Diagnoses began in Henry Adams and in Henry George. Was progress linked with poverty? Was the principle of the degradation of energy applicable to society? What was wrong? Muckrakers arrived on the scene, to be followed in our own generation by the social scientists with their statistical surveys. And yet America was still isolated and secure, a law unto herself, a prodigy of wealth and growing technological advance, having the *mystique* of its economic momentum. And in all this, I would say, no worse than Edwardian England or the France of the Third Republic.

But to return to what I have called the realism of the eighteenth century. The ideal set was that of the *mixed constitution* of Plato, Aristotle, Polybius, and Montesquieu. The aim was a balance between social groups, so recognized, with changes reflected in legislation only when practically conceded by all. Nothing hasty or merely popular should pass the system of checks and balances. Turgot in France criticized the scheme as qualifying sovereignty, while John Adams, the defender of natural aristocracy, defended it, as logically he should not have done if, as it would seem in his reply to Taylor of Caroline County, Virginia, he held that the abler always get their way, as it is right they should.

Now a study of this *static social realism* is important since it would appear that the United States is at long last entering a period of *dynamic social realism* as the social myths of the nineteenth century weaken. The interdependence of the Great Society demands, quite evidently, a reinterpretation of guiding premises in terms of community, the general good, and commonwealth. And this will be no easy matter. Yet it must be positive if it is to confront ideologies now rising all over the world. In my fledgling days I wrote a book, called *The Next Step in Democracy,* which reflected Charles Horton Cooley and Lester Ward and the impact of Shaw and Wells and the Webbs. Since it was written before the Russian Revolution and the rise of the Labor Government in England it can in these days hardly be called radical.

In Number Ten of *The Federalist* Madison expresses the classical tradition aforesaid. Parties are factions. The diversity in the faculties of men, from which the rights of property originate (a modified Lockian view) is not less an insuperable obstacle to a uniformity of interests. The protection of these faculties is the first object of government. From the protection of different and unequal faculties of acquiring property, the possession of different degrees and kinds of property immediately results; and from the influence of these on the sentiments and views of the respective proprietors ensues a division of the society into different interests and parties. Those who hold, and those who are without, property have ever formed distinct interests in society. Those who are creditors and those who are debtors fall under a like discrimination. A landed interest, a manufacturing interest, a mercantile interest, a moneyed interest, with many lesser interests, grow up of necessity in civilized nations and divide them into different classes, actuated by different sentiments and views.

Do we not have here a multi-group, economic formulation of ideologies? It is, of course, drawn in large part from Aristotle's *Politics* and Harrington's *Oceana.* The stress in the theory of property is upon psychological factors and is still incomplete sociologically; but it supplements Locke's. It would be well for Americans to bear in mind Jefferson's distinction between the *rights of personal competency,* such as the rights of thinking, speaking, forming and giving opinions—those afterwards at his insistence embodied in the Bill of Rights of the Constitution—and those which the individual could not exercise fully and perfectly apart from his relations with his fellows, such as personal protection, acquiring and possessing property, which are of *defective power* requiring the guarantee of society *for good and sufficient reasons.* The general good enters here as an absolute principle.

Since, as I have already indicated, the cultural climate changed with increasing economic individualism, growing nationalism tinged with romanticism, the cult of a classless society, rising industrialism, it is well for Americans to glance back now and then to this older realistic tradition and set it over against the folklore of the later nineteenth century. Daniel Webster was not a great thinker, but he was near enough to colonial times to appreciate the part played by economic factors. After describing the settlement of New England he adds: "Their situation demanded a parcelling out and division of lands, and it may be fairly said that this necessary act *fixed the future frame and form of this government.*" The italics are Webster's own. He was still thinking of the past and predominantly in agrarian terms, as did his intellectual guide, Harrington.

I have not the time to indicate the yeastiness of American social thought in the North until after the Civil War. Both religious and secular experiments in communal living were rife. Mormonism, of course, reflects this era.

It was after the Civil War and in part owing to its economic stimulation that the United States launched itself into industrialism, urbanism, and expansion of population through immigration. As in earlier England, there were few norms to control the impact of these activities. The new age of railroad and industrial barons ensued, a quite natural epoch. It was rationalized in terms of economic laws, social Darwinism, and the natural rights of property. The courts at first hesitated, and then fell into line. The Olympian note was added by Carnegie's moral doctrine of the stewardship of wealth. And Americans have a right to be proud of the final use of some of the great fortunes. What stands out, however, is the confusion in the social philosophy. What were means? And what were ends? Neither the individual nor society was clear about it all. Traditional religion, as Theodore Parker pointed out, served to prevent retrogression more than it helped to give direction. In these days when Sorokin and Sheen castigate the sensate and the secular, this point should be kept in mind. In my considered opinion only the humanists are frankly facing the job of working out moral principles within a naturalistic outlook. And systematic, cosmological materialism has in these days the intellectual job of showing that, at the human and social level, distinctive of this planet at least, morality is intrinsic to group life and expresses itself coordinately in moral conduct and in guiding norms. We have already noted that Jefferson, the best representative of the Enlightenment we have and, by reason of social conditions in America, affected by a very concrete democratic spirit, could discern no incompatibility between materialism and morality. The development of transfer-meanings by which the poor word "materialism" was made the scapegoat, was not yet fully under way. That is, materialism was not yet put into a vague, wholesale opposition to Idealism with a capital letter. So far as this country is concerned, Emerson and the Transcendentalists may be said to have inaugurated this contrast—in so doing, reflecting the romantic reaction against the empiricism and rationalism of the eighteenth century with, of course, the best of motives. But, surely, modern materialism has—to use an Hegelian expression—subsumed what was valid in Emersonian idealism in its more adequate expression.

In the middle period and well until the eighties American philosophy marked time, as did even European philosophy for that matter. There was need for the growth of biology, psychology, and the social sciences.

Moribund Scottish common sense, Cousin eclecticism, Spencerism, succeeded one another. But, by the nineties at least, Anglo-American idealism was in full swing, clearly a cultural phenomenon with small originality in any technical sense. Yet it stood against the extremes of the older individualism and unsocialized natural rights. With pragmatism the foundation was laid for the shift to the social sciences, but still with lack of clarity as to absolute principles. Quite naturally, it was the era of the *social process*. There was no clear attempt to relate the social process to a moral order and to criticize the actual moral order in the light of explicit normative principles. Society was not yet ready to face such an issue. That would come only as social forces and social claims got into dynamic movement again and a clarification of human values and ends became unavoidable. It is in such an epoch that the world now is, for good or bad, according to one's view. How the social and the human sciences will play into this situation I shall consider briefly in the sequel.

The twentieth century promises to be, then, an epoch in its own way analogous to other great periods such as the Greek Enlightenment, the Hellenistic era, the medieval thirteenth century, the eighteenth century—prepared by the seventeenth as the nineteenth century led to the twentieth by scientific and technological advances. There is no escaping the crucial fact; and merely to speak of the atom bomb is not by itself enough. It is the socially positive that we must have in mind. And here the United States has what can rightly be called a moral responsibility before the world that it cannot shirk.

And so I pass to what I have called the normative side of social philosophy. It will, I believe, interest my readers to find a materialist recognizing the normative as a guiding factor in the moral order intrinsic to group life. But, surely, group life and, with it, the socialized human being lifted to the level of humanity thereby, involves a moral order. The thing to do is to make it explicit and tentatively to extrapolate in the light of social trends. The job of the moralist is the clarification of moral principles. These—to use the jargon of English ethicists—are irreducible to non-moral terms. But that does not signify that they are non-natural, for man is, in group life, a moral being.

Primary to democracy is, then, the concept of a moral, social order in relation to cultural instrumentalities. And something of this has always vitalized the American Dream and ideology, however qualified by social forces and claims reflecting cultural conditions, such as pioneering, heterogeneity due to color and immigration, and the drive intrinsic to the capitalistic, economic system as it passed from phase to phase. It is an awareness of the reciprocal relation between an actual moral order and its social setting which the cultural realist must keep in mind. But he would be foolish not to realize that he has to do with a moving drama in which self-conscious personality operates in group fashion to set up moral claims in relation to social forces and so creates tables of value of a normative and guiding sort. Only in moral agents do normative principles operate. But that they do so operate is an empirical fact, to deny which constitutes moral nihilism. In so operating they constitute social morality. The job of the ethicist is to clarify and systematize normative principles. The job of the social reformer is to relate them to social conditions, expediencies, and possibilities. And here, of course, one can expect the whole spectrum from what Canadians call progressive conservatism to liberalism to radicalism.

It is a well known fact that there are more ways of going wrong than of going right. Christianity has long recognized this fact, for, at its best, it has not been sentimental about human affairs and human nature, though too inclined to give them up in despair in either a chiliastic or an otherworldly mood. And it has been a recurrent note that property and power, closely interwoven, have been the hardest to moralize. And in our multi-group society there are many forms of both.

But I can but bow to this question of social dynamics and pass on. To come back to the explication of democratic norms, I would suggest that they turn on the *absolute principle* of the moral dignity of human beings. This absolute principle seems to me irreducible. Its base is the natural and inevitable demand of self-conscious personality to receive just social recognition. And it flows from the moral inadequacy of any other principle, such as that of moral aristocracy. I consider social Darwinism as the last abortive attempt to confuse biology and morals. But it should be recognized that a moral norm is directive and regulative only as moral agents accept it. Moreover, the application of it is relative to social conditions and institutions, both of which require mastery—no easy achievement.

The burden of proof is, then, morally upon unequal opportunities for cultural development. And this principle implies that every range of value from health to art should be given normal vitality and presentation. To work such a principle out is the task of democratic statesmanship. In America, the genius of *political democracy* is the democratic process of compromise; and educational enlightenment should lessen the impact of social forces and claims. As we have seen, society cannot be conceived as statically these years as it was by Madison.

Curiously enough, in all this, modern materialism retains continuity with the age-old principle of natural, moral, law though without the supernatural sanctions and perspective often associated with it. It regards the breakdown of the idea of a moral order of a social kind into fixed "natural rights" as a declension which is being overcome in our days. Thus modern materialism is, in its ethical implications, neither sensate nor reductive but humanistically secular.

In conclusion, let me pass to the consideration of the primary theoretical question of our day; namely, the relation of social philosophy on its normative side to society as a going concern studied by the social sciences. Such sciences are necessarily causal and factual in their outlook and their methods. Must they, therefore, remain *wertfrei* or unconcerned with the normative?

Like the scholastics I would make a distinction. Working values are factual. That is, they are the expression in group and personal conduct of attitudes, sentiments, and volitions. As a man values, so he is. As a society values, so is that society. The whole moving complex of social myths, folklore, and *mystique,* intertwined with beliefs about man and his world, is factual. And all this, with its institutional setting, the social scientist must study with the best techniques he has. This material is full of working values. But these are of what the logician would call the *first order*. The normative of the ethical sort is of a second order; and it is of the normative of the second order that the social scientist is suspicious.

As I see it, the transition can be made by the principle of the *better than.* This principle appears in medicine, social work, political economy, political science. It unites the social sciences with reform movements. Its absence would signify that the social sciences did not reflect the dynamic of their subject matter. Man is a valuing animal; and valuing involves comparison. Health is better than sickness. Education is better than ignorance. Employment is better than unemployment.

It is the hitching of these *better thans* to the moral principles of human dignity and a true commonwealth that permits the social sciences to be integrated with the *second-order normative* while retaining their autonomy as sciences. If these are set forth by the social conscience as desirable ends, then the sciences can in some measure extrapolate their *better thans* into controllable and, in some measure, verifiable ends.

Such, clearly, would be the ideal of a rational social philosophy in responsible contact with the social sciences. The question remains, How far are the social sciences objective and scientific?

In my opinion, social anthropology is becoming the most objective of the social sciences. On the other hand, economics and political science still remain the least objective because the most tied up with social myths and folklore. But there are some signs of a change in both fields. The reason for this situation is, on the debit side, that they have been concerned with *institutions,* and, on the credit side, that they are beginning to stand back from institutions because of, first, events, and second, the growth of psychology, sociology, and cultural anthropology. But into the details I cannot here enter.

Ours is what the economist calls a *mixed economy* containing competition, semi-monopoly, and governmental enterprise of many types from education to road building and the TVA. Given the momentum of capitalism and the size and success of the economy, this mixed economy will in the foreseeable future remain, along with adjustments and modifications due to the growth of labor unions, the greater need for security, the clearer realization that business is, in last analysis, a means and not an end, the presence or absence of depressions, the continued liking for the social quality of our culture, etc. But it would be foolish to deny that the world is going to be the seat of many kinds of economy and culture between which there will be social competition of the normative sort. What is needed is peace and the lessening of dogmatism. The unfortunate factor is the institutional tradition of war as an early resort rather than a last resort. And here the lack of cultural synchronism is a danger. Both philosophy and science involve appeals to reason by their very essence.

MATERIALISM AND HUMAN KNOWING

by ROY WOOD SELLARS

FROM the historical approach to materialism we now pass to the expository and the systematic. Here philosophy and science inevitably overlap. The major part of the chapters in this section will represent the expert knowledge and modes of thought of scientists interested in seeing how their fields dovetail together and what continuity and what discontinuity in basic categories appear. Of what kind of diversified universe are we a part? And how does that gifted mammalian biped with his "new" brain, sensitive hands, and cultural accumulation learn to know what he knows about it all?

What is the role of philosophy in this division of labor? From the point of view of method a fairly modest one; namely, that of clarification. But this will go hand in hand with asking the sort of questions philosophers have been in the habit of asking since the days of the Greeks, when they put aside mythology and asked what things are made of. We can call these *general questions* about knowing and being. Much of our vocabulary was made by Greek thinkers.

We should not forget that science got really under way not much more than three centuries ago. Before this, philosophy had to handle the total scene as best it could and in as rational a fashion as it was able. There were, of course, cultural and technological forces playing into it. But it was not until the great seventeenth century that philosophy was hit by a major force which could not be denied, namely, science. Descartes, Locke, and Kant tried to make the necessary adjustments. These adjustments are still going on. The following passage from De Broglie's *Matter and Light* indicates one important condition of the advance of science:

> Every important step forward made by Astronomy, Physics, Chemistry or Biology had one essential condition—the previous existence or invention of certain apparatus; and as the sciences sought to extend their advance, so it became necessary for instrumental technique to develop and to expand in its delicate adjustments.[1]

And then De Broglie proceeds to show that it was the indications furnished by experiment that led to relativity and quantum-mechanics and the astonishing development of microscopic exploration.

To this development philosophy has not remained insensitive, though it recognizes that it does not have equivalent resources. What, then, has it tried to do? Two things, I take it. On the one hand, it has sought to clarify and improve its logical and linguistic apparatus and, on the other, to ponder its perennial problems in the light of the novel results gained by the sciences. As should be expected, some philosophical currents—usually called "analysis" and logical positivism—have emphasized the first project, while the second has been an affair of general growth and assimilation. When one runs over the roster of distinguished names in contemporary philosophy, one quickly notes representatives of both types, with much overlapping.

In the present chapter I shall be concerned with what seem to me the more realistic, and even materialistic, implications of the trends in both science and philosophy. But it is well to bear in mind the fact that, because of its very scope and generality, philosophy is bound to move slowly and to weigh every step taken. Special facts, alone, cannot completely determine its conclusions. Rather must it keep in mind the total field. Its traditional problems are so unavoidable and so basic that it has its own center of gravity and momentum. None the less, these must be constantly redefined in the light of the results obtained by the sciences with their great technical resources and methodology.

It is my expectation that this cooperative supplementation will show itself in this section, showing that the time is ripe for this interplay. A philosophy tied in with empiricism is not likely to be speculative in the romantic sense of that term. And a certain play of the imagination around generic issues is to be encouraged. That is why, for instance, I admire Whitehead's work while disagreeing with his point of departure, that is, his rejection of substance and his transformation of sensory particulars into eternal objects to play a substitute function.

Now it is quite generally granted that, in all its forms, materialism involves what philosophers call *realism,* that is, physical realism and not medieval, or Platonic, realism. In English-speaking countries particularly, realism is an epistemological term set over against idealism or mentalism. In the beginning of this century realism arose in England and the United States largely as a reaction against an idealism whose historical conditions were being outgrown. I shall not be able to consider idealism in this necessarily brief essay; but I believe that it can be shown that idealism always presupposes the defeat of realism. This is very apparent in Royce's writings, as in the study of the possibility of error; and it appears again in Blanshard's book, *The Nature of Thought.* They assume that to know an object is somehow *to be that object.* But is this not to confuse epistemology and ontology and to disregard the mechanism and referential nature of human knowing?

This realistic movement weakened idealism but did not, itself, achieve complete clarification or freedom from terminological differences and ambiguities. Into the details of these past disputes I cannot here enter. I am, however, inclined to believe that the time is ripe for a restatement which will do justice to analytic advances. What I shall argue for is a direct, referential realism built around the responding, discriminating and symbolizing human organism. And I do not believe scientists always realize the uniqueness and specificity of the cognitive claim which appears at the level of perception. Certainly, there is a nest of puzzles here which have kept philosophers confused. Once the correct guiding thread is found, they may well vanish. I have long argued that the directed cognitive claim is irreducible, though its conditions and mechanism can be studied. The tests of cognition, or of the truth of statements which constitute the content of cognition, are empirical and involve discrimination, verification, the power of prediction and control, all interworking. I see no good reason to doubt that we humans achieve such knowledge, of which perception is the lowest level. I would here point out the fact that much of the dispute about primary and secondary qualities stems from bad epistemology which takes knowing too much as an apprehension and not as a revisable predication.

Scientific knowledge is our most adequate knowledge; and many statements must be transformed to fit into it. They may be justified at the perceptual level and yet require translation for science. Thus we may continue to say that an object has a certain geometrical shape while refusing to admit that it has, literally, a colored surface.

I might put it this way: The philosopher must move from the macroscopic to the microscopic and back. His job, in short, is to be a conscientious monitor and not a pretentious arbiter, a companion of science with stored memories and large horizons.

It would not be misleading to say that the center of gravity of philosophy is man. It must keep its attention upon him if it is to ask—and answer—crucial questions. To some degree the physical sciences could ignore man, particularly if their thought was concentrated upon problems in their own field. Their primary linkage with man was in terms of methods and techniques. But this degree of disregard was impossible for philosophy. It was always concerned to ask how man knows and how he would fit into the world as it was conceived to be. Hence epistemology, the theory of the nature and reach of human knowing, was inevitably connected with ontology, the theory of being and of the general nature of things.

Another way of putting the difference of genius of the two supplementary cultural activities is to say that the sciences could go at their job in a rather piecemeal fashion, taking a step at a time, without too much concern with the total picture. Philosophy, on the other hand, always had the total outlook on its conscience even when it knew that systematization was premature.

What has happened of late is that the sciences are advancing with astonishing rapidity, technique and results being added in a sort of geometric proportion. And how about philosophy? It seems to me that its analytic capacity has never been surpassed. Something crucial is certain to follow from this intellectual situation.

I take it that materialism has always had the role of the *suppressed alternative*. It has loomed in the background. Surely it is time to bring it into the foreground, to consider neglected possibilities, to take it as something which should be studied in the light of every relevant objection. It is undeniable that there have been in the past essentially reductive forms of materialism, forms tied in with the scientific pictures of their day, before evolution was taken seriously.

All things considered, one would, I believe, be justified in saying that only in these days are the conditions being achieved in both science and philosophy for an adequate kind of materialism which can save not only *appearances* but *categories,* such as life, mind, personality, reasoning, values, and choice. It is what I would call an empirically minded materialism with a sense for the inner as well as for the outer, for the dispositions and organized "go" of things as well as for descriptive facts. And the new conceptions of field, configuration, and action give a sense of process which was lacking in traditional mechanics. It will take time for people to learn to live into this new outlook. But I doubt not that the new orientation will grow as old pictures and concepts fade.

It is not as well known as it should be that medieval Aristotelianism was empirical after its fashion, and that it sought to avoid the sharp dualisms of Platonism and of later Cartesianism. Aristotle had rejected Democritean materialism with its atomism and developed what is usually called hylomorphism. In a later paper there will be a discussion of its logic and peculiarities. Modern materialism might well be called evolutionary, formative, organizational materialism. It is emergentist but *not* holistic in a mystical sense. Much will depend upon the increasing naturalization of "mind."

It will be our argument that both Cartesian dualism and the various forms of idealism, subjective, objective, and absolute, represent compromises and speculative distortions. And there has always been something anthropomorphic about phenomenalism and experientialism. What we seem to need is a realistic empiricism.

I hope scientists will not be made uneasy by these philosophical terms, ontology and epistemology. They seem to me both relevant to basic questions and unavoidable. On the whole, I like the term ontology better than the term metaphysics. For one reason it is simpler and has fewer emotional overtones. It is my intention to consider matter both epistemologically and ontologically, using modern conceptions and stressing the nature and reach of human knowing. The stress will be upon concepts justified by scientific method and not upon *pictures* related to what philosophers call naïve realism. Perceiving is a very elementary, though necessary, level of knowing. It is macroscopic and largely practical. The scientist works out "observation" within it, as we shall see.

Now one can hardly have even the most sophisticated materialism without matter. The term must have application. But it is an historical fact that, from the days of Berkeley, Hume, and Kant, such application has been challenged. Phenomenalism is strong today and prides itself on its analytic sophistication. Nor is it easily refuted. We shall find it necessary to study the referential nature of human perceiving and its percipient, organic base. The cognitive value and claims of perceiving must not be allowed to be overwhelmed by either the *causal conditions,* external or internal, or the artificial, epistemological priority given, by some, to analytic sense-data, as alone hard and certain. We shall see that scientific stress on "observation" does not require such an assumption, and that it is *psychologically* not very defensible. I do not believe that the epistemology of perception should conflict with the psychology of perception.

Though the general idea of materialism is old, the word itself is relatively modern, appearing in the age of Boyle and the Cambridge Platonists. In fact, any one who believed in corpuscular matter—the term is Boyle's—as against the *materia prima* and the four elements of the Schoolmen or the hypostatical principles of the alchemists, tended to be called a materialist. Locke was so called. Boyle was influenced by the Democritean view but held that the corpuscles must be more vaguely and more experimentally conceived. Therein consisted his wisdom. Dr. Louis Trenchard More has brought this point out excellently:

> It was not Boyle's revival of the atomic hypothesis which started the ever-increasing activity in chemistry, for little or no practical use was made of it for many years; and it is doubtful whether such hypotheses are not at best impotent "aids" to experimental science. It was rather his definition that a chemical element was any substance which could not be further analyzed which gave the impetus to chemistry.[2]

Boyle also attacked the notion of substantial forms and rejected the notion that colors are intrinsic to things, a notion stressed by the alchemists and, I fear, held still by many realistic philosophers who do not understand the basis of the distinction between quantitative and sensuous predications. Only the recognition that perceiving is an elementary level of knowing in which the macroscopic and the microscopic are not yet sorted out can help on this point.

It was Berkeley who saw the threat. For him, any one accepting matter was *ipso facto* a materialist. Dualism was felt to be treacherous, as it actually turned out to be in large measure. The thing to do was to nip the threat in the bud by establishing immaterialism.

Now both common sense and science, if left to themselves, at least accept "material things." What is the human body if not something which has to be fed? I suppose from the times of early man the difference between a corpse and a living human being was outstanding. What is the nature of this perishing and corruption? Has something not quite material left its host? Or is it a breakdown of the most delicate organizational action? Are we growths which can act and choose in conscious fashion? Modern materialism cannot escape these perennial ultimates. Speech-gifted man, he was called by the Greek poets. Modern materialism can be no facile and unimaginative thing. It must have scope and comprehension from astronomer to poet.

When, as people are always informed with delight, Dr. Samuel Johnson kicked a stone to "refute" Berkeley, he was really appealing to bodily manipulation and action, for matter was a technological term concerned with falling bodies and obstacles confronting the organism. He felt in his bones it was no merely visual affair, no mere seeing of sensations. Was not the framework of organic percipience being ignored, the sensory cut off from the motor, and both from habits and know-how? But of this we shall have more to say in the sequel. The causal theory of perception was beginning to thrust man back into effects in himself written on a *tabula rasa;* surely, a vicious approach.

By ontological materialism I shall mean, rejectively, a position opposed to mentalistic idealism, dualism, and any form of mere experientialism. In a general way, I shall speak of it as *naturalism with matter.* But I shall not be thinking of "hard" atoms moving about in absolute empty space. I shall stress relations, patterns, process, levels. And I imagine the biochemist and the biologist will give the detail. Categories are in the making. But epistemology must be on guard also. We may need to appeal to a double knowledge of the human organism and develop a keener sense for the descriptive abstractness of the inorganic sciences.

If we start with some picture of the inert "stuff" of being, we are apt to regard the emergence of conscious awareness in animals as a paradox of the worst sort. But what have we to contrast it with in the realm of events and activities? Lucretius felt the problem and fell back on the rise of the sensate as an accident due to some kind of composition. But was not his difficulty greater than ours today because of his conception of the primordial atoms? There is need of philosophical delicacy here. Lucretius hardly possessed science as we understand it; but can we withhold admiration from his panoramic attempt?

Since science is chiefly concerned with facts and theories, it can be said that philosophy raises supplementary issues, issues, however, which it finds unavoidable and which have been debated perennially. I am persuaded that there have been many advances in the last fifty years in this domain. And what I shall try to do is to debate crucial points in epistemology, defend by apposition a realistic position, and then move briefly, in the conclusion, into ontology. Here I shall seek to develop the conception of *being in process,* that is becoming and perishing or, as Aristotle called it, becoming and corruption.

One of the vigorous enemies of ontological materialism has been mentalism. From mentalism sprang phenomenalistic empiricism in its various forms from Hume to recent logical positivism. Is there any defensible sense in which we can be said to *perceive* an external world? What do we *mean* when we say we "see" automobiles and trees? What do we *mean* when we say that we take hold of a tool—say, a spade or a brush?

When the word "matter" is brought forward in a group of philosophers an atmosphere of restraint becomes quickly apparent. Why is this? It is chiefly because certain basic factors in the theory of perception have not been sufficiently clarified.

In some measure, I take it, the fault lies in a neglect of the full-bodied background of actual, *plein-air* perceiving with its awareness of the organic self, poised for action or alert. Recently, in reading one of Whitehead's essays, I was struck by his emphasis upon the bodily background of Hume's sense-impressions. "Our sense-impressions are superficial and fail to indicate the massive self-enjoyment derived from internal bodily functioning." This I grant; but I would also stress an alertness directed to the environment, an awareness of concern and response, calling out symbolization and conceptual interpretation of things and events around us. The terms "intent," "response," "reference," have all been used to indicate this very significant factor. But it has not, I hold, been sufficiently recognized that such an attitude of alertness, expectation, and intent—found in animals likewise, as in a cat waiting by a mousehole—qualifies perceiving and makes it something quite different from a mere sensing of sensations or an apprehension of them. A kind of thin intellectualism, associated with the traditional formulation of the causal theory of perception in Locke and Descartes, pervades the formula of Berkeley that *to be is to be perceived,* and that apples are nothing but a complex of ideas. There is neglect of alerted attitude, pointing, demonstrative symbols, conceptualization, social objectivity, preparation for action with know-how.

It is this vectorial alertness and directedness of perceiving which makes it the center for interpretative references and symbolizations. Hence, I would stress not merely the so-called *thickness* of perception but its dynamic polarity as well. And it is this alert directedness which makes it continuous with overt action, such as the manipulation of objects. It is for this reason that I find no sharp break between perceiving a book and taking it from the shelf. In the first stage, as in the second, I am an organic self directionally concerned with something as real as myself and in the same world as myself. My interest and intent in full perceiving is with denotable and manipulatable things. There was something introspective, intellectualistic, and thin about the Locke-Berkeley-Hume approach.

I have stressed this contrast because it is pivotal for materialistic realism. Much of empiricism has been tied to this older perspective in which the prime assumption was that of acquaintance with disembodied states of a mind-soul, called by Berkeley self, mind, soul, or spirit. To challenge this perspective is an essential part of materialistic realism; and I feel sure that present-day psychology and biology would agree with the need for the shift in outlook. There is something anachronistic in philosophy still using the presuppositions of Locke, Berkeley and Hume.

It is an important point further because the axioms of analysis determine consequences to the uttermost theorem. Through the influence of scientific methodology, much emphasis is laid upon observation, verification, and confirmation. And there is danger of confusion between the macroscopic framework of human perception which attaches us to nature in a vital and practical as well as a conceptual way, and the logical function of "observation" which science stresses in connection with verification and confirmation of deductions and theories. Does the latter in any way challenge the realistic framework of perception? It will be my thesis that it does not, that there has been considerable confusion here which needs clearing up. In "observation" the stress is upon apprehensible discrimination, largely in connection with vision. And what is assumed is the significance of the data discriminated for the theory under probation. But, so far as I can see, it is less recognized that perception, as against such discrimination, is concerned with macroscopic, referential perception, like that which terminates on scientific instruments such as the thermometer or the spectroscope. Otherwise, surely, the larger framework of knowledge is denied and "observation" ceases to have a meaning beyond its own data. That is, there would be nothing objective to confirm. Much confusion as to the precise meaning of primary and secondary qualities has stemmed from this failure to distinguish clearly between "observation" and full-bodied perception, with its framework of organic self and environment. When we assign colors and shapes to things we are characterizing them under the cues of sensory data as these are used in interpretative perception. Things are "red," are so far from us, are of such a size, weight, etc. All this is predicative; and is significant only within the framework of perception and action. Thus, I find no chasm between my estimated size of a thing, as I run my eyes over it and recall past experiences, and the measurement size. But in "observation" I am concerned with a discrimination in my sensory field, such as a color in a spectrum, a pointer-reading, a mark on a thermometer as it *appears* in my field of vision. But I shall need to say more about this basic difference of framework later.

From Descartes to Russell, philosophers have had engrained in them the notion that they *ought to doubt* the framework of practical and operative perception, that it would be naïve in them to believe that they are "seeing" the keys of the typewriter they are hammering—although they know perfectly well that they bought the typewriter years ago and it needs repair—or that they are turning over the good earth with their spades, also bought. In all this there is willful abstraction both from biopsychological life and from society. It is, of course, quite right to ask, In what sense do we see and handle things? Intuitional notions of perception may well need to be rejected. But it is one thing to affirm that veridical perception involves complex attitudes, sensory processes, and interpretative operations, and quite another to say that we "see" only our sensations—which is a misleading statement. And yet one's whole philosophy depends upon the direction one takes right here. It is for this reason that the epistemological defense of materialism involves the careful consideration of phenomenalistic empiricism and its reasoned rejection.

Is "matter" an "observable"? Are material things "observables"? It is obvious that we must use language very carefully, and that the above distinction between perception and "observation" bears upon the answer to be given.

I take it to be fairly evident that we cannot intuit either corpuscular matter or macroscopic material things. Perceiving is not a case of intuition. But macroscopic things are *not* inferences, though they may be supported by reasoning, just as our bodies are not inferences. It is in this fashion that we have a physical framework. The electronic microscope by means of which, with new devices of polished glass, molecules can be denoted and "perceived" furnishes the transition to the theoretically inferable, the ultra-microscopic.

What, then, is an *observation*? It is a specialized perception in which a flash of light on a screen or a spectral line or a cloud path in a Wilson chamber is observed in terms of a visual datum. It is this narrowed and tested correspondence that is of such importance to science. But, if the observation did not work within the primary framework of general perception as in the use of instruments, *it would be merely sensory discrimination.* The weakness of much "sense-datum" theory is that it ignores the larger setting of cognitive perception and lapses into a search for "elements" of a maximum, intuitive certainty. The result is that the causal theory of perception dominates over cognition or that there is an isolated stress upon basic reports or sentences, as in logical positivism. The effort may then be made to "construct" things out of sense-data. It is felt to be very sophisticated. I shall try to show that it is bad logic and bad epistemology. If we cannot construct things out of sensations, it may be well to return to a realistic theory of perception as a frame.

Another point should be mentioned. If visual perception is such a conditioned achievement, should we expect it to enable us to "see" forces, integrative processes, organizing activities? At the best, it can give us clues selected, in part, because of our own awareness of activities. This organic self-perception helps to give *body* to the environment. But it, itself, is not a mysterious kind of intuition but an interpretative perception in terms of experiences. Categories are natural to perception, for they are perceptual meanings. Thinghood, endurance, causality, space-time framework, all go together. Hume was right in his protest against *a priori* rationalism; but he did not understand perception. When the physicist speaks of "binding forces" he has quantities and categories in mind. The context, in my opinion, must be that of dynamic substantialism. The weakness of the older atomism was its neglect of the indications of process, synthesis, causal connections, organization. It was a categorial weakness. As I have indicated, Whitehead has a sense for this; but his "reformed subjectivism" leans too heavily upon those artifacts "eternal objects" and timeless values. Yet if one throws out matter what else is there to do? Certainly, Russell's neutral monism has obvious weaknesses. It might be best for philosophy not to "kick against the pricks" and cheerfully resign itself to working out an adequate materialism. Such a materialism requires the cooperation of *all* the sciences. Both mass and energy *are* what they can do. Even Spinoza had an empirical feel for this principle. We cannot *a priori* know of what the organism is capable. I am afraid that philosophers must accept the brain as the seat of consciousness. But we shall take up this question in connection with Russell and the "under-the-hat" theory of mind.

Our tentative conclusion is that the word "matter" should be used for material things, macroscopic and microscopic. Do we not, all of us, readily speak of material things, such as automobiles, books, and garden tools? And then there are huge machines, factories, mountains, stars. And the scientist speaks about corpuscles which have a certain measure of endurance. In quantum mechanics he may recognize how indirect his denotable knowledge is and resort to statistics and waves of probability. But, if he has been affected by the virus of subjective empiricism, he may forget about his instruments and about society and about the social conditions of science itself, and speak only of actual and possible sense-data.

But materialism cannot, obviously, get very far from matter. Hence it must have an epistemology capable of defending a realistic view of denotative and referential perception within the human, organic framework. To cut science loose from this framework would be to cut it loose from its human and social source.

What I have in mind in all this argument is that there has been danger of reifying an abstract term, "matter," and regarding it as a something which one ought to be able to intuit but cannot. Locke's mysterious *substratum* into which entities, called "properties," were stuck, and so owned, also played havoc. But what is a property? It is an answer to a question about the characteristics and powers of concrete substances. And this answer gives what I call knowledge *about* or facts *about.* It is, thus, what I would call a disclosure about the nature of things. The conditions of such disclosure can be studied in detail; so can the linguistic and conceptual apparatus. But the claim of the human mind, thereupon, to make verifiable knowledge-assertions is just epistemologically ultimate. That is the situation we are in and the level that has been attained. Concepts have a cognitive function to perform; they apply, give tested facts about. According to their *species,* they disclose structure, powers, nomic routine and relations. And out of all this are woven the categories in terms of which we think nature. It is an active, exploratory affair, much of which has been historically and culturally achieved, as Emile Meyerson was fond of pointing out.

It has been one of the traditional duties of philosophers to study categories. Probably they have chiefly found them in language, as Aristotle did. This does not prevent additional development and clarification. Aristotle tried to accomplish this with substance, form, and becoming. It is not surprising that the tremendous development of modern science consequent upon new instrumentation and techniques has resulted in the rising to the surface of new categories and modifications of old ones. And this has sometimes been too hasty. As has often been suggested, science in the long run is a self-correcting process; still the philosophic monitor may be of assistance.

Since I have emphasized molar things and corpuscles in my ostensive, technological definition of matter, it may be well to mention the difficulties which afflicted the expression *materia prima.* As I understand it, prime matter and substantial forms are *principles of being* for scholasticism. Prime matter is unknowable but inferable, while substantial forms are, supposedly, in principle knowable. Both concepts bothered Descartes. As a rationalist, he wanted matter to be knowable through a defining attribute. And extension harmonized with geometry and mechanics in a way that dominantly qualitative elements would not. A fresh start was needed; and this turned out to be quantitative and experimental. Final causation and substantial forms did not seem to help. Descartes asked whence substantial forms come; and Boyle rejected stores of real qualities which are no "moods of matter." Science had to work out its own appropriate methods.

And so science asked questions and sought to answer them in terms of laws and bodies. The struggle over color, heat, and fire in chemistry illustrates the situation. Is color on the surface of things? What is heat?

Now I think there has been much misunderstanding about the epistemology of the so-called distinction between primary and secondary qualities. There was never any denial that color, for example, was a clue to external processes, and that red apples differ from green apples. What happened was a clearer realization of the mechanism of perception. But the danger was that the causal theory of sensation would dominate over the cognitive import of perception. It was empirical philosophy which fell into this trap. What science did was to develop measurement along with manipulations of instruments. Observation thus became subservient to instrumental realism; namely, that of rods and thermometers. In this, science followed and extended common-sense realism. As a deciphering and exploring activity of the organism, perceiving is bound up with the technique of the body. It is judgmental and interpretative. It includes categorial meanings. Qualities are immersed in referential relations. Suddenly to shift attention to "ideas" is to abstract from actual human knowing.

It has not been easy to work out an adequate realistic empiricism free from sensationalism on the one hand, and from mystical notions of thought on the other hand. Perhaps, the primary principle is to take empirical statements at their face value as referentially about objects. It is this framework of the organic self in correlated response to its environment that I have stressed. Categorial meanings dominate; and these are lifted to a conceptual, symbolic level. For instance, I, as self-conscious, set myself over against the things I am handling or even looking at. It is in such a fashion that a human being becomes a knower able to lift himself symbolically above his biological situation and become a cognitive spectator guided by intent. It is then no more difficult to think of a now non-existent Socrates than of the President of the United States. We designate by date and place.

The point is that the organism *uses* sensations and images within a referential framework and that, once this base is given, it can be built upon. It would seem that this further extension has been made possible for man by cortical processes and by language. It may well be that anthropology will throw light upon it. Tool-using and the awareness of others could be essential to an escape from *immersion* in a private play of experience. Cooperation, gesture, and speech lift to a world view.

The thesis of realistic empiricism is that human cognition is a *sui generis* achievement. Its tests must be worked out in terms of coherence, responsibility to data, prediction, and pragmatic control. From the beginning, however, it is objective in import.

Berkeley and Hume were too dominated by sensationalism and the causal approach; Kant made a valiant attempt to secure objectivity, but his objectivity was of a peculiar kind *without the biological base and hence not realistic.* What I would call things became things-in-themselves, unknowables.

I recognize that it is all very complicated historically. The wrong gambits were chosen, and led to a subjectivism which it was hard to overcome. To say the least, objective idealism did not mend epistemological matters. It was not until the turn of the century that a new effort was made to achieve an empirical realism. But, as I have already pointed out, it led to a stalemate. Then came the positivistic movement from Vienna, full of energy, conviction, and, let us admit, of ability, yet, until questions of language were introduced, very subjective. Principles of meaning were introduced. And so the question was heard, What do we *mean* when we speak of material things?

Even before this epoch was reached, Russell had tried to introduce scientific method into philosophy. What stood out, however, was his stress upon construction and upon the replacement of dispensable symbols by data felt to be hard and certain. The technique was taken up by the positivists.

In the meantime, Dewey and C. I. Lewis were developing pragmatism. In the case of Dewey the biological base became increasingly clear. But there went with it a note of experientialism and prediction. The result was a kind of realism without benefit of epistemology. As pragmatism and realism have come closer together, I have sought to be irenic and to clarify my own realism. But I still believe in epistemology, as will come out in my brief discussion of Lewis's position.

What, then, is the present situation? As I see it, the growth of science is making possible an evolutionary type of materialism capable of doing justice to categories like life, mindedness, personality, society. What is needed, in addition, is philosophical clarification and support. But, as we have argued, realism and materialism go together. So once more into the breach. What do we *mean* when we speak of material things? Can statements about them be translated into statements about sensations? I shall argue against such a thesis. Those who accept it cannot possibly be materialists, though they may well be naturalists. As is well known, the word "matter" in Greek had a technological origin; it meant timber, something one can handle and use. This origin fits in with the fact that perceiving and practical doing are closely connected.

I turn next to a brief study of those contemporary, naturalistic, empirical movements with which an empirical materialism must reckon. Since some of these will be examined in detail in later papers I here wish only to indicate critical points. I begin with Ayer because he raises so sharply the question of ontological statements. Are they meaningful? From him I pass to Lewis and Dewey; and I conclude with Russell. Consideration of Russell makes a good transition to ontology. Since I am concerned mainly with principles, I shall take Ayer's very readable *Language, Truth and Logic* as representative.

Ayer clearly assumes the validity of phenomenalism and argues that statements about material things can be translated into statements about actual and possible experiences of a more or less sensory sort. It is this thesis the materialist must challenge. For Ayer a slight technical emendation of Berkeley is sufficient:

> But the fact that he [Berkeley] failed to give a completely correct account of the way in which material things are *constructed* out of sense-contents does not invalidate his contention that they are so constituted. On the contrary, we know that it *must* be possible to define material things in terms of sense-contents, because it is only by the occurrence of certain sense-contents that the existence of any material thing can ever be in the least degree *verified.* And thus we see that we have not to enquire whether a phenomenalist "theory of perception" or some other sort of theory is correct, *but only what form of phenomenalist theory is correct.*[3]

Now, so far as I can make out, this early school is anti-realistic. Material-thing sentences are to be translated, even if capacities and dispositions offer apparent difficulty. Carnap represents a transition here. Yet we have many statements contrary to actual fact. If I were to drop this book, what would happen? and why? Do these not indicate ontological connections, to be known in laws? Are not laws true? Cases of knowledge about the world?

I have argued that there is an ambiguity about the term "observe," connected with two types of basic sentences. I can observe a sense-datum and regard it as evidential for a theory; and I can, in the framework of organic perception, referentially observe a thing. C. I. Lewis has been led to distinguish between verifiable, terminating statements and confirmable, non-terminating factual statements.

Can, then, material-thing sentences be translated into sense-datum sentences? And, if not, what is the alternative?

The best way to begin is to consider attempts to reduce material, or M, sentences to sensory, or S, sentences. Suppose I say, "This thing hanging on a hook on the wall is my hat." To begin with, we have a categorial concept, thing, which is in the same universe of discourse as my bodily self. Ordinarily I regard myself as something having, not only a complex internal constitution, but powers and dispositions. In the second place, the demonstrative is public in import and fits in with nod or pointing. In the third place, a hat-thing has a geometrical shape, was manufactured, and is made of a felt which itself has a history. Why should I regard all these testable concepts as illusory? It seems to me that I should do so only if realistic theories of knowledge are clearly absurd. In other words, I am persuaded that Ayer got on his hobby-horse too soon.

My conclusion is that phenomenalistic empiricism, like Berkeleianism, represents an inadequate analysis of perceptual experience with its references and claims. I agree with C. D. Broad that a translation of M-sentences into sentences about a hypothetical multitude of S-sentences of an "If-then" sort, contrary to fact, does not do justice to the situation. These "If-then" sentences revolve about the body of the agent. And is the body of the observer itself reducible to a prior set of hypotheticals? Is not all this a *tour de force?*

Perceiving is, undoubtedly, a far more complicated operation and experience than is usually assumed. One-sided beginnings of analysis, suggested by the emphases of the culture of the time, have been misleading. Thus, the so-called causal theory of perception, in its origins, was dominated by the notion of causal impact upon the senses and, thence, upon the soul-mind. But even the ancient Stoics had seen that interpretation and judgment were involved. And modern psychology regards the stimulus as just the incitation to intra-organic processes of a very dynamic sort. The organism is, as it were, alerted; or, more correctly, its alerted awareness is challenged by the stimulus. In my opinion, it would be wise for philosophers to speak of the *causal conditioning* of sensory data, rather than of a causal theory of perception. And the reason is that perceiving involves alerted reference, symbolizing and conceptualization. Of course, the individual does not literally transcend his experiencing; but his experiencing has structural and functional distinctions in which the percipient is set over against objects or *Gegenstände*. German is an expressive language here. And I do think of *awareness* as, basically, an activity. In man, a far more complicated and steady activity than in many other creatures. But psychologists can best take up such a point as this. What I wish to stress is the difference between the apprehension of sensory data and perceiving. Even of the first, there is no simple one-to-one correspondence with an external stimulus, as modern psychology has shown.

In much the same manner, I would reject traditional representative perception. While I do think we are justified in believing that visual data have a measure of correlation with the stimulus-situation, that belief is more of an inference from the practical and cognitive value of their *use* in perceiving than a datum of perceiving itself. We shall have something more to say about this point when we return to "observation" as against macroscopic perceiving. While I cannot apprehend an object to which I am alerted as I can my sense-data, I do denote and interpret it, as something over against myself. We are not naked souls immersed in our own states of mind, as the older dualism conceived the situation. Much of the mystery about "transcendence" stems from wrong assumptions. The essential thing is to understand the mechanism of knowing and its claims. It is the *claim* that is *irreducible.* I am denoting and judging this thing, other than my embodied, or organic, self.

Now, from all this analysis, it follows that a basic physical statement is not reducible to the mode of its verification. In ordinary perception, our alerted awareness and reference functions through an interplay of sensory data and conceptions. If we doubt, we try to get "better" data. But a perceptual judgment is *other than* the apprehension of sense-data. In fact, we are not, ordinarily, much aware of sense-data for their own sake. In scientific observation the situation is fairly different. The scientist is not interested in his instruments, rather takes them for granted in his artificial environment. He is interested in sensory data regarded as evidential of physical events confirming his theory.

While, then, M-sentences (that is, material thing sentences) are not translatable into S-sentences (sentences about sensory data) S-sentences are significant for M-sentences, because we can note that our concepts require them, though not as simply as was once assumed. I say that a penny is round, though, from this angle, it may well *look* elliptical. In scientific observation every effort is made to get "good data."

It is clear that the positivistic query must first be threshed out at the macroscopic level of common sense. After that, we can talk about atoms, electrons and quanta. It is measurement, mathematics, and instrumental technique that enable the scientist to penetrate beneath the denotative interpretations of ordinary perception and build up a frame of reference of space and time, which, itself, may break down with quantum mechanics. To the materialistic realist it is all quite understandable. We move *denotatively* from alerted sense-perception, which is an elementary kind of knowledge, to conceptually locatable microscopic denotables. But there must still be relevant, evidential sense-data, though the relationship is now very complicated. Theory and "observation" now are developed within sense-perception. My argument merely is, that if the macroscopic, organic frame ever were set aside completely, we should lose, not only things, *but our very selves.*

It follows from this argument *that empirical statements are ontological.* Both M-sentences and S-sentences are factual and about realities. In this sense—and in this sense alone—every one is continually talking ontology, as M. Jourdain talked prose. It is not speculative, but empirical, ontology. And I am arguing that that is what empirically minded materialism is.

In ridiculing metaphysics or ontology, hardly distinguished, Ayer and the logical empiricists have only been dogmatically affirming their phenomenalism. And yet how impressive it sounded, once the question of the reach of empirical propositions was thrust aside! "We men,"

Ayer wrote, "accordingly define a metaphysical sentence as a sentence which purports to express a genuine proposition but does, in fact, express neither a tautology nor an empirical hypothesis. And, as tautologies and empirical hypotheses form the entire class of significant propositions, we are justified in concluding that all metaphysical assertions are nonsensical." [4]

And so the question is really that of the reach and import of empirical sentences. I have been arguing that this reach and import is realistic in both psychology and the non-introspective sciences.

I wish I had the space to go into the syntactical and semantic developments of logical empiricism with Neurath and Carnap. At first, as I understand it, the emphasis was upon syntax with protocol sentences at the base of the pyramid. These were basic and only slightly corrigible. The proper concern of philosophy was, henceforth, with the language of science. There was still the firm conviction that the traditional disputes about the references and claims of perception were to be set aside as meaningless. But sentences are supposedly social in a communicative sort of way. I judge the psychophysics of communication was also regarded as involving no nonlinguistic quagmires. Philosophy moved only in the realm of language.

Before long, however, the limitation to syntax was felt to be suicidal. While some logical problems had been cleared up by the stress upon words and upon meta-languages, the distinction between strict verifiability and confirmability had arisen at the base. The result was an advance into semantics and semiotics under the guidance of C. W. Morris. What do words and other signs mean? Do not conventional, dictionary meanings rest upon, and presuppose, what C. I. Lewis calls sense-meanings? And are sense-meanings reducible to statements about data of observation? What is called pragmatics, the reference to the user and interpreter of signs, needed consideration. But were we not here back to the *full-bodied percipient?* And, if so, back to instruments, technique, society? And must not language itself be considered as a social technique? All this sounds realistic and far from Ayer's Berkeleianism. Only the continued conviction that a realistic, referential theory of perception cannot be worked out stands in the way.

And so we take leave of this type of phenomenalism. In trying to escape ontology it took the path of sensationalism; but a sensationalism enmeshed in an improved linguistic and logical technique. I have the impression that, among others of the school, there is the tendency today to start from a rather undefined common-sense realism and not to trouble too much about epistemology. But such a disregard of epistemology threatens to bring, in revenge, the traditional problem of Platonic universals for workers in logic and mathematics. This is particularly the case when conventions are separated from empirical meanings and what Lewis calls criteria of application. But into the complicated theory of symbols I cannot here enter.

C. I. Lewis has developed his conceptual pragmatism in an overtly naturalistic fashion in his latest systematic work. Explicit cognition emerges from the "know-how" of animal life and presupposes activity. Epistemology does not change human experience but seeks to make explicit the conditions and claims of human knowing. With all this I can fully agree.

Unfortunately, while he recognizes the fact of ordinary cosmology with its things, events, causality, and dispositional properties, he pays little attention to it. This I regard as unfortunate. Is it because he senses that it would involve the question of what he dismisses as the topic of the "metaphysical veracity" of knowledge? It is knowledge as predictive and conditional which is emphasized. But if objective facts are achieved—though, of course, never analytically certain—may not these facts give cosmological knowledge in a cumulative way?

Since, as a critical realist, I heartily agree with his recognition of private experience as something requiring what he calls the expressive use of language, I shall not linger upon his analysis with its biological setting. I only ask whether the "I" of conditional action is not the minded organism, and whether it and the *real connection* involved in statements to the effect that, if I were to do so-and-so, I should have such an experience are not cosmological in import. My point is that he constantly presupposes capacities and causality of an ontological kind.

Perhaps my difficulty can be best put as follows: Is an objective fact *translatable* without a remainder into the multiplicity of "If-then" testing statements? Do I mean by the statement that a piece of white paper is now before *me* merely that I can obtain a non-terminating series of sensory experiences? If so, we have something analogous to Ayer's attempt to translate M-sentences into S-sentences. What is the significance of objective facts for cosmology? I would myself hold that the white paper has the same existential status as Lewis's active self.

And is the self no more than its *possible* experiences? It seems to me that objective facts are left ungrounded because of his disregard of cosmology. And this disregard flows from his extreme emphasis upon prediction.

After a rejection of traditional epistemology resembling what Carneades might have delivered himself of in his attack upon Stoicism, Lewis permits himself the luxury of a note in which the whole problem of the status of sensory data is rather cryptically handled. It will be recalled that I have argued that sensory data function within dispositional, conceptual attitudes and meanings of the perceptual framework, and that perception, rather than sensing, is the cognitive unit. This and the categorial meanings involved are the reason why M-sentences are not translatable into S-sentences.

Since, as a philosopher, I have always been irenic and have held out the olive branch to the pragmatists as they increasingly became realistic and even materialistic, I should like, in conclusion, to comment on the note at the bottom of page 187 in Lewis's book. Let us remember that the critical realist holds to the referential directness of perception and not to the apprehensional immediacy of the *object* of perception. That is, he distinguishes between the *content* of perception and the *object* of perception. I stress this point because, in my opinion, the coming struggle is between pragmatism, critical realism, and Aristotelianism, so far as the theory of perception is concerned. I quote now from Lewis a passage such as I would write:

> That we may have before us some presentation whose character as given we can be sure of, and that at the same time we know, *through and by means of this presentation,* some objective thing or event, is not here denied but affirmed.

This sounds like realism. And then he proceeds:

> What is *immediate and certain,* however, is not the objective thing, event, or state of affairs which is known, but the content of experience which evidences it—as having some probability, which may be "practical certainty."[5]

And then he goes on to say that the process of verification *can* go on indefinitely. Of course it can. I long ago justified and confirmed the *belief* that this object is *my hand* pounding the typewriter; and, if I want to, I can regard each tap as the verification of a terminating judgment. The point is that the object can never be transformed into a sense-datum. The object cannot acquire the *apprehensible certainty* and immediacy of the sense-datum.

Now comes the note which brings in all the traditional epistemology Lewis had kicked out of the door.

> This statement [the one quoted above] has no implication of a dualistic or phenomenalistic interpretation of the relation of mind to reality [*sic*] in cognition. It is still possible, in terms of the conception here presented, to affirm that the content of presentation is an authentic part, or aspect, or perspective, which is *ingredient,* in the reality known. Such language is figurative . . . But the view . . . may be consistently and literally correct—provided one is prepared to accept the implications that an elliptical appearance may be a genuine ingredient of a real round penny, the bent stick in the water an ingredient of the really straight stick.[6]

The whole passage is crucial and very revealing. Both of us agree that the sensory presentation is conceptualized and used as evidence of the object. But I find myself more in agreement with Russell on the existential status of the evidentially used sensory presentation. It is *within* the brain-mind of the percipient. And to this I shall shortly come.

I need say little about Dewey since a paper will be devoted to his position. The usual quarrel of realists with him is that he redefines knowledge as that kind of warrantable assertion that satisfies inquiry and leads to the *reconstruction of experience.* "The true object of knowledge resides in the consequences of directed action." Is not this another hobby-horse?

Russell accepts the causal conditioning of sense-data, which he identifies with a causal theory of perception; holds that data correspond enough in pattern to external things to serve as a basis of scientific knowledge; regards physics as the most assured knowledge we have; argues that our knowledge of nature is abstract; rejects particles for events; holds that sense-data are "in" the brain; and substitutes neutral monism for materialism, thus attaching himself to William James and the later phases of the new realism. Let us now try to evaluate this complex of positions.

My own view has many points in common with his, but with a different emphasis. That should by now be clear. While I admire physics, I still think we cannot give up the organic framework of perception as a starting-point. In its own fashion we have assurance here. I would stress direct perceptual reference and be less skeptical and Humean; I would add to intellectual evidence and logical consilience the constant organic and technological testing of practice; I would not seek to translate M-sentences into S-sentences. Neutral monism seems to me to be an historical mistake based on bad epistemology *and radical experientialism.* In knowing, we get facts, or truths, about the structure, composition, and behavior of things and seek to answer questions asked. But I do not think that we should expect to intuit external *being* nor regard it as *like,* in nature, to our sensory experience. This does not exclude a partial correspondence of pattern. The relation of sensory experience to *being* comes in, rather, in the consciousness-brain problem. And our linguistic habits are not reducible to the sensory. Human knowing is a magnificent achievement, but why be too anthropomorpic in our demands? Russell's neutral monism strikes me as another instance of a powerful technique gone astray.

The theory that feelings and sensory data are intrinsic to neural processes I have long maintained. Here and here alone, I have urged, are we conscious participants in nature, on the inside of a highly evolved physical system.

Let us try to comprehend the situation in which we find ourselves. On the one hand, we are dominated by external perception with its knowledge-claims referentially directed to substantive things and processes. Our own body is, of course, included in this frame of being. By the very nature of the cognitive situation, no probing along these lines can bend back and attain and include the conscious act of cognition itself. In short, consciousness itself cannot be an object of any of the physical sciences. And we must include therein neurology. Epistemologically this fact should not surprise us, nor should it be made into a mystery.

But it does not follow that we may not have good reason to believe that the stream of consciousness is intrinsic to the neural processes. What we call *experiencing* is private and is inclusive of feeling, wishes, volitions, and the aforesaid acts of cognition. Upon all these we can make reports founded on what is usually called knowledge of acquaintance. What is more, all these experiences and reports are tied in with the organic self. Hence it can be said that we have a double knowledge of the organic self: one through perception and external investigation, and one more participative, reflexive, and intuitive.

The question will not down, therefore, whether there is anything about the external order of knowledge which precludes and shuts out this more intuitive kind of knowledge. Why may not a neural event "contain" consciousness as a qualitative dimension of its existential content? In this double-knowledge approach I have argued that what we are acquainted with is a *natural isolate* whose completing neural context cannot be apprehended in the same way. We can have external, factual *knowledge about,* but no external intuition. I agree with Herrick, Sherrington, and others that we have here a sort of impasse. But may it not be an impasse because we tend to expect too much from external knowledge? Such knowledge cannot be *participative.*

Materialism in the past was made inadequate by its pictorial atomism and lack of a feeling for pattern, dynamic relations and process. It was also weakened by an inadequate epistemology. Modern science realizes fully the inferential and deciphering nature of much of our physical knowledge. Why should it be difficult to acknowledge that there may be a qualitative content to existence, and that consciousness is an emergent sample connected with what Boring calls discrimination in its neural base? I would not overstress cerebral localization. And certainly the philosopher must leave it to the joint work of neurology and psychology to work out correlations and isomorphisms. But I myself feel justified in speaking of the mind-brain, while recognizing that the whole organism is the unit of behavior.

Such problems as these, positivism has largely ignored. They have been regarded as too speculative. But this kind of solution of the self-mind-body problem would simplify both science and philosophy. Other selves and minds would simply be other organisms to their degree. In the case of man, explicit knowledge, symbolic reference, and communication would merely climax the scene. We humans are both objects and subjects, "I = things" and persons.

I have spoken of consciousness as a natural isolate and as a privately given *feature* of an event in the brain. It is clear that there must be an adequate epistemological framework. I do not see how neurology and psychology can neglect the necessary epistemological distinctions much longer.

This apparent digression brings me back to Russell once more. He, being logical, decided that a sensation is "in" the brain, as an event may be in a more inclusive event. Unfortunately, he spoke of "seeing the brain" and found that few tried to understand him. What he meant was that a visual datum could be apprehended, and that it was, *in some sense,* an event in the brain-event.[7]

Now there are all sorts of complications here because discrimination appears to be a cortical function; and apprehension is discrimination. And yet the visual area seems to contribute the primary basis of such a *discriminatum.* I rather agree with S. Alexander that a sensation is, in itself, an activity to be "enjoyed," as we throw a throw or dance a dance. Professor Ducasse has been thinking along a similar line. Discrimination would then be a higher-order activity integral to alert awareness.

In concluding this section of my paper, may I revert very briefly to the status of "observation"? In observation, as I see it, we have *reports* which we regard as significant for theories about physical events, such as light rays, or the quantum activities within an atom, or the impact of an electron on a screen, etc. Now, once we accept the thesis that sensory data are significant for macroscopic, referential perception, I can see no theoretical difficulty in the verifying significance of such reports of apprehensions. It is, however, essential that we recognize two types of sentences which are not reducible to each other. "This book *is* oblong" and "This appears to me oblong" and "The sense-datum I regard as the sensory basis of this appearance is configurationally oblongish" are different kinds of statements. "I see a flash" and "I hear a click in this Geiger counter" are sentences which show how intimately connected are perceptual, referential judgments and sensory discriminations. I see an eclipse and confirm a scientific calculation and theory on the basis of a private sensory observation which, *as such,* was not predicted. The scientists assert that a physical event will occur which can be verified by personal observations. That is where the observer comes in. Without him and his perceptual framework, one could not connect science with the objective, material world. But the double-knowledge view shows that the private is also objective existentially and logically objective by *report*. All of which means that human beings have a dimension and level which does not exist in inorganic things or even in less highly evolved organisms. It is the dimension of interpretative, symbolic activity. And I suppose that is why the application to us of a thing-language is both fitting and unfitting. We have no fixed and static essence. Sartre, however, goes to an extreme in denying us an historical nature. But I cannot go into ethical theory here. Reductive materialism was false because it could not explain human knowing as a natural achievement.

To conclude this section, I offer a few words on that puzzling distinction between primary and secondary qualities. Does not the usual puzzle reflect an unordered mixture of linguistic, epistemological, and ontological points? If attention is directed upon sensory data, then configurational extensity and color are distinguishable but inseparable. If the object of thought is perceptual judgment about things, then a color-word already begins to refer to a standard color-appearance under normal conditions. It is then no surprise to discover that this appearance has external light-energy conditions as well as retinal and visual-area conditions. Physics studies the first set. In the meantime, the objective interpretation of things has continued in terms of comparisons, manipulations, and measurement. We should now speak of *facts* about things—that they are so large, weigh so much, have an internal structure and composition. The next job is to get adequate categories and ways of speaking. I prefer to speak of the extendedness, mass, energy, composition, and powers of things, leaving it to science to make these terms more precise. Categories are simply expressions of our most basic and general knowledge of the world. They declare what we take to be the case. I would reject Locke's unknowable substratum much as I would Aristotle's indeterminate matter. My suggestion, then, is that the historical distinction from Democritus and Galileo to Locke between primary and secondary qualities reflects, first, the recognition that sensing is different from objective perception and, second, that scientific method takes up and develops perceptual knowledge, emphasizing measurement and reallocating sensory data and clarifying physical categories such as mass and structure. Thus the distinction between primary and secondary qualities was not much more than a preliminary step. Epistemological and linguistic analysis must work hand in hand.

The primary task of a modern materialistic ontology is to clarify an adequate set of categories congruent with the results of science. It is easy to say that it rejects phenomenalism, mentalism, and substantive dualism. But that is not enough. It must be constructive and imaginative. Its job is to give ontological background to the new naturalism. There still is the burden of a gigantic cosmology now rightly left largely to physicist and astronomer.

Empirical materialism, refusing to accept the scholastic distinction between essence and existence, emphasizes the corporeally concrete but thinks it relationally and temporally. In this sense, *being* is process and existence is a temporality. Yet often an enduring, continuant temporality; in the case of man, substantial enough to look before and after and gifted enough to comprehend the universe in which he finds himself, a universe essentially non-personal endlessly weaving and unweaving its patterns. For knowledge of scientific range is an achievement conditional upon the invention of technique and methods. I do not overexalt it for its power, which can be used for good or evil.

To say that *this* table exists is a tautology unless it mean that I am *not* having an hallucination. In technical terms, primary existence is not a property added to something else called form or essence. It is, rather, a term for that which becomes and perishes in the dynamic patterning of nature. Neutrons and atoms can be said to exist in the same sense that tables and human beings exist—but after their kind. Is there a floor to *being,* a lowest level? It is that question which physics is approaching. And are not conservation and change correlatives?

The notion of levels is a philosophical speculation until the detail is filled in by biopsychology, psychology, and anthropology. Our co-operating scientists will, I doubt not, have much light to throw upon the question of levels and of the status of units in an integrative whole. The question of the relation of an elementary particle to its field is a burning one even for physics. How can justice be done to continuity and discontinuity in a more dynamic perspective?

Earlier in the paper, I mentioned the traditional contrast between mechanism and teleology. It would seem that both terms are undergoing sea-changes. Mechanism stands largely for structural distinctions, while teleology is increasingly thought of as involving directedness in processes, an intrinsic directedness whose opposite would be randomness. This directedness must be connected with organization at its various levels. It is hard, as yet, to verbalize what Cannon called the "wisdom of the body." Biologists are discovering such wisdom in the behavior of lowly organisms. We are still too anthropomorphic in our categories. Goal seeking may have many levels below cortical learning by experience and anticipation.

And what is mentation but a further development of the selective and varied, integrative activity of the brain as attuned to the vectorial alertness of the body? In man there develops an interfusion of natural and conventional symbols. If rats reason, as psychologists inform us, reasoning is an operation resting on integrative capacities and not on random throws. Logic is but its normative, linguistic clarification. If so, reasoning is a high-level causal process which psychology is only beginning to be in a position to describe. Scientific method is itself a cultural complication extending human reasoning. Such, I take it, must be the perspective of an evolutionary materialism. Empirically verified categories must be *saved*. The time is past for by-products and epiphenomena. The new concepts of the microscopic, of integrative organization, and of levels help in all this. And, probably, it is well to have a sense of internal "go" to supplement external observation. This signifies that causality has its levels.

I am impressed by man's novelty and uniqueness. Thus, knowing is a human achievement added to the know-how of animals-in-general. We can mean objects symbolically as well as respond to them; and, thus, knowledge can play over the universe *as though* it were an immaterial searchlight. Such is the operational basis of *symbolic transcendence,* as against organic response. To know a thing is not to be it or to possess a substantive form inherent in it, as Aristotle thought, but to make tested statements about it. And I have argued that this high, cognitive level must retain an enduring sense of its attachment to the organic framework of perception. Otherwise, we land in idealistic mysticism.

An empirical materialist can find a place for choice; for it seems to me as naturally prepared for as reasoning which intertwines with it. At the level of culturally developed personality, choice involves moral decision with its sense of responsibility. Here character, culture, and group connexity are coordinate. I have long felt that the historic opposition between freedom and determinism has been badly formulated.

The idea of levels of causality is relevant here. Ontological, immanent causality involves the intrinsic "go" of internally differentiated wholes. Internal directedness increases with life. Even worms and fruit flies adjust selectively. What is freedom in man but the power of projective, rational choice? Intelligence and education enlarge the scope of decision. And may it not be that the continued lure of the idea of "free will" points to our intimate awareness of alerted action as a self? In the past, science spoke too much about binding laws and blind necessity. It was also too reductive. Surely the human self is both a growth and an agent. Modern empirical materialism is far from puppetry and reductionism.

What I have tried to show in this paper is that the resources of philosophy—hitherto largely employed against materialism—may now be used in its favor. But it will not be the old materialism tied in with outgrown science and bad epistemology. One of the jobs is to rescue empiricism from subjectivism and phenomenalism. It is to this that the next paper turns.

References

[1] Louis de Broglie, *Matter and Light* (New York: Norton, 1939), p. 291.

[2] Louis Trenchard More, *The Life and Works of the Hon. Robert Boyle* (New York: Oxford, 1944), p. 254. The last two chapters discuss Boyle's criticism of scholastic science and alchemy.

[3] A. J. Ayer, *Language, Truth and Logic* (London: Gollancz, 1936), pp. 54–55.

[4] *Ibid.*, pp. 31–32. I take these as good formulations of logical positivism in its period of self-confidence.

[5] C. I. Lewis, *An Analysis of Knowledge and Valuation* (La Salle, Ill.: Open Court, 1946), p. 187. I have been accustomed to making the distinction between knowledge as objective and verifiable fact and what it is *about*. Lewis has replied to criticisms by Pratt and myself of his earlier work, *Mind and the World-Order*, on pp. 200–201. As his reply stands, I consider it to be a clarification with which I can agree. Sensory data are objective in their fashion and can be expressed in propositions. If we have reason to regard them as controlled by, and significant for, an objective thing or event, we take them as evidential for a statement about thing or event. Lewis formulates this relation in terms of identity of intention. If my datum were different I would assert a different objective fact. But the existences involved are distinct. Until Lewis tells us more clearly his idea of the existential locus of sensory data I shall not be satisfied. Our "common world," I take to be existentially and categorially one, referentially and ostensively one, and descriptively one.

[6] *Ibid.*, p. 187 n.

[7] The lamination of sensory areas in the brain, such as the visual and the auditory areas, indicates a reproduction of pattern. This is being explored by electrical methods. It probably has bearing on what the Gestaltists call isomorphism. The modern materialist is convinced that psychophysical research on the brain is going to pay dividends. The behaviorist has too much ignored the brain.

THE CATEGORY OF SUBSTANCE[1]

by

EVERETT J.

NELSON

Everett J. Nelson is Professor of Philosophy and Executive Officer of the Department of Philosophy, University of Washington, Seattle. Sheldon Fellowship, Harvard University, 1929–1930. Guggenheim Fellowship, 1939–1940. President, Pacific Division, American Philosophical Association, 1946. Consulting Editor, *Journal of Symbolic Logic*. He has published articles in *Mind, Monist, Philosophy of Science, Journal of Philosophy,* and other periodicals.

THE belief that we can learn from experience is not certified by data given in experience. This belief can be warranted only by principles in virtue of which a proposition reporting experience can be evidence of, or render probable, other empirically testable propositions not implied by it. Therefore, principles sufficient to validate empirical inference must entail that experiences are connected, and, consequently, must be formulated in terms of, or presuppose, modes of connection or of unity. Such modes of connection or of unity are metaphysical categories and are kinds of synthesis in terms of which the philosopher interprets experience.

I shall consider only one such type of synthesis—namely, substance—and shall argue that the proposition that substance is an ultimate category is presupposed by the belief that we can learn from experience. I shall defend the view that *if* empirical knowledge is possible, or if such notions as thing, property, cause, order, law, or even process are to have the objective significance they do have in our interpretation of the world and are to play the role they do play in our knowledge of the world, then the category of substance is indispensable. I am not going to argue for the proposition that empirical knowledge is possible, or that the notions we have just mentioned do have objective significance; hence, I am not categorically supporting substance. I confess, however, a firm and unequivocal belief in empirical knowledge. It is for this reason that for me, as it should be for any believer in science, a discussion of substance is serious philosophic business.

I shall introduce the problem of substance by considering the meaning and status of dispositional properties. I begin this way, not because I think that the acceptance or rejection of substance turns upon the analysis of dispositional properties, but because the issues raised by such properties lead directly to the problem of substance and thence to the relations between substance, causation, and natural law.

To say that gold is fusible, that sugar is soluble, that arsenic is poisonous is to attribute to these things dispositional properties. When I say that this lump of sugar is soluble in coffee, I do not mean that it ever was put into coffee and dissolved or ever will be put into coffee and dissolve. Nor do I mean simply that if it was put into coffee, it did dissolve, or that if it shall be put into coffee, it will dissolve. I mean also that if it *had been* put into coffee, it *would have* dissolved. Similarly, when we say that arsenic is poisonous, an essential part of our meaning is that if certain conditions *had been* satisfied, it *would have* poisoned someone.

Such properties must be distinguished from those which are not dispositional. Thus, when I say that a sense-datum is yellow, I am attributing to it a nondispositional property. When, however, I say that the case of my watch which is now in my pocket is yellow, I use "yellow" in a dispositional sense, meaning roughly that if anyone having normal vision had looked, or were to look, at the case in daylight, he would have had, or would have, a sensation of yellow. Of course someone might hold that my watch case is yellow also in a nondispositional sense: that the physical object is yellow independently of conditions of illumination or the presence of a perceiver. I hardly need to point out that most of the properties we use in identifying physical objects and defining their kinds are dispositional.

The notion of dispositional property leads to substance in the following way: When we assert, for example, that if this lump of sugar had been put into coffee, it would have dissolved, then we are asserting that the lump of sugar is "something which may be in various states, and may stand in various relations to other things at various times."

We are implying also that it "*might instead* have been in a different state or stood in different relations to the same or different things *at that time*."[2] And this implies that the sugar has a *nature* which does not necessitate its being in just this state or in just these relations to these other things at this time, and that it would have been the same thing even if it had not been in these states or in these relations in which it now is. The lump of sugar is then a *substance,* and its specific nature as such is constituted, at least in part, by certain of its dispositional properties.

Disquieted by the fact that relatively permanent substance seems in this way presupposed by dispositional properties, some philosophers have endeavored to show that dispositional properties are not ultimate and, in this way, have hoped to remove at least one reason for taking substance as a metaphysical category. They have tried to do this by expressing in nondispositional and nonsubstantive terms everything that we can sensibly express by employing such terms. Success in this project requires that statements in terms of the alternative set of categories be equivalent in the strictest intensional sense to the original statements. Such translatability is a *necessary* condition of the avoidance of dispositional properties and of substance, unless of course it can be shown that the very notion of dispositional property, or of substance, is infected with contradiction.

In the present positivistic and antimetaphysical milieu of philosophic thought, many thinkers have pinned their faith on the notion of "process" as the category most promising of liberation from metaphysics. I use the word "faith," because, though the recommendations of process are legion, closely reasoned expositions detailing precisely how a reconstruction in terms of it can be accomplished are astonishingly rare. C. D. Broad's argument in his *Examination of McTaggart's Philosophy* is one of the exceptions. In attempting to reduce substance to process, he does an excellent, though not entirely convincing, job until he comes to dispositional properties. There his attack takes the form of arguing that conditionals contrary to fact, which are expressions of dispositional properties, are nonsense in so far as they be construed to be about a singular subject and are sense only if they be construed to be about a class or kind, and that, when so construed, they are equivalent to functions expressible in the indicative mood.[3]

Thus, if in expressing my belief that a particular vase is fragile I say, "If this vase had been hit a sharp blow, it would have shattered," I am speaking nonsense if the subject of my proposition is *this* vase. And if I am not speaking nonsense, then I mean that if at any time any substance of the same kind as this vase were hit a sharp blow, it would shatter.

Though this language suggests that Broad is merely replacing a subjunctive conditional about an individual by one about a kind, and consequently that he has just shifted the problem from individuals to classes, I doubt that this is what he intends. Rather, I believe he means that the proposition about kinds is a functional law, which can be expressed in the indicative. Then he would reinterpret our original proposition about "this vase" as an instance of the law. Accordingly, the original statement that this vase is fragile would then have as its analysis the conjunction of the general law about vases and the following two propositions about "this vase": (1) If this vase ever was hit a sharp blow, it then shattered; and (2) If this vase ever shall be hit a sharp blow, it will then shatter.

On this argument I would comment as follows:

(1) Broad has not shown that it is nonsense to use a conditional contrary to fact about singular things. As far as I can gather from his discourse, his reason for rejecting such conditionals is this: If x had property ϕ at time t, then there is no sense in supposing that x did not have ϕ at time t. He asks what sense can be given to it, and from his admitted inability to supply an answer, he concludes that it has no sense. At least part of his difficulty seems to be due to his failure to see that the proposition that the world is so determined as to leave open no physical possibility does not imply that physical possibility is meaningless. Take the proposition: "If Roosevelt had not died on April 12, 1945, Truman would not have been President on April 12, 1945." Let us grant that Truman's being President on April 12, 1945, was a physically determined resultant of the particular state of the world eons ago. None the less, his being President on April 12 was as contingent as the laws of nature and as the particular state of the world at any previous date. Hence, though his being President then may have been physically necessitated, it was not logically necessitated, and the denial of it is not meaningless. Only if every truth about a thing were part of its essence—i.e., only if the most rigid theory of internal relations were true—would it be nonsense to contemplate Truman's not

being President on April 12, 1945. Though I can hardly believe that Broad could have held that if, as a sheer matter of fact or as a result of physical determination, a particular has a certain property, then the proposition that it does not have that property is meaningless, still I am at a loss for any other explanation of his position. Consequently, I must conclude that he has not successfully supported his denial of sense to conditionals contrary to fact about singulars, and, therefore, that he has not shown how to translate subjunctive conditionals expressive of dispositional properties into indicative equivalents not involving such properties.

(2) The denial of sense to subjunctive conditionals about singulars makes a travesty of much of our use of functional laws. Their application both in practical and in theoretical contexts often involves judging what would have happened if something had happened, or predicting what would take place in the future if such and such alternative were adopted. Moreover, even the functional laws themselves are for the most part idealizations never realized in fact. A good example is the law of inertia.

And finally, as I shall argue later, even if dispositional properties could be dispensed with in favor of events and their laws, still the very notion of law involves the notion of substance.

Before turning, however, to that matter, I want to mention one other attempt to avoid the consequences entailed by dispositional properties; namely, Professor Carnap's.[4] Beginning with a "language" not having dispositional words, he would introduce them into that language, not by definition, which he admits is impossible, but by the device of "reduction sentences." Such sentences state in terms of the initial language and the logic of material implication, sets of conditions under which the dispositional words may be used and other sets under which they should not be used. Suppose, for example, we want to introduce into our language the dispositional adjective-word "fragile." We stipulate: (1) If x is hit a sharp blow and shatters, then x is fragile; and (2) If x is dropped to the pavement and does not shatter, then x is not fragile. In this way we stipulate positive and negative conditions for the employment of the word "fragile." Such reduction sentences do not tell us the meaning of the word but enumerate conditions of its applicability and of its inapplicability. Additional reduction pairs enumerate further such conditions, with the result of a progressive determination of the correct application of the word. But, as Carnap freely admits, the determination will always be partial. With respect to the kinds of circumstance not enumerated, the expression "x is fragile" would, Carnap says, have "no meaning." This is sufficient to show that reduction sentences do not provide a definition.

On this mechanism of Carnap's I would remark as follows:

(1) Since the determination is always partial, the *meaning* of the dispositional adjective-word has not been introduced into his language. This would be true even if we could specify all the test conditions, positive and negative, of the application of the word, because such an exhaustive enumeration would be nothing but a *formal material equivalence*—not an identity—between the disjunctive enumeration of the positive conditions and the truth of the function, x is fragile, and a similar equivalence for the falsity of the function, x is fragile. Let us consider another example. Even though it were possible for a physiological psychologist to state an exhaustive set of conditions under which a human being may be said to be conscious, and an exhaustive set of conditions under which a human being may be said to be not conscious, still these sets would miss entirely the meaning of consciousness. Or, a corresponding statement of all the physical or physiological conditions under which one will have a sensation of red would not give the sensory content of the experienced red. However important such "behavioristic definitions" may be, we must not fail to recognize that they are not definitions in the usual sense—in the sense in which the *definiendum* may always be replaced by the *definiens* without any change in *meaning*. Carnap has not then shown us how to introduce into a nondispositional-word language the *meaning* of a dispositional word. All that his device of reduction sentences does is to determine to some degree the conditions of the correct application of such a word.

At least one reason why Carnap did not attempt to *define* dispositional property adjectives is that certain paradoxical consequences result from the use of the notions of the logic of material implication. These consequences follow principally from the fact that false propositions materially imply all propositions, and that functions may be vacuously true. An example of such a paradox is this: If we define "x is soluble in water" as "Whenever x is placed in water, x dissolves," we are driven to affirm of anything which never has been and never will be placed in water, that it is soluble in water, regardless of what it is made of.

Though I do not have a formal proof, I doubt that dispositional properties can be defined, or conditionals contrary to fact can be expressed, solely in terms of nondispositional terms and the concepts of material logic. I doubt it, not just because no one has successfully done it, but because formal implication and equivalence, being extensional functions, hold between many properties not only physically unconnected but totally independent in meaning, and also because propositions asserting them may be vacuously true.

I might add in passing that since the relation between the facts expressed by the antecedent and by the consequent of the expression of a dispositional property is not a relation belonging to logic, such a property cannot be defined in terms of the relations of a strict or intensional logic.

It is interesting to note that all attempts, or at least all attempts with which I am acquainted, to get rid of dispositional properties, either by reduction or by translation, possess one or both of two characteristics: (1) the exclusive use of a material logic, and (2) the exclusion of the notion of causation in any sense stronger than that of a mere constant conjunction in experience—i.e., in any sense not expressible in terms of a formal implication or equivalence.

Although I believe that dispositional properties involve connections not expressible by indicative conditionals of the "if . . . then" form, I do not object to expressing certain implications of propositions involving such properties by sentences of that form, provided we carefully distinguish between (1) the logical relation holding from the antecedent to the consequent proposition, and (2) the relation between the states of affairs expressed by these propositions. This latter relation is, as we have said, the one involved in dispositional properties; and, not belonging to logic, it cannot be expressed exclusively in terms of the notions belonging to logic.

I fully agree with the familiar view that this relation is *causal*,[5] provided the causal relation be synthetic and yet genuinely connective. I shall argue later that causation in Hume's sense is inadequate to ground empirical inference. I shall argue also that the synthetic connectedness required of causation presupposes substance, and that, consequently, causal law too involves substance. If this is right, no resolution of physical things, or even of minds, into processes or series of events exemplifying natural law could remove the need for substance. It would merely displace the locus of substance from things or minds to events and the relations between them.

I turn now to the relation between substance and law. The close relation between substance and causal law has been suggested by the fact that the conditional propositions expressive of dispositional properties are often stated in causal terms. I shall begin my discussion of this relationship by calling to mind Leibniz's view that the successive states of a substance form causal series, or, as some say today, form series which obey the laws of physics, and that the identity of a substance involves "the persistence of the same law of the series." Leibniz went so far as to say, "That there should be a persistent law, involving the future states of that which we conceive as the same, is just what I assert to constitute it the same substance." Thus he came close to identifying substance with law, but he did not make the identification. Russell, however, in discussing Leibniz's notion of substance, suggests "how easily Leibniz could have got rid . . . of the appeal to subject and predicate, and have substituted the unity of the law or series for that of the logical subject." [6] Such an identification seems to be what many recent philosophers have aimed at. Perhaps they have overlooked the fact that such an identification would drop out of causal series the connectedness between its terms, which makes it causal rather than coincidental.

But just what is meant by the unity of a law? In what does it consist? Do all laws have unity, or only some? What is the mark of its presence? I suspect that the use of such language without elucidation is a positivistic trick of smuggling in in disguise what is being denied. Such talk about unity seems to be either a concealed acceptance of substance or an attempt to introduce a generality or genuine connectedness not given in experience, without however admitting the inadequacy of strict empiricism to validate either conception. I think Hume was right in denying that we find in sensory experiences of allegedly causal transactions anything but conjunctions or successions. In them we find no necessary connection between cause and effect, no generality, and no objective unity. Repetition given in experience is essentially different from generality or universality. In empirical conjunctions we discover no constancy or generality which is other than that expressible by an enumeration of singular propositions. If there is any unity or generality expressed by a universal proposition, then that which makes such a proposition true transcends sensory experience. To supply this nonsensory element is one of the functions of substance, which therefore is a hypothesis explanatory of whatever repetition we do get in experience. Thus, the powers of Locke's substances or the activities of Leibniz's, or the "secret connexions" of Hume grounded the unity intrinsic to law and the constancy intrinsic to causal action. They were the stable generating agencies of those empirical series which may be expressed as laws.[7]

Russell has expressed one of his most widely known theses as follows: the "ground for assuming substances . . . is purely and solely logical. What Science deals with are *states* of substances, and it is these only that can be given in experience. They are assumed to be states of *substances*, because they are held to be of the logical nature of predicates, and thus to demand subjects of which they may be predicated. The whole doctrine depends, throughout, upon this purely logical tenet."[8] I do not wish to deny that this cherished doctrine of his has truth in it, or that it is an acute historical observation. None the less the metaphysical function of substance has not been simply that of a subject of predication. It has been, rather, also to provide the connection presupposed by the *stable* compresence of qualities and, let it be emphasized, of dispositional properties. It has been also, as we have already explained, to connect the successive states of a series exemplifying a law.

The unity presupposed by the stable compresence of qualities may be approached by reflecting upon Mill's definition of matter as a permanent possibility of sensation.[9] Thus, to say that my desk is material is tantamount to saying that it is a permanent possibility or, for example, visual and tactual sensations. It does not imply that it now manifests any such qualities as brown or hard but simply that under certain specifiable circumstances such qualities would be manifested. Thus, according to Mill, when I say that my desk is brown, I mean only that if certain standard conditions of illumination are fulfilled, then, if a perceiver looks in the proper direction, he will get a sensation of brown Similar definitions would hold for other qualities or properties of the material desk: for its rectangular shape, hardness, and weight, for its being combustible, destructible, etc. Hence, if Mill is right, a material thing is a set of compresent possibilities of several different kinds and related to one another in complicated manners.

Mill's choice of the word "possibility" is obviously misleading, however revealing it may be of his positivism. He meant more than logical possibility, for by a physical object he meant more than a permanent logical possibility, since anything less than a sheer contradiction would satisfy that description. Also he assigns to them a relatively fixed spatial location: "When we change our place we do not carry away with us the Permanent Possibilities of Sensation: they remain until we return." [10] In view of the function of these possibilities, they seem to differ little from dispositional properties or from the "powers" of Locke. To assert that nonactualized possibilities keep together, remain at a place, and will be manifested when certain conditions are satisfied is hardly less than to assert the presence of a permanent substance with its powers. Mill avoided substance only in name.

I would make similar criticisms of such treatments of physical things as Russell's construction of them out of sensibilia. His constructions are simply formulations of certain orders of data, or possible data, totally devoid however of any provision for the stability of those orders or for the laws governing changes in them. The conception of an object as a many-dimensional continuum of radii, each composed of a continuous order of sensibilia, utterly fails its metaphysical function because it provides neither a ground for, nor an explanation of, the formal unity and order so fancifully portrayed. As a logical analysis, it is worthy of the genius of Russell; but as metaphysics, it makes nobody the wiser.

Though I know that the word "power" is vague and figurative, and is abhorred by many, still I think it is useful in making explicit some of the problems involved in a metaphysical foundation of empirical inference. Accordingly, I shall state in more detail my conception of power, of its function, and of its relation to properties.

When I say that a substance has the dispositional property of, for example, fragility, *part* of what I mean is that it now satisfies some but not all of the necessary conditions of being shattered. Amongst these conditions may be certain qualities or relations. Part also of what I mean is that it provides the connection or *synthesis in virtue of which* (1) the necessary conditions it now satisfies and (2) the other necessary conditions are combined and together form a sufficient condition of being shattered. That is, the substance synthesizes conditions into a sufficient condition. This capacity to synthesize is the essence of power. To say that something has a certain power is to say not only that it has certain characters which, when supplemented by others, constitute a sufficient condition of the specified result, but also that it has the *capacity to synthesize* these conditions and thereupon generate the result, e.g., the shattering. To have a power is to have a power to do something, or to act in a certain way, when certain stimuli or influences are given.

I want to emphasize that, though having a certain power does involve certain necessary conditions, *power* itself is not a set of conditions in the same sense but is of a different order from that of the conditions or of the consequent manifestation. It is not a set of qualities or relations, but is that which makes qualities and relations relevant to other qualities or relations. Hence, to expect to have enumerated a set of qualities or relations in answer to the question as to what a power is, is simply to expect the wrong kind of answer. Such a set of qualities or relations would miss entirely the power.

I suspect that power is indefinable; but this does not entail that nothing of importance or enlightening can be said about it, or that it cannot be significantly related to other ideas and thereby clarified by them and they by it. It is just this sort of thing I have been trying to do and want to continue to do now by suggesting the hypothesis that causal action is the synthetic-creative activity of substance and finds its locus in substance. Thus, when I say that something is fragile, I mean, in part, that it right now has a nature which contains part of the cause of shattering. The addition of the other necessary parts of the cause then realizes the cause of the shattering, which is the effect. In a case of causal action, the substance accordingly does three things: (1) It supplies part of the cause; (2) It synthesizes this part with the other parts coming from outside it; and (3) It generates the "shattered-vase" situation called the effect.

In extending this elucidation by interrelation, I wish now to relate the notion of physical object to the conception of substance which we have just put forward. It is common practice to explain regular or orderly behavior by supposing the existence of objects possessing certain properties; and, conversely, we refuse to allow that a thing is a physical object unless its behavior conforms to rules, i.e., unless certain conditional propositions are true of it. An object must have the potentiality of manifesting or causing qualities in conformity with rules, qualities which do not now characterize it or which are not now exemplified, or even which it never has displayed and never will display.

Further, these rules or laws in accordance with which a thing behaves are, as far as experience reveals them to us, *synthetic*. The tie or connection between the events described by the antecedent and consequent of the law is not given in our experience of those events, and, as Hume also taught us, it is not given in any sensory experience. Now, either there is such a connection, or there is not. If there is not, then regular behavior is a matter of sheer chance, is inexplicable, and is not a valid indication of physical objects or of anything more than the given data themselves. If however there is such a connection, it must be granted a genuine status in the world. It is given that status by a hypothesis we already have at hand; namely, the hypothesis of substance with its synthetic-generative powers. Let me repeat: If the Humean analysis of sensory experience is correct, our senses are blind to genuine connections; and, again, if it is right, the ground of any stable orderliness sense-data have cannot be immanent in them but must be something transcending them. It must be, if we may use Hume's words, the "secret connexions" which bind events together. Our hypothesis is that this ground is substance.

Now, if law is general not only for a simultaneous cross-section of the world, but also through time, and so is stable, then the connective or synthetic function of substance, and therefore substance itself, must have a corresponding permanence. The significance of the permanence of substance is therefore not alone that of the existence of things through a duration but that of the stability of natural law. The analysis of this permanence and of the relation of substance to time is indeed fraught with problems quite as difficult and elusive as those involved in the notion of power. Though I do not pretend to know how to settle them, still I believe that their existence is not an objection peculiar to the category of substance. I believe this, because these difficulties will beset any hypothesis designed to account for the stability of law. For example, if a law is to be stable through time, it must transcend time. If it does not, we shall be threatened with difficulties similar to the one Descartes sought to solve by making God a conserving cause. And if law is to transcend time, substance or any other ontological ground we assign to law must do so too. To explain how this transcendence is to be conceived—whether, for example, by making time immanent in substance or dependent upon it in some other way—is, fortunately, beyond the scope of my topic. Now we must forsake these speculations for more down-to-earth considerations.

I have asserted that any evidence that the data of experience occur according to stable law or in an orderly manner is evidence of the existence of substance as a ground of that law or order. I fear that this proposition will be taken by many as anything but self-evident. It will be alleged that all possible data of experience are orderly and cannot fail to be orderly; and hence that, unless every possible experience is evidence of substance, no experience is. A favorite resource in support of this position is the truth that any given finite set of elements having certain quantitatively assignable dimensions can be shown to be an instance of an order, and that that order can be formulated in an equation. That is, a law can be derived which assigns to each element a specific place in an ordered whole. From this it is concluded that the demand for order cannot fail to be met, and, consequently, no ontological ground for order is needed. Now, I admit this mathematical premise; but I deny that the conclusion alleged to follow from it does follow from it. All that follows is that *ad hoc* orders into which the given data will fit can always be formulated. This however is not sufficient to scientific inference. No one today will deny that, to be acceptable to science, an empirical law or generalization must be fruitful in prediction. This means that the law or generalization must order not only the elements whose dimensional values have been used as data in formulating it, but also other elements of the same class whose dimensional values were not included in the data. It is no answer to say that an *ad hoc* law can be continually corrected as more and more instances are observed, because such a corrected law is, at every stage of the process, an *ad hoc* affair, which is descriptive of the data upon which it is based, but which is not a sufficient ground of probable success in predicting further data.

Let me give an example. Suppose that, at a given time in the history of an honest or perfect roulette wheel, the winning numbers in order of their selection be given. Then it is possible to formulate a law or function, such that the dependent variable will be the selected number, and the independent variable will indicate the ordinal position of the selected number. Now this function or law is of the kind I have called *ad hoc* because, though it holds of the data used in discovering it, it will not enable us to predict any future selection with a higher probability than that of any other selection of the same form. This means simply that we cannot learn from experience how to win at honest roulette. On the other hand, the hypothesis that we can learn to win at roulette entails that the wheel is not honest but has some constant bias in favor of some numbers as against other numbers. In that case, a law is derivable from past selections, which will make prediction, or winning, probable.

In general then we can say this: Anyone who believes he can learn from experience not just what experience has in fact already presented to him but what it will present to him presupposes not only (1) that certain orders exemplified by past events will be exemplified by those of the future as well, but also (2) that, in spite of the number of such orders fitting events up to any specified date, the data presented up to then render it probable that a certain finite set of those alternative orders contains the stable order which will not be invalidated by future events, and (3) that additional data will confirm some and invalidate others of the remaining alternatives. An accurate statement of these formal requirements is beyond the scope of this paper. What I am insisting is that the validity of empirical knowledge presupposes the truth of such formal requirements, which, in turn, have ontological presuppositions reaching beyond the data of experience. That is to say, in order that there may be genuinely prognostic laws, there must be some objective matrix which transcends the data of experience and which will be the ground not only of the truth, but of the very significance, of scientific laws and generalizations. The hypothesis of substance is designed to provide just such a matrix and ground.

Obviously, an analogous argument can be framed in terms of causation, which concludes that causation, as Hume defined it, is inadequate to the validation of empirical inference. Hume himself frankly recognized this; and, since it has been pointed out time and again ever since, it should not be necessary for us to discuss it anew. None the less, because it is still a commonplace to accept the Humean analysis and yet not to profess its skeptical conclusions, I shall repeat briefly, in causal terms, the preceding argument for an ontological ground for knowledge.

We must distinguish, as Hume at times did distinguish, the kind of *evidence* we have for the proposition that changes of kinds A and B are causally related *from* what we mean by their being so related. As I have said, I think Hume was right in holding that the only evidence presented in sense experience is particular instances of the conjunction of A's and B's. From these instances *we* generalize to the universal, "All A's are followed by B's," which is, on Hume's definition, just another way of saying that A's cause B's. Now generalizing is a valid mode of inference only on the credentials of a theory of the generation of events—of a theory implying that the occurrence of any change A involves a change B in virtue of ontological conditions such as we set forth earlier in discussing powers, and which we found to be essential to causal action. Hence, rather than causation being constant conjunction, it is that which explains constant conjunction and justifies extrapolation from some instances of conjunction to further instances.

We might well pause a moment in the presence of the fallacy of confusing the evidence with that of which it is evidence. This confusion has been technically refined, elevated to the status of a principle and precept, and, in this exalted role, it has been a favorite weapon of the antimetaphysicians. Bared of its technical dress, it is revealed as a trick deriving whatever philosophic power it may have from implicit assumptions. Its structure is essentially this: We have a class A of data, which are taken as evidence of B, and which would, accordingly, be explained by the hypothesis of B. Then we define, or to use more fashionable, albeit less perspicuous, langauge, we *construct* B out of the data of A; and so we have B as well as A, apparently without invoking any metaphysical dispensations. In justice to Russell I should say that he has never been quite taken in by this trick he so ingeniously perfected, but has always recognized that its philosophic employment has presuppositions transcending the given data—e.g., continuity, and irrelevance of space and time to laws, assumptions which reinstate the metaphysical problem. We might observe too that Hume himself was less guilty of this type of reasoning than many of his followers. Let us not forget that Hume did not deny, but actually affirmed, the existence of "secret" causes and of "secret connexions." What he denied was that experience teaches us anything more than "how one event constantly follows another." [11]

In regard to the definition of causation as constant conjunction, I want to make one further point; namely, even if the "constancy" of any experienced conjunction were not infinitely less than that asserted by a universal proposition—even if the known constancy were universal—still by itself it would have the status of a coincidence. It would be unexplained, would itself have no explanatory value, and would be no more a part of science than a statement of the number of grains of sand on the seashore. Universal propositions are significant for scientific knowledge only on the assumption that their truth is grounded in some sort of connectedness which explains the correlations they express. Perhaps we can put the point this way: The significance of the "general term" of an order is not simply that every particular term is an instance of it, but also that it expresses the *principle* of the order, which principle is ontologically prior to its specification in instances. Hence, our generalizing from particular terms to the "general term" is justified only on the premise that the data are so connected and generated that the "general term" is a *de jure,* not just a *de facto,* representative of all instances of their kind. If this premise is false, general propositions reduce to statements of accidents, staggering perhaps to our imaginations but still accidents. But in order that it may not be false, some such hypothesis as that of substance must be true.

A distinguished philosopher has recently said: "Nothing in experience or in events experienced either requires, or justifies, or would be illuminated by the hypothesis that causation is really some other sort of relation than that of regular correlation." [12] It is indeed true that nothing actually in experience or in events actually experienced requires anything more than regular correlation; in fact, I should go further and say that they themselves require nothing, not even regular correlation. Nor do they justify as brute data of sense any theory of causation at all. So far as I can see, nothing requires any justification for its sheer existence, unless it be a moral justification. But this does not imply that nothing needs justification. What does need justification is our belief that one happening is a cause of another in such a way that one of them is a reliable sign of the other. But this reliability does not follow from the theory that causation is nothing but constant conjunction. Not only that, but the Humean definition is not a *theory* of causation at all; nothing follows from it; it is, rather, a denial of the possibility of a theory explanatory of sequences of events. Unless we believe that there is something more to causation than constant conjunction, we might as well discontinue counseling the employment of the methods of science in the quest for knowledge.

Now I know that, influenced as we are by the great empirical tradition of modern philosophy and sensitive to the vigorous positivism and naturalism of today, few of us feel comfortable or at ease discussing, let alone defending, substance or powers or synthetic connections. I agree with these tendencies of thought in believing that it is healthy and just that every belief involving anything transcending experience should be viewed with suspicion and should be subjected to tests not only of truth but of meaningfulness as well. In this spirit, let us ask concerning the assumption of substance or power or connection, which can be neither confirmed nor invalidated by experience, just what cognitive meaning it has. Also, since every possible sequence of experience is consistent with it, what difference can its truth or falsity make?

In answering these questions, I want first to admit that the truth or falsity of such an assumption can make no experientially discernible difference; and that, therefore, any difference it makes cannot be found in the data of experience. But from this it does not follow that no propositions about experience would be true in one case but not in the other. Let us refer back to our distinction between order and stable order. No set of events can be inconsistent with the proposition that they exemplify a stable order, or with the proposition that they do not. Hence, at any given moment of history, the events of the past cannot be, by themselves, evidence for or against the proposition that they exemplify a reliable order holding in the class consisting of them and of future events. For all we know, the regularities recorded in history and used as the data of science may be purely accidental runs of events. At any specified date in history the empirical situation will be the same. But at any such date there are presumably events to follow, and the question then posed is this: Are these past data evidence of what will occur in the future? Though the answer will not be available, the question does have sense because we know an important and significant implication of each of the two possible answers; namely, (1) If past data are evidence of future ones, then scientific inference is valid; and (2) If past data are not evidence of future ones, then science is nothing but a blind illusioned faith, and any success it has is not its success but its *luck*. Accordingly, the difference transcendent connections or substance can make is the difference between the reliability and the unreliability of inference. This, I insist, is a meaningful difference. To say that events of the past are reliable signs of events in the future is to say something about those events. The difference might be compared to that between going up a blind road and proceeding to the destination. At no time before completion of the journey can we be sure that the highway is not a dead-end street; none the less the rationale of our continuing lies in the probability that not all roads are blind alleys. All of our practical activities, and all of pure science, presuppose that this is the case. This assumption, then, is the epistemological cash value of such a category as substance.

I realize that at every stage in my argument I have passed over problems inextricably involved in the problem of substance. For example, what is the relation between different substances? Can substances be parts of other substances? If so, are the properties of the whole derivative from those of the parts, or vice versa? Answers to these questions might have an important bearing on the nature of historical and social science. Nor have I said anything about the relation between those quasi-substances called events and the substance presupposed by an ordered series of events. These issues are part and parcel of two basic metaphysical problems raised by our thesis that substance is the metaphysical ground of law; namely, the qualitative and the quantitative problems of monism and pluralism. Into these questions I shall not go, except to say, in regard to the qualitative problem, that any theory ascribing to substance an inert or purely passive nature is inadequate to the synthesizing and causal role it plays and belies the dynamic aspects of existence. In regard to the quantitative problem, I want to say that in so far as there is law or unity in the world, there must be substance as pervasive as is the law or unity itself. The history of metaphysics may be read as the attempt of philosophers to steer a middle course between extreme pluralism, which would destroy knowledge by disintegration, and extreme monism, which would destroy it by making nonsense of all the distinctions attested by experience and presupposed by the very possibility of empirical knowledge. We can keep off the rocks of pluralism only by charting a course in terms of ontological *connections,* and off those of monism only by construing those connections as *synthetic.*

I have argued that the category of substance is required by any hypothesis providing for these ontological synthetic connections, and that therefore it is presupposed by the validity of empirical inference. As an ultimate category substance has the virtue of interrelating such basic notions as thing, property, causality, and law. As for its transcending experience, I would put the case this way: *If* we believe that we can learn from experience, then we have to admit that some ontological ground transcends the data of experience.

References

[1] This is a slightly altered version of "A Defense of Substance," *Philosophical Review,* Vol. LVI, No. 5 (Sept., 1947), pp. 491–509.

[2] C. D. Broad, *An Examination of McTaggart's Philosophy,* Vol. I, p. 149.

[3] *Op. cit.,* chap. xiv, esp. pp. 274–287.

[4] Rudolf Carnap, "Testability and Meaning," *Philosophy of Science,* Vol. III, No. 4 (Oct., 1936).

[5] C. J. Ducasse, "On the Attributes of Material Things," *Journal of Philosophy,* Vol. XXXI, No. 3 (Feb. 1, 1934), pp. 57–72.

[6] Bertrand Russell, *The Philosophy of Leibniz,* pp. 47 f.

[7] I wish to make explicit that in referring to Hume's analysis of experience, I advisedly limited my acceptance of it to *sensory* experience. I am not prepared to follow him in his assertion that in the introspection of, for example, voluntary action, we get nothing more than conjunctions. In chap. ii of his *Mind and Matter,* Stout has, in my opinion, shown the inconclusiveness of Hume's argument on this point.

[8] Russell, *op. cit.,* p. 49.

[9] John Stuart Mill, *An Examination of Sir William Hamilton's Philosophy,* chaps. xi and xii.

[10] *Op. cit.,* pp. 202 f.

[11] ". . . experience only teaches us, how one event constantly follows another; without instructing us in the secret connexion, which binds them together, and renders them inseparable" (*An Enquiry Concerning Human Understanding,* Section VII, Part I).

[12] W. R. Dennes, "The Categories of Naturalism," in *Naturalism and the Human Spirit,* ed. Y. H. Krikorian, p. 291.

MATHEMATICS

by

DIRK J. STRUIK

Dirk J. Struik is Professor of Mathematics at the Massachusetts Institute of Technology, where he has taught since coming to the United States in 1926. Previously he received his Ph.D. at the University of Leiden and studied under a Rockefeller International Fellowship in Rome and Göttingen. He has written papers and books on the differential geometry of more than three dimensions and the tensor calculus. He is also interested in the history of science and has just published a *Concise History of Mathematics* (2 vols.), and *Yankee Science in the Making.*

OUR MATHEMATICAL conceptions were formed as the result of a long social and intellectual process, whose roots lie hidden in the distant past. The beginnings may be traced back to the Neolithic period, when men changed from food gatherers to food producers, and the foundation was laid for agriculture, domestication of cattle, and eventually for the processing of metals. The remnants of Stone Age crafts, products of carpentry, weaving, basketry, and pottery, show how they may have stimulated the development of geometrical conceptions. Primitive counting, first simply in the form "One, two, many," gradually led to a more precise way of denoting numbers from one to ten and, later, larger numbers. There was a considerable Stone Age trade, which also stimulated the art of counting. Study of African or American Indian languages shows systems of numeration, often on a decimal scale, or on a scale of five, twelve, or twenty; here and there appear simple fractions.[1] This led to the abstract notion of number and form; when in Sumer and Egypt the first written documents appear, they reveal already some mastery of simple arithmetical rules. Such rules are realized when four appears

The author wishes to acknowledge his indebtedness to W. T. Parry for his valuable criticisms.

as two plus two, nineteen as twenty minus one, twenty as two times ten. Languages still show these relationships in their way of expressing the cardinal numbers. Patterns appeared in clothes, baskets, and rugs; ropes were stretched, wound and knotted; and some regular figures appeared as protective symbols in magical rites.

This process was accelerated in the next period of cultural development, that of the early civilizations of the Orient—Egypt, India, Babylonia, and China. Here mathematics appeared already as a science, but first and foremost as a practical, even empirical, science, indispensable for agriculture, land measurement, taxation, engineering, and warfare. The truth of the arithmetical and geometrical propositions and theorems was constantly tested in the dealings of man with nature and his own social structure.

This empirical-practical stage of mathematics was supplemented almost from its beginnings by a definite opposite trend, a trend toward abstraction. The creation of the concepts of number and figure themselves was such a deed of abstraction, which must probably be associated with a relatively high level of neolithic life. But as soon as these concepts are created they show a life of their own. Addition, subtraction, multiplication begin to be understood as abstract operations, first performed on objects, but later also on the symbols themselves. It was discovered that by addition the system of numbers can be extended indefinitely, and we can get a glimpse of the impression this must have made from the eagerness displayed by primitive agricultural peoples in playing with very large numbers. This is important for understanding how generalized mathematical conceptions can be created in the social process itself, because direct experience does not lead to a definite notion of any numbers but the small ones. The concepts of line, plane, and circle also began to assume a life of their own.

The early history of mathematics therefore bears out what John Stuart Mill observed a hundred years ago, that the original premises of this science

> from which the remaining truths are deduced are, notwithstanding all appearances to the contrary, results of observation and experience,—founded, in short, on the evidence of the senses.[2]

We now know that Mill's conception of these original premises was oversimplified, that there is more to the axioms of arithmetic and geometry than he believed. But it is true that mathematics as a science developed by the building of abstract concepts from empirical material, and then by letting these concepts live their own life. The general developed from the particular, the method from the example. This growth of an abstract science did not lead from objective facts to imaginative facts, but from direct empirical truth to truth on a higher level of generality. Where originally sets of small extent such as fingers were counted, now herds or armies could be enumerated. Addition, subtraction, and the beginnings of multiplication were extended from small numbers to larger ones. With the discovery that all numbers could be written in the framework of a system (usually the decimal system), that is, in the form $a_0b^n + a_1b^{n-1} + \cdots + a_{n-1}b + a_n$ ($a_0, \ldots, a_n$ less than b, b usually $= 10$), already an important arithmetical law was found—though, of course, not in this explicit form. In this interplay of induction and deduction, mathematics at its very birth showed already some of the aspects of a real science.

E. T. Bell remarks that the modern intuitionists, who accept the formation of the unending sequence of natural numbers as "original intuition," may have an unassailable starting point for an abstract construction of mathematics but their position is definitely unhistorical. Indeed, factually that intuition "is anything but universal among primitives who, presumably, are human beings." [3] The conception of the natural numbers was the result of a process of generalization applied in millennia of human practice to empirical data, a process constantly tested in the light of new experience. This experience widened with the coming of the oriental irrigation societies, but the process of abstraction also continued at increasing pace.

With the growth of ancient oriental civilization another development set in, which made mathematics divorce itself considerably more from the world of direct experience. This was the teaching of mathematics in the schools of scribes, in the temples and administration buildings of Memphis, Babylon, and other oriental centers.

The schooling of new administrators led to the formation of abstract problems for the sake of training, and this already began to assume the form of a cultivation of mathematics for its own sake. It led to a new abstract approach to problems concerning number and space, in which algorisms, theorems, and theories emerged. Babylonians of the second millennium B.C. knew the numerical relations between the sides of a rectangular triangle which we know as Pythagoras' theorem, and solved quadratic and some cubic and biquadratic equations. Some of this more complicated, mostly numerical and algebraic work can be explained by the demands of astronomy, but there clearly existed a cultivation of mathematics for its own sake. Mathematical relationships, which were found and studied independently of their direct applicability, were the result of the intrinsic logic and creative power of mathematics itself. The relation of this oriental mathematics with practice always remained pretty obvious, and the logical structure was still poorly developed. Yet, the testing of the numerical solution of a higher degree equation is no longer found in its application to taxation, geodesy, or even astronomy, but in the mathematical structure of the equation itself. This development, thus started, came to full fruition in Greek mathematics.

An instructive example of the manner in which new mathematical concepts grow out of the logic of the symbolism itself, and yet at the same time continue to express relations in the objective world, is the introduction of the zero. The Babylonians used a sexagesimal system of numeration (which facilitates fractional computation) superimposed on a decimal system (carrying in its base 10 the constant reminder that the number concept crystallized in the trading practice of finger counting). This sexagesimal system was expressed in a place-value system, itself a great discovery in mathematical formalism. The use of a special symbol for zero came as a necessary complementation of the place-value system, to bring out the difference between the notation for numbers such as $2\times 60^2 + 5$ and $2 \times 60 + 5$. Here the development of mathematical symbolism itself led not only to an extension of the number system, but also to the introduction of the symbol zero into mathematical reasoning. The history of this symbol, especially in Indian mathematics, connects it with the conception of the void, which also plays a role in Aristotelian physics.[4] Not only being but also non-being became the subject of mathematical operation, an early preparation to the mathematics of becoming, the mathematics of change. And again: this introduction of the zero did not mean that mathematics grew into idle speculation. It only simplified its dealing with objects characterized by natural numbers as well as fractions.

With the Ionian merchant class of the sixth century B.C. began the development of the logical structure of mathematics. This was one aspect of Ionian rationalism as a whole, which grew in an atmosphere of trade activities not too much hampered by oriental despotism. We know very little about the growth of this new approach to mathematics, though it is fairly certain that some of its discoveries—the irrational and the paradoxes of the infinite—developed as part of the ideological struggles between aristicracy and democracy in Greece's Golden Age. The logical structure of mathematics, the possibility of an axiomatic foundation of this science, was clearly revealed. The further elaboration of these foundations took place, first on the Greek mainland in the school of Plato, and afterwards mainly by professional scientists at the court of the Ptolemies in Egypt, and some other Hellenistic monarchs. The whole creative period of "Greek" mathematics lasted only a few centuries and took place in a highly exceptional social setting, the study of which still awaits careful analysis. The period began with the first appearance of a democracy in history—but a democracy coexistent with slavery—and witnessed the growth of a slave-owning aristocracy, of which Plato was a representative, that struggled with the remnants of democracy; it found its end in the early centuries of Hellenism, when Greece and Orient met under Greek hegemony. When with the Roman Empire slavery grew in importance and became more and more the basis of society, and Greece as well as Orient sank into colonial status, the ruling classes lapsed back into an easy mediocrity in which originality could not survive.

In the typical form of "Greek" mathematics, the immediate contact with practice was abandoned. The men who created this mathematics were indeed remote from trade and manual labor, and had been taught to despise it. They could devote full time to creative work of an abstract nature. In Euclid's "Elements" mathematics was placed in a rigorous deductive scheme. The theorems were derived from a small set of axioms. No questions were asked concerning the origin of the axioms, and no answers given. Though the choice of axioms and postulates as well as the language in which they are expressed still indicates their relation with the objective world, the theorems are demonstrated by reducing them to the axioms and postulates. All attempts at testing the truth of the theorems with experience are missing, though the significant fact remains that many of Euclid's theorems can be tested on material figures and be found correct within the limits of observation. There are, for instance, only five different regular polyhedra, as experiments with cardboard or plaster models and research on crystals amply prove. However, there are in Euclid mathematical concepts which can no longer be subjected to experiment, and it is here that the advance of mathematical reasoning beyond immediate experience becomes most apparent. The test between the commensurability and incommensurability of line segments lies in reason, not in experiment; and though we still can show by actual testing that the volume of the pyramid is one-third that of a prism with equal base and equal height, the proof of it needs the exhaustion method, that is, the framing of the pyramid in such a large number of small prisms that we better figure the proof out by reasoning alone. The reasoning itself has created its own laws; the test of truth in mathematics has now become the absence of contradictions. A theorem is true when it can be gradually reduced, by certain accepted logical operations, to a set of axioms, the truth of which is simply postulated. Modern mathematics has accepted this criterion of truth without reservation: the test of the truth of a mathematical theory is the absence of logical contradictions. In modern times the tests have moved from geometry to arithmetic, from arithmetic to logic. The different theories of the present time concerning the foundation of these fields all deal with methods to test possible contradictions in a mathematical system, or better, contradictions and loopholes (consistency and completeness). The question of testing the truth of mathematics as an image of the objective world becomes a remote one when such an approach prevails; many "pure" mathematicians are not even greatly interested.

Modern mathematics is the product of the rise of capitalism. The commercial towns of the later European Middle Ages were ruled by a politically conscious merchant class, which gradually emancipated itself from petty feudal lords and established its own commercial empire. The great difference between these merchants and the Ionians of two millennia before was the absence of slavery. Slavery in the long run frustrates technological improvement and, with it, stifles scientific originality. The merchant class of the later Middle Ages had no such impediment. There were free craftsmen, and the beginnings of a free working class. The possibility of great profits in the new capitalistic system led the merchants, as well as some of the princes, to cultivate navigation and astronomy. Arithmetic, algebra, and the new art of bookkeeping flourished in the towns. The possibility of using machines for productive purposes stimulated inventiveness. The increasing use of these machines led to the study of mechanics, and this again to the search for new methods in mathematics. Where the *Rechenhaftigkeit* [5] of the early bourgeoisie promoted arithmetic and algebra, the inventiveness of this class eventually led to the calculus. The sources of arithmetic and algebra were found in the Orient, those of the calculus among the Greeks, especially in Archimedes. And where, in the first enthusiasm of discovery, the logical structure of mathematics was often overlooked, the very nature of this science eventually required return to fundamentals. Where Kepler and Stevin were essentially experimenters in mathematics, almost as if it were a kind of physics, the great mathematicians of the seventeenth century were driven to develop mathematics for its own sake. The great discoveries of this period, the algebraic treatment of geometry and the calculus, were possible only because the mathematicians did not ask for immediate applications, but followed the dialectical logic of the science itself. Dialectical, because it established new relationships between fields separated before—between algebra and geometry, between the tangent problem and the determination of volumes, between the finite and the infinite, between mathematics and logic.

The fact that mathematics was developed for its own sake does not mean that the connection between theory and practice was lost. Mathematics, in the eyes of all great mathematicians from Descartes to Leibniz, was the key to mechanics, and mechanics was the key to the understanding of nature. Mathematics became not only the model for all science, it also provided the key to inventions. Typical of this whole period was the conviction not only that mathematics teaches the properties of matter, but that the harmony of mathematics somehow reflects the harmony of the world. In the early Renaissance days Aristotle was replaced, in many schools, by Plato with his Pythagorean belief in the universality of number, and this credo in the powers of mathematics became again, in modified form, a typical characteristic of the great rationalists of the seventeenth century.

The same intimate relation between "pure" and "applied" mathematics prevailed in the eighteenth century, and lasted until deep in the next—especially in France. For the Bernoullis, as well as for Euler, Lagrange, and Laplace, mathematics was above all the tool to the understanding of the cosmos. This is shown in the great works of the period: the two great mathematical works in which the seventeenth century culminated were the *Horologium oscillatorium* of Huygens and the *Principia* of Newton:[6] the two great works culminating the next century were the *Mécanique analytique* of Lagrange and the *Méchanique céleste* of Laplace. This virtual identification of mathematics and mechanics was not essentially broken by the remarkable discoveries of Euler and others in the theory of numbers, or by Lagrange in algebra.

A new period in the history of mathematics opened with the French Revolution. It is remarkable that the new scientific impetus came from the great political change; the influence of the underlying industrial revolution on the development of mathematics was much more indirect at first. England, which was the first country affected by the industrial revolution, remained mathematically sterile for many decades. The political revolution, on the contrary, affected opinions and outlook much more directly. It brought new classes into positions of influence and of power, classes interested in the promotion of technical education, in broadening the social bases of science and in new ideas of intellectual freedom. The Ecole Polytechnique, founded in 1795 at Paris to train engineers, became the prototype not only of an institution for scientific education but also for fundamental research in mathematics and natural sciences. The principles of the revolution in science and education spread to other countries, even those in which feudalism still maintained its power over the rising capitalism. Next to France rose Germany as a great mathematical center; other countries followed. The demands on science increased manifold.

In this social setting progress could only be made by specialization. Thus mathematics developed in full glory as a field of independent research, though not only mechanics, but also the new mathematical physics exerted a powerful influence. These two forms of approach, the "pure" and the "applied" one, were really never separated, even though the mathematicians themselves became more and more specialized. The number of cases where "pure" mathematics influenced the "applied" branch and vice versa was very large; it shows how despite all increased abstraction mathematics has continued to present a picture of relations in the objective world. Histories of mathematics recognize this fact to a certain extent, but the interaction of mathematics, physics and engineering is much more intimate than is usually recognized. The differential geometry of curves was developed under the influence of Barré de Saint-Venant's researches in elasticity, that of surfaces as a result of Monge's interest in engineering and that of Gauss in geodesy. Hamilton's study of light rays led to his theory of partial differential equations. Even the trend to rigor in modern mathematics received a powerful impetus from the study of trigonometric series, introduced by Fourier into the theory of heat; Riemann's rigorous definition of the integral was derived in his paper on trigonometric series. During the second half of the nineteenth century both Klein and Poincaré, the leading mathematicians of that period, stressed in their work the intimate relationship between mathematics and its applications, even when they revealed some of their most subtle thoughts. Klein stressed the importance of group theory in crystallography and mechanics, and saw in the later part of his life in the theory of relativity another application of his ideas. Poincaré's work can probably best be understood if we take as a starting point his work on celestial mechanics. It was Klein who promoted the foundation of the Institute for Applied Mathematics at Göttingen. This attitude is also reflected in Klein's lectures on the history of mathematics in the nineteenth century, which show in many places a materialistic approach. The recognition of this close connection between theory and practice, between the symbols and the world of which they represent an image is also felt in Hilbert's attempts to rescue the results of modern mathematics from the onslaught of the intuitionists.[6a]

The mathematicians of the seventeenth and eighteenth centuries had few doubts concerning the objectivity of the results of their speculations. Since pure and applied mathematics were not separated, mathematics for them was above all a way to solve equations, to find areas and volumes, solve problems in mechanics and engineering, and to find the laws of a mechanistic universe. Galileo said that only he can understand nature who has learned its language and the tokens in which it speaks to us; this language is mathematics, and its tokens are the mathematical figures. Even Leibniz, though believing in the "innate" character of necessary and eternal truths, understood them as "the very principles of our nature, as of the universe"; he saw in mathematics such a necessary truth serving as the universal exposition of possible forms of connections in general and their mutual dependency.[7] Number theory by its abstract character and utter "uselessness" might have offered an opportunity for idealistic speculation, but we do not clearly meet it in those early authors.

Idealistic reaction did not come from the mathematicians, but from Bishop Berkeley, whose *esse est percipi* was a direct attack on natural science, including the objective character of the mathematical conceptions.

Berkeley was perfectly clear:

> But it is evident, from what we have already shewn, that extension, figure, and motion are only ideas existing in the mind . . . That number is entirely the creature of the mind, even though the other qualities be allowed to exist without, will be evident to whoever considers that the same thing bears a different denomination of number as the mind views it with different respects. Thus, the same extension is one, or three, or thirty-six, according as the mind considers it with reference to a yard, a foot, or an inch.[8]

The reaction of the mathematicians may be judged from Leibniz, who brushed Berkeley's wisdom aside with contempt:

> The man in Ireland who impugns the reality of bodies, seems neither to give suitable reasons, nor to explain himself sufficiently. I suspect him to be one of that class of men who wish to be known by their paradoxes.[9]

Berkeley's criticism of the foundations of the calculus, however, remained long a challenge to the mathematicians.

During the first part of the nineteenth century the attitude of most mathematicians did not change much, even if Kant made some impression on their way of thinking. Gauss did not believe in the a priori character of our notions of geometry as Kant proclaimed. The euclidicity of space was for Gauss an empirical proposition:

> I come more and more to the conviction that the necessity of our geometry cannot be demonstrated. Until this is done we should place geometry in equal rank, not with arithmetic which stands purely a priori, but rather with mechanics.[10]

Gauss even took geodesical measurements on a triangle (formed by the tops of the mountains Brocken, Hohenhagen, Inselsberg) to find out whether the sum of the angles is 180°. He verified that within the limits of observation this sum is actually 180°.

Riemann, the central figure of nineteenth century mathematics, stated clearly:

When is our understanding of the world true?
When the interconnection [Zusammenhang] of our conceptions [Vorstellungen] corresponds to the interconnections of the things.[11]

And Weierstrass, in his inaugural oration of 1857, after pointing out that Greek mathematics had established the properties of the conic sections long before it was discovered that they were also the orbits of the planets, continued that he lived in the hope

that there would be more functions with properties such as Jacobi praises in his theta function, which teach into how many squares every number can be decomposed, how the arc of the ellipse can be rectified and which yet is able—and is the only function which is able—to represent the true law of oscillation of the pendulum.[12]

When mathematics during the course of the nineteenth century penetrated into deeper and deeper levels of generalization and abstraction and established a more and more involved technique, it began to appear, in the eyes of many people, as an independent structure, a creation of the human mind only. Science often developed separated from the social process in laboratory and academic hall; its social function was disregarded, and mathematics shared more than the other sciences this divorce from life. The increasing specialization of the individual mathematician tended to strengthen this isolation. The reconciliation of materialism with idealism in Kant found supporters among mathematicians, Kant's assertion of the a priori character of euclidean geometry [13] was for many years a powerful obstacle in the acceptance of noneuclidean geometry. In Hermann Grassmann's introduction to his *Ausdehnungslehre* of 1844 we find a Kantian touch in his belief that mathematics is a matter of thought alone:

Thinking exists only in relation to a being which stands opposed to it and of which thinking makes an image [ein Sein, was ihm gegenüber tritt and durch das Denken abgebildet wird], but this being is for the real sciences an independent entity which exists for itself outside of thinking, for the formal sciences however it is posed by thinking itself, which now again opposes itself as being a second act of thinking. Since truth in general consists in conformity of thinking with being, it consists especially in the formal sciences in conformity of the second act of thinking with the being posed by the first act of thinking, hence in the conformity of both acts of thinking. Proof in the formal sciences therefore does not transcend thinking itself into another sphere, but stays purely in the combination of the different acts of thought. The formal sciences therefore may not depart from principles [Grundsätze] like the real ones, but their foundation is formed by the definitions.

The formal sciences study either the general laws of thought, or they study the special entity posed by thinking. The first is dialectic (logic), the latter is pure mathematics.[14]

To this isolation of mathematics from life we can also ascribe what Klein has called Jacobi's "new humanism," [15] which saw the sole end of science in the "honor of the human mind" not asking for any social function:

It is true that Monsieur Fourier had the opinion that the main goal of mathematics was the public utility and the explication of the natural phenomena, but a philosopher like him should have known that the sole goal of science is the honor of the human mind and that from this point of view a question concerning numbers is worth as much as a question concerning the system of the world.[16]

In this period began a new and searching criticism of the foundations underlying the calculus. It was realized how much vagueness surrounded such conceptions as limit, continuity and convergence and the infinitesimal, and that neither the Newton-Leibniz "mystical," nor D'Alembert's "rational," nor Lagrange's "algebraic" approach [17] had been able to remove it. This actually led to false theorems, which again could lead to wrong applications to mechanics and physics. The program of clarifying the foundations of the calculus was carried out successfully by Cauchy, Abel, Riemann, Weierstrass, and many other mathematicians with the result that the calculus from now on could be used with confidence. It is easy to see how mathematicians, deeply engaged in carrying out this program of subtle reasoning, could gain the impression that they were freely engaging in a play of the human mind. It is also easy to see, in retrospect, that they were building up the calculus as a more perfect instrument to establish objective relationships; and it is due to their work that the calculus can now be applied with great confidence to extremely subtle problems in celestial mechanics, mathematical physics and the theory of probabilities.

This work on the foundation of the calculus was only one aspect—though an important one—of the whole reexamination of the principles of mathematics which began in the nineteenth century and had been continued until the present day. This led, in the second half of the nineteenth century, to a real struggle between different opinions concerning the nature of mathematics. "What are numbers?" asked Dedekind. "What is a limit?" asked Du Bois-Reymond. "What is the relation of mathematics to logic?" asked Frege. Such questions necessarily brought renewed attention to the ancient difficulties of Zeno and Eudoxus, as well as those of Newton and Lagrange concerning the nature of the calculus. The introduction of new and subtle mathematical conceptions—Dedekind's cut, mathematical logic, theory of aggregates—seemed to establish mathematics in increasing tempo as a science of pure thought, only incidentally related to nature. Mathematics, to many of its students, seemed to be nothing but a formal scheme, and this was only a step to the belief that mathematics was nothing but a game. Du Bois-Reymond, as early as 1882, warned against this position:

> A purely formalistic-literal skeleton of analysis, to which the separation of number and the analytical tokens from the quantity would lead, would eventually degrade this science—which in truth is a natural science—to a mere game of tokens, in which arbitrary meanings could be assigned to the written tokens, like to figures of chess or playing cards.[18]

Around this same time, Benjamin Peirce had defined mathematics as "the science which draws necessary conclusions," [19] stressing the formal reasoning at the expense of the content. His son, C. S. Peirce, who was one of the men who established mathematical logic, went further. For him mathematics was "the study of ideal constructions":

> The observations being upon objects of imagination merely, the discoveries of mathematics are susceptible of being rendered quite certain.[20]

This was the direct reverse of the older materialist sentiment of the great mathematicians of the past centuries, since it based the truth of mathematics on its absence of correspondence with objective reality. It was another version of the "chess play" interpretation against which Du Bois-Reymond warned; under such an interpretation the immense applicability of mathematics to mechanics and physics became only a remarkable coincidence. Subsequently Bertrand Russell, the leader of the logistic school which carried out Peirce's program, defined "pure mathematics" as "the class of all propositions of form 'p implies q' "[21] reducing all propositions of mathematics to propositions of logic. The formalist school, which concentrated on showing that the mathematical structure can be obtained by a series of hypothetical deductions from uninterpreted axioms, often did not see any thing else in mathematics but that, though Hilbert, its founder, saw clearly the real content in the abstract form. And the leader of the intuitionist school, Brouwer, interpreted mathematics also as a product of the brain only:

> Mathematics is a free creation independent of experience, it develops from a single aprioristic original intuition which can be called either constancy in change or unity in reality.[22]

This "original intuition" corresponds, as the basis of an abstract method of mathematical construction, to a dialectics of reality, and in Brouwer's work led to mathematical discoveries. However, it denied mathematical meaning to considerable sections of mathematics, and actually crippled not only its applicability, but also deprived it of some of its finest results. It aroused the ire of Hilbert: "No one shall drive us out of the paradise that Cantor created for us."[23] It was especially Hilbert, who, in his work for a faultless foundation of the whole of mathematics, developed a purely formal apparatus of tokens and rules of operation, but always stressed the harmony between form and content, between theory and practice, between human token and objective world.

This willingness of certain mathematicians to sacrifice content to form, or to consider their science as separate from nature, was—and is—part and parcel of a general academic movement which finds in concessions to idealism the solution not only to its scientific and philosophic, but also to some of its social worries.[24] This fact that in certain circles of mathematicians—namely, those who were interested in foundation questions—there existed a tendency to cultivate form rather than content, and to reduce mathematics to a mere skeleton of propositions, was received as a new liberation. Russell himself founded a philosophy on his "logical atomism," which in all modesty he believed to be "the same kind of advance as was introduced into physics by Galileo." [25] This attempt by Russell and others to understand the universe by starting from a formal scheme of logic [26] led by way of Mach and Avenarius eventually back to the subjective idealism of Berkeley.[27] It brought Moritz Schlick to the conviction that space and time are subjective,[28] Rudolf Carnap to the belief that many statements such as "time is infinite" are not statements about the world, but only about the way in which we use language,[29] and finally L. Wittgenstein to the discovery that mathematics is only a tautology.[30] This means, in the words of Professor Mannoury, that it is very easy to write a perfect mathematical book, as for instance:

$$a = a = a = a.$$ [31]

We see all these concessions to formalism and idealism in the last instance as the result of the separation of school and life, common under modern capitalism. But similar tendencies exist not only in the philosophical, but also in the historical field. Mathematics is often described as a pure succession of ideas, developed without any reference to the social setting in which it developed. As a result, there is no attempt to answer some of the most important questions. Why did the creative element in Greek mathematics stop with the growth of the Roman Empire? Why did the calculus originate in seventeenth century Europe, and not in Bagdad under the caliphs? Montucla, in the eighteenth century, still attempted to place the history of mathematics in a wider setting by showing its relation to mechanics and astronomy. Much of this disappeared in the nineteenth century, though there are traces left in Cantor.[32] It is one of the merits of Klein's lectures on the history of mathematics in the nineteenth century that he seldom omits to point to the relations between mathematics and the applied sciences, and even shows an open eye for philosophical and sociological trends.[33]

Against the idealistic approach to mathematics [34] the materialistic conception stresses:

a) the decisive influence of social economic factors in shaping the general character of mathematical productivity (or lack of productivity) in a given historical setting. We have already sketched how such a study may be conducted.

b) the impossibility of separating form and content, their interplay at all times, content eventually directing the progress of form, deciding its importance and survival. This relation of form and content pervades the whole of mathematics.

It is true the mathematician creates his symbols and the laws of operation to which they are subjected. He seems to be a free agent, a God creating his own world. His only laws are those of consistency, his structure must be free of internal contradictions; it may never lead to $1 \neq 1$. Many mathematicians, we have seen, stop here, and conclude that they are engaged in a game of meaningless tokens, or even in a game of fictions (as the *Als Ob* philosopher Vaihinger has claimed).[35] Others, led by the necessity inherent in the structure, claim that it represents some characteristic of the human mind or think that they are engaged in a tautology. But form and content are inseparable, they are endlessly interwoven. There is a "meaningful" mathematics, different from a game. It is applicable to the processes of nature, not in one way, but in many; it leads from one general aspect to another, it sets up connections between different approaches or different fields. The formal side may win for some time, and free construction seems to prevail, until the content catches up with the form, and dictates in its turn the course of progress. The history of mathematics shows how content always wins in the long run; our present mathematics with all its abstractions and seemingly free structures has an internal ramification and interconnection, and an applicability to the processes of nature, as never before. The search of consistency must reflect laws in the outside world.

The final criterion of truth must always be its correspondence with reality. A theory is true when its theorems can describe or predict occurrences in the real world. This can be easily understood for the beginnings of mathematics. But how is it with modern mathematics, which accepts the absence of contradictions as the criterion of truth? Is there any relation between the objective (the "philosophical") criterion for truth and the mathematical criterion?

This is not the place to discuss the different formulations given to mathematical logic. However, we must point out that logic does not consist in the free play of symbols, in a series of human-made conventions, but is itself a fundamental aspect of the real world as reflected in the human mind. There is again a form and a content. Take, for instance, the concept of identity: x equals y, with its laws of reflexivity ($x = x$), of symmetry (if $x = y$, then $y = x$), and of transitivity ($x = y$ and $y = z$, then $x = z$). This means on paper the assumption that we can recognize a token whenever it occurs. At the same time it expresses an essential quality of the world; namely, the invariance of an object. The world is in eternal flux, so that two things are never alike, and not even a single thing remains the same. Yet, it is possible to separate special aspects of this world and treat them as if they do not change. Professor Levy has called these aspects "isolates," and "isolates" can stay invariant and become an object of discourse. A straight line keeps its identity for us all, and for all generations, as does the number 4, the sphere, or an integral. The ball, which gave me the conception of a sphere, may move, get wet, or rot away; the sphere itself is an invariant conception. The laws of identity express the fact that I can reach correct conclusions by keeping the isolate unchanged throughout the discourse. It is clear that these laws of formal logic create the possibility of human understanding and activity, but do not in the least establish a divorce of mathematics from the real world. On the contrary, they make it possible for mathematics to present an image of reality.[35a]

Formal logic allows us to establish relations between objects (isolates), mathematical and nonmathematical. But they are, after all, trite (which does not mean that their study is trivial); and, while their use may be able to establish more and more complicated propositions, they can hardly make mathematics a creative science. Already ancient oriental science, with its close relationship between mathematics and reality, was infinitely richer. Where is then the secret of creative mathematics? In other words, what is its content? Why is not mathematics just an impressive tautology, as Poincaré has asked, and denied [36]— and as Wittgenstein has asked, and confirmed?

Mathematics, as an aspect of the real world, participates in its dialectics. Dialectics involves incessant creation. Mathematics by its very nature is therefore creative, transcending constantly the tautologies which may occur in its structure. We can express this by saying that mathematics is based on more than formal logic alone. The logic of mathematics, and especially of mathematics in its growth, is a dialectical logic. Much of the work accomplished in the last thirty years in the foundation of mathematics has been stimulated by the necessity to express in exact formulation the meaning of this creative element in mathematics. The intuitionists have stressed the principle of complete induction; the formalists have introduced "transcendental axioms," and have vigorously opposed attempts by logisticians to reduce mathematics to a tautology. Modern mathematical logic, as compared to the old Aristotelian logic, has become far richer in the process. Yet, it is doubtful whether a system of axiomatics will ever be found which will account for all mathematics; reality has more facets than an axiomaticist Horatio dreams of in his philosophy. The formalism of axiomatics itself has revolted against the attempts to reduce mathematics to a tautology, as is testified by investigations by K. Gödel and others. Though every school of mathematics has scored results, the full possibilities of mathematics have not been exhausted. Mathematics so far has refused to be bottled up in a set of axioms and interlinking rules, and probably never will be.

Engels remarked that the judgments of Hegel's dialectical logic, despite the arbitrariness of their classification, express universal ways of obtaining new information, the development of thought again appearing as the development of obtaining objective information.[37] These judgments can be considered in determinations of singularity, particularity, and universality.

This can indeed give us a picture of the way mathematical conceptions have developed—for example, our modern notion of geometry, which grew, first, by the observation that rotations preserve the metrical properties of a figure (pre-Euclidean), which is a determination of singularity. Secondly, it was found that certain properties remain invariant under different transformations, such as projective, affine, rotational ones (early nineteenth century), which is a determination of particularity; and, thirdly, every geometry is the theory of invariants of a certain group (Erlanger Program, 1872), which can be considered as a determination of universality. That such considerations may be captured in formal language can be seen from a sequence like the following: 1) seven is prime; 2) there are many primes; 3) the number of primes is infinite.

The progress of mathematics is along many paths. They can all be considered as dialectical judgments,[38] and some of the most fertile can be described as follows:

a) Passing from the specific to the general—e.g., from the theory of quadratic, cubic, etc. equations to Galois's theory:

> The subject matter of mathematics itself can no longer be described as simply form and number. These conceptions still form the foundation of all mathematics, but such subjects as projective geometry, topology, group theory transcend this classification. The boundary between mathematics and logic has disappeared as well.

b) Passing from the discrete to the continuous, from the finite to the infinite—e.g., from sums to integrals, from the rational to the real numbers, or in the use of the principle of mathematical induction:

> The transcendence of the finite into the infinite has been one of the most creative steps in the development not only of mathematics, but of understanding in general. "The infinite has like no other question moved so deeply man's mood, the infinite has like hardly any other idea worked so stimulatingly and deeply on the mind; the infinite however is also like no other conception so much in need of elucidation," wrote Hilbert.[39] Hilbert's attempt to show that the infinite can be eliminated not only from mathematics—an attempt already made by Eudoxus—but also from natural science "the infinite is nowhere realized" does not seem convincing; the infinite has a way of breaking through all limits set by man in a given historical period as the basis of his understanding.

c) Passing from quantity to quality—e.g., from metrical to projective geometry, and thence to topology. In passing from positive to negative numbers we bring into arithmetic the notion of one-dimensional direction, and in passing from real numbers to complex numbers we introduce a symbolism to denote a two-dimensional change of direction:

> Mathematics, though originating from the study of number and form, has so emancipated itself from its origins that few mathematicians are willing to define their science any more as that of number and form. The logic of quantum itself has led to quality in many forms. Leibniz was perhaps the first to detect this aspect of the growth of mathematics: "I believe that we still need another analysis, properly geometrical or linear, which expresses to us di-

rectly situs, as algebra expresses magnitude" (letter to Huygens, 1679).[40] However, the trend has been to show how mathematics can be constructed on the natural numbers alone, a curious vindication of Hegel's view that the end and the notion of mathematics is quantity, together with a rejection of his view that there is no growth and relation of ideas in mathematics.[41]

d) Principle of the permanence of formal laws—e.g., when we pass from arithmetic to the algebra of real numbers, and then to the algebra of complex and hypercomplex number systems, and from "real" to "ideal" domains:

> This principle was formulated by Hermann Hankel[42] in the words: "When two forms, expressed in general symbols of the *arithmetica universalis*, are equal to each other, then they shall also be equal to each other when the symbols cease to denote simple quantities, and hence the operations also receive some other content."

e) Principle of permanence of mathematical relations, so named by V. Poncelet, whom it inspired in the discovery of projective geometry (the "principle of continuity," for instance, allowed Poncelet to pass from known geometrical theorems to new ones, or to relate known theorems to each other):

> A special application of this principle was the work with imaginary elements in geometry, which led Cayley and Klein to the discovery that metrical geometry is a part of projective geometry, after Poncelet had derived the second as part of the first.

We can also list under this principle the fundamental conception of isomorphism, which allows us to interpret the same system of formal relations between abstract elements in different ways. Examples are polarity in projective geometry, and Hilbert's proof of the uncontradictory character of Euclidean geometry by its mapping on a linear algebra by means of coordinates. Here the form of a system corresponds to a multiformity of contents, and only receives its life from the content.

f) Principle of preservation of mathematical language—e.g., when we pass from three parametric systems applicable to space to four parametric systems, using again terms such as "point" and "line" for a "space" of four dimensions.

Much has been written about the confusing element in the use of language, also in mathematics. Mathematical logic has introduced symbols to eliminate words such as "or," "and," "all," and "there is." This trend has sometimes obscured the creative character of the use of words. By attaching wider conceptions to such words as "point," "space," and "vector" research into new fields has often been considerably facilitated. A good example is also the use of such terms as "function space," "orthogonal functions," and "probability density."

> The refusal of the Greeks to extend the term "number" to the irrational had a deterimental influence on the development of their mathematics. This should not be simply considered as an unfortunate accident. It was rather a result of the Greek emphasis on abstract geometry, itself a result of the seeming unwillingness of some of their leading mathematicians to accept the oriental conception of arithmetic and algebra, which can only be explained by the social cleavage between Greeks and orientals.

However, the fact that symbols and words are used to express mathematical conceptions should not lead to a statement like "Mathematics is the language of size," [43] which overemphasizes again the formal aspect of mathematics, and treats its content, its creative aspect as an image of the real world, as incidental.

This enumeration of some of the creative principles of mathematics could be continued; and cases could be analyzed where they overlap. When these creative principles are applied unconsciously, or semiconsciously, we may speak of mathematical intuition.[44] The feeling of harmony with the universe which the creative mathematician experiences expresses the agreement of his thoughts with the world. Here he treads on common ground with the artist and the mystic.

The deductive character, in which well organized mathematics appears before the public, should therefore not blind us to the essentially inductive character in which its results have been obtained. This goes back, in the last instance, to its being a study of nature—if only some of its most abstract characteristics, least susceptible to experimentation beyond elementary levels and to historic change—and furnishes the basic answer to the oft quoted question by Poincaré:

> The possibility itself of mathematical science seems an insoluble contradiction. If this science is only deductive in appearance, whence

comes to it that absolute rigor which nobody thinks of contesting? If, on the contrary, all propositions which it establishes can be obtained from one another by the rules of formal logic, why does not mathematics reduce itself to an immense tautology? [45]

We only add here that "absolute rigor" does not exist. The criteria for rigor in mathematics are historical ones; what seemed rigorous to Euclid or to Gauss does not seem rigorous to us. And we may expect—modern axiomatics seem to confirm it—that, even if mathematics could be reduced to a tautology in the eyes of one generation, it would escape the confines of its prison again at a later date.

The test of truth in mathematics—its noncontradictory character—is the test of its applicability to the real world. This is not a statement which can be proved like a theorem; the test between idealism and materialism cannot be decided on paper, or in theory, but has to be decided in the practice of life as well. The facts that mathematics is possible, that it is applicable to nature, and that it has a social function are all interwoven.

This does not constitute a utilitarian approach, because mathematics can develop only when it can be explored without a conscious search for immediate applications; nor does it mean that mathematics is an empirical science, as Mill claimed. As long as mathematics is empirical it has not reached the rank of science.

This does not exclude the fact that mathematical discoveries have been made by direct experiment. In the first place, every generation has to learn the fundamental concepts of mathematics for itself by direct testing with reality. Our conviction of the eternal validity of Pythagoras' theorems or the fact that $2 \times 2 = 4$ is not based on some *a priori* conception, nor can it be shaken by any clever mathematician who in a big book with formulas concludes that these theorems are mere convention. Our conviction is based on the fact that the theorems correspond to properties of the real world outside our consciousness which can be tested, and are accessible for testing to all persons from their earliest youth. Demonstration of Pythagoras' theorems and those attempts to prove that $2 \times 2 = 4$ which have existed since the days of Leibniz serve to connect these truths with even more elementary ones, even easier to test. The creation of a mathematical structure is necessary, is indispensable, for the discovery of other, less obvious truths, more difficult to test.

Relatively few mathematical discoveries have been made in modern times by experiment—those few mostly indirectly in attempts to account for phenomena in physics. An example is Fresnel's wave surface, discovered in the study of double refraction in crystalline media. Other indirect results of experimentation are the many solutions of differential equations obtained in the study of electrical or mechanical problems. Certain properties in the factorization of large numbers have been discovered by mechanical means, and the recent development of computing machines may lead to more discoveries. Some geometrical theorems have been discovered by means of plaster and wire models (e.g., Henrici's theorem of 1874 on the mobility of the straight lines on a hyperboloid). Such cases, in modern mathematics, are rare, and have so far never been of a fundamental importance.

This fact that relatively few modern mathematical discoveries are the result of direct experimentation cannot be used to argue that, whatever the origin of ancient mathematics may have been, modern mathematics at any rate is a pure product of the human mind. It does mean that mathematics has advanced to a stage where it can further develop to a great extent inside the framework of its own structure without waiting for experimentation to verify. The situation can be compared with that of the construction of new instruments (lenses, wave filters, etc.) which can be designed on paper with perfect confidence that they will perform the task expected of them, because of our exact knowledge of the laws of physics involved.

The specific mathematical criterion of truth enables us to find on paper, with pencil and pen, and by reasoning, relationships which are an image of objective relationships if the set of axioms from which we start is such an image. It is not, as we know, necessary for the mathematical reasoning to take the objective meaning of the axioms into consideration in future investigation, though it still may have an influence on the selection of the topics for research. A point may freely be taken as "Element A," a line as "Element B." The choice of axioms in almost every actually studied type of mathematics will be in accord with certain objective relationships. Here we agree with A. Tarski, himself a logician:

Thus one hears and even reads occasionally that no definite content may be ascribed to mathematical cencepts; that in mathematics we do not really know what we are talking about, and that we are not interested in whether our assertions are true. One should approach such judgments rather critically. If in the construction of a theory one behaves as if one did not understand the meaning of the terms of this discipline, this is not at all the same as denying those terms any meaning . . . A formal system, for which we are unable to give a single interpretation, would, presumably, be of interest to nobody.[46]

We may add that the very living of mathematicians as a group (not necessarily as individuals) depends on the fact that mathematics is meaningful. If it were different, then the university and high-school pay rolls would soon have few places for them. Some interested rich men would be willing to engage mathematicians as they now do chess players or bridge experts; others might be interested in helping mathematicians as artists. However, artists, as we know, find few protectors under capitalism, far fewer than scientists. It is essentially the constructive social role which mathematics played in the building of early and industrial capitalism that brought encouragement to the study of mathematics, even when it had to take more and more abstract forms to reach deeper levels of reality.

Many mathematicians of the nineteenth century believed in a "pure" mathematics cultivated only for the "honor of the human mind," and in a more or less separate "applied" field, often considered less worthy of effort. Titian's painting "Sacred and Profane Love," in the Borghese gallery at Rome, seemed to some of them to represent "Pure and Applied Mathematics." This distinction is losing rapidly in cogency as a fundamental form of classification, though it remains a convenient way to denote types of specialization. Any "pure" mathematical theory has found, or may find soon, its field of applicability. The mathematician, following on paper the strictly theoretical reasoning of his science, may find any moment that he has actually studied the laws of some field of physics, chemistry, or statistics. The classical example is the theory of conic sections, created by the Greeks probably as a result of their search for the trisection of the angle or the duplication of the cube, which was shown, two thousand years later, to be the study of the orbits of the planets. A modern example of a similar kind is the tensor calculus, discovered as a study of the invariance of quadratic differential forms, which several decades later was instrumental in providing a description of the universe according to Einstein's theory of relativity. Now we also know that tensors express fundamental notions in dynamics, in elasticity, in hydrodynamics. The tensor calculus can also be applied to rotating electrical machines and to the comparison of colors, and some of its more elementary conceptions have already found their way into psychology.

Such examples can be multiplied a hundredfold. One of the most abstract conceptions of modern mathematics is Lebesgue measure, which seemed to some mathematicians the very culmination of their science as a pure play of the mind.[47] Yet we now know that it forms the key to the understanding of the theory of probability, and of statistics; and this again makes it indispensable for the explanation of phenomena as far apart as the Brownian motion of particles in liquid suspension and the long-range behavior of mechanical systems.[48]

Already Jacobi observed how theta functions relate deeply hidden relations in number theory to the motions of the pendulum. Now number theory, one of the most abstract fields of mathematics, based on the so-called zeta function of Riemann, finds its way in problems of electrical engineering as well as parts of physics. Matrix algebra furnishes the basis of quantum mechanics and of the behavior of atoms in action. And Hilbert has pointed out how certain laws of genetics, in the case of the little fly Drosophila, obey the axioms concerning the notion of "between" as well as the linear Euclidean axioms of congruence.

It is therefore possible to maintain, as sometimes is believed (and the subjective idealistic conception of mathematics must necessarily lead to it), that the wide range of applicability of mathematics to nature and society is just a coincidence. The applicability of mathematics is too general, too universal, to take such a contention seriously. When the number of such "accidents," "coincidences," "lucky hits" increases so manifold, we should look for a more rational explanation. All scientists are engaged in a cooperative enterprise to discover the behavior of the world, and while their paths and results diverge widely at times, the fundamental unity of the universe makes eventual harmony of all results possible. It is this author's conviction that a belief in this fundamental unity of all things in existence is shared by all serious scientists, and that that belief gives them their deep-lying conviction that their research is meaningful.

Practice as well as theory has thus amply justified our belief that all mathematical activity is meaningful in the sense that it gives an image of some aspect of the real world. It seems to agree with Leibniz's opinion as expressed by Schrecker:

> Whereas according to the utilitarian knowledge is true because it is useful, it would be more adequate according to Leibniz to state that if knowledge is true, it must be useful, and that thus usefulness is only a confirmation, not a constituent element of truth. True knowledge, indeed, represents the objective and real order of the universe.[49]

Hilbert, because of this intimate relationship between thought and nature, between experiment and theory, as modern mathematics reveals, has been willing to accept Leibniz's notion of "prestabilized harmony." But he saw in the relation between theoretical mathematics and its applications even more than this "prestabilized harmony":

> Without mathematics present-day astronomy and physics is impossible; these sciences in their theoretical parts dissolve, we can say, in mathematics.[50]

It is to this unity of thought and nature that the development of modern mathematics itself has led.

References

[1] D. E. Smith, *History of Mathematics* (Boston: Ginn, 1923–1925), Vol. I, pp. 6–18.

[2] Mill, *A System of Logic* (New York, 1848), p. 364.

[3] Bell, *The Development of Mathematics,* 2nd ed. (New York: McGraw-Hill, 1945), p. 561.

[4] C. B. Boyer, "Zero: The Symbol, the Concept, the Number," *National Mathematics Magazine,* Vol. XVII (1944), pp. 323–330.

[5] This expression is due to W. Sombart (*Der Bourgeois,* München, 1920 ed., p. 164).

[6] The paper by B. Hessen, "The Social and Economic Roots of Newton's *Principia,*" read at the International Congress of the History of Science and Technology held in London in 1931, published in *Science at the Cross Roads* (London: Kniga, 1933), pp. 151–192, has introduced many scientists to the understanding of the materialist approach to the history of science. See also R. K. Merton, "Science and the Economy of Seventeenth Century England," *Science and Society,* Vol. III (1939), pp. 3–27.

[6a] The social background of mathematical research in the different periods of history is sketched in more detail in Dirk J. Struik, *A Concise History of Mathematics* (New York: 1948, 2 vols.). See also L. Hogben, footnote 43. A deeper understanding of the social forces active in the development of mathematics can only be reached when historians of mathematics begin to take cognizance of the vast territory uncovered by economic historians. Combined with this should be the study of the history of technology, still a relatively unexplored field.

[7] Ernst Cassirer, *Substance and Function* (Chicago: Open Court, 1923), p. 92.

Bertrand Russell, *A Critical Exposition of the Philosophy of Leibniz* (London: Cambridge Univ. Press, 1900), p. 70.

Gottfried W. Leibniz, *The Monadology and Other Philosophical Writings,* transl. Robert Latta (Oxford: Clarendon, 1898), pp. 233–234.

[8] George Berkeley, *A Treatise Concerning the Principles of Human Knowledge* (Dublin, 1710), as included in *Works,* ed. G. Sampson, Vol. I, pp. 183, 184.

[9] B. Russell, *op. cit.*, p. 72.

[10] Letter of Gauss to Olbers, 1817. Gauss, *Werke,* Vol. VIII (1900), p. 177.

[11] B. Riemann, *Ges. Math.* (1892), p. 523. Riemann died in 1866.

[12] Karl Weierstrass, *Mathematische Werke* (Berlin, 1894–1927), Vol. I, p. 226.

[13] This, at any rate, was the common interpretation of Kant's doctrine, based on the "transzendentale Aesthetik." There are other places in Kant which allow a less apodictic interpretation, e.g., in the "Schematismus des reinen Verstandesbegriffe."

[14] H. Grassmann, *Die Ausdehnungslehre,* in *Werke,* Vol. I, Introduction.

[15] "Naturwissenschaftlich gerichteter Neuhumanismus."

[16] C. J. G. Jacobi, *Werke,* Vol. I, p. 454, letter of July 2, 1830.

[17] The terms are due to Karl Marx, see D. J. Struik, "Marx and Mathematics," *Science and Society,* Winter, 1947–1948, Vol. 12, pp. 181–196.

[18] P. Du Bois-Reymond, *Die allgemeine Funktionentheorie* (Tübingen, 1882), pp. 53–54.

[19] B. Peirce, "Linear Associative Algebra," *American Journal of Mathematics,* Vol. IV (1881), p. 97.

[20] *Century Dictionary,* art. "Mathematics." See J. B. Shaw, *Lectures on the Philosophy of Mathematics* (Chicago: Open Court, 1918), p. 59.

[21] B. Russell, *Principles of Mathematics* (Cambridge, 1903), p. 3.

[22] L. E. J. Brouwer, *Over de grondslagen der wiskunde* (Amsterdam-Leipzig, 1907), p. 179.

[23] D. Hilbert, "Ueber das Unendliche," *Jahresb. Deutsch. Mathem. Ver.*, Vol. 36 (1927), p. 207.

[24] Cf. E. Colman, *Predmet i metod sovremmenoj matematiki* (Moscow, 1936, 316 pp.), esp. chap. x.

[25] B. Russell, *Scientific Method in Philosophy* (London: Oxford, 1914), p. 4.

[26] This overestimation of the role of formal logic also appears in the "logical" foundation of probability theory in the school of Keynes.

[27] M. Cornforth, *Science Versus Idealism* (London: Lawrence, 1947), *passim.*

[28] Schlick, *Allgemeine Erkenntnisslehre* (Berlin, 1925 ed.), p. 224.

[29] R. Carnap, *Logical Syntax of Language* (New York: Harcourt, 1937).

[30] L. Wittgenstein, *Tractatus logico-philosophicus* (1922), in English (London, 1922), pp. 154, 160.

[31] G. Mannoury, *Mathesis en mystiek* (Amsterdam, c. 1925), p. 32.

[32] Moritz Cantor, *Vorlesungen über Geschichte der Mathematik* (4 vols., Leipzig, 1900–1908).

[33] F. Klein, *Vorlesungen über die Entwicklung der Mathematik im 19. Jahrhundert* (Berlin, 1926–1927), Vol. I.

[34] A related criticism of idealistic and formalistic methods in E. Colman, *loc. cit.;* also in E. Colman, "The Present Crisis in the Mathematical Sciences," *Science at the Cross Roads* (London, 1931), pp. 215–229.

[35] Vaihinger's point of view has been attacked by the mathematician E. Study, *Die realistische Weltansicht und die Lehre vom Raume* (Braunschweig, 1923). Study gives a spirited exposition of the thesis that there is an outside world independent of consciousness.

[35a] Compare the "logical machines" in N. Wiener, *Cybernetics, or Control and Communication in the Animal and the Machine* (New York, 1948), pp. 147–148. This remarkable book, which overcomes the limitations of mechanical materialism by an analysis of the modern concept of machine, also contributes to a materialistic understanding of mathematics.

[36] H. Poincaré, *La Science et l'hypothèse* (Paris, 1918), chap. i.

[37] F. Engels, *Dialectics of Nature,* transl. and ed. C. Dutt (New York: Internat'l Pubs., 1940), pp. 237–240.

[38] Cf. J. B. S. Haldane, *The Marxist Philosophy and the Sciences* (London: Allen & Unwin, 1938), chap. ii, "Mathematics and Cosmology."

[39] Hilbert, *op. cit.,* note 23.

[40] See H. Grassmann, *Werke,* Vol. II (1894), p. 417. The direct answer to Leibniz's quest has been the vector and tensor analysis, but the portent of his remark is much wider.

[41] Hegel, *Phänomenologie des Geistes* (Lasson ed., 1927), p. 37.

[42] *Theorie der complexen Zahlensysteme* (1867), p. 11.

[43] L. Hogben, *Mathematics for the Million* (New York: Norton, 1937), p. 68.

[44] "Rigor and fecundity are two complementary aspects of the same reality, when we place all our attention on the one we lose sight of the other" (R. Duval and G. T. Guilbaud, *Le Raisonnement mathématique,* Paris, 1945, p. 147). A beginning of the study of this mathematical intuition and inventiveness has recently been made by J. Hadamard, *An Essay on the Psychology of Invention in the Mathematical Field* (Princeton, 1945, 143 pp.).

[45] H. Poincaré, *op. cit.*, pp. 9–10.

[46] A. Tarski, *Introduction to Logic and to the Methodology of Deductive Sciences* (New York: Oxford, 1941), p. 129.

[47] Criticism of some idealistic conclusions of Russian mathematicians concerning this subject and related ones is found in E. Colman, *Predmet i metod sovremmenoj matematiki,* p. 290. See also his *Kritický výklad, symbolické metody moderní*" (Praha, 1948), p. 299.

[48] See N. Wiener, *Cybernetics, etc.,* chap. ii, which shows the connection between the work of Gibbs on statistical mechanics and of Lebesque on integration.

[49] P. Schrecker, "Leibniz and the Art of Inventing Algorithms," *Journal of the History of Ideas,* Vol. VIII (1947), pp. 107–116, esp. 115–116.

[50] D. Hilbert, "Naturerkennen und Logik," *Gesammelte Abhandlungen* (1930), pp. 378–387. It is sometimes stated that, according to Hilbert, mathematics is a meaningless game. This paper shows that such a statement does not express Hilbert's full understanding of mathematics.

AN ASTRONOMER'S VIEW OF THE UNIVERSE

by

ROY K. MARSHALL

Roy K. Marshall (Ph.D., University of Michigan, 1932) is director of the Fels Planetarium, Franklin Institute, Philadelphia, and has been astronomer of the Cook Observatory of the University of Pennsylvania since 1940. He is science editor of the *Evening Bulletin,* and a radio and television entrepreneur, promoting scientific telecasts on the NBC network. He is a member of the American Astronomical Society, Royal Astronomical Society of Canada, British Astronomical Association, and a Fellow of the Royal Astronomical Society (London). He has written extensively on astrophysics and spectroscopic analysis.

THE INITIAL impressions of our remote ancestors with respect to the heavens were inextricably intermingled with their religions and superstitions. Some of these lingered even until the seventeenth century, when it was quite common, in diagrammatic representations of the universe, to put at the outer rim a strange region in which a magical supply of energy, the *primum mobile,* was located. Even today, the average citizen is likely to worry about why the Earth continues to rotate on its axis and to pursue its orbital revolution about the Sun. He does not know that Galileo essentially explained the motions of the universe in a series of statements which might be condensed into this: "What's to stop them?"

The outstanding characteristic of the universe as we know it today is empty space. From the practical viewpoint, it is quite empty. The average density of the universe is less than that of normal air by a factor of at least 10^{16}. With the largest telescopes in the world, space can be penetrated to see objects at distances of a thousand million light-years, the equivalent of more than 5×10^{21} miles, and this very fact is an admirable proof of the essential emptiness of the space between the agglomerations of matter, which themselves consist of small masses of matter separated by wide distances.

This picture of an open-spaced universe is one which has been thrust upon us by the overwhelming evidence of observation. A casual examination of an object in the sky does not permit judgment of either size or distance, and the early observers could only speculate concerning the possibility that the tiny flickering stars might in reality be large bodies like the Sun, diminished in apparent importance only by distance. Primitive estimates of the distance of the Moon in terms of that of the Sun were derived from observations of the phases of the Moon, and these, added to realization of the cause of eclipses of the Sun, first established the important fact that the distances of various objects were different.

The first measure of the circumference of the Earth was accomplished by the Alexandrian Eratosthenes, almost twenty-two centuries ago, by a method fundamentally sound and precisely that which is employed today for a similar purpose. A century later, Hipparchus estimated the distance of the Moon to be 59 Earth-radii, a value very close to the truth. This result, combined with the ratio of the distances of the Moon and the Sun as derived by Aristarchus, resulted in a value of about 1,200 Earth-radii for the distance of the Sun, a result which was practically universally accepted up to the beginning of the seventeenth century. Then, although the value was believed to be in error, the only changes were arbitrary and not based upon observation.

Late in that century, observations by a French expedition gave Domenico Cassini of the Paris Observatory the means of deriving a value for the distance of the Sun equal to 360 times the distance of the Moon, or about 10 per cent less than the modern value of a little more than 23,500 Earth-radii.

The relative distances of the planets were well established with the enunciation of the laws of planetary motions by Johann Kepler, early in the seventeenth century, and their mathematical justification by Isaac Newton later in the same century. With the discovery of the law of gravitation and the invention of the calculus, it became possible to put much speculation about the planets on a firmer basis and to determine their distances from the Sun in terms of the Earth's distance. By the end of the century, then, the solar system as known at the time, including the planets Mercury, Venus, Earth, Mars, Jupiter, and Saturn, was mapped fairly accurately.

Beyond the planets lay the stars, but not one stellar distance was measured until 1838. True, the Danish Tycho Brahe had tried to measure their parallactic shifts and had used his failure to accomplish the assignment as a principal reason for rejecting the Copernican heliocentric theory of the arrangement of the solar system. If the Earth revolves around the Sun, Tycho reasoned, we should see the near-by stars shift their places with respect to those in the distant background. His instruments were the best produced in his time, yet he failed to detect the displacement which we know today is at best only 1 or 2 per cent of Tycho's smallest measure. But it was with Tycho's unrivaled measures that Kepler worked to do away with the circles upon circles which had been adopted, but in vain, to explain the non-uniform motions of the planets. The firm results of Kepler, added to the observations by Galileo, with his new telescope, of the phases of Mercury and Venus and his discovery of the satellites of Jupiter, revolving around some center other than the Earth, served to swing the balance in favor of the heliocentric theory.

The first proof of the motion of the Earth around the Sun came in 1725, when James Bradley attempted to determine stellar parallactic displacements. Instead, he discovered the aberration of light, which is traditionally compared with the phenomenon of the tilt of an umbrella in the direction of motion. The finite velocity of fall of the drops of rain can be combined vectorially with the speed of motion of the person carrying the umbrella, to determine the optimum tilt to the umbrella required to shield the person from the falling drops. If the umbrella is carried vertically, the person will walk into some of the falling drops.

Similarly, a telescope must be tilted forward, in the direction of the Earth's motion around the Sun, to guarantee that the light from a star will pass unhampered through the tube of the telescope. Actually, it is not quite so serious; the star can still be seen, with an untilted telescope, but it is shifted by a maximum amount of more than 20 seconds of arc, because of the finite ratio of the speed of the Earth in its orbit and the speed of the light. In 1728, the correct explanation of aberration occurred to Bradley. It is generally agreed that no plausible explanation of aberration, other than an annual motion of the Earth around the Sun, is possible, so that its discovery constituted the truth of the heliocentric theory.

The first measures of stellar parallax were made in 1838 and 1839 by Struve at Dorpat, Bessel at Königsberg, and Henderson at the Cape of Good Hope. All their values were somewhat wide of the truth, gauged by modern standards; but they were of the right order of size and can be accepted as the second proof of the revolution of the Earth around the Sun. The diameter of the Earth's almost-circular orbit is 186,000,000 miles; observations of a near-by star from the two ends of a diameter should disclose a measurable displacement with respect to the more distant stars beyond. The displacement for the nearest star is such that the distance of the star is about 275,000 times as great as the distance from Earth to Sun. Today, the distances of several thousands of stars have been determined by this trigonometrical method.

A third proof of the Earth's motion of revolution came with the application of the Doppler-Fizeau effect, by Huggins in England and Vogel at Potsdam. The lines in the spectra of the stars are displaced by changing distance from the Earth. Part of this displacement, a constant for an ordinary star unhampered by a companion, is due to the motion of the star with respect to the Sun. The remainder is a variable amount, repeating its variation in an annual period, and is due to the motion of the Earth. At one season of the year, we may be approaching a given star; six months later we shall be receding from the same star. The amount of the variation of the displacement of the spectrum lines in the light of the star is a measure of our velocity in our orbit around the Sun. If, as we find, we travel in our orbit with a speed of 18½ miles per second, and a year of seconds is required for us to complete this cycle, we can multiply 18½ by the number of seconds in a year, to obtain the circumference of the Earth's orbit, hence the distance of the Sun. This value checks those derived in other ways.

The discovery of other planets—Uranus in 1781 by William Herschel, Neptune in 1846 by Galle of Berlin, as a result of the mathematical work of Leverrier (with independent British calculations by John Couch Adams that fell before almost-blind eyes), and Pluto in

1930 by Tombaugh, with the calculations of Lowell guiding him (and again, an almost ignored William Pickering working independently) —served to expand our ideas of the solar system. The comets that dive into the neighborhood of the Sun for a few brief weeks are known to travel out even beyond the most distant planets, and the thousands of minor planets or asteroids—and untold myriads of meteoroids—are now known to trace their courses through what were formerly believed to be regions untenanted by any regular members of our system.

That same Herschel who was first to discover a planet in historic times was also the first to examine the sidereal system systematically, with a view to discovering the extent and arrangement of the universe. He devised and used a statistical method which is, in essence, that used today to glean the observational material for the same broad purpose. He realized the futility of embarking on a program of intimate examination of every area of the heavens, or even of the portion visible to him in the high northern latitude of England. He counted the stars in regions of the sky selected with a certain careful randomness, and found that the number of stars per unit area varied from region to region. He came to the conclusion that our system of stars, while full of irregularities and clumps and clusters that defied accurate description, is roughly disk-shaped, with the direction of greatest extent marked out fairly well by the Milky Way. Moreover, the number of faint stars increases remarkably as we approach the Milky Way. Herschel had to assume that, in general, the stars are of the same intrinsic luminosity, and that apparent faintness must be attributed to great distance. The increase in number of faint stars, then, meant that in the direction of the Milky Way the stars extended to far greater distances. The Milky Way itself is irregular; and in the direction of the part of the Milky Way just above the southern horizon for England the densest star clouds occur. Herschel established the method and the initial general indications of a finite system of stars, of which the Sun makes one. Today, our dimensions are different, but the essential idea is the same.

Modern measures, certainly subject to some revision, but not substantially far from the correct values, reveal that our Sun is one of perhaps 100,000,000,000 stars distributed throughout a volume of space that is roughly globular, and of the order of 100,000 light-years —about 6×10^{17} miles—in diameter. Almost all these stars are strewn together throughout a discoidal region of the foregoing major dimension, but only about 15,000 light-years in average thickness. Our Sun is located about 30,000 light-years from the center of the disk. There is a considerable nuclear bulge to this disk, and considerable congestion as compared with the region where the Sun is. Around the disk, filling out the globular volume of which it is an equatorial plane, a few hundred millions of stars are loosely strewn, along with a few score globular clusters of stars, each consisting of perhaps a million stars.

In addition to the stars, there is at least an equal mass of material scattered through this discoidal region in the form of electrons, ions, atoms, molecules, and even dustlike particles. Some of this material is luminous by scattering and reflection of the light of neighboring stars. Some of it shines by a fluorescence process, absorbing the ultraviolet radiation of hot involved stars and emitting the energy in visible form. Still other regions of this material remain unilluminated, but reveal their presence by the obscuration of the stars lying beyond them. The stars are dimmed but, fortunately, they are also reddened; the spectra of the stars can tell us what their colors should be, and the amount of reddening can tell us something of how much material lies between us and them. This interstellar gas and dust make an interesting problem of the task of peering out to the edges of our Milky Way system, or galaxy. Here and there we find small windows through which stars can be seen relatively undimmed, and studies of these regions permit outlining of the system.

This stellar system or galaxy is rotating on an axis which is, as one might suspect, perpendicular to the plane of the discoid. As a first approximation, the mode of rotation is like that of the solar system: bodies near the center perform their revolutions about that center in shorter periods. This should be true of any system in which there is concentration of mass toward the center. The stars which lie between us and the center overtake and pass us; we overtake and pass the stars which lie farther from the center than the Sun. Our speed around the center (which is in the direction of the tail of the Scorpion, just above the horizon for northern United States, in July evenings), is about 150 miles per second and, at our distance from the center, one revolution requires about 200,000,000 years.

This manner of motion guarantees that a photograph of our galaxy from outside will reveal a different structure as time goes on. The outer portions lag with respect to the nuclear region. Almost every star has its individual motion; our Sun moves with respect to its neighbors at a speed of 12 miles per second, in a direction not too far from that of the bright star Vega. Each star revolves around the center of the system in a noncircular path, much as the comets revolve around the Sun. The congestion that might be suspected, because the intermingled stellar orbits all pass close to the nuclear region, does not occur, because the stars travel faster and spend less time in the neighborhood of the nucleus. This is clearly analogous with the cometary system; while the total population may be high, at any moment a given volume of space is occupied by very few comets, even in the Sun's neighborhood, where each of them must return periodically.

Herschel's ideas concerning the general shape of our galaxy have been amply confirmed by modern observations, but the dimensions are considerably beyond anything that he would have been willing to admit. During the course of his surveys, Herschel was especially interested in the nebulae and star clusters. Some objects were readily resolved into individual stars by his largest telescopes, while others were amorphous objects in which, even with his highest magnifying powers, the individual stars could not be seen. He was willing to believe that these, too, with sufficiently great instruments, might be resolved into stars; but many of them were proved, after the middle of the nineteenth century, to be truly gaseous objects—true nebulae. Their spectra were not what should be obtained from aggregations of stars but were, instead, emission spectra as emitted by gases at low pressure. Still others revealed spectra resembling those from clusters of stars, yet defied even the best telescopic attempts to detect the individual stars. These, today, we call the galaxies. Many of them have been resolved into stars, and we have many kinds of evidence that the others, too, consist of stars; but again we must say that our instruments are not capable of performing the resolution, so great are the distances of these galaxies.

When we leave our Milky Way system behind, and begin to study the other galaxies, we are for the first time sketching the structure of the universe. It may be that higher degrees of organization exist; and it is with this possibility in mind that Harlow Shapley speaks of the observable volume of space as the metagalaxy. Whether we think of it as the metagalaxy or as the observable universe, the volume of space that we can examine with our largest telescopes has the galaxies as its particles.

The two nearest external galaxies are of irregular shape and are easily visible to the unaided eye, appearing like detached bright portions of the Milky Way. They can be seen only from southern latitudes, and they are known as the Magellanic Clouds, or Clouds of Magellan. It was while studying the stars of the Magellanic Clouds that Henrietta Leavitt of the Harvard Observatory discovered the first clue to the distances of these and other galaxies.

There are in these clouds a great number of variable stars. They change their brightnesses in very definite patterns that make it possible to assign them to the class of variables called Cepheids. From statistically estimated distances of Cepheids in our own galaxy, we have today a relationship between the period and the intrinsic luminosity of Cepheid variables that is a most important tool for determining the distances of the galaxies.

Miss Leavitt noticed that the Cepheids in the Small Magellanic Cloud could be arranged on a graph in which period of variation is plotted against apparent mean brightness. She reasoned that the Cloud was far away from us as compared with the thickness of the Cloud, hence it must be that we could consider all these Cepheids as approximately at the same distance from us. If this were true, then the relationship between period and *real* luminosity must prevail. Some nonvariable stars in the Cloud were of types known in our neighborhood, and their intrinsic luminosities could be assumed to be the same as for the neighboring stars. This gave initial estimates for the distance of the Cloud. Estimates of the distances of near-by Cepheids in our galaxy gave a zero-point which agreed with what was demanded for the Cepheids of the Small Magellanic Cloud, to put them at the distance suggested by the nonvariable stars of recognizable types.

As a final general result, we have at our disposal today a curve of relationship between intrinsic luminosities and periods of Cepheid variable stars, wherever we find them in the universe. If we discover a Cepheid in another galaxy, we can recognize it by its regularity of variation and the shape of its curve of variation. We can observe its maximum and minimum brightnesses, and take a mean of some kind. This is the observed or *apparent* mean brightness, of course. From the length of the period, we can determine the *intrinsic* mean brightness, by consulting the period-luminosity curve we have at our disposal. As soon as we know how bright the star appears, and how bright it really is, we can calculate its distance by a simple algebraic formula.

In this way, the distances of some of the near-by galaxies have been determined, because they fortunately contain recognizable Cepheid variable stars. But the Cepheids are not among the very brightest stars. These latter are assumed, for the nearer galaxies, to be of the same intrinsic luminosities as the brightest known stars in our galaxy and in the Magellanic Clouds. Their brightnesses as we observe them are compared with the probable intrinsic brightnesses; and the distances check those derived from the Cepheids. At least, they agree well when we consider the assumptions that must be made. There is a possibility that some stars of our galaxy may be projected before another galaxy, so that the few very brightest stars in a galaxy are rejected, before a mean is taken of the apparent brightnesses of the next few brightest stars.

When we have thus derived the distances of a few score galaxies, by using Cepheid variables and other recognizable bright stars in them, we can begin to correlate distances of galaxies with apparent total brightness, and with apparent dimensions. The more distant a galaxy is, the fainter it will appear, and the smaller. This kind of correlation works pretty well for the few score galaxies whose distances have been more or less directly measured; they lie along straight lines when we plot distance against apparent brightness or distance against apparent diameter. So we make a very broad but apparently justifiable assumption, that the galaxies are, on the average, of the same total intrinsic brightness and of the same general dimensions.

This is the same kind of assumption William Herschel made about the stars, and we know now that the stars range in intrinsic luminosity from fainter than to brighter than the Sun by factors of the order of 100,000 times. The uniformity of the galaxies is far greater than this, however. There are some supergiants and some dwarfs among them, in luminosity; but most of the galaxies are embraced within a range of 1,000 times, as compared with 10,000,000,000 times, at least, for the stars. For all except about 150 of them, we cannot see the individual stars, and so must resort to some statistical method for determining the distances for the remote galaxies.

Right away, we must be careful about our measures of apparent brightness. William Herschel recognized a systematic arrangement of his so-called "white nebulae" which today we call the galaxies. They are found in greatest numbers when we get to the greatest distance from the Milky Way—the actual starry veil through our sky. As we get close to the apparent borders of the Milky Way, the galaxies begin to thin out and, except in very special places in and very near the Milky Way, galaxies are missing. This preferential distribution with respect to the stars of our own system helped to prevent earlier agreement as to the nature of these external objects. If their distribution was conditioned by the distribution of the stars of our system, one might justifiably, without further evidence, conclude that the galaxies are but small objects, near by, and actually integral parts of our system.

In 1885, a bright stellar point was observed near the nucleus of the spiral-shaped galaxy in Andromeda. It faded after a few days and became invisible. Since that time, such outbursts of stellar objects in many galaxies have been observed; and the performance is the same as for the so-called novae, new stars or temporary stars in our own galaxy. These objects appear to possess some kind of instability that at last forces them to throw off their surface material in a brief but exciting flare-up of excess energy during which we see them grow to perhaps 10,000 times their previous brightnesses. At maximum, such stars are about 25,000 times as bright as our Sun, within a comparatively small range. They are among the recognizable stars which can be used to determine the distances of the galaxies in which they have been observed.

Heber D. Curtis, about 1925, emphatically insisted that these outbursts in external galaxies were like those of galactic novae, and perhaps hastened the acceptance of the metagalactic character of Herschel's "white nebulae." Today, there is no doubt that these are great aggregations of thousands of millions of stars, comparable in every way with the Milky Way system which is our own galaxy.

The systematic distribution, in which the Milky Way itself is avoided, is now known to be due to the layer of absorbing material, the interstellar gas, which lies through the discoidal major distribution of the stars of our galaxy. We are unable to see out beyond the bounds of our galaxy, in the direction of the Milky Way. What is particularly gratifying is the evidence, in scores of photographs of other galaxies, that they are similarly afflicted with interstellar material. Dark bars cross them from end to end, when we see them on edge. We cannot see into them, along a line that spans their greatest extent. Observers inside these galaxies could not see out, to observe our galaxy.

Wherever, in the Milky Way or near it, large numbers of galaxies are seen, we know we have found a "window" through the interstellar medium. It is by examining the most distant stars near the edges of these windows that we are able to determine the maximum extent of our own galaxy. Elsewhere, we are afraid that obscuring material of the interstellar medium has vitiated the apparent brightness of the stars. It is always a little surprising to know that, at the poles of the Milky Way, as far as we can get from the thick layer of obscuring material, the galaxies photographable with our greatest telescopes actually outnumber the stars of our own galaxy.

From surveys of hundreds of selected areas, made with large telescopes, it has been estimated that, with the 100-inch reflector at the Mount Wilson Observatory, approximately 100,000,000 galaxies could be photographed, in all the heavens, if the obscuring effects were not present in our galaxy. If space were uniformly populated with galaxies, and no other complicating factors were present, we should be able to photograph almost 1,000,000,000 galaxies with the 200-inch aperture of the Palomar Mountain telescope. The most distant ones are of the order of 1,000,000,000 light-years distant—approximately 6,000,000,000,000,000,000,000 miles. With a sphere of a thousand million light-years radius containing a thousand million galaxies, the density is of the order of one galaxy per 10^{18} cubic light-years. In general, we might say that galaxies are about a million light-years apart.

Some of our own neighbors are closer than this. The Magellanic Clouds are so close that we must consider them as satellites or companions of our own galaxy. The Large Magellanic Cloud is 75,000 light-years distant; the Small Cloud is almost 85,000 light-years distant from our Sun. Next beyond the irregular-shaped Magellanic Clouds we recognize the so-called Sculptor galaxy, of a nonnucleated but slightly centrally condensed character, at a distance of about 250,000 light-years. A similar galaxy in Fornax is about 500,000 light-years distant, while an irregular galaxy designated as NGC 6822 may be a trifle farther away. Another irregular galaxy, IC 1613, is about 900,000 light-years distant.

Two beautiful but dissimilar spiral galaxies lie at about 750,000 light-years: one of them rather loose and ragged, M 33; and the other more compact and brighter, M 31. M 31 has two companions, M 32 and NGC 205, which are of amorphous, spheroidal nature, only recently and with difficulty resolved into stars by the use of infra-red radiation which eliminates the blurring effect of the scattered light of shorter wave lengths.

Including our own Milky Way system, then, we know of eleven galaxies within a radius of a million light-years, which is considerably more than the earlier estimate of one galaxy per 10^{18} cubic light-years. In our neighborhood, we have a density more than twice as great; but we realize, of course, that observational selection has something to do with this. Some of the known near-by galaxies would not be noticed at distances of a few hundred million light-years. Indeed, the two thin galaxies, in Sculptor and Fornax, were discovered only through systematic surveys in which, fortunately, photographic plates of accidentally extraordinary sensitivity were used.

The two appear to be of a very new type of galaxy, large in size but low in population; there are other spheroidal galaxies, but the star density in them is about ten times as great as in these two systems. The spheroidal galaxies belong to the general class known as elliptical, totaling about 17 per cent of all galaxies. Some of the ellipticals appear as though seen exactly edge-on, and they then are seen to be spindle-shaped. There was for a time considerable confusion about the true nature of these objects. In the 1941 meeting of the American Astronomical Society at the Yerkes Observatory, theoretical proof was offered to the effect that the ellipsoidal galaxies consisted of clouds of dust surrounding extraluminous stars. Two or three years later, photographs were made at Mount Wilson Observatory, using infrared, that definitely resolved some of them into individual stars.

About 80 per cent of all galaxies are spirals of two seemingly different types, of various degrees of concentration and openness of spiral structure. There are the barred spirals, which consist of a nucleus, through which runs a more or less straight bar, from the ends of which spring the spiral arms, roughly concentric with the nucleus. The other galaxies are the normal spirals, in which the arms spring directly from the nucleus.

The remaining 3 per cent are of the type of the Magellanic Clouds, irregular in structure.

Except for these few irregulars, the galaxies appear to possess rotational symmetry; and, when the spectrograph is employed, the rotations can be detected and measured. The velocities of rotation are of the order of the speed found for our own galaxy, so that every galaxy has, for some intermediate radius, a period of several millions of years. There was considerable confusion about the direction of rotation, because for many of the galaxies it is impossible to determine which side is nearer to us. For a few of them, however, it is obvious that one side or the other is nearer, because the dark interstellar material is arranged so as to be silhouetted against certain details of the structure. From these, it has been rather definitely determined that a galaxy turns in a way such that the spiral arms trail and lag behind.

There are a few regions of disagreement between various schools of observation and thought about the galaxies. For example, the Mount Wilson Observatory (and, presumably, the Palomar Mountain Observatory group, which widely overlaps the Mount Wilson school) refers always to these external stellar systems as nebulae. They are not nebulae, of course, by the standards of American dictionaries, which state specifically that certain distant aggregations of stars appear to be nebulae. The word "nebula" should be reserved for the gaseous amorphous clouds which shine because of reflection, scattering or fluorescent excitation of the light of adjacent stars. We should not be hampered by the deficiencies of early telescopes. The word "galaxy" pertains, of course, specifically to the Milky Way, but we have coined a phrase embracing all the stars in our own system, some of which give rise to the visible appearance of the Milky Way. We call this the Milky Way system or the galaxy, or our galaxy. Other aggregations that, to observers inside, would lead to similar appearances, we call galaxies, aggregations of stars like our own. On such small and really insignificant points, much time is wasted and much confusion is engendered in the minds of the nonspecialists of the general public. The word "galaxy," in the plural form, should be soon specifically designated to indicate stellar aggregations of thousands of millions of stars, like the one in which we live. The word "nebula" should be specifically reserved to indicate clouds of particles such as molecules and atoms, or even dust motes. This is the view of the eastern astronomers, particularly at the Harvard College Observatory.

Between the Pacific and Atlantic experts, there is another realm of disagreement. The reflector type of telescope used at Mount Wilson is potent for detailed analysis; but only a small portion of the sky can be included in one shot. At the Harvard College Observatory, wide-angle refractors, or lens-type telescopes, have been largely used. These embrace a wide area of the heavens in one photograph, but on a scale that is necessarily less than that possible with the large reflecting telescopes.

At Mount Wilson, considerable reliance has been placed on sampling, or the use of selected areas of the sky. While the selection is a random one, with no preference to one area or belt of the heavens, there is always the danger that approximations and generalizations made from such selected areas will be far too general, and that localizations will be ignored in the final smoothing process. As a result, the Mount Wilson observers and students of the observations fail to agree with the Harvard experts in the matter of clustering. Mount Wilson astronomers readily recognize the obvious clusters of galaxies that are found in Virgo, Coma Berenices, Boötes, Ursa Major, Corona Borealis, and Pisces. But the Harvard galactic specialists contend that clumping and irregularities are the rule, rather than the exception, in the structure of the metagalaxy. Until these two views are reconciled, all conclusions concerning the structure of the visible universe are subject to reinterpretation. But the new work will be only quantitatively different from that which has gone before, and the major tendencies will be revealed again. Over enormously large volumes of the universe, the clumpings that are insisted upon at Harvard break down into a roughly smooth distribution such as that insisted upon by the Pacific observers.

The Lowell Observatory at Flagstaff, Arizona, in the second decade of this century, made spectrographic observations of several spiral galaxies, to determine their line-of-sight velocities by means of the Doppler-Fizeau effect—the shifts in the lines of the spectra of the galaxies, as compared with the standard or laboratory-observed positions of the lines. Almost without exception, the lines in the spectra of the galaxies were shifted toward the red, by amounts exceeding the shifts previously observed for any other type of object. This redward shift was interpreted with considerable success as a motion of recession, and the only galaxies not showing it were the larger, presumably nearer ones. The others displayed shifts that were vaguely related to their apparent brightnesses.

Today, we know that the velocities of approach for the nearer galaxies are only apparent, and are caused by the rotation of our own galaxy. We are being carried toward them by galactic rotation of the order of 150 miles per second, which cancels out their own motions. The interpretation of the apparent recession for the others—the expanding universe effect—is one of the most important problems in astronomy and physics.

The first attempt at an explanation was made by Harlow Shapley, who referred to the principle of equipartition of energy. Studies of stellar velocities had revealed that, for large numbers of stars, on the average, the more massive stars traveled more slowly. So Shapley said that the correlation between velocity and faintness for the galaxies might be in reality a correlation between velocity and mass, the fainter galaxies being probably the less massive ones. This was based on a tacit assumption that the galaxies were all at about the same distance from us, as so many students of the problem believed in those days. Shapley added, however, that the correlation might be one between velocity and distance. Today, we are converted to the latter view and believe that the galaxies are, to a broad first approximation, of the same order of mass.

To determine the apparent brightnesses and apparent or angular diameters of the galaxies constitutes a considerable problem. A galaxy is comparatively dense at its center, thinning out at the edges. Many of them are thinner at the edges than others. The lack of high-density population at the margins cuts down on the amount of light per unit area, on the face of the sky, so that the outlying portions of a galaxy do not impress themselves strongly on the photographic plate. For a near-by galaxy, this effect is not serious, because there are many stars of sufficient brightness to record themselves on the sensitive emulsion. For distant galaxies, the luminous density at the edges is so low that it cannot even overcome the threshold intensity of the sensitive emulsion, and no image can be built up. In other words, while ordinarily the prolonging of an exposure results in a stronger and stronger image on the emulsion, when the incident light is too far below the limiting intensity required to overcome the inertia of the emulsion no amount of prolongation of the exposure can result in a stronger image. The most distant galaxies photographable today reveal themselves as slightly fuzzy patches, scarcely to be distinguished from stars. Actually, these patches are images only of the nuclei, and not of the outlying spiral arms.

Even when the outer portions of a galaxy are recorded on the photograph, the human eye can distinguish them only when the darkening on the negative has reached some limiting value. There are instrumental methods for detecting degrees of darkening on the negative that would completely escape the examination by the eye. Such are the methods employed in various forms of the microphotometer. A beam of light is passed through the negative, and its intensity is recorded as received by a photoelectric cell or other impersonal device. The microphotometer can detect differences in intensity far smaller than the least the eye can see; and by means of such instruments the dimensions of all images of galaxies have been shown to exceed considerably the earlier eye estimates. It is not uncommon for the microphotometer to yield a diameter for a spiral at least five times as great as that estimated by a careful observer using only his eye, on the same photograph. The feathery edges of the images of galaxies do not completely record themselves, because of threshold considerations of the emulsions used; but only the microphotometer can begin to decide the amount that has actually been recorded.

The nearer spirals are of about the same order of size as our own, by more or less direct measures, supplementing ordinary examination with microphotometric study. Those in the near middle distance appear to be only slightly smaller, when carefully studied; from what we know of the deficiencies of the photographic process, we should agree that for the most distant galaxies we fail to record all of the total light, and we are unable to record any of the light from the outer margins.

All studies involving the brightnesses and dimensions of distant galaxies contain inherent inaccuracies of this kind, and every measure of apparent brightness or size thus far recorded is subject to revision. That a revision must be made is apparent to everyone; what the order of the revision will be is a subject for argument. One other important deficiency in our observations arises from the fact that the photographic plates used for the surveys are sensitive to limited regions of the spectrum, particularly the green, blue, and violet. This becomes important because here we are concerned with the Doppler-Fizeau shifts of the spectrum lines, or at least a redward shift that is proportional, for each line, to the wave length of the line.

When Doppler first explained the variable pitch of a moving source of sound, thus giving his name to the Doppler effect, he tried to extend the idea to phenomena in light. He suggested that red stars were those that were receding from us, while blue ones were approaching. Reasonable velocities for the stars would not permit a great amount of change, however, because a shift to the red will pull a little more invisible ultraviolet into the visible violet, while a shift to the violet will pull a little more invisible infrared into the visible red. Fizeau stated that the shifts of the spectrum lines, as referred to laboratory sources, would permit the detection and evaluation of stellar line-of-sight velocities, and they were at length detected. But the stellar velocities are too small to produce any color change.

The distribution of energy through all the wave lengths radiated by a star is by no means uniform. The peak of intensity is determined by the temperature of the star, in accordance with what is known as Wien's displacement law. Approximately, the wave length, in angstrom units, of the place of maximum intensity in the spectrum of a star is given by dividing the constant 28,800,000 by the temperature of the star in centigrade degrees counting from absolute zero. For example, a star whose effective temperature is 2880 degrees absolute will display a spectrum with maximum intensity at 10,000 angstroms, in the infrared. A star with twice the effective temperature will have its maximum intensity in the green, at 5000 angstroms. The apparent maximum, in a photograph of the spectrum, will be altered in accordance with the reflectivity of the mirrors of the telescope, or the lack of uniform transmission of the lenses, the spectral transmission of the prism of the spectrograph, and the curve of sensitivity of the photographic emulsion used. By means of certain types of standardization of the photographic plate, these effects can be largely eliminated, especially if a standard light is studied through the entire optical system, once for all.

A galaxy is an aggregation of stars. They are moving, hence their individual spectra, if separately observable, would reveal Doppler-Fizeau effects. For this reason, because of the small random motions of the many stars of a galaxy, the lines in the spectrum of a galaxy are not sharp, compounded as they are of the identical lines in the spectra of many stars, all shifted by different amounts. In general, the background intensity curve for a galaxy is compounded of the background curves for all of its stars. There are predominant types of stars, however, and galaxies almost uniformly show colors and background curves resembling those of stars of about the same type as the Sun—

a star with an effective temperature of about 6000 degrees absolute, and a maximum intensity at about 4750 angstroms.

Velocities indicated by Doppler-Fizeau shifts for the stars are of the order of only a few score miles per second, at best. For the galaxies, the maximum measured shift corresponds to a velocity of about 25,000 miles per second. The shift is revealed by the shifts of the lines in the spectrum; but the whole spectrum background is shifted, as well, and a shift of this amount will move the wave length of maximum intensity from 4750 angstroms in the blue-violet to 5400 angstroms in the green. In other words, the color of a galaxy should be seriously altered by this shift; and all measures of apparent brightness as previously made, on photographic plates which do not record light of all wave lengths, are subject to careful correction in accordance with the shifts of the spectrum lines.

Whatever the cause of the shifts of the lines, the amount of the shift can be used as an indication of the correction that is necessary. But the amount of the correction will be different, for a given shift, for a different cause of the shift. This point will prove to be of importance in our summary of the problem of the galaxies.

Deep surveys of selected regions of the sky have been made at the Lick and Mount Wilson observatories, with reflecting telescopes ranging from 36 to 100 inches in diameter, the larger ones at Mount Wilson. At the Harvard College Observatory stations at Oak Ridge, Massachusetts, Arequipa, Peru, and Bloemfontein, South Africa, surveys not quite so deep have been made of every square degree of the sky. The differences in distribution in various areas, as recorded by the Harvard observers, have yet to be given their complete interpretation, but there are obvious clusterings in various regions, some of them investigated rather thoroughly at Mount Wilson. Statistical studies of dimensions and apparent brightnesses, as related to shifts of spectrum lines, have been made, particularly by Hubble at Mount Wilson, and it is from these that most of the problems are posed. The important pioneer work of V. M. Slipher at Lowell, in measuring red-shifts, has been continued at Mount Wilson, largely through the efforts of Milton Humason.

The greater the red shift, the more distant the galaxy. For a first approximation, the red shift is proportional to distance, as derived from measure of apparent size or apparent brightness. Suppose we count galaxies down to one limiting brightness, then count them down to an apparent brightness only one-fourth as great as the previous limit. This should mean that a sphere of twice the radius has now been included, and so there should be eight times as many galaxies included in the second count as in the first count. Of course, the second count includes all the galaxies in the first count.

When such deeper and deeper counts are made, it is found that the proper ratio is not achieved. When we go to a galaxy twice as far away as another, as judged by its apparent brightness, we do not include eight times as many galaxies in the second sphere as in the first. The factor is less than eight, as though the galaxies were thinning out in all directions from us.

From earliest truly scientific days, we have learned to shun any kind of universe centered on the observer. The Mediterranean Sea is not really in the "middle of the land," nor is the Earth the center of the universe. The Sun is but one of many, many stars, and it is not at the center of the galaxy of which it is a member. Our own galaxy appears to be but one of many millions of similar stellar aggregations. We must, if we can, avoid any acceptance of an apparent universe that is centered on our neighborhood in space. To be specific, we must search thoroughly for some way to avoid accepting the counts of galactic surveys as they have come to us, when they indicate a thinning-out as we go to greater distances in all directions.

There has been some mention of the necessity for correction of observed brightnesses of the galaxies. The existence of a red shift that varies with apparent brightness demands a correction, regardless of the cause of the shift. A redward shift is a shift toward longer wave lengths, or lower frequencies. Lower frequencies mean lower energies, and so the observed energies must be corrected. If it is a simple loss of energy, from an unknown cause, one kind of correction is demanded; if it is a loss of energy by dilution of the quanta, as the galaxies move bodily away from us, the correction is of another kind.

Without going into the mathematical and physical details of the picture, it can be said here that, when the correction demanded by the red shifts as interpreted as Doppler-Fizeau effect is applied, the distant galaxies are brightened too much. The appearance is then that the galaxies become more numerous as we go to greater distances, as though we lived in the least crowded region of a universe that becomes more and more crowded as we go to greater and greater distances. Again, we arrive at a universe centered upon us, and we don't like it.

There is a way to avoid the appearance, and that lies in the acceptance of a kind of universe that transcends perception. As the surface of the Earth is two-dimensional, curved in a third dimension, so our universe might be three-dimensional, curved in a fourth dimension. The uniformity of distribution of the galaxies might be restored by a proper choice of radius for the four-dimensional universe. Without dwelling on this possibility, which will be detailed in the next essay, let it be said here that, on the basis of the observations of 100,000,000 galaxies out to distances of 500,000,000 light-years in all directions, the radius of the universe is such that the total population is only 400,000,000 galaxies, and the 200-inch telescope will reveal all of the universe. It has a grasp of eight times the volume included in the deepest surveys of the 100-inch telescope.

When the corrections to the apparent brightnesses are made solely as a means of restoring the energy loss that is revealed by the red shifts, a uniform distribution of galaxies, to the deepest surveys, is obtained. This is somehow quite satisfying, because there then is no preferred region of space, and we do not look out into a man-centered universe. It gives rise to a possible acceptance of a new principle of nature—a light-fatigue. Light loses energy, in the very act of traveling, and the loss is proportional to the distance traveled. This is, somehow, a reasonable idea, although there is nothing in the existing theory of light that permits or even suggests such a loss. Our physical theories are largely earth-bound, of course, and when we begin to reach across many millions of light-years we can expect to receive a surprise or two. In view of the anachronism introduced when we interpret the red-shifts as due to Doppler-Fizeau effect, it may well be that the simpler alternative will be to build into our theory of light a loss of energy, a light-fatigue, heretofore unsuspected.

The observational crux of this matter is likely to arrive within the next few years, when the work of the 200-inch telescope has caught up with and surpassed that of the 100-inch. When homogeneous surveys with this new instrument are at hand, a decision will be possible.

ON THE STRUCTURE OF OUR UNIVERSE

by

L. INFELD

Leopold Infeld was a lecturer at the University of Lwow, 1929–1934, a fellow of the Rockefeller Foundation at Cambridge, England, 1934–1935, and has been Professor of Applied Mathematics at the University of Toronto since 1939. He is the author of *The World in Modern Science* (1934), *The Evolution of Physics* (with Albert Einstein, 1938), *Quest: The Evolution of a Scientist* (1941—awarded Anisfield-Wolf Award), *Whom the Gods Love: The Story of Evariste Galois* (1948), and has published some fifty papers on theoretical physics, some in collaboration with Born and Einstein.

THE science of our universe is new. We can tell the year in which it was born: 1917, when Einstein's paper on "Cosmological Considerations in General Relativity Theory" appeared.

In different religions, in poetry, art, and philosophy, we find beliefs, pictures, and speculations about the universe in which men live. All such attempts to penetrate into the unknown by faith or imagination are as old as the history of our civilization. But only some thirty years ago did this old problem shift into the field of science. There it will remain for a long time to come.

Summarizing the result of three decades of experimental and theoretical investigations, let us say: *Our universe is a universe of islands.* It consists of islands of matter (or nebulae) on the sea of emptiness.

Imagine that we travel through space with the greatest *known*, and the greatest *possible* speed, that is, with the speed of light. In a matter of minutes we leave the Sun behind us. In a matter of hours we leave our entire solar system; in a matter of years we reach the nearest stars. Thus we judge distances now by light-years; the years that it would take us to traverse these distances while journeying with the speed of light.

Our solar system and all the stars that we see on a bright night form *our* nearest neighborhood; they are a part of *our* galaxy, of *our* nebula; they are a part of the island on which we live. But this galaxy (of which the Sun, the planets, the stars visible with the naked eyes, are members) is only one of the very many islands, one of the very many *nebulae* of our universe. The nebulae—the great conglomerations of stars—are islands of matter in a sea of empty space. Our galaxy is only one of them. After thousands of years of traveling with the speed of light, we should find ourselves outside our galaxy; then to reach the nearest neighboring island, the nearest conglomeration of stars, we should have to travel almost a million light-years more! There is nothing fantastic about this; and there is no reason to become emotional about the extent of emptiness and the rarity of matter in our universe. There is even less reason to become upset about this than about the rarity of gas stations on a desert road, because we shall never travel along these highways of the universe. The light rays that reach our eyes from the distant nebulae are the only messengers that do travel; and they don't mind the emptiness. On the contrary, they could not reach our earth if they met too much absorbing matter on their long voyage.

Let us examine the evidence brought to us by these light messengers and caught by our most powerful reflectors. Hundreds of thousands of these nebulae-islands have been photographed. The farthest from us which are visible, though very faint, are about half a billion light-years away from us. This is as far as we can penetrate today. By building better reflectors (like the 200-inch reflector which has recently been completed) we shall be able to penetrate still deeper into space.

The average nebula is about 20,000 light-years in diameter, and the average distance between the nebulae is about two million light-years. I repeat: islands on the sea of emptiness.

The astronomer Edwin Hubble gives the following picturesque comparison: Imagine tennis balls fifty feet apart scattered through a sphere five miles in diameter. Each tennis ball stands for a nebula consisting of many millions of stars. Five miles represents the distance to which we can penetrate today. The fifty feet between the tennis balls represents the rarity of matter and the commonness of empty space in our universe.

Such is the structure of or universe as revealed through observation and through simple theoretical interpretation of the observational results.

We are interested in the structure of our universe *as a whole*—that is, in its broad characteristics, in averages, ignoring small irregularities and cosmologically unimportant deviations. Similarly, when planning an airplane journey around our earth, we are interested in the distribution of landing fields and very little in the villages between them. For such a purpose we consider the earth as a sphere with points representing landing fields. But at other times, while attending to the business of our daily lives, we must care, and we do care, about our neighbors and the happenings in our back yards.

While viewing the universe as a whole we are little interested in the small irregularities, in the fact that each island—nebula—has its own peculiar shape, size, age, history. We consider the islands as all alike and disregard the differences in their sizes and in their distances from one another. Our picture of *equidistant* nebulae of *equal sizes* is a highly idealized one. Here as always in science, we simplify and idealize; then we complicate our original simple picture under the impact of new observations. After some time the increasing complications make the entire picture so ugly in its complexity that it has to be rejected and a new, simpler picture sought. But in the still young science of cosmology we have not progressed far beyond the first few steps. Our picture is still very simple; perhaps too simple!

Now we come to the most characteristic and puzzling feature of our island universe. It, too, has been revealed to us by observation. I shall state the result first in technical language: *The spectra of the nebulae show a red-shift.* Or, in less scientific language: *The nebulae seem to run away from us.*

An explanation of the two equivalent statements can be given only in terms of Physics. The pitch of a whistle on an engine seems to an observer at a railway station to be higher as the engine approaches than when it stands still. Again, the pitch seems lower when the engine travels away from the station. This fact, well known in acoustics, is called the Doppler effect.

We find a somewhat similar phenomenon in ordinary life. Imagine a party traveling by car and sending to you messages every hour by motorcycle. The messengers will arrive every hour while the party is just resting at a tourist home. But if the car continues to travel away from you, you will receive the messengers at longer intervals than an hour; if the car travels toward you, you will receive them at intervals shorter than an hour. As a matter of fact, from the frequency with which the messengers arrive you could deduce the speed at which the car moves toward you or away from you, knowing the speed of the motorcycles and the frequency with which the messages are sent to you. The same is true in the case of the engine whistle. The pitch measures the frequency with which the voice-messengers arrive; it is higher (that is, the frequency is higher) if the engine moves toward the station, and lower when it moves away.

A very similar effect, also well known to the physicist, is the Doppler effect in the field of optics.

A spectroscope is an apparatus that analyzes light. For example, if the source of light is a gas through which passes an electric current (as, say, in the case of the neon tube), then what we see, looking at the source through a spectroscope, are thin bright stripes on a dark background. The vapors of different elements give different systems of lines. There are no two elements with identical systems of lines, just as there are no two men with identical fingerprints. Thus, the system of lines uniquely characterizes the element to which it belongs, and every element is characterized by its system of lines.

By analyzing the light from stars or nebulae we can detect the presence of elements that we know and have analyzed on our earth. The lines of hydrogen or helium have the same structure whether they come from our earth, from the sun, from the stars of our galaxy, or from the nebulae.

Yet, if we compare the spectrum of an element on our earth with the spectrum of the same element in a nebula we not only see the same structure (otherwise we couldn't say that it is the same element) but also recognize some differences. The whole spectrum—that is, *all* the lines that characterize the element—is slightly shifted. This again, as we know both from theory and from experiment, should happen and does happen if the source of light (neon tube, star, nebula) moves away from us or toward us. It is the same effect, the Doppler effect, that we have recognized in the example of the messengers or the engine whistle: the system of lines is shifted toward the red end of the spectrum if the source of light moves away from the observer, and toward the violet end of the spectrum if the source of light moves toward the observer. The shift toward the red end indicates a diminished frequency of the light messengers, and the shift toward the violet end indicates an increased frequency of the light messengers. As in the case of the whistle and the messengers we could calculate from such a red or violet shift the speed with which the source of light moves away from us or toward us.

The question arises: Why do the nebulae behave as though they were running away from our galaxy? The simplest answer would be that the nebulae behave as though they were running away from us because they do run away from our galaxy. But then the question is: Why do they run?

If the red shift and the running away of nebulae had been discovered in biblical times we might by now have had some explanation that would appear satisfactory. (The nonsensical character of this statement does not escape me!) We could have assumed that in each galaxy there are planetary systems, and that our earth is not the only one populated by "intelligent" beings. Yet our planet is the one on which Adam sinned and the only one on which men kill men. Therefore, all the other nebulae have a deeply rooted antipathy to our galaxy and try to get as far from us as possible.

Yet we can hardly be satisfied with such an explanation. Even if the inhabitants of other nebulae could see what is happening here, they would see *now* what was happening millions of years ago, because light from our earth takes millions of years to reach them. Secondly, there is another curious, indeed very curious, point. The red shift *increases* with the distance. That means, the greater the distance from our galaxy, the greater seems the speed of the running nebulae. This is baffling! Why should the aversion increase with the distance? The law of this increase in red shift is, in itself, extremely simple: the greater the distance, the greater—proportionately—the red shift. A nebula a hundred million light-years distant seems to run away from us ten times as swiftly as a nebula ten million light-years distant. This law connecting the red shift with the distance seems to be fairly accurate, with some small systematic deviations; in spite of them it is good enough even to allow us to determine the distances of the far removed nebulae.

We return to our question. What is the reason for the law of the red shift?

In search of an answer, we leave the region of observation and enter the region of speculation: that of General Relativity Theory. There is a bridge leading to this region—an important principle belonging partly to the field of observation and partly to the field of speculation.

If we turn our reflector telescopes in different directions we see that—statistically—no one direction stands out sharply from the others. We find, generally, as many nebulae in one direction as in any other. Neither do we see that the number of nebulae per unit volume changes with the depth to which our reflectors penetrate. The universe seems to be fairly uniformly filled with matter. Of course, there are some irregularities—but small enough for us to assume, with good approximation, that there is no great difference between directions or points in space.

Thus we conclude that the universe is *uniform*. We may have rushed too quickly to that conclusion. We know only a fragment of the universe, and the new, larger reflector may reveal further irregularities and some systematic deviations from uniformity. Yet if the universe is not uniform we shall have to know how it changes in direction and in depth. Obviously, to say that the universe is uniform is to make the simplest possible assumption; and in making that fundamental hypothesis we do not contradict experience.

The assumption, based essentially on observation, has been taken over and much sharpened by theory. It has become, so to speak, a moral commandment for our universe. We claim: the story of the universe—taken as a whole—must be the same, whether written from our galaxy or from any other nebula. Let us imagine, since no limits have been set to our imagination, that we send to each nebula an observer properly equipped with brains and instruments. The history of the universe will be the same for each of these observers. This is what we mean by the principle of uniformity. There will be small irregularities, of course, but a smoothed-out and idealized universe will be reflected in the same way in the scientific descriptions of all these scientists on different globes in different nebulae.

Now we have a powerful principle restricting the possibilities in the structure of the universe. The model of the universe must agree with the principle of uniformity!

We return to the previous question: How do we explain the red shift? Now the question becomes more general and more difficult. Under the principle of uniformity the observer on a nebula outside our galaxy notices the red shift: the nebulae seem to run away from him too! Thus they do not run away from our galaxy alone but run away from one another—unsociable creatures, full of mutual aversion.

But even this conclusion is slightly premature. Perhaps assuming that the nebulae run away from one another is not the only way to explain the red shift. All that we do assume at this moment is that the observer in each of these nebulae would confirm the existence of the red shift, and that he would find that that red shift is proportional to the distance.

Thus we are led to another question: What possible structures of our universe are consistent with the principle of uniformity? Here the story of the structure of our universe becomes intermingled with the story of Relativity theory, more specifically with that of General Relativity theory.

Thus we must interrupt the tale of our universe and say a few words about geometry and its connection with physics. In doing so we shall have to consider a three-dimensional curved space. This is a difficult concept, but we can simplify it by talking only about two-dimensional curved surfaces and explaining with their help, at least some of the essential ideas of modern cosmology.

We imagine thinking creatures living on a two-dimensional plane. We can watch and even be moved by their actions as anyone knows who has shed tears in a movie. But we must not take the movie comparison too seriously. We imagine the screen infinitely great, forget the perspective and visualize flat creatures with only one profile like those on an Egyptian painting. We assume too that these creatures have brains and act of their own accord. For them the two-dimensional plane is what three-dimensional space is for us. If they are intelligent they may, in time, develop the knowledge of plane Euclidean geometry—the geometry that we learned in high school. Once they start a journey along a straight line they will never return to their point of departure; two parallel lines will never meet, and the circumference of a circle will be 2π times its radius. These creatures—we may imagine—even have a primitive kind of physics. They may have experimented with light rays, they may have developed the concept of time and velocity; they may have found that the velocity of light—as in our three-dimensional space—is 186,000 miles per second.

Now let us proceed to the second chapter in our story of the two-dimensional creatures. At some moment when all these creatures were asleep, someone has transplanted them to the surface of a sphere—one so big that, in the beginning at least, they do not detect any change. Their communications are not sufficiently developed to discover that a journey begun "straight ahead" will ultimately end at the point of their departure. In drawing a small circle, they will not find that its circumference is slightly smaller than 2π times its radius. But as generations of two-dimensional creatures die and are born, as their science and technique becomes more and more perfected, they will find out that something is wrong with their heritage of Euclidean geometry. They will conclude that it is more convenient and more consistent with their observations to use the non-Euclidean geometry of a sphere! For some time the conservative elements of the community will resist such an innovation and perhaps burn in a two-dimensional fire, creatures preaching non-Euclidean geometry. The conservatives may say that the rods used were not perfectly rigid, that some differences in temperature accounted for the apparent breakdown of the Euclidean geometry. But finally science will win in such a struggle, as it always does. Slowly the two-dimensional inhabitants of the sphere will recognize that it is much more convenient to assume that their geometry is that of a sphere. Thus, they will learn that a "straight line" (great circle to you) is always closed; that a light ray sent from any point P returns to the point of departure. They will pronounce this true even if they cannot travel all around the sphere, even if a hundred generations must be born and die before an actual experiment demonstrates that a light ray does return to its point of departure. They will deduce these results from the fact that in their neighborhood the geometry of a non-Euclidean character describes their phenomena better, more economically, than the old Euclidean geometry. A scientific revolution will have taken place among these two-dimensional creatures!

The story is not so fantastic as it sounds. Indeed, in some features it reminds us of our earth and the way in which its spherical shape came to be recognized.

We return to the third and last chapter of our tale of the two-dimensional creatures. A new change has taken place. Again something has happened suddenly to them while they were asleep; but this event has been in the field of physics instead of geometry (if there can be said to be a clear-cut distinction between geometry and physics). Picture these creatures living on the sphere, and single out two opposite points on this sphere called the North and South pole. The temperature of the sphere, which has been uniform, undergoes a sudden change. It is cold at the poles, warmer away from them, and hottest at the equator. At the poles the temperature is absolute zero. This means, so we assume, that the dimensions of all the living creatures, of all the rigid rods, shrink to nothing as they approach the poles. Thus the creatures traveling toward the poles become smaller and smaller, their dimensions, their steps, smaller and smaller; and although they may travel along the equator or another circle of latitude, they will never reach the poles. Traveling along the circles of latitude, they may find, if the temperatures are adjusted properly, that every such circle is just as long as the equator; because their rods and their own dimensions have shrunk so as to account exactly for this very fact; the circles become smaller, but so do their measuring rods.

Thus, our intelligent two-dimensional creatures are faced with an entirely new situation; and they have two ways of adjusting their science to their changed world. If their two-dimensional bodies are not sensitive to the change of temperature, then they may assume that they live now, not on a plane, not a sphere, but on an infinite cylinder. It will be infinite for them because they can never reach the end while going north or south. But it will be finite if they travel along parallel circles and all the circles have for them the same radii because they know nothing of the change of scale that we noticed looking at their sphere with the advantages of three-dimensional human beings.

On the other hand, if they are susceptible to cold and heat they may prefer to assume that they still live on a sphere, and that on the sphere there are now two very singular points which they will never reach because the temperature there is absolute zero.

No one knows what will be the choice of these creatures. It depends on many circumstances which we do not wish to analyze. They may even have two rival theories. They may start a two-dimensional atomic war between these two world philosophies.

Our story has a deep moral. It shows how intimately physics is connected with geometry. Remember that the two-dimensional creatures have a choice between assuming differences in temperature and spherical geometry on the one hand, or, on the other hand, no differences in temperature and the geometry of a cylinder (which is essentially a Euclidean geometry).

We, three-dimensional creatures, are in a similar situation. This is what the General Relativity theory has taught us. We must treat geometry and physics as *one* system. Our scientific task is to formulate such a single system, most consistent and convenient for the description of the phenomena of nature. The system is good if it works.

After this digression into the field of geometry, we return to cosmology. We are looking for a model of the universe consistent with the principle of uniformity—a model that will explain the red shift observed from all the nebulae. Here mathematical analysis takes over, and all that we shall do is to quote and explain some of the results.

True enough, the principle of uniformity and the law of the red shift restricts possible models of the universe. Yet, many models are possible, and the evidence of observation is not sufficiently conclusive to allow choice of a single one. Whatever the character of the universe we live in, we know at least that it is either *open* or *closed*. This important statement does not sound too impressive. It may remind you of the trivial fact that a door can be either open or closed. Yet the recognition of two such possibilities is a great discovery. Before the General Relativity theory the statement that the universe is closed would have been meaningless. What are the characteristic features of an open, and of a closed, universe?

Let us start with a closed universe. The universe of the two-dimensional creatures living on a sphere would be a closed one. For them, we remember, a light ray sent out returns ultimately to the point of its departure.

Similarly our universe is possibly a closed universe although it is more difficult to picture than to describe mathematically a three-dimensional spherical space. Yet we can at least imagine in principle a crucial experiment telling us whether our universe is closed or not. Send a light ray into open space. If, after some time, the light ray comes back, then the universe is closed. If it never comes back, then the universe is open. Of course such an experiment has some technical difficulties; but we may ignore them. The biggest difficulty is that we have too little time; according to our present knowledge it would take light billions of years to navigate our world and come back to us. Yet there is a chance that with the new 200-inch reflector we shall be able to find out, in a roundabout way, whether our universe is open or closed.

We can picture our universe as closed by suppressing one dimension and comparing it to the universe of the two-dimensional creatures living on a sphere. Pursuing this comparison, let us imagine golden points rarely, but uniformly, distributed through such a sphere; they represent to us the nebulae of our world. What about the red shift? In answering this question we must slightly complicate our two-dimensional picture. Imagine that a sphere expands like a balloon under increased air pressure. This expanding sphere, rather than a sphere with an unchanged radius, is the two-dimensional model of our universe! We see that such a model satisfies both the principle of uniformity and the law of the red shift. Indeed! Our nebulae—the golden points on the expanding balloon—will remain uniform because they were dotted uniformly and because the expansion preserves the shape of the sphere and changes only its radius. The distances between the nebulae measured on the balloon will increase. An observer on any of these nebulae will see that others recede from him. It is also clear that very near to any chosen nebula the speed of the expansion will appear to the observer proportional to the distance.

We shall examine now the other possibility—that of an open universe. Here it is unnecessary to suppress one dimension, and we may return to the three-dimensional picture of our space. It is best to understand this open-type universe from a historical perspective.

Once upon a time all the matter of our universe was concentrated in a very small volume. In our idealized mathematical model we may say that it was concentrated in a point. Thus all the nebulae were squeezed tightly together; then something happened, and the whole world of matter exploded like shrapnel. The nebulae began to run away from one another with constant speed. Thus, as seen from our galaxy, those nebulae which had a greater speed than others moved away farther than others. Today they still move uniformly. We see why such a history of our universe gives us the law of the red shift (proportional to the distance) and also satisfies the uniformity principle. The farther away the nebulae are, the greater their speed, because they had this greater speed when the universe was created and they retain it because they move uniformly. The nebulae nearer to us have lesser speeds because they had lesser speeds at the moment of creation and they retained them. We also see, although this is slightly more difficult, that the principle of uniformity is not violated. Indeed all the nebulae were once together, and although we can say that they began to run away from our galaxy the same can be said by the inhabitants of any of the nebulae. The speediest of them would have a speed approaching that of light, and the entire matter of the universe is concentrated inside a sphere with a radius equal to the velocity of light c times the epoch t_0 that has passed from the moment of creation. Each observer can draw such a sphere for himself, and such a statement will be true for any observer. The transition from one system (that is, from one nebula) to another is governed by the transformation formulated by the Special Theory of Relativity. The so-called Lorentz transformation tells us how to describe phenomena in one system if we know the description in another system. Take, for example, our galaxy as a point O and a very far-removed nebula as a point P. Then P will be near the edge S of the sphere with the radius ct_0 drawn around O. But the observer at P will imagine himself in the center of such a sphere too. All the nebulae between P and S will seem to lie on a contracted shell for the O observer compared with the P observer. This is because they move quickly. It is the result of the famous Lorentz contraction known to everyone who has studied the Special Relativity theory. For the same reason all the nebulae farther than O will appear to lie on a contracted shell for the observer on the nebula P. The history of such an open universe would be the same for any observer on any nebula!

It is only by a detailed calculation that we can show more explicitly how both the law of red shift and the uniformity principle follow from such a picture.

When was our universe created? From the observation of the present red shift we can deduce that the expansion started some billions of years ago.

Now, since we know at least in outline the two possible characters of our universe we may ask: Is our universe open, or closed? As I said before, there is not enough evidence to answer the question. We may ask a more modest one: Do we prefer an open or closed universe? This is, of course, a subjective question, and different scientists may provide different answers. Yet, I believe that a great majority of those who work on cosmological problems would prefer our universe to be a closed one. There is more mathematical beauty in a closed universe; such a universe is finite although it has no boundary. (The question what is beyond a three-dimensional sphere is meaningless; there is no beyond, just as there is no beyond for the two-dimensional creatures living on a sphere.) The mathematical superiority of the closed universe is apparent if we consider any physical problem on such a cosmological background. In the open universe we have to worry about happenings at infinities because we have infinities of time and space in such a universe. We do not have them in a closed universe; and, to be technical for a moment, the problem of an electromagnetic field, for example, becomes an attractive boundary value problem, fitting much better into the general scheme of modern physical theories than when treated on the background of an open universe.

This century has changed the picture of our world. From atoms to the structure of our universe we see revolutionary changes, a rapid development which can hardly be compared with any other in the short history of mankind. This development has sprung partially from needs, and if we look back it seems essentially determined by the previous state of science. But it would be wrong to assume that the entire development of science is utilitarian. It is not. Many of our speculations about atoms and about our universe were created because of man's curiosity, because of his desire to penetrate deeper and deeper into the unknown. The utilitarian value of many of our theories may be nil; but they help us to comprehend the world we live in.

One such highly speculative question is: Is there any connection between laws governing the atom and those governing our universe? Some scientists believe there is one, and Sir Arthur Eddington devoted many years of his life to speculations on this very problem. His views are shared, at least partly, by Schrödinger and Dirac, both leaders in the field of modern physics. On the other hand, to many physicists such an idea seems repulsive and almost ridiculous. They do not believe that the microphysical world of atoms reflects in any way the macrocosmos of our universe. Even in science there are subjective views and tastes. My own view is that there is no possible connection between the microcosmos and macrocosmos if our universe is open, but there might be a connection if our universe is closed. Substantiation of my belief would have to be too technical for this place. But even if it could be included here the arguments would of necessity be too vague to be convincing for holders of different views. On the frontier of science, in which men are at work, in which only scaffolds can be seen and the architecture of the future building predicted with great uncertainty, scientists are divided in their views. Their divergent views may reflect different scientific environments and even different social attitudes.

It is a temptation, in talking about our universe, and the distances between nebulae (remember? two million light-years), to frighten the receiver of such information with the loneliness of matter in vast space, with the mysteries of the universe, with the audacity of the high priests of learning who have glanced into it, with the mathematical genius of its Creator, with the insignificance of our lives and human affairs compared with the harmony and beauty of nature. All this is, of course, utter nonsense, although books written in this vein usually sell well as long as people value muddled emotional thinking more than the rational approach, and as long as they regard understanding as a poor substitute for metaphysical thrills.

We are living on our earth, and nothing is as important for us as the social, ethical, economical climate we live in. Here on our earth were our cradles, and here will be our graves. Here we must live with our fellow men, and here we must do our best to bring about a better world. Yet it is a pleasant escape to reach above and beyond our earth, to contemplate problems that have little to do with our daily lives. But it seems silly to bring back from such a journey into space and time contempt for our surroundings because our earth is small and because the nebulae are far away. The moral of such a journey, as of any journey into the field of science, seems to me obvious. Scientific method combines observation and speculation. It acts dispassionately, rejecting theories that do not work, accepting and pursuing those that do. This is the lesson that we could learn from science and apply to our social affairs. It may take some time. Let us not be too pessimistic. Our world is still young, and in it science is only three hundred years old.

The modern picture of our universe, like all scientific creations, is the result of the work of many men. Some of them have been mentioned in our story. Let us quote a few of the very important names omitted: the Dutch astronomer, de Sitter; the Russian, Friedmann; the Belgian, Lemaître; the American, Robertson. But there are also many others. Science is a cooperative venture which does not know racial or national boundaries, and in which scientists of the civilized world collaborate successfully, if allowed to do so.

QUANTUM MECHANICS

by

MELBA

PHILLIPS

Melba Phillips is assistant professor of physics at Brooklyn College. Since completing her graduate work at the University of California she has continued research and taught at various institutions, including Bryn Mawr College, the Institute for Advanced Study, and the University of Minnesota. She is the author of numerous technical papers, mainly on the theory of atomic spectra and the theory of light nuclei.

THE universe contains energy in one or the other of two forms, commonly called matter and radiation. Both are atomistic, or "quantized," not continuous. Quantum mechanics is a description of this fact, a method of taking account of the atomicity or discreteness of nature. Pre-quantum, or classical, physics suffices whenever the assumption that matter is continuous is justified, that is, when the atomicity does not make any difference because many, many atoms and/or quanta are involved. For atoms, molecules, crystals, free electrons, and radiation, quantum mechanics gives a complete and adequate description—within limits which we shall have to examine at the end of our discussion. Within this same realm, on the other hand, classical physics often gives quite wrong and misleading answers—answers which do not correspond with experimental results. Which is just another way of saying that it fails to account for the atomicity which exists in the world.

There has been much confusion and misunderstanding in the interpretation of the principles and concepts of quantum mechanics. I shall not soon forget the remark of a colleague from an unnamed department in an unnamed university: "I'm happy about modern physics. At last the physicists admit that they don't know anything for sure, either." This is an extreme case of misinterpretation of a technical word, "uncertainty," but it is by no means isolated. Even within the field of physics there was for a long time difficulty in comprehending and accepting fully the radically new ideas of the quantum mechanics.

New ideas are always difficult to accept. But the principles and conclusions which become a part of the body of any science are the inescapable consequences of experimental research. This has been so with the principles of quantum mechanics. Physicists hope to improve their ideas tomorrow, as new facts are discovered; but, as far as it goes, today's physics is right. It has been substantiated by all the tests that could be devised, and has given rise to almost countless applications. For the future, there is, in the words of Franklin D. Roosevelt, "science, the endless frontier." The multitude of unsolved problems will surely, sooner or later, lead to ideas as radically new as was the quantum hypothesis, but science will lose nothing but ignorance.

Of course scientists do make mistakes. But mistakes do not stand the test of time and the repetition (with variations) of experimental procedures. Scientists even, like other people, learn from mistakes. Classical physics, however, was and is no mistake, but a success, a triumph. In a sense one of its triumphs is that it gave birth to quantum mechanics.

The roots of quantum mechanics are deep in the history of physics, particularly that portion which deals with light. It was in the field of light, which had come to be coincident with that of electromagnetic radiation, that it was necessary to introduce the quantum hypothesis in 1900. This was twenty-five years before the mathematical theory was developed, twenty-five years in which the evidence was accumulating to make the famous and rather unfortunately named "uncertainty principle" inescapable.

In the second half of the seventeenth century there was a controversy over the nature of light. It had become evident, from the astronomical observations of Roemer and others, that light travels at a finite speed. But what is it that travels? Mechanics suggested two alternative possibilities, particles and waves, the behavior of both being well understood. A particle is like a billiard ball, only smaller; and everybody has seen waves on the surface of a liquid. In spite of the success Huygens achieved in explaining the observed optical phenomena in terms of a wave postulate, the contemporaneously more acceptable idea was that light consisted of minute particles, whose degree of fineness determined the color of the light. All Newton's great discoveries in the field were explained by him on this basis, and his vast prestige sufficed to discourage any serious questioning of the hypothesis for more than a century. It must be admitted that the evidence at hand could be equally well described one way or the other.

But progress in science is relentless, if uneven in rate. By the early nineteenth century, crucial experiments were designed to answer the question, "Particle or wave?" The experiments of Young and Fresnel proved, once and for all, that light is wavelike. The exhibition of interference effects, such as are shown by two waves on a pond, may almost be taken as the definition of a wave. Interference experiments are repeated in every elementary physics laboratory and in a host of applications today. But the question which Young and Fresnel correctly asked, and to which they found the correct answer, proved, nearly a century later, not to be the right question at all. This of course they could not possibly know.

The nineteenth century was a highly fruitful one for physics. Newtonian mechanics had been made at once more elegant and more powerful by the mathematical techniques of Lagrange, Hamilton, and others. Brilliant discoveries in the field of electricity and magnetism flowered into the electrodynamics of Faraday and Maxwell, with the prediction that light itself consisted of electromagnetic waves. The confirmation of this prediction constitutes one of the most beautiful examples of the interlocking roles of scientific theory and experiment. In heat the development of thermodynamics and the statistical mechanics of Gibbs and Boltzmann not only became well substantiated, but served as the basis for the gigantic chemical industry.

Except for a few unsolved problems physics seemed to be sitting on top of the world. Nearly everything was explained, the end of the road was in sight, the riddles of the universe—of physics, at least—were almost completely answered. Not everybody thought so, of course, but such an attitude was almost inevitable for Lord Rayleigh, of whom it has been said that he solved all the problems of theoretical physics which he could have known about. Even Michelson thought it unlikely that there would be more great discoveries, and in his view physics was doomed henceforth to investigate the fifth and sixth decimal places. In this beautifully clear sky—ceiling unlimited—Kelvin perceived two clouds. One of them, the Michelson-Morley experiment, led directly to the theory of special relativity. The other was the distribution of energy in electromagnetic radiation at equilibrium in a cavity, the famous "black body" problem.

The answer given by electromagnetic theory and statistical mechanics to the question of how energy is distributed according to frequency (at a given temperature) was straightforward and unambiguous. It was also quite wrong—i.e., it was in complete disagreement with the result of experimental measurement.

This paradox was resolved by Planck in a manner which could be described as main strength and awkwardness, except that the answer was rather elegant. The problem he set for himself was not "How can this be understood in terms of the properties of matter and radiation?" but "What assumption is necessary to produce a formula which can be made to agree with experiment?" To answer this question he had to postulate the quantum; that is to say, he had to disregard some of the axioms of physics and conclude that the energy of an electromagnetic wave of frequency ν cannot be assigned arbitrarily, but has only the discrete values $E=nh\nu$. Here n is an integer, and the size of the constant h is determined to make the formula fit the experimental distribution curve quantitatively. It follows that the mechanical oscillators, which absorb and emit the radiation, have corresponding discrete energy levels.

The value of Planck's contribution is not lessened by its initial arbitrariness. In the first place the condition for validity of any hypothesis is that it be compatible with experiment. In the second place he broke the ice, however timidly, into a whole new world beyond the scope of nineteenth century physics. Historically it does not matter much that Planck himself failed to follow through, and spent much time and effort trying to find a less radical solution. Other people, notably Einstein, grasped the significance of this revolutionary idea. There began the building of a theory, the fundamental cornerstone of which was Planck's hypothesis.

It was Einstein who postulated the existence of particles of light, called "quanta" or "photons," each with energy equal to $h\nu$. In terms of the quantum he explained the puzzling variation of the specific heats of solids with temperature, and the photoelectric effect. All this did not by any stretch of the imagination mean a return to the corpuscular theory of Newton's time. No single bit of evidence for the wave nature of light had been disproved: interference and diffraction effects, as well as increasingly many other experiments on radiation, still stood to show that light consisted of electromagnetic waves. It was only that light *also* behaved like particles.

What this means is that for a given frequency ν, no smaller amount of energy is emitted or absorbed, or can be detected in any way, than $h\nu$. The only way we can have smaller amounts of radiant energy is to have lower frequencies, for which the quantum is smaller (not in size, but in energy). The reason quanta remained undetected for so long is clear from a consideration of the size of h — 6.61×10^{-27} erg seconds. A quantum of green light, say, has an energy of about 3×10^{-12} ergs, or 3×10^{-19} watt seconds, and a quantum of radiation from a typical radio broadcasting antenna has roughly a billionth as much. The senses cannot distinguish such small amounts of energy, and experiments have to be carefully devised to record them.

The evidence for light quanta became quite irrefutable. The hypothesis not only received the somewhat indirect confirmation of Einstein's work mentioned above: experiments by Compton and Simon indicated that light travels as corpuscles, i.e., that quanta are sufficiently well localized in space to act like particles in collisions with electrons. To describe such a collision one must define what one means by the momentum of a photon; but the theory of relativity had provided a guide for this—if the energy equals $h\nu$, then the momentum p is given by $p = h\nu \div c$, where c is the velocity of light.

By this time it must be clear that the answer to the question "Is light wavelike or corpuscular?" is "Both!" In terms of our nineteenth century mechanics concepts light is dualistic in character. It is possible not only to define the wave length, frequency, and velocity of light, all of which characterize a wave, but also the energy, momentum, even position, of a photon. There are limits on the definiteness with which we can ascribe to light these attributes of a particle, limits readily acceptable because they are obvious in terms of the wave picture. For example, no one would ever say, "The wave is localized at this geometrical point," and every student of physics knows that a perfectly monochromatic wave is infinite in extent.

The apparent contradiction lies in our concepts "wave" and "particle," modeled after macroscopic mechanical phenomena which can be experienced directly by our senses. If consideration of the corpuscular nature of light, in addition to its wave aspects, is necessary for the understanding of a given experiment, we are in the realm of what we call quantum phenomena, for which there *is* no classical analogue. There is thus no visual model, and we have to use two apparently contradictory models simultaneously.

Meanwhile light could not be, and was not, considered apart from its interaction with matter. The quantum mechanical description of matter grew out of the context we have been describing, with its own but much the same kind of conceptual difficulties. There were amends: the complete theory achieved a unified description of matter and radiation which is one of the most brilliant successes of science to date.

The first direct application of the quantum idea to matter was made by Bohr in 1913, when he applied the energy levels of Planck's oscillators to Rutherford's model of the atom. Its success in accounting for the empirical Ritz combination principle and other features of atomic spectra was most gratifying. Today the original Bohr theory looks crude and unsatisfactory. It was based on a number of *ad hoc* hypotheses which were in direct contradiction with what could be expected on the basis of classical physics, but it involved no change in the ideas of the particles composing the atom. Bohr's electrons and nuclei were particles after the billiard-ball model, except that they behaved in a peculiar way as regards possible energy states, etc. But in this connection Bohr introduced a most important and fundamental principle, called the "correspondence principle." It states that in the limit of large quantum numbers, or actions large in comparison with *h*, Planck's quantum of action, the laws of quantum mechanics are the same as those of classical physics. That is to say, if you apply quantum mechanics to problems where the atomicity or quantum nature of matter and radiation makes little difference, you get the classical results. Newtonian mechanics and classical electrodynamics appear as a special case, so to speak. Which, in view of the vast amount of substantiating evidence for the classical results, constitutes an argument for the correctness of the quantum theory. A necessary, although not the sufficient, condition for the validity of any new theory is that it not be in contradiction with older and well established results.

Put forward about ten years later than Bohr's atom, De Broglie's hypothesis was the complement of Planck's. It stated that matter itself is wavelike. Analogous to the definition of the momentum of a photon as $p = h\nu \div c$, or $p = h \div \lambda$, define, for particles, a wave length $\lambda = h \div p$, or $\lambda = h \div mv$. This hypothesis in itself added nothing to the theory of the atom. Its only virtue was the supreme one of experimental verification. When the test of a wave was applied to electrons, i.e., "Do they exhibit interference?" the answer given by experiment was "Yes."

What was now necessary was a mathematical mode of describing atoms and atomic phenomena consistent with Bohr's energy levels, De Broglie's hypothesis, and the many experimental results which had been or could be obtained in this field. Actually two such schemes were developed: Schrödinger's formulation, called "wave mechanics," made direct use of De Broglie's hypothesis. A different, but entirely equivalent approach, due to Heisenberg and others, started from Bohr's correspondence principle plus the principle of quantization. Heisenberg's "matrix mechanics" is more formal, depends less on any visualization, but is like the wave mechanics in that it demands correlation with experiment only in the results, not the intermediate steps, of any physical process. Both make use of classical mechanics, and, as we noted, both methods amount to the same thing. Together they constitute what is today called quantum mechanics.

The details of these theories do not here concern us, but their basis does, together with its implications. We must note that the conservation laws of energy and momentum are still valid, and that the sense of the correspondence principle is maintained. The new axioms express the limitations of nineteenth century mechanics and electrodynamics: they constitute not so much a renunciation of the old axioms as a statement of how far the old axioms can be pressed. They also indicate the path to be followed outside the limitations of classical physics.

The fundamental axiom of quantum mechanics is the uncertainty principle. It is expressed in terms of the concepts of the particle picture, and specifies the limits within which that picture can be applied. If x is a space coordinate, describing position, there is an uncertainty in the specification of x which is called Δx. Similarly the momentum p, which is the mass times the velocity in the x direction, is indeterminate by an amount Δp. The principle makes no statement about each of these uncertainties separately, but it does say that their product is not less than h, Planck's constant, divided by the numerical factor 4π. Mathematically it is often stated $\Delta p \Delta x \sim h$, where $\sim$ means "is of the order of magnitude." The same statement is true of uncertainties along the other two space coordinates and their corresponding momenta. It is also true of energy and time: $\Delta E \Delta t \sim h$.

The uncertainty principle applies to both light quanta and to material particles. If valid for one it must be valid for the other, for conservation of energy and momentum. This principle is the key to the whole of quantum mechanics, if properly understood. To its understanding Niels Bohr has undoubtedly contributed more clarity than any other single individual, and much of what we shall say here is due to him.

The basic idea, in terms of the concepts "wave" and "particle," is the duality of both matter and radiation. Both behave sometimes or partly as waves and sometimes or partly as particles. These two forms of energy are of course not identical: although the wave concept is useful in describing matter, indeed necessary, the waves are of quite another kind from light waves. Matter waves are complex, in the mathematical sense. An analogy may be helpful. Minkowski and Einstein found it convenient and enlightening to treat time as a fourth dimension in complex space-time; but that does not mean that anyone would confuse a clock with a meter stick, or that because we represent time geometrically along the imaginary axis it is any the less physically real. This despite the fact that time and space get "mixed up" with each other in any transformation to a relatively moving system of coordinates. So, also, although both matter and radiation have the dual characteristics of wave and particle, they are essentially different, convertible into each other in accordance with the now famous equation $E = mc^2$, but quite easily distinguishable.

Bohr (e.g., *Physical Review*, Vol. XLVIII, 1935, p. 696) has pointed out that our difficulties in visualizing quantum phenomena arise from the inadequacy of our classical concepts. What right have we to suppose that we can get a full understanding of these things in terms of billiard balls and waves on a pond? We must be prepared to accept as what actually happens the findings of carefully designed and performed experiments, whether they correspond to what one would expect from our visual models or not. The test of an adequate theory results from the proper identification of the theoretical predictions with those findings. The concepts of the theory, its vocabulary, must be related, directly or indirectly, to something measureable.

Now all experimental atomic data are somewhat indirect. What we actually observe, with our senses, is not the phenomenon itself, but is geared to it by the most ingenious and foolproof arrangement we can devise. The result of an individual measurement we interpret as one of the classical concepts like position, or momentum, or frequency; but what we *see* is something triggered or set off by an atomic process which is completed in the making of our single record. Immediately the question arises, Is this due to nature or to the inadequacy of our measuring instruments? One characteristic of quantum mechanics is that the theory itself gives no way of following the intermediate steps, or details, of the process. Is this a failure of the theory? Or does it not make sense to ask for a more complete description? It is possible to ask meaningless questions. Perhaps no one would ever be guilty of trying to find the color of Middle C, but physicists of sixty years ago were trying very hard to find out whether we move with respect to the ether or drag it along with us. It was hard to accept the answer that we *neither* move freely through, *nor* drag, the ether.

In our case it does turn out not to make sense to ask for a more complete description, at least for ordinary atomic processes. The variables in terms of which the state of a particle is described correspond to the concepts of Newtonian mechanics: space coordinates and time, or energies and momenta, such as are used in Newton's second law of motion. Naturally these are the quantities we devise experiments to measure. The uncertainy principle means that we cannot blithely assume that in atomic physics the system, or object, has definite values of all these variables. The uncertainty is not in our knowledge, but in the quantity to be measured. In other words, the uncertainty principle applies to nature, whether we happen to look at it or not. (The inappropriateness of the word "uncertainty" becomes apparent.) In classical physics it was natural to assume that any variable has a definite value, even though its value is unknown, because in principle it could always be measured. The meaning of the dual aspects wave and particle is that this is not entirely so, either for atomic particles or for photons. It is true only within limitations.

These limitations can be fully expressed in terms of classical concepts if one examines the process of measurement. It is by analyzing the process of measurement that Bohr has shown that the quantum mechanics is self-consistent and complete over its whole range of applicability. In classical physics a measurement can be made, in principle, without affecting the object measured. In quantum physics one must remember that measuring apparatus consists of matter and radiation which are subject to the same uncertainty relations as the system on which the measurements are made. The measurement of any variable *necessarily* disturbs the system, so that it cannot be assumed that it is in the same state whether or not a measurement is made on it.

This is shown quite clearly by an examination of the experiment by which Young originally established the wave nature of light. We know now that the same experiment can be performed with the substitution of a beam of electrons for the light ray. The apparatus and the results are indicated in the drawing. A beam of monochromatic light (or electrons) from the source falls on a pair of slits, whose length extends perpendicular to the page. The intensity distribution on the screen, or amount of blackening on a photographic plate, is indicated by the curve. In terms of waves the pattern on the screen is easily understood, and can be predicted by means of Huygens' principle. But what is the interpretation in terms of particles?

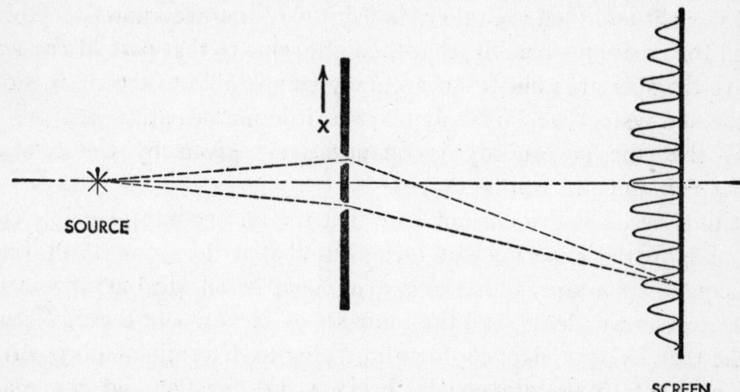

To a classical physicist it seems clear that each photon or electron reaching the screen passes either through the top slit or through the bottom one. It would follow that he could do the experiment twice, with the same photographic plate serving as a screen, once with the lower slit covered and again with the upper one covered, and get the same intensity pattern. Each trial would constitute a measurement of x, the coordinate perpendicular to the length of the slits and parallel to the screen. But this is simply not so. The blackening on the plate from the two experiments bears no resemblance to that obtained when both slits are open. In other words a measurement of position, to the extent of answering the question "Through which slit did the particle come?" completely destroys the interference pattern.

Yet the particle nature of the electron or photon is still there. If the source gives off only one electron or light quantum it will produce a single spot on the screen. The full pattern is produced by a succession of particles. Knowing the pattern gives some information about the result for a single particle, however, in that it indicates the probability with which any electron or photon will strike a given portion of the screen. In this sense the laws of physics which follow so simply from the wave picture have only statistical validity in terms of particles.

Because a good diffraction pattern can be obtained only with a nearly monochromatic beam of light (or a stream of electrons all having nearly the same velocity) and the pattern can be calculated from the wave length, Young's experiment is essentially a measurement of momentum, including the component of the momentum in the x direction. Our attempt to measure simultaneously the position, by closing first one slit and then the other, failed. Of course we know something about the position—namely, that the light came to that part of the wall where the slits are; but to an accuracy comparable to the dimensions of the slit system we failed. It takes a little mathematical analysis to show that the uncertainty is quantitatively given by the relation $\Delta p \, \Delta x \sim h$, but this can be done.

It thus becomes evident not only that the uncertainty principle corresponds to the experimental facts, but that it does not result from inadequate apparatus. Our slit system could be an ideal arrangement, as perfect as we please, and the same set of facts would occur. Nature is like that. We got slapped down in trying to determine both position and momentum simultaneously, because the question did not make sense. We were trying to impose our nineteenth century billiard-ball model on a situation to which it did not apply. In other words, electrons and light quanta are only somewhat, not altogether, like billiard balls.

Bohr has called pairs of variables to which the uncertainty principle is found to apply—like position coördinates and the corresponding components of momentum, or energy and time—"complementary." The word comes from the fact that the combination of *both* aspects of physical phenomena, say position and momentum, characterizes the method of classical physics, so that they are complementary to each other in this sense. In quantum phenomena we may measure one of two such aspects as accurately as we please, but at the cost of renouncing precise knowledge of the other. In this "freedom of choice," says Bohr, "we are concerned with a *discrimination between different experimental procedures which allow of the unambiguous use of complementary classical concepts.*" (Italics Bohr's.) The limitations on the use of classical concepts, which are imposed by the nonclassical nature of the electron or photon, correspond to the impossibility of carrying out the simultaneous measurement of two complementary variables.

There has been much discussion of causality in quantum mechanics. Physical laws are descriptions of the behavior of physical systems under given conditions, and are useful because they enable us to predict future behavior from present knowledge. Have we given this up in any sense? The answer is a decided "No!" It is true that we cannot follow the path of an electron as we can that of a billiard ball; but the reason is that an electron is not a billiard ball. Wave mechanics is concerned precisely with a wave function describing the state of the system, and a wave equation which tells us how this function changes in time. It is the business of quantum mechanics, like the rest of physics, to make predictions. These predictions are substantiated by experiment, and the important ones are just those which were impossible to make on the basis of classical physics. "In fact," according to Bohr, "it is only the mutual exclusion of two experimental procedures, permitting the unambiguous definition of complementary physical quantities, that provides room for new physical laws, the coexistence of which might at first sight appear irreconcilable with the basic principles of science."

Our discussion up to now has been concerned with the nonrelativistic quantum mechanics founded by Heisenberg and Schrödinger. For the phenomena within its range of validity this theory is now as well substantiated as classical physics. But, like every other advance in science, it has its own limitations. Quantum mechanics as it stands today is no final answer, but only a beginning. There are many problems it leaves partially or wholly unsolved.

It is the relativistic quantum mechanics which is not entirely in order. Even before the advent of quantum mechanics it was clear that relativity would have to be considered in any theory, since Newtonian machanics is an approximation valid only for velocities small in comparison with the velocity of light. Relativisitc effects can be considered as corrections in Schrödinger and Heisenberg mechanics. Great advances have been made by Dirac, Pauli, and others toward a consistent theory, with relativity built in, so to speak, and not merely tacked on. Dirac's relativistic quantum mechanics of the ordinary (negative) electron led to many predictions confirmed by experiment. It even made possible an understanding of the positive electron, or positron, when it was discovered in 1933. It has cleared up a number of points in the nonrelativistic theory, notably the special axiom which was necessary for the treatment of identical particles (Pauli's exclusion principle). But for very high energies, and very small distances, such as are involved in atomic nuclei, there is as yet no adequate theory. It is somewhat embarrassing, to put it mildly, that present theory often leads to mathematically infinite answers in the computation of effects which are in reality small. The interaction of a free electron with radiation, and the "self-energy" of an electron, are examples of quantities to which the theory gives infinite answers. Sometimes it is possible to interpret the results physically by keeping only certain terms of a divergent series, or by the *ad hoc* introduction of a "cut-off radius" to make infinite integrals converge; but such tricks are obviously not satisfactory.

Just when physics will break through these difficulties and repeat on a higher level the process of pushing back the boundaries of knowledge cannot be said. Experimental evidence is accumulating which should serve as a basis for new theory. Studies on cosmic rays, and experiments which will be possible with the powerful machines now under construction for accelerating particles to high energies, ought to throw light on possible paths. Bohr has already suggested that perhaps it is wrong to expect an adequate theory of the electron (both positive and negative) by itself. Twenty years ago it was thought that all matter was composed of positive protons and negative electrons. The list of "elementary particles" now includes not only electrons and positrons, protons and neutrons, but also at least two distinct kinds of mesotrons (with masses intermediate between those of the electron and proton). There is evidence for the existence of two different "neutrinos," if energy and momentum are to be conserved. Most of these particles are unstable, and "decay" into other particles or radiation. Perhaps the next major step in theory will be a formalism into which all of these particles fit, or at least which simultaneously describes several of them. But these things are not yet clear.

Physical theory at any given time in the history of science is the best and most consistent description, in language and mathematical symbols, which can be made of a whole range of physical phenomena and their interrelations. It cannot rely on abstract thinking, but is built only in very close contact with experiment, involving the interplay of suggestions back and forth between the laboratory and the mathematical analysis. Where conflict between theory and experiment occurs, persists, and is confirmed, the theory must be revised. How it is revised depends in detail on the experimental discoveries. The present state of affairs, with infinities cropping up in the theory which have no physical counterpart, and with the experimentalists still discovering new elementary particles in 1947, may seem discouraging. But the very recognition of the existence of so many unsolved problems is encouraging. We are in little danger of repeating the closed outlook of Michelson, Rayleigh, and other great physicists of fifty years ago. The speed with which science achieves new marvels depends on motivation, as well as personnel and technical resources, and on the extent to which cooperation is possible between scientists everywhere. These things we have left out of account, but they are the basis for greater worry today than the purely technical difficulties ahead.

INTERACTION OF PHYSICS, CHEMISTRY, AND BIOLOGY

by

J. B. S.

HALDANE

J. B. S. Haldane is Professor of Biometry, University College, London, and a Fellow of the Royal Society. Hon. Doctor of the Universities of Paris and Groningen. Editor of the *Journal of Genetics.* Chevalier de la Légion d'Honneur. Principal publications: *Daedalus* (1923), *Enzymes* (1930), *Callinicus* (1924), *Possible Worlds* (1927), *The Inequality of Man* (1932), *The Causes of Evolution* (1933), *Science and Human Life* (1933), *Heredity and Politics* (1938), *The Marxist Philosophy and the Sciences* (1938), *Science and Everyday Life* (1939), *New Paths in Genetics* (1941), *A Banned Broadcast* (1946), *Science Advances* (1947), *What Is Life?* (1947).

A MATERIALISTIC approach to biology involves the answering of the following questions, among others:

(1) Can we give an account of the phenomena of life in terms of existing physics and chemistry?

(2) Is it likely that this will be possible at a later date?

(3) Is it likely that such an account will be possible in terms of physics and chemistry as developed later on?

(4) Is it likely that living beings developed from nonliving ones without the intervention of other living beings?

My own answers are: (1) No. (2) I am doubtful, but I think not. (3) Yes. (4) Yes. Five years ago I would have given a firm negative to question 2. Now I am not so sure. Clearly one cannot pose question 4 so as to demand a categoric answer until living beings have been made synthetically, or systematic attempts to make them have failed, and until we know much more about what the earth was like a thousand million years ago.

The existing account of life in materialistic terms is, so to say, patchy. A complete account would give a schedule of all the atoms in a simple organism such as a bacillus or a unicellular alga at a certain time, and in the relevant parts of its environment, with such properties of them (e.g., energy levels) as were needed. The system would then be followed through until we had two comparable bacteria or cells, each change being shown to be of the kind and degree predicted on the basis of physics and chemistry.

Such an account is of course beyond our powers in the case of the simplest chemical reaction, and perhaps always will be. We can merely describe the behavior of typical atoms, and apply statistical methods to large aggregates. This gives extremely satisfactory results in chemistry, because we are dealing with a few kinds of molecules, and a great many of each kind.

It has a limited application in biology because the functional unit of life, such as a cell, usually contains only one or two molecules of certain species, notably genes, and because the number of different molecular species is exceedingly large. So far we have only described molecular species, of which the number per cell is to be counted in millions or at least in thousands.

Thus a single bacterium, according to McIlwain,[1] contains about 100,000 molecules of nicotinic acid, 1,000 of folic acid, but only one, or some small number, of the catalyst responsible for making pantothenic acid from lactate, β-alanine, and inorganic salts.

It will be seen that any materialistic account of life must be fundamentally an account in terms of chemical change. At is simplest level, life is just a self-perpetuating pattern of chemical reactions. In the course of these, some sort of form is built up. But we do not distinguish different kinds of bacteria by their forms. Movement of a gross character is not an essential of life. Some kind of feeling may be, but we have no evidence on this matter. Such an account of life at a low level is of course very incomplete; but, as we shall see, there are no facts which suggest that we cannot approach it indefinitely.

Supposing such an account to be possible, we have further to ask whether a simple organism could have come into being from inorganic matter, and whether it could have evolved into the various types of living organism existing today. The former question has hardly been tackled seriously, though it has not been neglected. The latter has been very seriously considered by Darwin and his successors.

Before we return to them, let us deal with the physicochemical basis of life. Theoretically, it might seem best to deal wholly with bacteria or protista; but there is no doubt that they have a capacity for self-regulation and healing of injuries, and these processes can be better followed in higher organisms.

Living substance is built up of the same kinds of atoms as are found in non-living material. Most of its weight consists of water; the rest, of a great variety of compounds including proteins, carbohydrates, fats, nucleic acids, and various intermediates, such as nitrogenous polysaccharides and lipins. These have skeletons of carbon atoms and commonly contain—besides hydrogen, oxygen, and nitrogen—phosphorus (always pentavalent) and sulphur (usually bivalent). Other elements occasionally found in the large molecules are iodine, magnesium, zinc, copper, iron, and probably manganese. Boron may perhaps be so associated. Cadmium, vanadium, and other rare elements seem to be so occasionally. Sodium, potassium, magnesium, calcium, chlorine, and sometimes silicon, exist in ionized solution or ionic crystals, chlorine being incorporated into a few organic molecules by some molds. All the above are probably essential to life, though all are not so in all species. No sort of atom is peculiar to life, nor is there any evidence that anything leaves the body at death. A certain pattern of chemical events comes to an end, but there is no suggestion that vital spirits escape.

Life is characterized by certain transformations of matter and energy. The energy is ordinary energy, as the matter is ordinary matter. The energy is derived from two sources. On the one hand radiant energy is used to synthesize organic molecules from water or hydrogen sulphide, carbon dioxide, nitrates, sulphates, and the like; oxygen or sulphur being liberated. On the other hand energy may be derived from the oxidation of organic, or more rarely inorganic, molecules or from the rearrangement of the atoms of organic molecules, as when yeast produces alcohol, carbon dioxide, and a little free energy, from the fermentation of sugar. The energy liberated in this way appears as heat, kinetic and potential energy, sound, light, and electrical potential energy. There is nothing to suggest that any peculiar form of energy characterizes life. The balance sheet between the energy available from food and oxygen and that put out in various ways is remarkably accurate. This is notably so in man, where it might have been expected that energy would have been converted into metaphysical forms (e.g., will or thought) or derived from metaphysical sources.

Organisms appear to obey the second law of thermodynamics as completely as the first. Certainly they decrease their own entropy over long periods; but they do so by extracting negative entropy from their environment—for example, from sunlight and from food plus oxygen. Entropy increases during the process taken as a whole, which may be compared to the action of a water hammer in raising some of the water in a falling stream to a high level, at the expense of the energy of the remainder, or of a steam engine in operating an arc lamp at a temperature higher than that of its furnace.

Sixty years ago scientists who admitted this nevertheless thought that it would be hopeless to follow the fate of the atoms of food after they entered the cell. The word "protoplasm" was used not only to cover our ignorance of intercellular events but to suggest that they were insusceptible of further analysis. Since then a large number of enzymes have been isolated from cells, each of which can catalyze a particular step in metabolism. Thus one enzyme catalyzes the loss of two hydrogen atoms from one carbon atom of a sugar, and thus the local oxidation of the sugar molecule; another enzyme, the breaking of a sugar molecule into two molecules of a three-carbon sugar, and so on. Another builds up glucose-phosphate molecules to form starch and phosphateions. All enzymes appear to be proteins, though many, perhaps all, have a non-protein prosthetic group such as a porphyrin-metal complex, attached to a larger mass of protein. Given the existence of about a thousand species of enzymes in a cell, it seems extremely probable that the whole of its metabolism can be accounted for. The isolation of all the enzymes in a particular type of cell does not seem an impossible goal, even if only a fraction have yet been isolated from any particular type.

Enzyme action seems to differ in no essential way from any other chemical action. We can not merely describe it, but predict it. Thus Briggs and Haldane produced the fundamental equations for the kinetics of a simple type of enzyme action according to which, when an enzyme is introduced into a solution of its substrate, the enzyme-substrate compound is produced at a certain rate. Later it was found that certain enzymes changed color on combining with their substrates; and eighteen years after Briggs and Haldane, Chance (1943)[2] showed that peroxidase follows the laws which they had deduced. Colored enzymes are important in another way. Keilin has followed the color changes in oxidative enzymes within a living cell, and shown that they are precisely the same as those undergone when purified solutions of the same enzymes are acting on their purified substrates. This disposes of the idea that enzymes are only dead fragments of giant living molecules of protoplasm, and that their action inside the cell is governed by laws of a special nature.

Enzymes exist which build up complex molecules, but it is far from clear how they build them up into the highly specific patterns which seem to characterize the proteins. We do not know whether all the molecules of, say, insulin or hemoglobin in a given animal are precisely alike, apart from isotope substitution and occasional accidents, as all its glucose molecules are alike. But certainly their patterns must be very similar. Proteins are built up from about 20 amino acids, and a typical fairly light protein such as hemoglobin contains about 600 amino acid residues. The possible diversity of molecules of this size is as near infinity as human thought can easily reach. According to Eddington there is only enough matter in the universe to make about 10^{74} such such molecules. The amount of matter in all the galaxies within five hundred million light-years, and therefore possibly photographable, is far less. The total number of possible proteins of 600 amino acids is 20^{600}, or 10^{781}, in fact exceeds the tenth power of the above number. An aggregate consisting of one molecule of each of all the possible 60 residue peptides would weigh much more than the known universe. This simple fact shows that the whole diversity of living organisms may have an extremely simple chemical basis. We must suppose that, in certain cases at least, the enzymes which build up proteins are provided not only with the raw materials, the amino acids, but with the specification for the particular pattern to be built up. What form that specification may take, we shall consider later.

Within a century it is quite probable that biochemists will have prepared all the catalysts in a given type of cell, or all that are needed for its routine activities, and will have determined with sufficient accuracy how they are arranged within it. Perhaps they will not have synthesized all these catalysts; but they will have synthesized some, and prepared others from cells of the type under study. It should then be possible, with the above catalysts and other materials of a structural nature, to produce a model or synthetic cell which will carry on for a considerable time the ordinary vital activities—for example, a yeast cell which will make alcohol, a leaf cell which will make sugar when illuminated, a muscle fiber which will repeatedly contract when stimulated and fed sugar and oxygen.

It may be remarked that actin, the main contractile protein of muscle, is an enzyme which changes its molecular form in the course of transforming its substrate, adenosin-triphosphoric acid.

Such a synthetic cell will have at least a certain measure of self-regulation. So does a steam engine with a governor. It will regain its original form after some enforced changes in it. So does a football or, to take a better example, a candle flame. It will not presumably be capable of reproduction. Nor is a castrated horse. Whether such a model cell will be regarded as alive is a matter of definition.

However, living organisms possess the capacity for self-regulation in a far greater degree than any machine, and that for reproduction, which no machine possesses. Nevertheless the analogy of a flame on a gas-jet or candle shows that non-living systems can possess both in a slight degree. The flame will restore its original form when it is blown out of shape, but not blown out, and will light an indefinite number of other similar flames if brought into contact with appropriate material. This is because the flame, like a living organism, is a pattern of chemical changes rather than a pattern of molecules. Primitive men were as right in thinking flames were alive as Descartes in thinking that animals were machines, at least of the type known to him. A pattern of physical processes—for example, a fountain—will often restore its original form after disturbance, but will seldom reproduce. On the other hand a crystal is less apt to restore its original form but more apt to reproduce itself. In particular this reproduction may be specific. Some substances can exist in several crystalline forms. If a crystal of one of them is introduced into a supersaturated solution or a supercooled melt of the substance in question, it will reproduce more crystals of its own type, and not of any of the other possible types.

A cell is somewhat of a compromise between a machine with a number of stable components, such as cogs or electronic valves, and a flame in which each part is being very rapidly replaced. The large molecules, such as enzymes, are not permanent, like the parts of a machine, but occasionally exchange atoms with their environment, as has been shown by the use of isotopes as indicators. However, a given atom of nitrogen stays in its place for an average time which is often measured in days, and is rarely less than about six hours. An enzyme may often transform 100 molecules of its substrate per second, sometimes much more. So the part of the enzyme containing this atom may perform some hundreds of thousands of operations before it is made over. And the carbon atoms are a good deal stabler than the nitrogen.

A synthetic cell such as we have imagined would be quite comparable to a machine such as a steam engine converting chemical energy into heat and work, or an automatic unit in a chemical factory performing some process as long as it is fed with the appropriate materials. It would have a very limited power of self-regulation, and no power of reproduction. These are among the reasons why most biologists do not agree with Descartes's theory that organisms are machines.

But before we adopt this view it is important to see just what we mean by the word "machine." I shall not define this word, but shall say a little about its history. Just when a tool becomes a machine is not clear. A machine must, I think, have several parts capable of relative motion. A knife is certainly not a machine, a pair of scissors doubtfully so, a hand mill almost surely so. The first at all complicated machines were clocks. A clock is intended to imitate the motions of the solar system, so as to indicate the direction of the sun and perhaps also of the moon and planets. Now the solar system is almost frictionless. Its movements are described by equations which are not appreciably altered when the sign of the symbol representing time in them is changed. If in 1948 I want to calculate the position of Jupiter at a date in 1958 I can do so. Precisely the same set of calculations gives me its position in 1938 if I suppose all the motions of the system to be reversed. Moreover the internal motions of the solar system are so unaffected by the other stars that millions of years will probably have to elapse before any such effect can be measured.

A clock has similar properties. Most of its mechanism will work backwards. Above all it is isolated from its environment in two distinct ways. First, it is designed to be independent of environmental changes such as temperature and perhaps even barometric pressure. If it is to be moved over the earth like a ship's chronometer it must be independent of variations in the earth's gravitational field, and cannot include a pendulum. Secondly, it has no means of correcting its performance by reference to the environment. We hope that its hairspring, pendulum, or vibrating crystal will make it keep good time. If it does not, it is occasionally reset by man. It would be entirely possible to design a clock which was reset on every cloudless night by a photoelectric cell when a certain star passed the meridian. (Actually one would probably have to use two or three different stars.) However, no such clock exists as yet.

The clock then has nothing corresponding to receptor organs which enable it to modify its performance in response to environmental change. This is as it should be, for the solar system is isolated. And it has no proprioceptors, to enable it to adjust what would otherwise be an inadequate performance. The hairspring or pendulum is hardly a proprioceptor, for, once an error has been made, it cannot be corrected.

The higher living organisms possess exteroceptors and proprioceptors. The exteroceptors include the sense organs which allow us to adjust ourselves to our environment, notably by movement in animals, and the various devices which cause a plant's leaves to grow towards the light, and its roots towards water. It is not certain whether bacteria have organs of this kind, though many protista certainly have them.

Again the higher animals have proprioceptors. My brain receives messages from the muscles, tendons, and joints, which allow a very fine regulation of movement. When for example I try to grasp my left hand with my right hand I can do so even with my eyes shut. The most characteristic symptom when the proprioceptive system goes wrong is tremor. The muscles overshoot their mark, then come back past it, and may never be able to settle down to rest.

Machines can now be fitted both with exteroceptors and proprioceptors. Both have been especially developed for the purposes of war, where there has been a demand for pilotless aeroplanes, for torpedoes which move towards a sound, for shells which burst in the neighborhood of a hostile aeroplane which they detect by radar, and so on.

Finally, machines can be provided with something analogous to a memory. This is best seen in the Eniac calculator, which has two recording systems. On the one hand the results of former calculations are recorded on punched cards, which can be automatically used to motivate a subsequent calculation. On the other hand the results of the current calculation are kept in being as a system of electrical pulses passing through a mercury trough and then repeated by a series of valves so as not to lose any precision. They can thus circulate for a considerable time, becoming available again at a later stage. Further, the action of such a machine is quite irreversible. Time has a definite direction for it.

It is quite certain that a living organism is much more like a machine of this kind than it is like a clock or a steam engine. It seems to me at least possible that a living organism is such a machine, though I shall later consider some arguments against this view. It is perhaps unfortunate that we use the same word, "machine," for systems with exteroception, proprioception, and memory, as for machines with none of these properties, like a medieval clock which had not even a pendulum to act as a governor.

However that may be, it is certain that the study of such machines will throw a great deal of light on biology and particularly on the action of the nervous system. Ordinary mechanics explain a great deal about the action of the bones as levers, the heart as a pump, and so on. Ordinary thermodynamics and chemistry explain a great deal more about the phenomena of life. In a very suggestive paper to which I am indebted here and throughout this article, Wiener [3] has suggested how the study of machines with the properties mentioned above may explain many of the properties of the nervous system. It is particularly striking that a neurone resembles an electronic valve in that it discharges completely or not at all, though in either case the time of discharge may be determined by a very complicated system of stimuli. The pathology of servo-mechanisms, that is to say their tendency to "hunt" under certain circumstances, is already throwing light on the pathology of the nervous system as exemplified by tremor; and the Eniac calculation can solve not only mathematical but logical problems, and therefore at least suggests what may be the physical basis of thought.

There are, however, several reasons against supposing that one can regard a living organism as a "supermachine" of this kind apart from emotional objections and the carryover from traditional metaphysics. The history of science shows that a materialistic explanation at a given level may be of great service but yet finally inadequate. The Cartesian mechanistic theory gave the first rudiments of a scientific physiology. The theory of atoms as indestructible units was of immense value to the development of chemistry, but equally broke down. Newtonian mechanics, after two centuries of triumph, had to be recast.

Again, a study of cellular chemistry suggests the need for caution. In the nineteenth century we gained a fair idea of the properties of acids and bases, which was greatly clarified by the ionic theory. It then turned out that the constituents of proteins, the amino acids, were both acids and bases. They form ions with both positive and negative charges. In consequence they possess quite novel properties, as do the proteins formed from their union. Other unique or at least uncommon properties of proteins depend on the flexibility of the chains of which they are composed. It is a commonplace in physics and chemistry that a system can exhibit novel properties as the result of the union of opposites in such a way as to abolish or diminish the external force field of the components. For example, the electric force between two protons is 2.3×10^{39} times the gravitational force. Only when protons are associated with an electron apiece is the gravitational force detectable. Apart from such residual properties which appear when the more striking field components are abolished, there are other novel properties which appear simply as the result of the size of a system. Thus a hydrogen molecule has a far more complicated system of energy levels than two hydrogen atoms. It does not seem impossible that a cell as a whole, or an organism as a whole, might have properties not at present deducible from those of its constituents, associated perhaps with systems of energy levels like those of molecules, but with a finer structure.

If this is true, everything suggests that, while the study of living organisms may reveal new properties of matter, these will be explicable by previously unknown but not unverifiable properties of its elementary constituents. The wavelike properties of electrons were first detected by the study of atomic spectra—that is to say, of electrons as atomic constituents. They were then found to hold also for electrons in beams, and the electron microscope became a possibility. It is possible that the course of science will be otherwise, and that the data of atomic physics will allow of the prediction of properties in larger aggregates, some of which will be found to explain vital phenomena.

Thirdly, a thoroughly materialistic mathematical theory of evolution has been built up in recent years by Wright, Fisher, and Haldane in particular, based on the known properties of genes. The fundamental property of a gene, its capacity for orderly, but not absolutely orderly, self-reproduction, is taken as given. It may turn out (though I think it most unlikely) that is property of genes will remain forever inexplicable on materialistic lines. But a failure so to explain it would not invalidate the above theory. In the same way the relations between neurones may be formally so similar to those of valves in an Eniac that the theory of the Eniac will also be that of the cerebral cortex. But even so it is possible that the neurones will be found to have properties not explicable in terms of present-day physics and chemistry.

We have so far shelved the problem of reproduction. The facts to be explained are as follows. A cell divides into two daughters indistinguishable from it. How are the different constituents formed? If we X-ray the cell we can produce changes in any of its molecules. If these changes are not fatal, one of two things happens. Either the descendants of the original cell revert completely to the normal type, or a changed condition is perpetuated. Where sexual reproduction allows the necessary analysis, it is found that the changed condition is due to a change in one or more chromosomes. This may be a sharply localized change which we describe as a mutation in a single gene. Or it may be a rearrangement involving two or more breaks which are subsequently rejoined to give an inversion, a translocation, a deficiency, or a duplication. It is doubtful whether a sharp line can be drawn betwen the two types of change. The chromosomes are reproduced in their altered condition, and the character produced by the change is inherited according to Mendel's laws. If a similarly reproducible change occurred in the cytoplasm, it would be transmitted mainly in the maternal line. Such changes occur; but they are very rare and can often, perhaps always, be explained by change induced in symbionts or viruses. Thus the races of *Paramecium aurelia* fall into two groups (Sonneborn, 1947).[4] Group A shows no cytoplasmic inheritances; group B shows several examples, including the cytoplasmic agent partially responsible for "killer" character. As various species of Paramecium certainly carry symbiotic algae, and as the cytoplasmic factors are borne only by one race of *P. aurelia,* it seems that their presence is not a fundamental character of the species, and that they may at least provisionally be regarded as symbionts.

With few exceptions at most, then, we may say that in each cellular reproductive cycle the molecules of the cytoplasm are not copied from preexisting molecules. The chromosomes and perhaps other nuclear structures such as centrosomes, are so copied. One can regard this process either as the reproduction of an existing structure, or as its copying by the cytoplasm. The distinction may be only verbal, as no experiment can at present be suggested which will distinguish between the two hypotheses. The chromosomes consist of nucleoprotein. So do molecular viruses, which are also copied in a similar way. It is perhaps a matter of taste whether we say that a tobacco mosaic virus molecule, introduced into tobacco cytoplasm, proceeds to reproduce in this favorable environment, or that the cytoplasm proceeds to make copies of the virus molecules introduced into it. The essential difference between a gene and a virus is that the reproduction of the gene is synchronized with that of the other cell constituents, and that it is a part of a chromosome which is regularly distributed.

The fundamental problem of reproduction from the physicochemical point of view is then, "How does a gene or a virus reproduce?"

There are at least two possibilities. We can rule out the hypothesis of growth of qualititatively similar material until the aggregate becomes unstable, like a large drop of water. The results of irradiation make it clear that a gene does not consist of a number of like parts, but must be regarded as a single molecule, even if it is regarded as a portion of a still more gigantic molecule, the chromosome. Either a gene G is copied, a new gene G' being laid down alongside it; if so G must clearly be spread out as a sheet not more than one amino-acid or nucleotide residue in thickness; or the gene G is copied onto a "template" g, and g in turn copied by two new genes G_1 and G_2. The latter method is of course that used in photography, where a positive is copied as a negative, from which one or more positives are produced. This is not the place to give the arguments in favor of these two hypotheses in any detail. The first postulated process resembles crystal growth. The second has analogies with antibody formation. Here a foreign protein induces the formation of antibodies which are also proteins that somehow fit it in such a way as to combine with it but not with closely related proteins. This is not a specifically vital activity, since Pauling has produced antibodies in the laboratory. It is tempting to speculate that a gene can exist in two forms *G* and *g*, of which one consists primarily of nucleic acid, the other of protein; that is to say that the essential pattern can be expressed in either of these substances. The fact that peptide and nucleic acid chains have almost identical spacings renders the hypothesis plausible. On the other hand nucleic acid chains are built up of only four types of units; protein chains, of about twenty. It is, however, striking that all self-reproducing proteins are nucleoproteins. Further there is evidence that ribonucleic acid is concerned in the synthesis of cytoplasmic proteins. And above all we have the fundamental discovery of Avery, McCarty, and Macleod that a nucleic acid can induce bacteria to produce its like indefinitely, and also to make a characteristic polysaccharide. Even if it turned out that their nucleic acid contained a small fraction of peptide or other residues, it is clear that the specific pattern can be expressed in a pattern which consists primarily of nucleotides.

To sum up, we can say that the problem of gene reproduction may be soluble in terms of the chemistry of nucleoproteins and of the enzymes which build them up from simpler materials. It may turn out that some wholly new principle is involved. But it is quite certain that the problem of reproduction will not be solved until the chemistry of the nucleoproteins has been thoroughly investigated.

Given the existence of genes which are generally but not always reproduced exactly, the problem of evolution appears to be soluble in principle. It is a matter of observation that the substitution of one gene for another can produce the most startling changes in physiology and anatomy. It is a matter of observation that new genes are constantly arising by mutation, that is to say by imperfections in the copying process or by the copying of altered models. And it is a matter of observation that selection can cause a new type of gene to spread through a population. The main difficulty which arises is that in many cases several simultaneous gene changes would be needed to produce a new balanced system. The work of Sewall Wright in particular suggests how this may have happened. It has been said that all gene changes are regressive. It is not clear to me how a change lengthening a rabbit's hair and one shortening it can both be regarded as regressive. Moreover X-rays will change a gene for normal eye color in Drosophila to a gene for white eyes and later change the white-eye gene back again to normal. Both changes cannot be regressive, or regarded as injuries or inactivations of the gene. I am aware that some of the statements made in this paragraph must appear dogmatic. It is difficult to summarize one's life's work in a paragraph without the appearance of dogmatism.

I now come to the question of the origin of life. If it took place on earth it took place very long before the Cambrian period, which started five hundred million years ago; for the main invertebrate phyla were well developed in Cambrian times, and pre-Cambrian fossils of many of them exist.

It is highly probable that the oxygen of our atmosphere is due to photosynthesis, and the fact that before Laurentian times ferrous compounds predominate in sedimentary rocks, and afterwards, ferric compounds, suggests that photosynthesis began at this time. If so life began in the absence of oxygen. The fact that even in the higher organisms many essential processes are anaerobic (for example, oxygen is not needed for muscle contraction, though it is needed for the recovery process making future contractions possible) at least bears out this view.

The primitive atmosphere of the earth probably consisted mainly of hydrogen and inert gases, of which the hydrogen and helium at least soon flew off into space, as the surface temperature was very high. When the surface cooled, a secondary atmosphere was formed from gases combined or occluded in the solid and liquid body of the earth. This secondary atmosphere probably contained ammonia and methane like those of the outer planets, and carbon dioxide like that of Venus, besides water vapor and hydrogen sulphide. Ultraviolet radiation was not, as now, absorbed by ozone and oxygen at great heights. Various metastable organic compounds were formed, by the action of ultraviolet radiation on the atmospheric gases, and dissolved in the primitive seas. As there were no bacteria to destroy them, they must have reached a fairly high concentration. Suitable food for primitive anaerobic organisms was thus available, and also considerable numbers of large organic molecules. Once the simplest kind of organism was in existence, it would have had relatively little difficulty in propagating itself, and accidental variations could have given it the possibility of evolution. We must not, however, overlook the very great difficulties involved in giving a plausible account of its origin.

It may of course be found that some nucleoproteins will reproduce themselves in an environment containing amino acids, sugars, purine and pyrimidine bases, and phosphate. If so, it is easy to imagine the origin of such a particle by chance, and its indefinite self-reproduction. But it is at least arguable that a virus or a gene needs for its copying not merely raw materials but a whole battery of enzymes capable of synthesis, but synthesizing nucleoprotein, or one of its two major constituents, in accordance with a preexisting pattern. If so the original organisms must have been much larger than molecules. Parker-Rhodes (1946) claims to have shown, on mathematical grounds, that any organism must contain more than one loculus—that is to say, enclosure surrounded by a semipermeable membrane and containing catalysts and their substrates. If his reasoning is correct, this implies a considerable complexity. Catalysts of various kinds doubtless arose in the primitive ocean; but, unless they were so collocated as to form a self-preserving and self-reproducing system, they would merely destroy the available foodstuffs.

To suppose that so complex a system arose by chance may appear ridiculous. However, we must remember that the space available for its formation was an ocean covering a large fraction of our planet, and the time probably more than a billion (10^9) years but less than three billion. When we know enough biochemistry to be able to specify the magnitude and complexity of the smallest possible self-reproducing system, and can form some estimate of the concentration of organic molecules of different types in the primitive ocean, we shall be in a position to say whether the probability of such a random synthesis was near to unity.

To object to the hypothesis that probability must be considered in such a context, is to show a surprising ignorance of the facts both of physics and of morality. I boil a kettle with full confidence in the outcome although I know that the process of heating depends on the random motion of vast numbers of molecules. The probability that the flame will not heat the kettle is extremely small, but it is calculable.

Moreover the theory which gives it has been applied to the case of fluctuations in gases near their critical point, and shown to give correct results where it can be checked. When I drive an automobile I take certain precautions. If I do not do so tonight it is highly unlikely that any harm will come. But if I neglect them for several years I am fairly sure to injure a pedestrian. If my chance of killing a pedestrian in a lifetime were one in a million I should be a fool to take the precautions which I do. Morality is based on probabilities of this kind. When I sow a field there is perhaps a 10 per cent chance that any particular seed will not germinate, but a practical certainty that enough will germinate to give me a crop. It is at least possible that the conditions on the primitive earth were such as to give this kind of certainty that life would originate. If it can be shown, on the one hand, that they were not so and, on the other, that life could not have been brought to the earth by spores from an extraterrestrial source, it will be time enough to evoke other hypotheses.

It has been urged that primitive organisms must have been capable of synthesizing all their constituents from inorganic material like green plants, or at least from very simple organic compounds. And it is suggested that modern organisms have mostly lost some of this primitive synthetic capacity. I do not agree. If the primitive organisms arose in a natural culture medium they would have had to be selective rather than creative. Their life processes would have been slow because the large majority of the organic molecules available would not have fitted their catalysts. On the other hand every step towards autotrophy would have been of considerable selective advantage in allowing the use of simpler foodstuffs. But if the primitive ocean contained trioses as well as hexoses, acetic acid as well as stearic, and so on, the steps could have been rather gradual.

The remarkable uniformity of the chemical basis of life and, above all, the fact that all living organisms use the same set of sugars and amino acids in their vital processes, and none use their optical antipodes, suggests strongly that all life on our planet derives from a single origin. A few bacteria make appreciable quantities of some of the "looking-glass" amino acids and incorporate them in antibiotics, but they do not seem to form part of the living substance. However, the fact that they can be made in this way suggests that "looking-glass" organisms might have arisen and may have done so on other stars. Probably, however, within a few thousand years of the origin of life on our planet, most of the materials for a second origin were already used up, especially if the primitive organisms had a d-amino-acid oxidase.

However, life must have gone on in a very halting way until some kind of photosynthesis was achieved. Once radiant energy could be harnessed, the need for organic materials disappeared, and once oxygen was liberated in appreciable amounts most of the primitive organisms must have been killed, as anaerobes are killed today, and the methane of the secondary atmosphere and the organic solutes of the primitive oceans must have been oxidized, while the curtain of ozone slowed down the synthesis of new ones. Both on morphological grounds and from the presence in them of metalloporphyrins not unlike chlorophyll, it is probable that the higher animals, as well as plants, are descendants of the first photosynthetic organisms. Many of them, including all animals, have now ceased to be autotrophic, and need a variety of sugars, fats, proteins, and vitamins ultimately derived from plants. But this loss of chemical function probably occurred after the world revolution produced by photosynthesis, when living organisms became common enough to allow one to live by eating others.

The above ideas are, of course, common currency. They and others have been developed in great detail by Oparin and others. In case, however, I am accused of plagiarism, I may add that I published them about 1927 in the *Rationalist Annual,* and that they were reprinted in my book *The Inequality of Man.* The main change in my views has been that I now regard it as improbable that a giant molecule such as a gene or virus could have reproduced itself in the primitive ocean.

It will be seen, I think, that the main gap in our materialistic account of life lies between our account of enzymes, on the one hand, and of cells on the other. From the point of view of ordinary chemistry the properties of enzymes are remarkable, but not inexplicable. An enzyme can be extremely selective, attacking only one of a pair of stereoisomers or completely incapable of dealing with a substrate molecule containing a single extra methyl group. It can be extremely active, transforming up to 100,000 substrate molecules per second, though such a turnover is probably never achieved in life. And it can perform remarkable feats of synthesis, such as that of starch from glucose phosphate. Nevertheless we understand pretty well how it works. Again given a cell such as a simple flagellate, we can see how evolution may have occurred, and fill in the details, as paleontologists and geneticists are constantly doing, with remarkably little change in the fundamental ideas laid down by Darwin and his contemporaries. But the gap between enzyme and cell in our knowledge is serious. I do not believe that there is, in the nature of things, any particular mystery to be unveiled in this gap. The gap is there for technical reasons. We cannot, with a microscope, observe structures much smaller than a wave length of light. And our chemical methods give us rather sketchy knowledge of molecules whose weight is over 10,000. In other words we know very little about objects between 10^{-6} cm. and 10^{-4} cm. across (an increase of a millionfold in bulk). We are gradually learning about them with X-rays, electron microscopes, ultracentrifuges and other physical methods, and also by biological methods such as genetical analysis. If our eyes could see with X-rays and not with light, there might be a gap elsewhere. We might know how protoplasm worked, but not about the cellular organization of our own bodies. The mystery or gap in our knowledge would be at a different level.

I have of course said nothing about consciousness, which is associated with at least some kinds of life, nor can I say more than a few words in this brief essay. If, as some philosophers hold, things in themselves are not at all like our perceptions of matter, then conciousness is an inexplicable and irrational mystery. If, as plain men believe, the world is like what we feel, see, and hear, it follows that our sensations, thoughts, and so on, are like the things in the external world. Perhaps they are like matter because they *are* matter—namely, the matter in our brains, or rather certain of its properties; for, since many of the properties of external matter do not give rise to sensations, it would follow that the corresponding properties of the matter of our own bodies are not sensations. If our consciousness is the self-knowledge of matter, the physicochemical account of matter may be substantially true, but is certainly very incomplete. That is one of the reasons why, though a materialist, I have hesitated to reply in the affirmative to question 2 of the opening paragraph.

The ideas here put forward may seem to some readers to be of a kind totally cut off from the main stream of human thought and, in particular, incompatible with any elevated morality. This is not the case. I will say nothing of the great Asiatic philosophies except that such views have some affinity with the Indian Sankhya philosophy and very little with the Vedanta philosophy. To turn to Europe, we have to distinguish two tendencies. On the one hand the followers of Plato have drawn a sharp distinction between mind and matter. Plain men have seldom done so. They generally thought that a spirit left the body at death, but they thought it had a shape, size, and other properties of matter. The life of the body depended on its union with this spirit. If we substantiate for the visible but not tangible ghost a pattern of metabolic changes we can adopt something like the plain man's view. St. Thomas Aquinas held that the human soul was the substantial form of the human body, a formulation which has much to commend it. But his evidence that it could be separated from the body seems to me to lack cogency. However, throughout Christian as well as non-Christian thought, the view that there is no sharp line between body and soul persisted, and was formulated whenever it was safe to do so.

In particular Milton in Book V of *Paradise Lost* puts the following speech, made to Adam before his fall, into the mouth of the Archangel Raphael:

So from the root
Springs lighter the green stalk, from thence the leaves
More aerie, last the bright consummate floure
Spirits odorous breathes: flours and thir fruit,
Man's nourishment, by gradual scale sublim'd,
To vital spirits aspire, to animal,
To intellectual; give both life and sense,
Fansie and understanding; whence the soule
Reason receives, and reason is her being.

Raphael tells Adam that all created things are created from "one first matter," and "if not deprav'd from good" may evolve towards God,

Till body up to spirit work, in bounds
Proportion'd to each kind.

Naturally Milton's formulation must be amended in view of the greater knowledge of the world gained in the last three centuries. But the view that spirit is a flowering of matter did not prevent Milton from having lofty moral principles and (with inevitable lapses) living up to them. It need not prevent those who hold such a view today from holding moral principles and living or, when necessary, dying for them.

References

[1] Henry McIlwain, in *Nature,* Vol. CLVIII, p. 898 (Dec. 21, 1946).

[2] Britton Chance, in *Journal of Biological Chemistry,* Vol. CLI, p. 553 (Dec., 1943).

[3] Norbert Wiener, "Time, Communication, and the Nervous System," in *Annals of New York Academy of Sciences,* Vol. L (1948).

[4] T. M. Sonneborn, "Recent Advances in the Genetics of Paramecium and Euplotes," *Advances in Genetics,* Vol. I, p. 263 (1947).

A BIOLOGICAL SURVEY OF INTEGRATIVE LEVELS

by

C. **JUDSON HERRICK**

C. Judson Herrick is now living in Grand Rapids, Michigan. His publications include about two hundred scientific articles, chiefly neurological, and several books: *Introduction to Neurology* (1915—5th ed., 1931), *Neurological Foundations of Animal Behavior* (1924), *Brains of Rats and Men* (1926), *The Thinking Machine* (1929—2nd ed., 1932), *The Brain of the Tiger Salamander* (1948). A major interest is the *Journal of Comparative Neurology,* of which he has been Editor since 1894. During World War I he saw military service as Major, Sanitary Corps, in charge of Pathology at the Army Medical Museum, Washington. He is Professor Emeritus of Neurology, University of Chicago.

THE first concern of biology as a natural science is accurate description of living things and what they do. But this is merely the foundation for a superstructure of classification, generalization, and explanation of how they do what they do and why. The material of which living bodies are composed and its organization have no meaning for biology, except in terms of vital activity. Life is process, and the goal toward which all biological study is directed is the understanding of this process in the interest of more efficient control of it.

The material structure of the living body is a mechanism. The biologist, then, must be some kind of materialist (whatever else he may be too), because, as Herbert Spencer pointed out, the vital process is essentially the correspondence of the living mechanism with the other natural mechanisms of the world about. The material body must adjust its own activity to those of other material things; but, since matter is now defined and described only in terms of its action, the biologist's materialism must be conceived in dynamic terms. His concern in the upshot is not with the body alone nor with its action alone; it is with the *relations* existing between bodies (organic and inorganic) and their reciprocal adjustments one with another. Neither anatomy nor physiology has any biological significance apart from the other. Anthropology, psychology, and sociology have similar relationships.

We must, then, first inquire into the properties of mechanisms in general. Machines make things, and what they make is something different from the raw materials out of which it is made. This creative process and the nature of the product manufactured are determined by the intrinsic organization of the mechanism at work. This is equally true of natural machines, like river systems and animal bodies, and those constructed by artifice of man. An external agent may initiate the process; but what is actually made by the mechanism is determined by its own structure, and structure in last analysis is organization.

It is the province of science to find out how the different kinds of mechanisms make their products. It must be kept in mind that a machine—whether natural or artificial—is not inert structure operated by forces external to it. It is an active participant in the process, and it has a restricted range of freedom of action; otherwise it could not make anything.

D'Arcy Thompson wrote, in his great book *Growth and Form*, "From the physical point of view, we understand by a 'mechanism' whatever *checks* or *controls*, and *guides into determinate paths*, the workings of energy." (The emphasis is mine.) This control, which is an active process involving expenditure of energy, is the distinctive characteristic of all mechanisms, and it implies *directive action.*

These properties of natural mechanisms are everywhere apparent, as may be illustrated by the simple process of making water by chemical combination of hydrogen and oxygen. The process is initiated by an external agent, say an electric spark; but what happens thereafter is determined by the intrinsic properties of the constituent elements.

The formula written by the earlier chemists, $2H + O = H_2O$, is now outmoded. The equality sign is replaced by an arrow, an energy factor is included, and also a factor of pattern of organization. The revised formula expresses, not a balance but a process, and this process is directive, not random.

It may be questioned whether, if all the facts were known, any such thing as random activity could be found. There are no isolated phenomena in nature, and chance has no place in the natural order. An apparently random movement is random only within some particular frame of reference. Even the movements of electrons are not lawless. If they were, they could not be systematized statistically. The laws of probability imply order, not chaos. It has been shown by Guye's computations, made so much of by Lecomte du Noüy, that the probability that a molecule of protein would be produced by chance combination of the constituent atoms is as 1 to 100 multiplied by itself 160 times. This product would be a mass of matter much greater than that of the whole known universe. To this *reductio ad absurdum* another complication may be added. The computation assumes that the atoms after combination to form the molecule remain unchanged. This is not true, and so a practically unlimited series of additional variables is injected into the problem. Chance explains nothing. What we observe is orderly directive action. The "final cause" of these directive trends we do not know.

Empirical science (as distinguished from the normative, or analytic, sciences like logic and mathematics) is an integrated body of knowledge about things of which we have experience and about ourselves as experiencing subjects. If in our experience of natural things and events there is an apparent break in the continuity of process or in the lawfully ordered relations of things among themselves, this is a challenge to science. Because science is concerned with the relations of things, a chaotic or dismembered world could not be investigated scientifically. For the naturalist, then, a dualistic or pluralistic philosophy of nature is a confession of defeat.

When the laws in accordance with which natural events take place are adequately known, we can discover causes. In a causal situation there is always a directive. We are interested in causality because knowledge of causes may enable us to control the direction taken by natural events or, if that is impossible, to control our own conduct in adjustment to them. Man-made machines and human social organizations are designed for this purpose. The naturalist's interest in causality is strictly operational. There is no causal agent which acts as a *deus ex machina* upon a natural process. The active agency is in the process itself; indeed it *is* the process. It is an inexact use of words to say that any cause controls its effect, for the control is exercised within the event, not upon it. This "immanent causality," as Sellars calls it, is nothing other than the directive activity which is inherent in every mechanism and is the distinguishing characteristic of mechanism as such.

If, then, we regard the living body as a mechanism, we must recognize it for what it is as *mechanism*—a creative causal agency capable of fabricating out of inorganic materials a living substance with properties quite unlike those of the constituent ingredients. The directive quality of vital activities—organic evolution, individual development, regeneration, adaptive behavior, purposive action, and all the rest—is unique, not in being directive, but in the range and complexity of its manifestation and in the capacity shown for self-regulation and self-determination of novel patterns of performance.

With rare insight Claude Bernard wrote in 1878, "La vie, c'est la création." There is still much that is mysterious about this creative power and the mechanisms employed, but nothing is gained by appeal to mystic agencies that lie beyond the realm of the natural order. The human capacity for inventing new things and original conceptions is the outgrowth of those creative powers that are inherent in all living substance, and the successive steps in the acquisition of this capacity are open to inspection. This vital creativity, in its turn, has its roots in that directive quality that is apparent in every causal situation, organic and inorganic. Making novelties seems to be nature's chief industry.

The avowed objective of most physiological research has been to *reduce* vital processes to the physicochemical categories of the inorganic realm. This has been remarkably successful up to a certain point; but a limit is soon reached beyond which it fails to explain the observed facts, because actually these processes face the other way about, forward not backward. The innumerable physical and chemical processes of inorganic type which have been recognized in vital processes are combined in patterns that are novel and distinctive, and this creation of new patterns has been carried on at an accelerated rate during the course of organic evolution.

The key problems in all scientific inquiry are not analytic but synthetic. This is because the new properties that emerge in directive activities are unique combinations integrated from elements which lack these properties. A study of the history of creative evolution reveals successive levels of more complex and efficient integration. As Novikoff has remarked in a survey of integrative levels:

> Each level of organization possesses unique properties of structure and behavior which, though dependent on the properties of the constituent elements, appear only when these elements are combined in the new system . . . The laws describing the unique properties of each level are qualitatively distinct, and their discovery requires methods of research and analysis appropriate to the particular level.[1]

The foregoing general topics, some of which are treated more fully in other sections of this symposium, are recapitulated here because they are essential for an understanding of the relations between vital phenomena and those of the world within which they are set and of which they are part. The integrity of this cosmos and the orderliness of all natural processes is the basic induction of modern science.

In a search for integrating agencies which hold the world together and preserve the unity and the individuality of its constituent parts, that is, for the causes of the orderly sequence of events, we look for directive trends in the phenomena under observation. This, as just pointed out, is the most obvious characteristic of living bodies.

In the course of development of the individual from egg to maturity there is successive increase in the complexity of structure and behavior, with enlargement of the variety and range of directive activities. There is also ample evidence that in the hundreds of millions of years during which life has existed on this planet similar changes have resulted in greater efficiency of adjustment of living beings to environment, including a larger measure of control of the environment itself. This control may change the physical features of the terrain (coral reefs, beaver dams, irrigation projects), it may revolutionize the flora and fauna of a continent (by replacing forest and prairie with farms), and at all levels of vital organization there is some measure of social control within the group and from group to group (with, in human society, elaborate instrumentation in education, political administration, and so on).

The directive movements are often called progressive, but progress has been so variously defined and so often debated without definition and with covert transfer from one connotation to another that much of this dialectic is futile. For our present purpose progressive organic evolution may be defined as change in the direction of increase in the range, variety, and efficiency of adjustment of the organism to its environment. Progress in the development of the career of any individual may be gauged by similar criteria—by his success in meeting the emergencies of life with strength, skill, and versatility that yield a larger measure of satisfaction. If he is content with cheap satisfactions, his life is correspondingly impoverished.

In the animal kingdom viewed as a whole, we recognize progressive changes in two directions toward radically different types of successful adaptation. Adjustments of the first type are primarily in the interest of the individual animal, its survival and the progressive diversification and enlargement of the scope of its activities, with more varied needs and enhanced satisfactions of these needs; they involve also increase in the self-sufficiency of the individual and ability to adapt to a wider range of external conditions. This may be termed the *individually modifiable,* or plastic, type of adjustment. In the domain of human social organizations we call it democratic.

Adjustments of the second type may be of a species or other group as a whole to some niche of the environment or to some characteristic mode of life. In this *totalitarian* type of adjustment the welfare and autonomy of the individuals are subordinated to the group, as seen in the beehive and the ant colony. It may or may not be progressive as here defined. In the case of many parasites, for instance, it is regressive—a successful regression from the standpoint of survival of the species, but at the expense of individual competence and range of adaptability of the species.

The individually modifiable and the totalitarian types of adaptation are not mutually exclusive; for all animals, from the lowest to the highest, show some capacity for self-improvement and at least a rudimentary kind of learning ability, and in all ranks of life there is some measure of group adaptation and social control. But in the higher ranks one or the other of these directive trends is manifestly predominant, so that we recognize two rather sharply contrasted types of progressive differentiation of both individual and social organization.

In the organization of both the individual body and the social group there are always two components. One is a stable, relatively rigid system of characteristics common to all members of the species or group. In the body these characteristics are typified by reflexes and instincts, which are fixed in the genetic organization of the species; in human society we find something similar in established codes of behavior transmitted from generation to generation by what has been termed social heredity, that is, by example, oral tradition, written documents, legal enactments, etc. Sharply contrasted with the stereotyped patterns of this system are other characteristics which are individually acquired by personal experience, including learning and all the higher mental capacities related with it. Some learned patterns of behavior may be so stabilized as habits that they are hard to distinguish from instincts; but the habits are not inherited, and, like all other cultural accomplishments, they must be reacquired by each succeeding generation. This implies that the second component of behavior patterns has a plasticity that the first component lacks.

In the human brain the apparatus that performs the two kinds of functions is conspicuously different. The reflex and instinctive acts are controlled by a relatively rigid arrangement of nerve cells and fibers which is substantially the same in all persons. Permeating this stable fabric there is a looser reticulum that we call neuropil, which in some way as yet unknown provides for conditioning of reflexes and other modifiable behavior. In addition, the brain stem is enveloped by a gray mantle, the cerebral cortex, which is the specific organ of the higher mental functions, with structure which is exceedingly variable from person to person. In all animals with well developed nervous systems these two types of component nervous structure can be recognized, and in man the apparatus of intelligent control of conduct is so greatly enlarged that it makes up more than half the total mass of the brain.

In the course of animal evolution, one line of progressive specialization of totalitarian type has culminated in the insects. These are very successful organisms. More than two-fifths of the 2,500,000 known species of animals are insects. There are more than 3,5000 species of ants, and Wheeler estimated that there are now more ants in the world than there are individuals of all other terrestrial animals in the aggregate. The group of ants is plastic; the several species are adapted to every possible situation. Within the species there are specialized castes with refined division of labor. Each species and each caste shows amazing perfection of adaptation of structure and behavior for performance of specific duties which are rigidly circumscribed. These adaptations of each group are biologically determined for the group as a whole by stable genetic, nutritional, and other factors, and the individual ant has a very limited range of abilities. They have some freedom of choice about what they do and some capacity for learning, but these are narrowly restricted and most of their activities are standardized in the interest of the colony as a whole, not of its separate members. Every ant must conform to the predetermined pattern of stereotyped reflex and instinctive behavior or perish. They do perish in enormous numbers; but there are plenty of ants, and the cruel wastage of ant-power is compensated by great fecundity.

The ant colony is a totalitarian type of social organization in which the welfare of the individual is ruthlessly subordinated to that of the group. The integration of the group is maintained by virtue of its intrinsic organization, that is, by the interplay of the constituent castes or classes in a dynamic equilibrated system, with no dominant overlord in control. This clearly is a very efficient device for assuring survival of the groups and their adaptation to a wide range of conditions; but the efficiency is at a low level of integration as measured by biological criteria. The insects as a class are ranked lower than the mammals despite their more extreme specialization. In evolutionary time they appeared about 150,000,000 years before the earliest mammals, their specialization was in a different direction, and from the Carboniferous Period until now they have spread horizontally on this low plane. In sharp contrast, the mammalian series of animals, which has lived for a much shorter time, has progressed in a different direction and at a constantly accelerated rate up to man, who claims to sit on the top of the world.

Another type of totalitarian organization is seen in those groups which are dominated by a powerful master or dictator, as seen in the pecking rank of barnyard fowls, the harems of the fur-seal rookeries, and unlimited monarchial and fascist human governments. Here preeminent aggressive ability of an individual, or an oligarchy, succeeds in imposing forcible control upon a population composed, not of robots but of individuals endowed with a larger measure of plasticity, initiative, and intelligence than any insects possess. The integrative agency here resides in a head or central power; and, in human societies, if this power is administered with skill and firmness, the efficiency of the organization is far greater than anything that has been attained by equalitarian or communal organization.

But this is not the best way to manage human affairs, for the history of human culture teaches unequivocally that no form of totalitarian organization is equal in efficiency as a mechanism of cultural progress under present conditions to the type of adjustment which was characterized above as individually modifiable, or democratic. The many attempts that have been made to establish communities on an equalitarian basis have proved to be utopian. Either the community disintegrates from internal friction, or else it survives under the dominance of a dictator or an oligarchy. And no absolute monarchy or dictatorship is stable. Sooner or later, if not transformed by democratic process, it is destroyed by rebellion. We have ample experience of the advantage of democracy, and this, as we now see, has sound biological justification.

All the progessive changes which have been mentioned involve specialization of the individual body or of the social group, with local differentiation of parts, each of which has some capacity for independent autonomous action. This local autonomy, however, must always be kept in subordination to the dominant control of the body as a whole. Otherwise conflict arises, resulting in impairment of efficiency and, if carried to an extreme, in death, as, for example, from cancer. Or else, if the central dominance is of low order and local autonomy is highly developed, the integrity of the individual may be sundered, with resulting fission into two or more separate persons, as happens in the budding of polyps and the segmentation of tapeworms. In human social organizations comparable processes are observed in uninhibited nationalism (which is a cancerous growth) and in successful factional rivalries which split a social unit into separate organizations.

In the development of every living body and every social group there are these two trends which are in some respects antagonistic; namely, progressive differentiation of parts with local autonomy, and, opposed to this, the necessity for maintenance of the integrity of the individual. Successful living depends on progressive development in both directions in proper balance. Integration is the primordial requirement for survival. The individuation of parts takes place within the integrated whole and must be kept in subordination to it. From this it follows that discovery of the integrating agencies is a cardinal problem in biology. This is even more evidently true in sociology, which is fundamentally a biological discipline.

Many of the organic integrating agencies that have been recognized are similar to those seen in inorganic mechanisms, such as adjustment for the distribution of mechanical strain, various ingenious mechanical devices for regulating the flow of fluids and changes in temperature, the physical properties of surfaces and the permeability of membranes, chemical reactions in infinite variety and the associated changes in electrical potential.

There are other integrating mechanisms for which there are no inorganic counterparts. With increase in the size and complexity of animal bodies there is demand for conductors adapted for speedy transmission from part to part. The flow of blood with its contained chemical messengers meets some of these requirements. Ordinary protoplasm also is a conductor of physical, chemical, and electrical energies, though the transmission is slow and diffuse. Slender strands of protoplasm are especially modified to secure more rapid conduction without decrement for long distances by insulated pathways. Transmission in these nerve fibers involves well known physical, chemical, and electrical processes, but these are combined in patterns of action which are unknown in the inorganic realm. In all except the most primitive animals, the nervous system is by far the most important apparatus of integration, and this is its primary function.

The simplest nervous systems known are in coral polyps, jellyfish and their allies, where the nerve fibers are woven into a network which is spread almost uniformly throughout the entire body. The jellyfish's body is more perfectly integrated than that of a sponge of equal size, because the sponge has no nerves. The diffuse network keeps every part of the body of the jellyfish in communication with every other part. There is no head or other central control station. Integration is effected simply by the interplay of a system of conductors which facilitates coordinated action of all parts in the interest of the welfare of the whole body.

In higher animals with more complicated bodies, the nervous system shows progressive increase in size and differentiation in two directions, which may be termed analytic and synthetic. Various organs of sense are developed, each of which is attuned to respond to a specific kind of environing energy—pressure, sound waves, light waves, and many others. These sense organs and the related nerves and central adjustors comprise the apparatus for analysis of sensory experience. On the motor side there is similar analysis in the organs of expression. Out of the total repertoire of possible responses to stimulation, those and only those are selected which give behavior appropriate to the situation as registered by the sense organs.

The diffuse nervous network seen in jellyfish would be incapable of making the refined analysis of sensory and motor experience of stimulus-response type that is done by higher animals. A central adjusting apparatus is needed to sort out the different kinds of incoming sensory messages and to direct them into the appropriate outgoing channels. Accordingly, parallel with the elaboration of the analytic apparatus which has just been mentioned, the central nervous system is progressively enlarged and complicated, to include also the synthetic apparatus which assures the integration of all local activities and their coordinated action.

The central dominance of the integrating apparatus assumes progressively greater importance as we pass from the lower to the higher ranks of animals because of the increasing complexity of the problems of behavior to be resolved. In the lower ranks most of the behavior is stereotyped in heritable stimulus-response patterns which we call reflex or instinctive, with relatively little ability to change these patterns by learning through personal experience. In the higher mammals the primitive stereotyped patterns are not lost, but they are supplemented by progressively increasing ability to regulate behavior through postnatal experience. This increase in learning power is correlated with enlargement and complication of the cerebral cortex, which is preeminently the organ of learning and all those mental capacities which are dependent upon it.

In the series of backboned animals, from fish to man, the fundamental plan of the brain is similar, but the modifications of the plan in adaptation to various modes of life are amazingly great and diversified. Only one illustration can be cited here, and it concerns the origin and significance of the cerebral cortex.

The most primitive existing animals that possess a well differentiated cortex are the turtles, though imperfect rudiments of it are seen in some fishes and amphibians. The fossil record shows that from primitive reptiles now extinct two lines of progressive evolution diverged, one leading up to the present birds, the other to the mammals. In all living birds the stem portion of the cerebral hemispheres is enormously enlarged, but the overlying cortex is reduced and in some species scarcely evident. In all mammals, on the contrary, the stem portion of the hemispheres is diminished to less than the reptilian size and the cortex is enlarged and diversified, and progressively so we pass from lower to higher species of mammals. Why is this?

The answer is plain. The bodies of birds are more highly specialized than those of mammals, and in the brain the stem part of the hemispheres and the related structures of the thalamus are far more elaborately differentiated. It is well known that these cerebral structures are concerned chiefly with the control of the instinctive and emotional components of behavior; and these components are more highly elaborated in the birds than in any other class of animals. Birds, like insects, are very successful animals. They mark the culmination of a directive trend in evolution, with emphasis on heritable, stereotyped patterns of behavior at a high level of efficiency. The number of species is large, and they are adapted to a wide range of environmental conditions. This adaptation is of the species as a whole, as in insects, though the method employed is different from that of the social insects. Birds are more intelligent than ants, and their lives are far richer in diversified experience; yet the individual bird is not very adaptable, and the capacity for learning is far inferior to that of the higher mammals. Birds have dominated the air, but now the inventiveness of man has surpassed them in the control of their own domain.

Mammalian evolution took a different direction, with emphasis on the adaptability and educability of the individuals rather than on diversification of the species of which they are members. In the most primitive mammals these capacities are not highly developed; but they all possess a specialized cortical gray mantle of the cerebral hemispheres which is organized on a plan different from anything found elsewhere in the brain, and which has practically unlimited potentialities for further elaboration. In mammalian evolution this cortical gray expanded at a very rapid rate (as measured by evolutionary time) ; and, correlated with the progressive differentiation of this tissue, the intelligent type of adjustment was correspondingly augmented.

In the reptilian ancestors of mammals most of the behavior was inflexibly reflex and instinctive, under the control of the brain stem. In existing reptiles and birds, as just pointed out, the stem part of the cerebral hemispheres and the thalamus are enormously enlarged to perform these functions. But in the reptilian cortex we see an incipient stage of development of a structure of different type, which marks the appearance of an integrating apparatus at a higher level—a new pattern of organization which in the mammals assumes control of all activities of the underlying brain stem. This control is intelligently directed, and intelligence is not heritable; it is always individually acquired.

The successive steps in these transformations of behavioral capacity and the related bodily organs have been carefully studied. There are few wide gaps in our present knowledge of the continuity of the series of changes as we pass from the inorganic through the ranks of the animal kingdom up to and including mankind. The two most critical points are marked by the transition from the inorganic to the organic and from brute to man.

The gap between the inorganic and the organic realms is obviously bridged in so many ways that there is no occasion for invoking any mystic immaterial agencies. All materials and energies found in living bodies are derived from the inorganic realm, and they are returned to it. The new thing that has emerged is the pattern of performance, and this sort of thing we find throughout the inorganic realm also, as when water is made out of hydrogen and oxygen. It is directive action in all cases.

Pattern is not a nonphysical entity, an empty verbalism, or merely an abstract concept. It is an observable property of everything there is, from atoms to galaxies, from ameba to man. Some of these different patterns are overtly discontinuous, so that evolution seems to be saltatory; but under the superficial appearance of every one of these apparent jumps there is continuity of process. The gap between the inorganic and the living has been bridged by the discovery of what Needham calls "mesoforms." For instance, in both intrinsic structure and patterns of behavior, the known viruses intergrade with the non-living protein molecules, on one hand, and with living protoplasm, on the other hand.

The gap between ape and man may now be regarded as successfully bridged so far as concerns bodily structure. Recent paleontological discoveries have brought to light so many intermediate forms between extinct species of apes and fossilized specimens of primitive man that the main features of human ancestry are now before us.

There remains, however, one wide gap in our knowledge of the evolution of man that has not been satisfactorily filled. The brains of the most primitive races of men now living are about twice as big as those of any apes of comparable body size. What is the meaning of this apparently saltatory change? Most of the increase is in the cerebral cortex and its immediate dependencies. We know that this cortex is the specific organ of our rational life, and this knowledge opens up the question of the evolution of mind and the more fundamental problems of the relations between mentation in general and the physiological functions which are obviously colligated with it.

The colligation of our mental life with its bodily instrumentation, to which reference has just been made, is so intimate and so well validated by adequately controlled scientific evidence that it must be accepted as an organic relationship. Our bodies move themselves and their members by means of well known organs, the action of which is fairly well understood, though much remains obscure. In a similar way our bodies feel and think, and the organs by which these acts are performed have been recognized and described in great detail. The evidence that these two kinds of performance are executed by their respective organs is of similar nature, it is clear-cut, and it is equally convincing in the two cases. But we do not know as much about how the apparatus of mentation actually works as we know about muscular contraction. Though we do not yet understand how we understand, perhaps we can find out.

The great difficulty with which we are confronted in this enterprise resides in the disparity between our perceptual knowledge about our own bodies and about all other objective things, on one hand, and, on the other hand, the subjective processes by which this knowledge is manipulated in the acts of perception and reasoning. The things and events of our naïve objective world are framed in three-dimensional space and linear sequence of time. These events have been systematized and explained in terms of Newtonian mechanics, Euclidean geometry, and Aristotelan logic. We now know, however, that the principles just mentioned are not universals. They are applicable in what Sir James Jeans called "the man-sized world"; but in the domains of subatomic physics and astral space they must be supplemented by the principles of relativity and quantum mechanics. It remains true that all we know about this objective world indicates that it is a lawfully integrated unitary system.

The subjective domain also is lawfully ordered in accordance with principles which have been codified in the sciences of introspective psychology, logic, linguistics, and cognate subjects. The laws of this order are radically different from those of the objective domain. For instance, they may be entirely emancipated from the limitations of space and time. All thinking is here and now, but this "specious present" may, with the aid of symbols, embrace unlimited space and time. Abstract concepts of universals, like "truth," disregard space and time.

This apparent discontinuity between the realm of objective nature as we know it through perceptual evidence and the realm of subjective experience as we participate in it has not been satisfactorily explained. No structure-function models designed in accordance with the principles of either Newtonian or quantum mechanics have been devised which satisfactorily bridge this gap, and an increasing number of competent authorities incline to the belief that such a construction is impossible. When it was found that Newtonian mechanics was inadequate in the domains of subatomic and astral physics, quite different systems of relationships were discovered. This analogy suggests that it may be necessary to find a still different frame of reference, as yet unknown, before the body-mind relationships can be clarified. The acquisition by mankind of ability to think in terms of symbols of abstractions (words, numbers, conceptual configurations of various sorts) apparently marks a step to a higher level of integration than has been achieved by any subhuman creatures. We somehow manage to experience the process of cerebration as an active participant on the inside of the works, not as a spectator looking at the apparatus through perceptual channels.

This unique immediate awareness cannot be reduced to the level of the systems of structural and functional organization from which it emerges. It tells us nothing directly about the organic apparatus involved, though, as we have seen, it is possible to learn a great deal about its relations with the underlying subsconscious processes by objective methods of inquiry. All naïve perceptual experience is framed in space and time, but conceptual experience may be free to disregard this limitation. This is why the subjective and the objective realms of experience seem to be disparate and incommensurable. The metric employed in physical, chemical, and physiological investigation is not applicable in the psychic realm.

The scope of our conceptual experience and its inventive skill has been progressively enlarged. The three-dimensional space and one-dimensional time of perceptual experience have been united in a concept of four-dimensional space-time with a different metric, and this is now a useful tool of scientific investigation. The mathematicians have gone further in this direction and postulate still higher dimensions, of which we find no analogies in perceptual experience. It may well be that the realms of conceptual (introspective) experience and perceptual (extraspective) experience are related in terms of dimensions not yet recognized and given scientific expression, accepting Oliver L. Reiser's definition of a dimension as "any manifold which can be ordered." [2] Appeal is made here to the principle that, if integrated order cannot be observed at any dimensional level, it may be found at a higher dimensional level.

This is the problem that baffles us, and until this mystery is resolved we must work with such tools as we have, always alert for better methods and new formulations of our problems and always confining our search within the domain of verifiable experience with no appeal to mysticism.

A conscious experience has no existence except at the moment of its exercise. As a bodily activity it is where it is made, just as truly as the location of the magnetic field of a dynamo is determined by the place where the apparatus that generates it is set up, and it occurs only when the apparatus is in appropriate action. The mechanism of the conscious act has locus in space and time, but the product made, the thought, is patterned on different principles.

What may be the mechanism involved in the conscious act, and how it differs from those of its unconscious precursors and accompaniments, is still unknown. In this connection it is well to remember that the most characteristic nervous functions of the brain are circular reactions, not one-way traffic as postulated in the conventional stimulus-response formula. When waves of sound impinge upon the ear a nervous impulse is transmitted to the brain, and this is immediately followed by a nervous outflow back to the receptive organ, to the intrinsic muscles of the middle ear and probably also to the organ of Corti itself. When a muscle contracts there is a report back to the central nervous system which registers there the location and character of the movement. The thalamus and the cerebral cortex are reciprocally connected in such a way that any activity of the one is immediately registered in the other, so that both are involved in every cortical activity.

There is evidence that consciousness emerges genetically within bodily activity and is conditioned upon it. From this it has been inferred that

> the consciousness of a sensation is probably never attained until there has been a kinesodic response to it and it is not unlikely that it is the reflected current rather than the direct one which enters consciousness. It is in this way that the storage of vestiges in the cortex may be explained in such cases where the original stimulus never reached consciousness.[3]

The stream of consciousness is not an uninterrupted flow. But the subconscious activities out of which consciousness emerges are continuous. There is no break in the flow of the vital process. This opens up an avenue of approach to our problem that promises well.

This promise is supported by several lines of current investigation which employ recently invented instruments, new technical methods, original engineering concepts and mathematical processes, and, above all, the convergence upon specific projects of the skills of specialists in diverse fields. To mention a single illustration, in the construction of improved electronic computing machines the engineering principle of the feed-back is so applied as to give results that are strikingly similar to those that we get in the mental operations of observation, memory, logical analysis and generalization. The mechanisms employed in the machine and in the brain are radically different, but the principles involved have much in common.[4] We seem to be on the threshold of a new domain of psychobiology.

Though every conscious act is solipsistic in the sense that it is strictly personal and private, just as every reflex is, neither of these acts is an isolated event. The mental act has antecedents and consequences, some of which are consciously experienced and some not. In short, the conscious act is an integral member of a causal situation, and these causal relationships are observable. The study of relationships is a cardinal scientific method. In fact, all that we know about anything is its relationships, and every scientific explanation is an exposition of these relations.

A thought is a private possession and as such it cannot be regarded as a datum of science. Not directly, but if it is expressed, the utterance is an overt act and, if written as a proposition, it becomes an enduring object that can be examined and reexamined scientifically. By this and other indirections a science of introspective psychology is practicable. Again, since every mental act has antecedents, accompaniments, and consequences that are objectively discoverable, these physiological, behavioristic, and other relations furnish the data for the legitimate sciences of physiological and comparative psychology.

These studies, which now are far advanced, have brought to light, in the objective domain, so many data of both human and animal economy that we may safely say that consciousness emerges within behavior as a new pattern of performance in much the same way that life emerges from the non-living and that every other novel pattern arises by directive action intrinsic to the appropriately organized structure. The distinctive properties of our so-called spiritual life arise within us as naturally as do our breathing and our muscular contractions. It is as natural for the brain to think as it is for the heart to beat.

Nature, as known to mankind, is defined by Santayana as "the sum total of things potentially observable, some observed actually, others interpolated hypothetically." From this it follows that we are justified in "regarding nature as the condition of mind and not mind as the condition of nature." [5] When nature, including human nature, is thus examined realistically, we are at once impressed by the polarization of the observer (the self) set over against the things observed (the objective world). This polarization is not something peculiarly distinctive of human experience. As we have seen, every living thing is an integrated unit which is polarized in a similar way against the things that comprise its environment. Every organism is a self in this biological sense. We also observe something similar throughout the inorganic realm. A molecule of water as an integrated unit differs from every other thing with which it stands in relation by virtue of its own intrinsic properties.

Everything that is, is unique; otherwise we could not define it as a thing. Even repetitive processes are not circular in pattern; they are spiral. Nothing in nature is ever exactly repeated. Human experience marks the culmination (so far as we know) of an increasingly complex series of directive activities. It has unique properties like everything else in nature; but these properties have developed through eons of "emergent evolution" by a continuity of process, the main outlines of which are now clearly before us. Human individuality, the acquisition of hands and related cerebral apparatus for invention and use of tools, the polarization of the self against the not-self, the directive quality of human purposive action, human freedom of choice of a present act in the light of intelligent appraisal of possible future consequences (by what Korzybski calls "time-binding"), the acquisition of symbolic thinking with the aid of language, mathematics, and other semantic tools, the fabrication and codification of practical rules of conduct in accordance with general principles of utility and aesthetic and moral standards—all these distinctively human perquisites have their roots in various subhuman activities which have been identified and more or less fully described.

The moral standards properly top this list of human attributes because the whole history of human culture teaches that in our present types of social organization they have actual survival value. Without the intelligent practice of a large measure of subordination of personal, group, and national advantage to the welfare of other groups and of the population of the world as a whole, the social structure disintegrates, and we perish with it. And this subordination must be voluntary, that is, intrinsic to the mechanism in operation, not enforced by an outside power.

Conformity with moral standards of decency, honor, and social responsibility is the price that must be paid for social stability and cultural advancement. Civilized man has succeeded very well in controlling for his own use his physical environment and the resources of plant and animal life, but he has dismally failed to understand his own nature and learn how to keep the peace with himself and his neighbors. He has not grasped the significance of the essential differences between his own human nature and the rest of nature, and so too often he tries to make his adjustments in accordance with the laws of the jungle. Thousands of years of human experience, and especially the experience of the present generation, have shown beyond question that the social standards of the anthill and the wolf pack do not fit our situation. A code that is good enough for a skunk or a hyena drives man to perdition.

It is doubtless true, as has been emphasized by Sewall Wright and A. E. Emerson,[6] that it is in large measure the populations that are the units of evolutionary change, yet the qualities of the individuals composing these populations play a progressively larger part in shaping the course of events in the competitions of populations for survival. This is why in the higher ranks of life the individually modifiable types of adjustment have the advantage over the totalitarian types, and why the moral standards of the individuals are decisive factors in human survival.

Fortunately, under the surface of present disorder there is a substrate of sound, vigorous, enterprising, and decent human nature. I have faith in humanity because we have only to be true to those qualities of our own nature which have emerged from a brutish ancestry to assure successful adjustment in an ever changing world. Given time (a lot of time, from present indications), we shall learn how to get along with ourselves as well as we manage to do with the rest of our natural surroundings.

We already have the necessary knowledge and the available skills to conduct our affairs in the light of reason, rather than of greed, national supremacy, racial and other traditional prejudices, irrational dogma, and wishful thinking. The human brain and the life of reason with which it endows us are the natural products of a long process of emergent evolution, and we may cherish the faith that nature will not be defeated by its own machinery. But we must find and apply some new patterns of thought if we hope to succeed in this quest.

References

[1] Alex B. Novikoff, *Science,* Vol. 101 (1945), No. 2618, pp. 209–215.

[2] Oliver L. Reiser, *The World Sensorium* (New York: Avalon Press, 1946).

[3] C. L. Herrick, *J. Comp. Neurol.,* Vol. 6 (1896), p. xxi.

[4] There is an extensive literature dealing with this and related subjects, as illustrated by the following works and others there cited: Arturo Rosenblueth, Norbert Wiener, and Julian Bigelow, *Philos. Sci.,* Vol. 10 (1943), pp. 18–24. F. S. C. Northrop, *Science,* Vol. 107 (1948), No. 2782, pp. 411–417. L. K. Frank, G. E. Hutchinson, W. K. Livingston, W. S. McCulloch, and N. Wiener, "Teleological Mechanisms," *Annals N.Y. Acad. Sci.,* Vol. 50 (1948), Art. 4, pp. 187–278. Herbert H. Jasper, *Science,* Vol. 108 (1948), No. 2805, pp. 343–347. Norbert Wiener, *Cybernetics, or Control and Communication in the Animal and the Machine* (New York: Wiley, 1948)—abstract by the author in *Scientific American,* Vol. 179 (1948), No. 5, pp. 14–19.

[5] George Santayana, *Reason in Common Sense,* 2nd ed. (New York: Scribner, 1928).

[6] A. E. Emerson, *Trans. Ill. Acad. Sci.,* Vol. 39 (1946), pp. 9–18.

LEVELS IN THE PSYCHOLOGICAL CAPACITIES OF ANIMALS

by

T. C.

SCHNEIRLA

T. C. Schneirla, Sc.D. (Michigan, 1928), Curator, Department of Animal Behavior, American Museum of Natural History; Visiting Professor of Psychology, New York University. Formerly Fellow of the National Research Council and of the John Simon Guggenheim Memorial Foundation. Field work in Mexico and Central America on problems in animal behavior, since 1932; laboratory investigator on problems in learning, insect behavior. Coauthor of *Principles of Animal Psychology* (1935) and *Recent Experiments in Psychology* (1938). Articles on research and theory of problems in animal psychology, in *Journal of Comparative Psychology, Biological Bulletin,* and other periodicals.

THE concept of psychological levels in its modern form is due especially to the investigative attack of experimental science upon evolutionary processes. To a large extent these lines of research have been materialistic in the sense that their principal method drives for explanations of events in terms of properties discovered through systematically broadened and controlled investigative experience. Such empirically grounded methods have been introduced broadly into investigation and theory as well, challenging in both of these departments the predominantly deductive and subjective procedures which have infiltrated science from preexperimental philosophy through mystical and animistic conceptions of nature. An inevitable characteristic of the materialistic approach to problems is the drive for naturalistic explanations.

The term "levels" is a convenient conceptual device for developing a systematic theory of different patterns of adaptation to the given conditions of existence in different organisms. Our methods of investigating, describing, and explaining the similarities and differences which prevail among different animal types must adjust themselves as precisely as possible to the real state of affairs prevalent in each case. Both Mechanists and Vitalists seem to have missed this course by divergently emphasizing different phenomena; the former by endeavoring to fit all adaptive capacities directly under physicochemical rubrics, the latter by setting out to bring all cases under a universal supernatural causal principle. Both seem to have erred in generalizing too widely an incomplete characterization of a different portion of the animal series. In effect, both have slipped into what Sloane (105) aptly terms the error of "reductionism"—they have tended to reduce organisms to a single level by distracting attention from the nature of differences among levels. To offer seriously a theory of human thinking couched throughout in terms of brain biochemistry is vague in that the nature of the general capacity is lost in a welter of unorganized details. To offer an explanation of food-taking in a protozoan organism as "purposive striving" is assuredly vague in a somewhat different sense, in that a humanized label is applied which has barely more than a literary suitability in the given situation.

It is necessary to ask what questions are properly subject to investigation by animal psychologists—that is, what constitutes a psychological problem in animal behavior? A classical answer has been rephrased by Bierens de Haan (10), who considers Psychology as a science of "psychic realities" which man can first know in himself through introspection, and then study in lower animals through "sympathetic intuition." The difficulty is not merely that such an approach to the subject is ethnocentric and limits procedures mainly to anthropomorphically colored analogies, but—even more serious—that human introspection as the proposed source of concepts offers a most unsound point of departure. Modern experimental psychologists studying human capacities employ introspection only with numerous reservations as a secondary adjunct to method, admitting such data as evidence only after adequate checks and balances have been imposed. Many difficulties await one who operates through analogy on a phenomenalistic basis such as the above.

The general problem of the animal psychologist is the nature of behavioral capacities on all levels of accomplishment. He must contrive to understand how each animal type functions as a whole in meeting its surrounding conditions; what its capacities are like and how they are organized in admitting given functions of individual-unit or of group. The principle of levels has come into current usage through a recognition of important differences in the complexity, the degree of development, and the interdependent organization of behavior functions through the animal series. The evidently superior properties that appear on a new level of organization are not to be explained as due to a new kind of energy (85) or new vital properties (83), but as functional properties arising from a new system of organization which differs in given ways from "lower" and "higher" systems. Thus local autonomy in food-taking is less in the snail than in the jellyfish, the learning of social insects is subject to limitations evidently not typical of mammals, internal condition can have a more or less restricted significance in the general behavior of different animals, and so on (75).

The terms "part" and "whole" must be regarded as convenient abstractions which have a different relationship to each other on different animal levels. For example, in the sponge behavior of the individual aggregate is little more than a summated action of individual parts or chimneys, whereas in a food-snatching kitten the details of local muscle contraction are subsumed under superior functional organizations describable in part as learned habits. The problems of animal psychologists, then, involve discerning the similarities and differences in capacities and whole-functioning on different levels.

A reminder is essential at this point. A comparative study of capacity for organization does not presuppose a reduction of psychology to biological terms. We are cautioned by Novikoff (85) that the error of reducing all properties of the organism to the physicochemical is not to be corrected by ignoring biochemistry. Psychological properties must be regarded as derivatives of biological processes—hence the construction of appropriate new concepts must be undertaken when required by evidence at progressively higher levels. Put in another way, experience in behavior investigation reminds us not to expect the "wholes" of lower levels to be encountered as specific constituent parts on higher levels. If the lower-level wholes appear to be represented as subsystems in the higher organism, these are likely to be differentiated qualitatively by the nature of the given more inclusive system in which they occur. For instance, it is superficial and really misleading to say that "instinctive man" is like a given lower animal, since this implies that by removing the top layers we encounter substratal units which duplicate lower-animal behavior. A social group, as another example, is involved very differently as a unit in a population than an individual as a unit in a social group. The student of levels in capacities must be alert for qualitative differences as well as for similarities.

Theoretical validity is endangered in fundamental ways when concepts such as those offered by Vitalism are generalized *a priori* to all animal levels. Along with Vitalism have been inherited from preexperimental times the practices of a predominant deductivism, of widely generalizing certain unquestioned and uninvestigated concepts regarded as basic, thus imposing a strait-jacket upon whatever investigation may be attempted.

Anecdotalism

An inevitable outcome is the practice of anecdotalism, in which there is a selection and mustering of instances which fit given preconceived explanations at the expense of a broad study of relevant events. Anecdotalism is chronically subjective and not experimental in tendency. Here we are confronted with a curious explanatory procedure in which a final interpretation exists in advance of any appreciable amount of evidence. This practice is by nature restrictive and non-statistical, promoting the selection of given events for description without much consideration of the wide population of events in the classes to which these belong. It can lead irresponsibly to an emphasis upon instances or of characteristics which may well be exceptional in nature and unrepresentative of their classes. One who sets out to demonstrate that protozoan organisms or any others have the mental characteristics of man may convince himself at least, provided he singles out opportunely the brief episodes which seem describable as instances of perception of danger, of reasoning, or what not. By the same method, the absence of reasoning in man can be proved with ease.

Another difficulty with anecdotalism lies in its dependence upon the false assumption that an uncontrolled perceptual observation must possess some intrinsic validity of its own. The shortcomings of observational memory and its corollary procedure of unchecked verbal report have been emphasized repeatedly by general psychologists, from Stern to Bartlett (6). The best intentioned subjects typically report their observations with alterations, additions, and various types of motivated rearrangement in the material. Such defects emphasize the basic importance of a dependable technique and method for studying animal capacities. Actually, observation involves techniques subject to improvement through practice, just as do more formal methods of experimentation.

It is a safe rule that rigid distinctions, particularly those offered with pretensions to fundamental significance, should be held as highly tentative in scientific procedure and not accorded fundamental explanatory roles in advance of adequate evidence. Yet the separate existence of "mental" and "physical" realities still enters almost without question into the theorizing of many scientists and philosophers about animal nature. When we admit the dichotomy mind *vs.* body without challenging its applicability to scientific investigation, anecdotal practices are a foregone conclusion as ingrown features of method. For the concept "mind" offers a convenient ground against which seemingly representative instances can be selected perceptually to the exclusion of others. And the blanket concept of the animal's "psyche" offers a convenient device for relegating the biological actualities underlying adaptive existence to limbo in favor of hypothetical agencies such as "purpose," "vital principle," or "mental faculties."

It is possible to introduce anecdotalism without seeming to do so, by selecting evidence which emphasizes apparent similarities among animal levels. To say that a particular instance of behavior is a case of "learning" does not explain it and assuredly does not demonstrate that it is necessarily related very closely to other instances in which the same term has been used. The similarity may be so partial and superficial that use of the common term actually misrepresents the various phenomena considered by minimizing the existence of wide areas of difference among them. Has an amoeba "learned" in any important sense when in the course of repeated head-on exposures to a beam of light it extends progressively fewer pseudopodia? (77) The phenomenon appears to resemble light adaptation more closely than it does learning in a higher animal, especially since it evidently involves a progressive reduction in the biochemical action of light which has a distinctive and relatively short time limit. It is doubtful whether Jennings (59), merely by using the term "learning," suggested an adequate explanation for his discovery that individual starfish can be induced to use much less frequently two of their five radial arms originally used predominantly in moving from a set of restraining pins, especially after another investigator has shown that the results can be duplicated by persistently rubbing the given arms or by applying acid to them. It is questionable whether Bramstedt (14) by using the term "conditioned response" has found the most suitable conceptual device to indicate what has occurred in given paramecia which remain predominantly in darkened water, out of a lighted area, without then requiring a temperature difference initially present in the two areas. At first sight these cases appear to have the essential aspects of "conditioned response" and "learning." Yet there are reasons to believe that this generalization has been very premature. Grabowski (42) found that paramecia would react as did Bramstedt's subjects even though they were kept from the experimental areas until the final "tests" and the water alone was subjected to the light-temperature combinations used in the training procedure of Bramstedt. The term "learning" seems to be very misleading for phenomena in lower invertebrate behavior which resemble instances of sensory adaptation and muscle fatigue more closely than they do a representative learning through experience. The breadth of the difference is suggested by the fact that no persistent and progressive changes of the species behavior system have been demonstrated in the lower invertebrates, at all comparable to what "learning" may involve in higher animals. On the strength of such evidence as Bramstedt's, Chauvin (19) believes that the psychological similarity of lowest and highest organisms has been underestimated. It is more likely that an uncritical generalized use of the higher-level concept has tended to distract attention from the vast area of difference separating these phenomena.

When terms such as "learning" are used in sweeping fashion on widely separate levels they encourage thinking conclusively of homogeneous agencies presumably understood in the various cases, rather than processes of very different nature still requiring explanation. Such practices have the characteristic of mysticism inherent in Vitalism, as well as its effect of distracting attention from the need for further analysis and comparison.

Analogy

A serious charge to which vitalistic theories are vulnerable is that their premature generalization of concepts such as "mind" and "purpose" tends to vitiate the close comparison of animal levels which evolutionary doctrine encourages. If vitalistic precepts were generally followed, scientific procedure in studying animal capacities would be reduced to a mere general description of events under the label presumed to apply (cf. 49). For a dynamic theoretical process based upon inductive method would be substituted a system of concepts derived from initial "intuition" and enforced by authority, or prestige, or by the sheer inertia of wide acceptance. Matters have not been improved when concepts are imposed upon lower levels anthropocentrically, as the term "learning" has been generalized widely by some writers and "perception" by others (e.g., Russell, 92). Inevitably, an insistent generalization of mentalistic terms throughout the animal series, whether or not it is designedly vitalistic, has much in common with vitalistic thought-ways.

These procedures both involve centrally a dominant deductivism, which elevates the use of analogy at the expense of analysis. The term "mind" suggests close qualitative similarity wherever it is used, evading explanation but at the same time implying it with such propagandistic success that the issue seems fairly settled. The word then effectively infers a causal agency *sui generis,* in a procedure which lacks little to become animistic (52). A very similar strategy is accomplished through the generalization of terms such as "instinct" to several animal levels. Actually the practice is atavistic in the sense that the discussion of phenomena is transferred to preexperimental conditions under which it becomes easy to overlook or ignore evidence that does not agree with the given position.

A sound generalization deriving from the comparison of a wide variety of levels in animal capacity is that a given behavioral adjustment (e.g., food-taking) may be based in different instances upon very different patterns of cause-effect relationship. When an author asserts that an amoeba extending a pseudopod and a man asking for a sandwich are both acting "purposively," readers may be justified in taking the statement to allege that a similar "intention" underlies both acts. Whether the author really means this, or merely wishes to call attention to a similarity in the adaptive adequacy of behavior in the two cases, the effect of the common term is to imply that a closely related organization of underlying processes exists in both instances. A common feature of Vitalism, Animism, Mentalism, and other procedures featuring the use of analogy is that the organization of processes underlying behavioral systems is not subjected to very close study. Seldom do these doctrines encourage a critical comparison of presumably similar phenomena in different animal forms. Actually the analogies are preliminary and descriptive; the common terms, nothing more than tentative labels. Yet the customary emphasis upon a central theme tends to crystallize the terms and to obscure the unsoundness of applying them in purported explanatory roles to very different orders of events.

Idols of the Theater

Many of the difficulties we have been discussing rest upon a failure to recognize that concepts are ways of representing and thinking about things and their relationships; explanatory symbols which should change and develop with advances in our evidence about things and relationships. For example, in the pre-mating behavior of birds there are special activities which have been called "display" because, after Darwin, they have been regarded as special appeals designed to win over a desired individual of the opposite sex. For Pycraft (88) and some later writers such as Armstrong (4), the strutting and posturing of a male bird which serves to expose brilliant and striking plumage (not seen ordinarily) can have no other explanation. However, on further investigation, difficulties have arisen with this view. New factors of different nature have been discovered, which have led recent investigators such as Marshall (76) and Lack (64) to abandon the purposivistic concept of "display" for the notion that plumage is exposed incidentally in the course of behavior not designed to expose it as an appeal for mating, but appearing rather as a product of a generalized emotional excitement. Marshall came to the conclusion that the concept of a conscious sexual selection, as proposed by Darwin, must be replaced for birds by the view that such behavior is emotionally and not deliberately aroused. The other bird may be attracted through the behavior, but not because of a deliberate enticement, and in many cases the only identifiable adaptive role is that of promoting glandular processes. The behavior remains; our conception of it has been greatly improved.

Many instances may be found in which traditional concepts through long usage have come to represent presumable real forces underlying animal capacity. Frequently, after the example of Aristotle, students of animal ways have concluded that, because highly appropriate activities often seem to be without benefit of special experience, the impulse toward such activities must logically be inborn, or "instinctive." Modern animal psychology has had to struggle against the tremendous weight of authority always found behind this concept, and its seeming reasonableness. However, a growing body of experimental fact and theory now favors the view that "instinct" denotes a wide variety of bahavior processes all influenced in one or another way by hereditary factors, rather than inborn urges to carry out a given process. In different animals, it now appears, the hereditary factors may be of very different nature, and may influence the appearance of given behavior patterns in different ways and to different degrees (75). The word "instinct" is reductionistic and fallacious in the sense that it tends to level over these important group differences, and to obscure the real nature of their influence.

As Warren (114) has shown very succinctly, conceptual devices such as "instinct" and "mind" are products of a major nominalistic error, in that they involve substituting a mere name for a problem requiring solution. For a long time after Aristotle, while it was confidently proffered and widely accepted as standing for an explanation, the word "instinct" served to distract attention from the need for serious study of the subject matter. Increasingly in recent decades scientists with good reason have balked at following the instinct dogma. Distinctive processes have been found in the rise of individual behavior in different species as well as in the broadest groups, the animal phyla; very different processes which are not adequately represented by the word "instinct." Coghill's (21) investigations, for instance, have shown that aquatic locomotion of salamanders arises mainly through the maturation of given neural centers and connectors, whereas the research of Kuo (63), Shepard and Breed (101), and other investigators has revealed that pecking in domestic fowl is dependent upon the maturation of given part-process activities (e.g., head lunging at bright objects, and swallowing reflex) and a learning to use them together (75). In the chick's typical environment one type of learning becomes possible and the typical pecking pattern appears; under changed extrinsic conditions other learning occurs and the resulting pattern is quite different. Neither pattern is "instinctive" in the sense of resulting from an inborn urge to perform it as a system. This holds even more forcibly for the development of behavior in mammals, which in the higher orders involves learning to relatively greater extents, and eventuates in patterns which differ very plastically in relation to the special external conditions of development. Thus, although the word "instinct" loosely represents a type of problem, it no longer meets the requirement; namely, to express the relationships between hereditary factors and behavior patterns on different animal levels.

Animal psychologists can point to some five decades of real progress in the materialistic and empirical study of animal capacities (75, 81, 82, 113). However, some of their own concepts, which lead into lines opposing comparative practice, have developed into reductionistic procedures operating almost as special disciplines within science itself. An example is the concept of "dominance" in social study.

The idea of dominance relationships in an animal group arose most specifically through the work of Schjelderup-Ebbe (93), who was first to demonstrate a "peck order" in his investigation of domestic fowl. Since then "dominance hierarchies" have been revealed in the group relationships of many other species of birds and other animals from fish to (and, of course, including) primates (1).

Typically the concept implies an aggressive type of relationship, in which one member of the group forces another to submit by actually attacking it or by threatening attack (25). It affords a convenient way of quantifying the behavior of individuals in a group, and for this reason alone its popularity is understandable. However, it is doubtful that the "dominance" concept is qualified to serve as a chief theoretical device for understanding group organization. Aggression dominance is not necessarily coupled with other important characteristics of group behavior such as ascendance, prestige, and (especially in higher types of social organization) social approval. However prominent a characteristic of group behavior it may be in many instances, dominance after all emphasizes part-processes, the discrete aspects of individuals and of specific individual interchanges, and serves to distract attention from the broad problem of accounting for group unity on the various social levels. It is doubtful whether "dominance theory" alone, as dictating a method of study, would ever lead to an investigation of factors which are involved in the formation of groups and in the socialization of individuals under varying conditions.

Here is an example of a way of thinking which tends to restrict the comparative aspect of animal psychology. On different animal levels there are pronounced differences in the quality and complexity of group unity, and capacities for plastic change in such unity, which dominance theory does not prepare us to understand (95). The essence of social organization consists in the approach-relationships of individuals, yet dominance thinking emphasizes withdrawals. Summated, withdrawals describe one prominent aspect of many groups; however, this aspect clearly is secondary to the factors which brought the parts together in the first place and keep them together long enough for dominance relationships to develop and pass through various changes (2). Actually, dominance relationships as such are absent in many effective types of social organization from primates (18) down through insects.

Although it has arisen from an effort to introduce quantitative method into the study of animal societies, the "dominance" procedure thus tends to lead away from the central question of group organization, and tends to discourage a thoroughgoing comparative study of groups. The trouble is that a partial and really descriptive procedure has become confused, in "dominance" emphasis, with the broad problem of investigating and explaining group unity. "Dominance" theory is reductionistic in this sense, as well as in the sense that it stresses partial similarities among groups on different levels, at the expense of studying other similarities and differences which may be much more significant for the nature of social organization.

But these are similar to the difficulties which we find in animistic conceptions of group organization, such as Maeterlinck's "spirit of the hive" on the insect level and McDougall's "crowd mind" on the human level. Such concepts implying a social psychic agency either are used frankly as literary conceits, or are fraudulent devices substituted gratuitously for any real effort to study the factors underlying a given level of group performance (22). They are simply descriptive, and circular—as for example, to the "spirit of the hive" may be attributed any properties which are noted in the collective performance of bees, whatever these may be. This type of concept is misleading, not merely because it tends to crystallize descriptive and observational errors in literary metaphors, but also because the metaphors furnish a veneer for ignorance. Thus "group mind" offers a spurious explanation for human social phenomena, in that it implies the existence of a close similarity between group function and individual mental function, with no more than anecdotal suggestions to support the analogy. This concept, far more than "dominance" doctrine, evades the issue of accounting for the origin and nature of social organization (16, 84).

We have considered some ways in which animal psychology has deviated from comparative method at the expense of scientific validity. One, the reifying of concepts into presumed forces, is often paralleled in its results by practices which have no apparent relation to Animism. When a single aspect of behavior, such as dominance, is studied on different levels without adequate attention to its origin and its background in the whole phenomenon, significant differences in addition to the most essential similarities may be obscured. Fallacies of metaphor are involved when terms are applied to different orders of capacities so loosely that the essential similarities are blurred and the important differences among capacity levels confused or ignored. Thus, nervous conduction in an individual may be assumed analogous to communication in a social group; but the similarity actually seems to have only an introductory or descriptive significance, and to lack any particular utility for explaining the nature of individual and social group comparatively. The procedure is "reductionistic" (105) in the sense that it isolates part-functions or single characteristics from their respective whole settings without adequate consideration of their relations to and dependence upon the wholes to which they belong. The chief shortcoming of "organism-superorganism" theory (37) lies in the fact that it is based upon this same kind of procedure (95).

We may consider two further examples of concepts which are often generalized in misleading ways. The term "stimulus" has been variously applied to causes of behavior ranging from specific energy effects to complex systems in motivation and perception. In the first sense it is frequently used in a positivistic manner by an experimenter who assumes that, because he has made no deliberate change in the external situation, no extrinsic difference can exist from a preceding observation. With his impression that the "same stimulus" is effective externally, he may refer prematurely to unknown internal processes to explain the difference in behavior. Through forgetting that the term "stimulus" actually is a convenient conceptual device which may or may not denote delimited and invariable causal factors, an inadequate control of extrinsic factors often is introduced which vitiates a realistic theory. The same type of positivistic and artificialized delimitation often is involved in speaking of "*the* environment" of a given organism, or of "*an* environment" which is optimal for different organisms. The development of ecological investigation and of methods for studying animal sensitivity and adaptiveness has shown that the term "environment" must be used in a statistical sense, keeping in mind what range of conditions is optimal for a given animal and what consequences ensue when conditions vary beyond this range. Through scientific investigations of animal adjustment it is becoming truistic to say that "the environment" of a given animal form is relative to the nature of its biological properties (e.g., temperature sensitivity and tolerance) and psychological capacities (e.g., learning capacity). Yet it is often forgotten that the "same environment" beneath a particular tree is very different for sitting rabbit and crawling slug on the "same" patch of grass. In a similar sense, when an animal psychologist refers to "the problem" which he has presented to animal subjects, the very expression may stem from a positivistic leveling effect in perception which scarcely prepares him to be alert for possible important differences in "the problem" for various individuals.

Purposes of "Purpose"

No conceptual term has tended to obscure differences in capacity level more than generalized "purpose." Recently Bahm (5) has discussed concisely some of the chief logical weaknesses of the concept "purpose" as it is involved in teleological writings on natural history subjects. Closest to our present discussion is his reminder that the teleological purposivistic argument is always *post hoc,* since it ignores the fact that "survival of purpose does not imply survival for a purpose." This fact seldom dissuades purposivists from resorting to Animism on one or another basis.* A common ground for such practices is a presumption of proof through elimination. A traditional proponent of purposivistic theory in biology and psychology, William McDougall (70) held steadfast to the argument that, since materialistic procedures in science cannot account for the phenomena of *a*) growth and *b*) adaptivity in behavior, only Animism remains adequate as a basis for metaphysical theory. McDougall (71) held persistently to the weight of point *a* although through the next two decades the sweeping conclusions of Driesch (34) from experimental embryology, on which it was based, were progressively carried toward negation by the researches of Spemann, Child (20), and other investigators. The second argument bears more directly upon animal psychology, where its considerable contemporary influence is evident in the writings of Tolman (111), Lorenz (68), and Russell (92) in particular.

Undeniably, behavior generally is describable as adaptive. From bacteria to man, living organisms universally tend to behave in ways beneficial to survival. Dating mainly from Darwin's work, this fact has been accepted as a widely prevalent characteristic of animal activities. However, the purposivists customarily underplay a corollary fact that even among contemporary species the adaptive aspect of behavior is a relative and not an absolute value throughout the population. In animal species maladaptive behavior commonly accounts for a death curve of individuals ranging from early to advanced ages. The biological factors underlying adaptive behavior, on one level or all levels, are by no means covered by the term "purpose." Mounting evidence favors the view that more or less complex processes of mutation in germ plasm compounded with the intricacies of propagative process and of environmentally enforced selection (32, 78) underlie the appearance of new or changed biological processes and animal types. The relative significance for adaptation of given biological factors is in the long run critical for survival, with mechanisms which promote maladaptive behavior constituting potential causes for elimination in the processes of so-called natural selection. To take an extreme example, a species of protozoa which through mutational innovations possessed organic

* How effectively this ancient practice becomes accepted in a particular social setting through institutional propagation of concepts encouraging non-logical and non-empirical thought processes, is clearly apparent, for example, in Rosenfield's (91) valuable treatise on the Cartesian controversy.

mechanisms favoring consistent movement toward the source of intense stimulation and away from weak stimulation, assuredly would be wiped out in the course of time. Survival is favored, on the other hand, when factors arise which favor the reverse of these types of response. Adaptive behavior, directly or indirectly dependent upon biological factors on whatever level it occurs, is basically attributable to the processes of organic evolution which condition the phyletic development of such factors. It is strange to find these processes slighted or even ignored by writers who set out to account for the basic nature of adaptive behavior.

Adaptivity is an inevitable characteristic of all levels of adjustment. But is "purpose"? A basic mistake inherent in all Vitalistic and Animistic thinking is to confuse a fact, the great predominance of adaptive or life-promoting behavior throughout the animal series, with generalized "purpose." The latter term thus used is ambiguous, from the standpoint of science. Experimental psychologists find that "purpose" can be identified on the human level as "anticipation of a goal." "Purpose" in this scientifically acceptable sense of acting persistently and appropriately with reference to anticipated results, is a difficult technique which is present in the human child not automatically but only by dint of much gradually accomplished learning through experience. Hard come by in development, it is a capacity not to be taken lightly.

To what extent are such capacities, not readily acquired even by man, possessed by lower animals? From evidence on mature adjustments in the mammals, purposive behavior when it arises may be considered as the product of ontogenetic development. The adaptivity of purposive acts is devious and is relative to the given situation, as discussions of ethical and moral standards in different human cultures illustrate. In contrast, the behavior of animals on respective lower levels is more and more directly conditioned by organic factors, and hence its predominantly adaptive trend is attributable more and more specifically to the processes of evolution and heredity (75, Chapters 7 and 12). The kind of teleological doctrine which asserts that "purpose" is present wherever adaptive behavior exists either has theological implications which are hardly relevant to scientific theory, or rests upon a gratuitous *a priori* endowment of all living animals with higher-level psychological functions.

A great variety of biological processes underlies adaptive behavior functions on different animal levels, as is abundantly demonstrated in descriptive summaries of food-getting and other behavior such as those offered by Warden, Jenkins, and Warner (113). It is well to distinguish constantly between description and analysis, remembering the rule that similar adaptive consequences may result from very different causal processes. To refer to classes of behavior such as "protective behavior," "courtship," and "food-getting" behavior throughout all animal levels is entirely permissible on a descriptive basis which emphasizes the kind of adaptive result obtained; however, such a scheme has no essential validity at all for explaining the ontogenetic causal processes involved in producing given behavior in one or another animal type. For example, "protective behavior" may depend upon a shock-elicited tonic immobility of a given physiologically determined duration, as studied by Hoagland (50) in the lizard, or it may involve anticipated evasion of the source of disturbance, as is possible in a socialized chimpanzee or human child. The manner in which effective food-taking occurs in the starfish is explicable as a "community of reflexes" (112), a pattern of local reflex functions systematically unified through the generalized conductile properties of a nerve-net system (45); but in contrast, chimpanzees are able to bring in food out of reach by constructing simple tools, and the "table manners" of a human child are essentially the product of socialized learning. We have used very wide contrasts here only to emphasize that broadly similar adaptive results may depend upon lower-level or higher-level processes. Certainly we are not implying the fallacious distinction that in lower animal groups behavior is "instinctive" and in higher animal groups behavior is learned. Differences in developmental patterns are not that crude and simple.

Levels in Adaptive Behavior

Perhaps the most basic problem in adaptive behavior concerns the manner in which animals on all levels avoid some types of stimulation, generally injurious, and approach other types which are generally adaptive or beneficial in effect. In the lower invertebrates such responses as "approach" tend to involve the whole body, and they are characteristic of the species without evident benefit of learning (75). The nature of the responsible hereditary mechanisms is suggested by some of the relevant evidence. A significant fact is that approaches toward the source of stimulation, as in food-taking, typically occur in response to effectively weak energies of stimulation, whereas withdrawals occur in response to effectively intense energies of stimulation. The earliest clear demonstration of opposed response types dependent upon quantitative aspects of stimulation was offered by Jennings (58) from his studies on protozoa and other invertebrates. In the invertebrate groups which have specialized receptors, the differentiation of response occurs in dependence upon strength of stimulation in various fields, such as light-, chemical-, and contact-sensitivity. The shift in "sign" of adjustment is not an "all-or-none" process, but occurs much as in the light responses of earthworms in Hess's (48) experiment, in which there was a gradual decrease from a maximum of approach reactions and an increase to a maximum frequency of withdrawal when a source of light was changed from low to high intensity.

The critical matter underlying such differences must be the amount of energy delivered to reactive tissues, since Hess found that adaptation to light causes earthworms to turn toward light of abnormally high intensities and to turn from the source only when intensities at the upper end of the scale were much higher than in worms unadapted to light. In contrast, dark adaptation (by effecting an increased sensitivity to light) lowered the entire scale of relationships. The nature of other important biological mechanisms basically involved in adaptive approach and withdrawal in these organisms is not altogether obscure (75). In the earthworm the principal effector systems are also differentiated in thresholds of responsiveness, with the circular muscles (extending the body forward by thinning it) first and predominantly aroused when stimulation is weak, the longitudinal muscle system (drawing back the body by thickening it) predominating when stimulation is strong. When stimulation is very intense the threshold of the most rapid conductor lines in the nervous system, the "giant fibers," is exceeded, and the invariable response is a highly adaptive backward jerking of the entire animal. This we may term the *principle of differential organic thresholds* underlying the adaptive orientation of behavior.

We are reminded here that in the lowest animals adaptive orienting responses can involve movements of the entire organism with respect to the stimulus source. The basis evidently lies in the evolution of generalized organic processes differing appropriately in threshold of arousal. Moreover, these responses appear directly upon the maturation and functioning of heritable structures. The literature on tropism and orientation offers abundant evidence for the broad applicability of this theory among invertebrate animals (38, 75).

The principle of adaptive-threshold systems seems applicable in the case of vertebrate animals, as well, although there evidently exist wide group differences in the nature of heritable mechanisms involved and in the relative directness of their influence upon the eventual behavior pattern. Complicating factors, rather incompletely known at present, are involved on all levels, with learning variously influencing the outcome especially in mammals (98). On the whole, there is no doubt that the unlearned components are more directly effective in the submammalian group than in the mammals. And among the submammalian classes, birds appear to rank above the others in this respect. For instance, the typical lower-vertebrate forward lunge, highly important in feeding, is regularly given to small moving objects in a mainly stereotyped way; whereas we have seen that the pecking response of some birds to edible objects evidently arises through the initial presence of a similar part-process but one eventually combined with others into a pattern through an early learning process.

In the mammals, and especially in man, adaptive organic thresholds seem to be most complexly and deviously influential in behavior development. With a very few doubtful exceptions, whole-body patterns are no longer attributable directly to maturation. The evidence suggests that certain local mechanisms of the reflexive type are present, first clearly demonstrated in Sherrington's (104) finding that the extensor-thrust response of the spinal mammal has a distinctly lower threshold of arousal than the limb-flexion reflex. Combine these facts with the further fact that weak stimulation has a typically localized effect, whereas intense stimulation of the neonate mammal produces a widespread mass action as Carmichael and Smith (17) reported, and it becomes apparent that these differential effects of stimulative energy furnish a broad basis for the establishment of specialized adaptive adjustments through learning (98).

Evidence for such underlying mechanisms may at first sight seem to be lacking in the case of man; yet there are scattered suggestions of their presence, as in the case of the plantar response (41, 87) and of an unlearned arm withdrawal to intense local stimulation (103). The latter fact seems very important, yet limb extension to weak stimulation remains to be demonstrated clearly in early neonate behavior. Careful studies made with graded intensities of stimulation are essential. A general hint of what may exist may be gathered from Watson's (116) trio of "love," "fear," and "rage" responses in the very young infant, in that he elicited "love" (simply a pacified effect, with relaxation and some limb extension) by mild stimulation such as patting, and the "fear-rage"—better, "excited"—responses (high excitement, crying, generalized contraction, and limb flexion) by definitely intense stimulation. Significantly, there is a suggestion here of an unlearned basis for a differentiation of the emotional component, in that craniosacral autonomic signs predominate with weak stimulation, and sympatheticoautonomic signs with strong stimulation. To be sure, Sherman's (102) critique of Watson's emotional trio demonstrated that "fear" and "rage" were not differentiable in early neonates as Watson claimed, but neglected to examine comparatively the more excited ("fear-rage") and milder responses ("love") reported by Watson. Bridges's (15) description of an originally undifferentiated basis for emotion in the human infant after the scheme of Stratton (106) has no substantiation, because she did not work with infants below the age of three months, when some differentiation was found. Although the evidence is at present rather meager, the possibility is worth examining experimentally, that organic mechanisms such as those mentioned above provide an initial basis not only for the overt adaptive adjustments of man to his world, but also for their differentiated emotional backgrounds (98).

How these indistinctly glimpsed organic processes provide an initiating basis for purposive adaptive behavior in man can only be suggested here. Purposive reaching is centrally important, but arises only gradually as an outcome of a lengthy developmental process. In Halverson's (44) study of grasping it seems significant that six-weeks-old infants responded at first to a small cube of sugar (i.e., weak visual stimulus) by a somewhat variable extension and abduction of arm, together with a rolling of eyes toward the object (visual "regard"). These first arm movements in the situation seem to constitute incidental products of the mild stimulative change, and to be not at all purposive in the sense of representing "attempts" to reach or get the object. The initial dependence of such movements upon organic maturation is indicated by the fact that after the age of three months the record steadily worsens for a number of weeks, in that the infant's arm is extended variably sideward and farther from the object than in earlier tests. The reason seems to be a more rapid maturation of the abductor muscles than of arm-extensor muscles at this stage (44). The act has all the aspects of an incidental "getting the arm out" upon excitation, rather than a directed reaching in anticipation of obtaining something. Circumstances indicate that the latter condition develops slowly through learning, as Holt (51) suggested. During early months the hand virtually never reaches to and touches the seen object. Then a reasonably efficient pattern of reaching out directly, grasping, and pulling in ordinarily appears, at seven or eight months of age, only after several months of variable activity. It is a reasonable hypothesis that this eventual directed, anticipatory pattern is a perceptual system which develops through organic maturation and learning-in-use from the initial physiological process of incidental arm extension to weak stimulative effects.

Levels: Common Factors and Heterogeneities

It would appear that the initial physiological mechanisms underlying approach and withdrawal responses are broadly similar on several animal levels. Wide differences appear, however, in their relation to the eventual behavior pattern. On the mammalian and especially the primate level the process is most indirect and involved of all, and the appearance of the eventual purposive pattern is most influenced by special learning. Here ontogeny plays the foremost role, with individual variation and capacity for plastic modification as outstanding features. This plasticity is effective also in the influence of visceral components upon the development of perceptual and emotional processes.

The fact that systems of approach and withdrawal behavior are widely adaptive on all animal levels often causes them to be treated as though they were effectively similar throughout the animal series. Our evidence is sufficient to show wide stages of difference. On the lowest animal levels their function is present through maturation alone; the physical properties of stimulation are effective in a similar stereotyped fashion in an animal's life from beginning to end. It is thus a serious error to apply the word "perception," as does Russell (92), to the "food-getting" and other adaptive responses of invertebrate and lower vertebrate animals, as if these animals could sense a meaningful environmental pattern by virtue of *anticipating* further stages of the process and the eventual significance of the object to them. The disordered and confused epistemology involved in such errors can be corrected only through comparative study of the underlying processes. A survey is not comparative if it deals with the acts in cross-sectional manner as mere episodes of accomplishment, taking adaptive significance as adequate proof of a similar process of underlying "purposeful perception" in all cases. To be adequate, the survey must be carried out in a consistent longitudinal way, with cross-sectional investigations at suspected turning points.

There is ample evidence from developmental experiments with human infants that "perception" of the nature of objects, and "purposeful striving" to deal with them in given ways, result from a complicated ontogeny involving much learning and social-selective influence (cf. 90). Such evidence is lacking for inframammalian forms in particular. Unless we rest content with the gratuitous assumption that "innate knowledge" is possessed by lower organisms such as starfish and spiderling which give *initially* appropriate reactions, detailed comparisons will be made which show that the latter must be regarded as qualitatively different from mammalian "perceptual" adjustments.

Impressed by apparent signs of qualitative equivalence, writers often prematurely generalize particular concepts so that significant functional differences are placed subordinately or are even overlooked. Thus the term "perceptual pattern" has been used to imply a meaningful visual organization equivalent to that of man, whereas in fact the nature of visual organization may be significantly different from that of man. For example, the work of Mathilde Hertz (47) on visual discrimination in bees was impressive, especially in demonstrating what a variety of "patterns" of intricate design could be discriminated. Taken as a matter of Gestalt differentiation, the process appeared to lie qualitatively close to the human level. However, Wolf's (119) results suggest that the process in the bee involves a differentiation of gross flicker effects rather than the appreciation of inclusive figural patterns involved in mammalian perception. Thus although "pattern" has been a convenient term in studying behavior systems on various levels, the time has come to use it with greater care so that qualitative heterogeneity is not obscured.

The fact is that organic maturation makes very different contributions on different animal levels. Adjustment patterns so called appear on widely different bases in ontogeny. The feeding pattern of the jellyfish is largely present through maturation alone, whereas systems such as food-pecking in birds are complexes resulting from a close and progressive interaction between maturation and learning. This learning is much more generalized and qualitatively simpler than learning generally is in human ontogeny. It would seem advisable to avoid dogmatism concerning the sense in which adjustive patterns as such may be inherited, even on lower levels such as social insects in which complex behavior systems seem to arise without benefit of learning. (As a matter of fact, insect social patterns *do* involve some learning.) For no animal inherits its environment except in an indirect sense, and behavior patterns must always be considered as the products of an intimate interaction between organism and environment. For example, the behavior pattern of an army ant colony, with its intricate system of daily raids and nightly migratory movements, constitutes an impressively complex and highly stereotyped system (96, 99). The pattern is the outcome of a cumulative interaction of processes contributed by colony queen, developing brood, and worker individuals in the characteristic environmental setting. Broadly considered, it is the outcome of genetic properties, yet in no sense is it inherited as a pattern even by the colony queen who functions as "pacemaker." The significance of this statement is indicated by the fact that learning functions at certain strategic points; and, although simple and rudimentary in nature, the learning component is essential for the rise and maintenance of the pattern (97).

Levels in Subsocial and Social Adjustment

Actually, phenomena such as the above represent complex systems of interrelated individual and subgroup adjustment patterns. They constitute one level in the scale of social phenomena—"social" because the integrity of the group depends upon the interdependence of individuals and upon their mutual responsiveness. The nature of such interdependence and the complexity of intragroup relationships differs widely among animals exhibiting social behavior. Group systems may be termed "subsocial" (118) when interdependence is incidental to the presence of other individuals and their role may be replaced by given environmental effects such as temperature. Allee (2) has demonstrated the broad adaptive significance of grouping in numerous lower phyla, in which an incidental kind of "cooperation" occurs. Or on the other hand, the interdependence may hinge qualitatively upon the nature of the composite effect of other members of the group as individuals with given properties. The great popular and even scientific prominence which the struggle and destruction aspects of evolution have received has tended to obscure the significance which "mutual aid" assumes in phylogeny on a wide variety of levels (62). "Cooperation" may be systematically present on the basis of a simple stereotyped system or on qualitatively specialized grounds. Other individuals of the species, or other animals, always must be considered as members of the effective environment of each individual, variously influencing the trend of its adjustments both pro and con on one or another qualitative level.

How similar and how different are social levels? A common factor evidently involved in the origin and maintenance of any social aggregation is based upon the biologically prepotent effect of weak stimulation in eliciting turning-toward reactions (95). The process seems to underlie interindividual responsiveness on all levels of complexity and qualitative elaboration in social behavior. This factor, which after Wheeler (118) may be termed "trophallaxis," is basic to the development of both stereotyped social patterns (as in insects) and more plastic social patterns (as in mammals). Its elaboration in lower-level societies involves learning only in a simple and secondary form delimited by hereditary mechanisms; in mammals its potentialities for plastic modification and elaboration are relatively greater. It is basic to and accounts for the gregariousness of individuals, however that gregariousness may be expressed and modified in a variety of ways through social heritage and special learning. The fundamental role of trophallactic processes in socialization derives from the fact that, from the first moment, interchanges which canalize and mold the early learning processes occur between the newborn mammal and its surroundings. Factors of relative dominance, ascendancy, or tendencies toward seclusiveness and the like, must be considered as of secondary and modifying significance, influencing the form of relationships in the social organization without being themselves basic to the *fact* that a social organization of some kind occurs.

Although the initiating factor in social aggregation evidently is broadly similar on levels from insects to man, differences of the widest magnitude appear in its expression in various social patterns. Such patterns are all adaptive in some important sense. In natural selection those organisms would appear to be favored which develop one or another mechanism of interindividual facilitation (2, 62). But it must also be recognized that the adaptive significance of a capacity for mutual assistance and its general role in selection may differ considerably according to the psychological level of its process. While mutual assistance on the insect level, developing on the basis of direct trophallactic interchanges, is limited to a relatively simple interindividual facilitation (95, 97) the chimpanzee can anticipate the result of joint effort in relation to a group goal (27). The possibilities on the human level are vastly greater, and moreover are psychologically cumulative. While any environmental changes effected through the "interindividual facilitation" to which insects are functionally restricted are typically standard for the species through innumerable generations for eons, important changes may occur in human society within a matter of years.

Of all the factors conditioning the potentialities of individual development and socialization on different levels, the most crucial is the extent to which the central nervous system has evolved. Although it appears that some capacity for learning plays an essential part in socialization on all levels, differences in the learning potential undoubtedly are of first importance in setting limits upon socialization, as upon the relative plasticity of adaptive functions in general.

Learning capacity, definable as susceptibility for effective individual changes through experience in the organization of the characteristic behavior pattern, has been demonstrated experimentally even in lower invertebrates such as flatworms (53, 75). Though learning can occur in the absence of cerebral cortex (65), experiments with lower animals show convincingly that it is qualitatively much reduced (29). The maximal accomplishments possible in inframammalian animals such as insects, although impressively complex in some respects, nevertheless show qualitative limitations such as a proneness for stereotypy and a sluggish development of habit organization. For example, the learning capacities of ants, evidently at their best in the Formica species, are relatively situation-bound and rotelike, resembling the showing of lower mammals (e.g., rats) deprived of much of their cortex (94). The behavior changes which have been reported for invertebrates such as protozoa and echinoderms appear to belong on a distinctive sublearning level, especially since they represent transient effects which do not alter the characteristic behavior pattern in any effective way.

Unfortunately psychologists have paid insufficient attention to the analysis of differences in learning capacity through the animal series. An influential contemporary learning theorist, Hull (56), endeavors to account for learning in general by applying the conditioned-response concept deductively. Various limitations of this approach have been pointed out by critics (66). A serious shortcoming of the Hull doctrine is its basic implication that differences in learning are secondary to the homogeneity which all cases are held to possess. It is characteristic of conditioned-response learning, however, that emphasis is upon the situation as set for the animal (e.g., by the experimenter). The role of the animal is relatively passive, with the pattern of its acquisition canalized by the prescribed stimulus-combination. Simpler instances, like the varieties of "habituation" or "negative adaptation," are similar in this respect. On the other hand, the "selective learning" or "trial and error learning" which is accomplished when an animal is free to act in terms of its own behavior resources, appears to be qualitatively distinct from and superior to "conditioning" in important respects. One critical aspect distinguishing "selective" learning, as Culler (28) and Maier and Schneirla (74) have pointed out, is that here the response of the animal changes the effective situation so that new types of adjustment may occur permitting a learning to anticipate the terminating condition, which can become a "goal." Through conditioning a child may be taught to pull a string until an object is encountered, then to pick it up and play—whereupon disconnecting string from object in a test will not inhibit pulling. When, however, through selective learning the child masters a more highly organized response in which string is pulled in relation to toy, then he both anticipates future play while pulling and notices a disconnected string before pulling. The qualitative inferiority of a conditioned-response learning often is not perceptible until the subject is required to use it in a changed situation (60).

It would appear very significant that in the lowest levels on which learning has been clearly demonstrated, the flatworms (53) and the annelids (26, 46, 121), conditioned-response patterns are possible but there is no clear evidence for selective learning. When Formica ants and rats are tested in an objectively identical maze pattern, the ants begin their specific learning with locally restricted unitary processes of a conditioned-response character, and selective learning enters gradually, whereas the rats evidence selective learning and intersegmental relationships at an early point (94). Such results suggest that, in addition to a qualitative difference between conditioning and selective learning, there exist different levels of qualitative accomplishment in selective learning itself.

In mammals, and particularly in the psychologically highest orders of mammals, maturation alone provides few specialized adaptive behavior mechanisms, whereas large repertoires of relatively stereotyped behavior are found in the lower groups. Among mammals as a rule the general adaptive pattern is initially unformed or very loosely formed. Their deficiency of organically stereotyped activities is coupled with an initial period of slow maturation in the atmospheric environment, typically under parental protection. Participation of the parents in the selective learning of young, a process first seen in birds, broadens the social environment according to degree of learning capacity. Organic factors such as those underlying nursing and brooding facilitate a prolonging of early trophallactic relations into a period of family life and perhaps higher-level socialization as well. Thus in various ways the mammal's superior learning capacity greatly broadens its environment and introduces more degrees of freedom under changing environmental conditions. Yet along with this progressively increasing adaptive plasticity, through a linkage of intervening stages, new possibilities for maladaptive behavior are also introduced (40). Thus among mammals according to group psychological capacities, "adaptive" and "maladaptive" become more relative to special value systems than they are in lower animals.

When "learning" is used as a generalized term, it is necessary to remember that a longer ontogenetic preparation usually combined with superior cortical equipment in the "higher" mammals introduces not only greater complexity in attainments but also a greater qualitative variation in the organic traces of experience. The inevitable outcome is a greater qualitative heterogeneity in the eventual adult pattern in dependence upon special conditions. Only man has the time, capacity, and special social assistance adequate for the guidance of learning by reasoning and long-term anticipation or special planning. Yet often through hampering conditions or conflicting special factors his individual and group attainments are arrested on lower stages.

One of the most important contributions of the kinds of selective learning admitted by the progressive evolution of cerebral cortex is that a more effective interrelationship becomes possible among the animal's organic processes and behavioral capacities. Thus visceral processes underlying emotion and motivation can enter into wider relations with capacities of the whole individual such as perception and anticipation in environmental adjustment. Lower mammals to some extent and man to an extent great in potential may thus learn to inhibit or divert hampering emotional and motivational processes.

A most important criterion of higher status in the psychological scale would appear to be group capacity for variable and plastic adjustments. The young individual in inframammalian and lower mammalian orders receives a rather standard preparation for social participation; hence the outcome is more or less typical for the standard environment. There is good reason to believe that organic differences (e.g., brood patches) exist among bird species which account for the young of one species taking more readily to a solitary life than a social one, or the reverse. In man the influence of surrounding individuals upon selective learning is vastly greater from the start and is potentially more variable —witness the striking differences which eventuate in children according to the nature of the "social heritage" dominating their upbringing (7). There is no evidence for the "instinctive" prepotency of individualistic or egocentric attitudes in man (31, 54, 79). The relative predominance of patterns such as competition or cooperation depends upon what system of cultural influences canalizes and guides the socialization process, not upon any known racial or national differences in germ plasm (79). When an educational program is unscientific in that it emphasizes a mass acquisition of predigested categorical results and discourages questioning and search for better answers to old questions, the conditioned-response pattern of learning obviously is in the ascendance and the intelligence potential of the given society is broadly wasted (39).

Drives, Motivation, and Goals

One necessity is to understand the relation of goals to the basic organic energizing conditions which are conveniently denoted as "drives." We owe to Jennings (58) the first adequate emphasis upon an important basic fact about adaptive behavior patterns, that a given organic disturbance or deficiency leads inevitably to an increased variability in behavior, through which readjustment may occur by chance. An organic change which merely disturbs the subject in a generalized way may be termed a "lack." In organisms capable of learning through experience to the essential extent, "lacks" can become effective as "needs," since through conditioned-response or selective learning a special direct adjustment may be added to the behavior repertoire. Thus chicks learn to peck at grains when hungry. The effective need then becomes the focus of a "drive" or energizing tissue condition leading to given readjustments, and the special stimulus pattern promoting a given readjustment process may be termed an "incentive." Special incentive patterns the properties of which are not directly apparent but are anticipated in terms of their expected outcomes may be termed "goals." Here activities are more or less efficiently organized into a unitary system controlled by special "stimulus cues" and really projected into future time. Token-reward solutions as demonstrated for certain carnivores and primates illustrate "goal-wards" adjustments (120).

In situations of deficiency or "lack," the lowest organisms respond on a direct organic basis governed by the immediate biochemical stimulation, according to its intensity. Much the same is true of higher organisms at early stages before ontogenetic specialization has begun. On this level potentially harmful objects may elicit approach reactions much as Jennings's (58) observations disclosed—provided the effective stimulus is weak. Thus, at first the human infant does not "reach," but *gets the arm out* on appropriate stimulation. The difference is that, through experience, animals on successively higher levels can become "conditioned" or can learn selectively to respond according to the special properties of objects, i.e., what *kind* of object is involved. Frequently, as in orthodox Freudian doctrine and in typical "purposive" psychology, a given set of goals and perceptual processes is viewed as innate. Such practices are possible when the significance of ontogenetic psychological development in a given social setting is not really taken into account. Ontogenetic study of mammals discloses no innate "perception"; rather, "appreciating the nature of the object" in simple or involved ways depends upon the given animal's capacity to learn and its opportunity to learn through experience. The stages of perceptual learning are most numerous and complex in man, whose knowledge of objects and effective environment can expand progressively through reaching, crawling and walking toward the finally "calling"—that is, through codifying socially the anticipation of a desired object or situation. It is only through a developmental study of the socialization process, in which the interrelationship of successive stages is adequately considered, that the dependence of advanced stages of perceptual anticipation of "goals" upon initial non-perceptual processes of organic "lack" may be appreciated.

As Dashiell (30) puts it, "A man's interests and desires may become ever so elaborate, refined, socialized, sublimated, idealistic; but the raw basis from which they are developed is found in the phenomena of living matter." To say that fundamentally all behavior derives from and is motivated by the organic processes of the individual is not, however, tantamount to claiming that everything from impulse to attitude and purpose is traceable *directly* to a specific "drive" or energizing tissue condition. Those who insist upon such a narrow interpretation of the materialistic viewpoint underestimate the levels of complexity involved in mammalian, and especially human, psychological development. Yet progressive research in child psychology shows with increasing clarity that the relationship of motivated conduct to organic processes is at first insistently direct in the infant, and later steadily more indirect and devious. The sequence of interlocking stages involved in the education of motivational processes may be suggested by the progress of individuals in attaining their effective incentives and goals, as described by Shaffer (100) and other students of human adjustive behavior. Earliest to become recognizable are sustenance motives clearly related to tissue conditions; then are evident the more specialized "security" motives, and in different relative strengths "dominance," "social approval," "special sex motives," and so on.

Socialized human motivation functions on widely different qualitative levels, according to the complexity of the satisfactions afforded, and to the closeness of the relationship between basic organic factors and accepted goals. Only a failure to consider evidence from the ontogenetic processes of socialization can explain the neglect of the function of organic factors at all stages. Shaffer (100) has pointed out how each of the principal types of motivation, from sustenance to social approval, arises through the involvement of given initially reflexively functional tissue conditions in stimulative interchanges between infant and environment. The earliest situations inevitably combine more or less uniformly the various physiological states of interruptive (disturbance) or vegetative (relief) character with given environmental changes which through conditioned-response learning come to serve as special cues (e.g., the infant's response to special sounds much as to feeding). Then selective learning enters the picture and the infant becomes able to respond differentially to cues (e.g., turning toward one sound, "mother's voice," rather than another). The mother's voice soothes him as did feeding or patting originally, and thus functions as an early "substitute satisfaction." The selective process in time leads to a versatile anticipation of given social results and an initiation of his own cues as a means of manipulating and controlling these events. For example, the statement "Bub hungry" may become a special device if it has served to set the feeding process into action or hurry it along. Thus language symbols become involved in an infinite variety of ways both as especially efficient cues (e.g., "Love me?") and as anticipated ends in themselves (e.g., working hard, anticipating "We're proud of you!"). Here we realize that any attempt to write a social psychology based on individual motivation must fall short, since, highly individualistic or not, whatever system of effective incentives and accepted goals may prevail is a product of training in some kind of social environment.

The weakness in Lewin's (67) valence-vector conception of human motivation is that it presumes the existence of given adult systems of effective incentives and goals, without examining variations dependent upon the determining role of an ontogenetic socialization process effective according to selective conditions in the given social heritage and culture. In mammals such as rodents and carnivores social heritage is limited to secondary and relatively disparate influences like structure of the burrow or parental activities in dealing with prey, so that nature of incentives and goals and the entire picture of motivation remains closely related to the basic integral organic processes themselves. In man, culture and intellectual heritage as selective agencies have so thoroughgoing an influence that even sustenance and security adjustments may become rather completely controlled and modified by factors of prestige, dominance, social approval, and the like. If one neglects ontogenetic development and does not endeavor to trace the influence of organic factors (i.e., the basic drives) up through the various stages of socialization, it is easy to forget that these organic factors are always involved directly or indirectly in adult behavior. Hence mystics and occasional idealistic philosophers may gain adherents for the view that sophisticated, well sublimated purposes and goals never have any relation to man's vulgar organic processes, but are present intuitively or instinctively. These last words denote procedures of evasion.

The elusiveness of the connection between the initial organic states, including processes such as trophallaxis on the one hand and the stages of psychological elaboration in socialization on the other, has permitted sophisticated men to forget that the organic factors are implicated as facilitators and reenforcing agents on all levels of development. The connection is readily overlooked or denied mainly because organic processes seldom appear in relief on higher psychological levels, but are modified and merged in qualitatively new adjustment patterns. Thus socialized man even under stress of extreme organic need or persistent frustration does not regress to the "brute level." Rather, he shifts to some eccentric and distorted variation of his ordinary personality, which varies from his prevalent socialized make-up according to the degree of integrity and organization attained by that adjustment system. The view that man's "higher psychological processes" constitute a single agency or unity which is capable of being sloughed off under hypothetically extreme provocation is a naïve outcome of the mind-body conception of man's nature which stands in need of correction.

Mind, Adaptive Behavior, and Reasoning

"Mind," ostensibly a term for a generalized functional entity, a very impressive term, actually is only an introductory expression for all of man's intellectual capacities and attainments considered as a system.

It is only in a relative and not at all an absolute sense that the processes denoted by terms such as reasoning, thinking, imagining, knowing, perceiving, anticipating, learning, and attitudinizing constitute a unitary and integral system. Attempts to conceive these functions as constituting a single non-corporeal agency, distinct at all times from "body," have failed dismally as a basis for prediction in science. Notable examples may be found: from the Kantian prediction of complete failure for an experimental psychology since "mind" was held to be non-organic and hence not subject to measurement, to the endeavors of the "formal discipline" school to train "memory" as though it were a unitary and discrete thing rather than a term for a set of deviously related characteristics of learning and recall.

The various forms of mentalism in psychology tend to give spurious answers to the problems of reality and of knowledge. They confuse the evasive *phenomenon* of "awareness" with a postulated general causal agency, a functional or structured "consciousness" to which are imputed various descriptively familiar properties such as "knowing" and "choosing." As Holt (52) has put it, for an explanation of these functions is substituted a "little man inside," endowed *a priori* with all the properties to be explained. Unfortunately this preexperimental and non-scientific procedure is insistently maintained by a social pressure grounded in social heritage and propagated in our everyday vocabularly and dictionary as in our mores. The *reductio ad absurdum* is reached when the capacities of lower animals are attributed to "animal mind," when animals are spoken of as "instinctively knowing," and when anthropocentric ideas dominate comparative psychology to the detriment of a really comparative investigation.

In endeavoring to understand the nature of higher psychological processes, it is dangerous to accept one characteristic as if it were critically representative of the whole system, or central to it. Early American experimenters in animal psychology (23, 24, 43, 107) thus endeavored to test for the presence or absence of "ideas" or "imagery" in lower mammals, as somehow critically indicative of thought processes. The results were not at all conclusive (75, 115). Even in man, where imagery may be studied with far greater directness than in lower mammals, various experimenters (13, 86) have found its role generally of secondary importance in reasoning, if not actually detrimental to best results. Theories such as Binet's (11) and Titchener's (110) which account for reasoning in terms of the association of memory images are at best very incomplete.

The concept of imagery denotes only the sensory aspect of representation, which is but one phase of the capacity for dealing perceptually with objects or situations in their absence. Its relation to an action basis, or lack of such basis, is highly significant, as Werner (117) has shown ontogenetically. Significantly, the principal contribution of delayed-response method has been made in the demonstration that to relatively different extents rodents, carnivores, and other mammals below primates possess capacities for the representation of absent situations. Differences are found, with anthropoids superior to lower mammals, both in the time limit and in the qualitative complexity of the represented situation. This capacity both widens the boundaries of the immediate spatial environment and extends the effective temporal limits of integrated environmental adaptation.

The term "anticipation" signifies the more dynamic type of representation, in which the organism projects itself into an organized sequence of specialized adjustments of representational character dominated by the expected development of a given outcome—a "goal." Although orthodox teleologists generously endow all animals with this capacity, its presence has been demonstrated adequately only in the mammals. Comparisons are helpful here. The excitatory function in insect "communication" is performed in a stereotyped way without any evidence of expecting given results; whereas the shoulder-tapping gesture of a chimpanzee in a joint rope-pulling problem clearly involves an expectation of producing given changes in the partner, with a readiness to join in the projected future activity (27). The nature and elaboration of symbolic cues in anticipatory behavior appears to depend upon the relative development of cerebral cortex as a basis for advance in perceptual learning. Thus the chimpanzee's inability to advance beyond gestural cues in his anticipatory adjustments, to the mastery and employment of verbal language cues, does not seem to lie mainly in an incapacity to make the sounds, but rather in his restricted ability to organize meaningful relationships in anticipation. In view of the fact that the perceptual anticipation we have been discussing is an instance of thinking, the lower primates may be considered as chronically inferior to man in the qualitative nature of these processes.

Qualitative differences in thinking often are somewhat confused through the use of the term "insight." Thus Thorpe (108) has considerably exceeded the scope of his evidence by generalizing the insight concept to some insect accomplishments which superficially appear to involve "insightful" processes. If "insight" is taken rather vaguely to mean "seeing through to the solution of a difficulty," such an analogical extension of the term may seem justifiable, for insects often do overcome difficulties in ways which might appear similar to primate solutions. Thus, numerous observers have reported Ammophila wasps tamping down earth with a pebble in closing their burrows. However adaptive, such behavior seems more susceptible to explanation as an act arising spontaneously in the course of stereotyped activities than as problem-thinking (8). Neither is the complexity of insect behavior in learning problems, or the relatively sudden improvement in efficiency which sometimes occurs, any necessary indication of "insight" processes, for analytical study of such accomplishments reveals that they have a much simpler character within the limits of rather stereotyped selective learning (94).

It seems necessary to study instances of suspected "insight" not only in terms of the given problem situation, but also in the ontogenetic background of preparation for the event. Thus, in working toward a fuller understanding of the stick solutions reported for chimpanzees by Köhler (61), Birch (12) found that previous use of sticks in play, although not in food-getting, provided a generalized background of preparation for the accomplishment of "insightful" food-attainment solutions with sticks. From our theory of the ontogeny of purposive action, it may be suggested that the basis for solution was provided by the previous perception of stick-in-hand-lengthening-arm, which now can lead to an anticipation of stick-in-hand when the food is seen beyond arm-reaching distance. A relationship of this kind was in fact suggested by Köhler (61) himself.

On the human level, comparable differences in action experience seem to condition the occurrence of "insight" in surrogate ways. In Durkin's (35) experiment with human subjects assembling a complex patchwork puzzle, insightful or sudden-integration solutions were accomplished most frequently by subjects who had previously worked with the component sections of the complex problem as subpuzzles, but scarcely at all by those subjects who had no previous experience with any part of the puzzle. It is significant that the latter subjects were the ones who worked most persistently with their hands, by "overt trial and error," whereas the "insight" subjects spent more time thinking—that is, in anticipating or dynamically representing the prospective results of their working processes. The trial-and-error subjects merely perceived the pieces as belonging to a puzzle to be solved, the "insight" subjects more readily perceived them in terms of an anticipated use in-relation-to-something-else in a possible type of solution. An intermediate "gradual analysis" solution type combined features of these two.

Human thinking has many types, from simple representation and anticipation through more complex daydreaming and free imagination, from simple rationalization to rather elaborate autistic patterns, and from creative imagination to more or less systematic reasoning. All these types involve two characteristics in particular—various meaning-systems are dealt with in terms of representative processes, and these processes (or "concepts") function in a highly reduced (i.e., schematized) form which under the most efficient conditions obviates recourse to overt behavior. The ontogeny of human thinking is a long process, proceeding from an early basis of direct perceptual adjustments, to the development of a capacity to represent and anticipate absent situations, and next the imaginative interrelating of represented meaning-systems. Infrahuman primates fall far behind the human infant in the basic perceptual and object-meaning acquisitions (57), quite evidently through deficiency in the organic prerequisites for complex learning (i.e., cortical equipment). This deficiency may well account for their inability to master the use of sounds as symbols, an accomplishment which is well under way in the human infant, as a rule, shortly after one year of age. The chimpanzee reaches his limit at the level of representative (conceptual) cues which grew out of the meaning-system itself and remain qualitatively similar to it—as do simple gestures.

Findings in comparative psychology lead to the conclusion that lower primates, and even many psychologically lower mammals such as dog and rat, are capable of solving problems through identifiable processes of thinking. Maier's work (73) suggests that processes which serve as cues for overt adjustments may be reorganized implicitly even in rodents; the studies of Köhler (61) and of Yerkes (122) demonstrate this for lower primates. The above conception of animal reasoning has been arrived at inductively, through experimental investigation; it might well be used as a simple definition of the basic and essential process in human reasoning. In this sense, on experimental grounds, we are able to recognize that a capacity to reason is present in lower mammals.

The qualitative superiority and immensely greater versatility of human reasoning is of course undeniable. However, the difference although great is a relative one. T. V. Moore (80) has endeavored to make it absolute, through the following dialectic argument:

> Do animals reason? Reasoning in human beings has a specific meaning: the deduction of conclusions from general principles. This is the sense in which the term is used in most works on logic. To depart from this meaning is likely to give rise to various ambiguities and any such clouding of expression must by all means be avoided.

If we recognize that the nature of reasoning must be worked out in scientific investigation and cannot be limited *a priori* through categorical speculative procedures, this argument loses its basis. The "specific meaning" favored by Moore would in fact lead to the categorical elimination of vast areas of human reasoning, from the rambling generative processes of "creative imagination" to the inductive processes which underlie and permeate scientific theorizing.

The evidence from lower mammals indicates that their reasoning is characteristically a matter of synthetic processes in which relatively simple recombinations and reorganizations of learned representational systems permit overcoming difficulties in ways not covered by unmodified recall of experience (75). Man at his best is of course vastly superior in such accomplishments; however, for an adequate comparative study of human capacity it is necessary to study him also in his varying degrees of efficiency and of preparation, and to examine his progress through the ontogenetic stages underlying various types of adult thought patterns. In the lower levels of intelligence and of education, and in early childhood, we find that human reasoning is not at all conveniently divisible into deductive and inductive patterns, any more than it is in lower mammals (31, 54, 69). On the other hand, in the unsophisticated struggles of young children (3, 90) or of poorly prepared adults with new problems requiring reasoning (35, 61) we note significant features basically similar to the reasoning of lower primates as described by Yerkes and Köhler.

Man and Lower Animals

There are two extreme views concerning man's relationship to lower animals: one, the non-scientific position that man possesses an immortal soul which sets him sharply and forever apart from the "brute"; the other, the scientifically developed evolutionary conception of man as a higher animal who has emerged gradually by a process of continual evolution from ancestral forms similar to what he now calls "animals." The latter approach, experimentally grounded, has opened the way for a recognition of basic similarities to lower animals on essentially biological levels, and of important potentialities for superior development on psychological and social levels (33). Such a comparative procedure has guided the foregoing discussion.

The comparative study of man in the various sciences, from biology to psychology and anthropology, assuredly does not mark human beings off as different from lower animals in absolute ways. The differences are of course striking and outstanding, when one considers the impressive continuity and development of man's languages, his literary and artistic creativity, his social and political institutions, his long-term propagation and improvement of knowledge in history and in science. There is one capacity in particular, man's facility in the technique of articulate language, which seems to be prerequisite to his superior attainments (9, 89). Yet his qualitative distinction is not an absolute or complete one in this respect, since the most essential psychological characteristic of language, the formulation and delivery of symbols in directive, purposive ways, has been demonstrated in the lower primates (27). Furthermore, man is not absolutely different from lower animals in his capacity for thinking and reasoning, because levels of difference have been demonstrated among lower mammals both in the capacity for implicit representation and self-signaling essential to thinking and in the extemporaneous reorganization of different meaning-systems central to problem-solving thought or reasoning.

Neither is man absolutely different in social respects from lower animals. Fundamentally similar biological factors are traceable in the processes underlying gregarious behavior on very different social levels from insect to human society. The outcome of their influence, and the nature of behavior patterns producible through their elaboration, naturally differ according to the nature of psychological capacities and other special factors (e.g., sexual rhythms, social heritage) involved on the different levels. Lower-level societies exhibit social heritage in different but always limited respects, from the presence of particular nest constructions and prevalent chemical patterns as in insects to the parental and family influences upon selective learning in the ontogeny of various mammals. Culture in the ethnopsychological sense is not absent from lower primates, as witness Köhler's (61) report of observing self-decoration and crude quasi-ritualistic group dancing in chimpanzees, and Tinklepaugh's (109) note that monkeys (like chimpanzees) often pluck fur with evident anticipation of an adornment effect. These last similarities, particularly, are outgrowths of the trophallactic basis of social unity.

It is of course truistic to say that man's ways of life are far more complex and plastic than those of lower animals, in relation to infinitely more variable ontogenetic contributions in his case. Lower animals always exhibit marked stereotypy although to different extents in their constructions and dwellings, strongly in contrast to man's versatility in artistic forms and in architecture. Potentially, man's degrees of freedom are far greater through his superior learning and thinking capacities, his incentive and goals far more extensive and elaborately specialized beyond the bounds of initially effective and physiologically dominated sustenance motivation, than those of lower mammals. Man is capable of goals and purposive behavior on many different levels. Unfortunately, this superiority is often misused to the point of maladaptiveness. It is a prevalent hazard of the human level of psychological versatility that superior logical attainments may be used ingeniously to favor the propagation of illogical and unscientific practices in society, and that superior social groups may beat each other down. The systematic institutional propagation of mysticism and narrow stereotyped patterns in human society is responsible to no small extent for the fact that, contemporaneously, human science is far ahead of social capacities to utilize its advances.

Scientists and philosophers, who are bound to be intimately concerned professionally with the principles of validity in reasoning, must consequently become interested in the verifiability and validity of the ethical and moral precepts which are influential in their society. Such attitudes represent a full appreciation of the fact that man's supremacy in cortical equipment permits his attainment educationally of a superior capacity level on which episodes of reasoning may extend into organized sequences of plans and programs. However, when this superior capacity of ontogenetic versatility leads into the cultivation of barrier-building techniques and fetishistic intergroup conflicts, the potentialities of reasoning are blunted inevitably in individual and group, and there occur widespread lapses to lower-level types of adjustment among the human possibilities.

Conclusion

The foregoing discussion has emphasized the fallacious nature of a generalized teleology which argues for a purposive agency in all organisms, and thereby obscures the fact that somewhat similar effectiveness in adaptive behavior may exist on rather different biological and psychological levels of organization. Indicating some of the pitfalls which are introduced through a reliance upon analogy, we have tried to suggest the manner in which comparative study reveals the actual nature of similarities and differences among the many adaptive levels. The levels considered lowest are those on which specific biological processes account directly for the character of adaptive behavior, without further hierarchies of complexity in the organization; the progressively higher levels are marked by the presence of progressive linked stages of organization typified by increased qualitative complexity in perception and learning; the highest levels are those of plastic adaptive adjustments arising through widened learning capacities and the entrance of thinking. Reasoning arises as a specialized problem-solution type of thinking. Biological processes are involved indispensably at all levels, yet their discrete functions and simpler interrelationships do not account directly for the superior capacities of the higher organisms as mechanistic theorists have claimed. On the other hand, the inadequacy of Mechanism at higher levels does not warrant resorting to Vitalism. The far sounder alternative is the practice of continuing to study all levels comparatively, discarding concepts and dichotomies which are outgrown, and constructing theories which better represent the nature of similarities and differences in animal capacity throughout the series.

Bibliography

1. Allee, W. C., 1942. "Social Dominance and Subordination Among Vertebrates." *Biol. Symposia,* 8:139–162.
2. Allee, W. C., 1938. *The Social Life of Animals.* New York: Norton.
3. Alpert, A., 1928. *The Solving of Problem-Situations by Preschool Children: An Analysis* (Contributions to Education, No. 323). New York: Teachers College, Columbia Univ.
4. Armstrong, E. A., 1942. *Bird Display.* London: Cambridge Univ. Press.
5. Bahm, A. J., 1944. "Teleological Arguments." *Sci. Mon.,* 58:377–382.
6. Bartlett, F. C., 1932. *Remembering: A Study in Experimental and Social Psychology.* New York: Macmillan.
7. Benedict, Ruth, 1934. *Patterns of Culture.* Boston: Houghton.
8. Berland, L., 1935. "Quelques traits du comportement des Hyménoptères Sphégiens." *Ann. Sci. Nat.,* 10th Series, 18:53–66.
9. Bierens de Haan, J. A., 1930. "Animal Language in Its Relation to That of Man." *Biol. Rev.,* 4:249–268.
10. Bierens de Haan, J. A., 1947. "Animal Psychology and the Science of Animal Behaviour." *Behaviour,* 1:71–80.
11. Binet, A., 1899. *The Psychology of Reasoning.* Chicago: Open Court.
12. Birch, H. B., 1945. "The Relation of Previous Experience to Insightful Problem-Solving." *J. Comp. Psychol.,* 38:367–383.
13. Bowers, H., 1935. "The Role of Visual Imagery in Reasoning." *Brit. J. Psychol.,* 25:436–446.
14. Bramstedt, F., 1939. "Ueber die Dressur-Fähigkeiten der Ciliaten." *Zool. Anz.,* 12:111–127.
15. Bridges, Katherine M., 1931. *The Social and Emotional Development of the Pre-School Child.* London: Kegan Paul.
16. Brown, J. F., 1936. *Psychology and the Social Order.* New York: McGraw-Hill.
17. Carmichael, L., and M. F. Smith, 1939. "Quantified Pressure Stimulation and the Specificity and Generality of Response in Fetal Life." *J. Genetic Psychology,* 54:425–434.
18. Carpenter, C. R., 1934. *A Field Study of the Behavior and Social Relations of Howling Monkeys* (*Alouatta palliata*) (Comp. Psychol. Monographs, Vol. 10). Baltimore: Johns Hopkins.
19. Chauvin, R., 1947. "Les Progrès de la psychologie animale moderne et leur intérêt en psychologie humaine." *Rev. Quest. Sci.,* 20:188–204.
20. Child, C. M., 1924. *Physiological Foundations of Behavior.* New York: Holt.
21. Coghill, G. E., 1929. *Anatomy and the Problem of Behavior.* London: Cambridge Univ. Press.
22. Cohen, M. R., 1931. *Reason and Nature.* New York: Harcourt.
23. Cole, L. W., 1915. "The Chicago Experiments with Raccoons." *J. Anim. Behav.,* 5:158–173.

24. Cole, L. W., 1907. "Concerning the Intelligence of Raccoons." *J. Comp. Neurol. Psychol.,* 17:211–261.
25. Collias, N. E., 1944. "Aggressive Behavior Among Vertebrate Animals." *Physiol. Zool.,* 17, 83–123.
26. Copeland, M., 1930. "An Apparent Conditioned Response in *Nereis virens.*" *J. Comp. Psychol.,* 10:339–354.
27. Crawford, M. P., 1937. "The Cooperative Solving of Problems by Young Chimpanzees." *Comp. Psychol. Monogr.,* 14:1–88.
28. Culler, E. A., 1938. "Recent Advances in Some Concepts of Conditioning." *Psychol. Rev.,* 45:134–153.
29. Culler, E. A., and E. Mettler, 1934. "Conditioned Behavior in a Decorticate Dog." *J. Comp. Psychol.,* 18:291–303.
30. Dashiell, J. F., 1937. *Fundamentals of General Psychology.* Boston: Houghton.
31. Deutsche, Jean M., 1937. *The Development of Children's Concepts of Causal Relations* (Child Welfare Monograph Series, No. 13). Minneapolis: Univ. of Minnesota Press.
32. Dobzhansky, T., 1941. *Genetics and the Origin of Species.* 2nd ed. (rev.) I. New York: Columbia Univ. Press.
33. Dobzhansky, T., and M. F. Ashley Montagu, 1947. "Natural Selection and the Mental Capacities of Mankind." *Science,* 105:587–606.
34. Driesch, Hans, 1908. *The Science and Philosophy of the Organism.* 2 vol. London: Black.
35. Durkin, H. E., 1937. "Trial and Error, Gradual Analysis, and Sudden Reorganization." *Arch. Psychol.,* No. 210, pp. 1–85.
36. Emerson, A. E., 1942. "Basic Comparisons of Human and Insect Societies." *Biol. Symposia,* 8:163–176.
37. Emerson, A. E., 1939. "Social Coordination and the Superorganism." *Amer. Midland Nat.,* 21:182–209.
38. Fraenkel, G., and D. D. Gunn, 1940. *The Orientation of Animals.* Oxford: Clarendon Press.
39. Freeman, E., 1940. *Conquering the Man in the Street.* New York: Vanguard Press.
40. Galt, W., 1940. "The Principle of Cooperation in Behavior." *Quart. Rev. Biol.,* 15:401–410.
41. Goldstein, K., 1939. *The Organism.* New York: American Book Co.
42. Grabowski, U., 1939. "Experimentelle Untersuchungen über das angebliche Lernvermögen von Paramaecium." *Ztschr. Tierpsychol.,* 2:265–282.
43. Gregg, F. M., and C. A. McPheeters, 1913. "Behavior of Raccoons to a Temporal Series of Stimuli." *J. Anim. Behav.,* 3:241–259.
44. Halverson, H. M., 1933. "Acquisition of Skill in Infancy." *J. Genet. Psychol.,* 43:3–48.
45. Hamilton, W. F., 1922. "Coordination in the Starfish: II, Locomotion." *J. Comp. Psychol.,* 2:61–76.
46. Heck, L., 1920. "Ueber die Bildung einer Assoziation beim Regenwurm auf Grund von Dressurversuchen." *Lotos Naturwiss. Ztschr.,* 68:168–189.
47. Hertz, Mathilde, 1931. "Die Organisation des optischen Feldes bei der Biene." *Ztschr. vergl. Physiol.,* 14:629–674.
48. Hess, W., 1924. "Reactions to Light in the Earthworm, *Lumbricus terrestris L.*" *J. Morphol. Physiol.,* 39:515–542.

49. Hingston, R. W. G., 1929. *Instinct and Intelligence.* New York: Macmillan.
50. Hoagland, H., 1928. "On the Mechanism of Tonic Immobility in Vertebrates." *J. Gen. Physiol.,* 11:715–742.
51. Holt, E. B., 1931. *Animal Drive and the Learning Process.* New York: Holt.
52. Holt, E. B., 1937. "Materialism and the Criterion of the Psychic." *Psychol. Rev.,* 44:33–53.
53. Hovey, H. B., 1929. "Associative Hysteresis in Flatworms." *Physiol. Zool.,* 2:322–333.
54. Huang, I., 1930. "Children's Explanations of Strange Phenomena." *Psychol. Forschung.,* 14:63–182.
55. Huang, I., H. Yang, and F. Y. Yao, 1945. "Principles of Selection in Children's 'Phenomenistic' Explanations." *J. Genet. Psychol.,* 66:63–68.
56. Hull, C. L., 1944. *Principles of Behavior.* New York: Appleton-Century.
57. Jacobsen, C. F. and M. M., and J. G. Yoshioka, 1932. *Development of an Infant Chimpanzee During Her First Year* (Comp. Psychol. Monographs, Vol. 9). Baltimore: Johns Hopkins.
58. Jennings, H. S., 1906. *The Behavior of Lower Organisms.* New York: Columbia Univ. Press.
59. Jennings, H. S., 1907. "Behavior of the Starfish, *Asterias forreri de Loriol." Univ. Calif. Publ. Zool.,* 4:53–185.
60. Katona, G., 1940. *Organizing and Memorizing.* New York: Columbia Univ. Press.
61. Köhler, W., 1926. *The Mentality of Apes.* New York: Harcourt.
62. Kropotkin, P. M., 1917. *Mutual Aid: A Factor of Evolution.* New York: Knopf.
63. Kuo, Z. Y., 1932. "Ontogeny of Embryonic Behavior in Aves: IV, The Influence of Embryonic Movements upon the Behavior After Hatching." *J. Comp. Psychol.,* 14:109–122.
64. Lack, D., 1940. "Pair-Formation in Birds." *Condor,* 42:269–286.
65. Lashley, K. S., 1932. "Integrative Functions of the Cerebral Cortex." *Physiol. Rev.,* 13:1–42.
66. Leeper, R., 1944. "Dr. Hull's Principles of Behavior." *J. Genet. Psychol.,* 65:3–52.
67. Lewin, K., 1935. *A Dynamic Theory of Personality.* New York: McGraw-Hill.
68. Lorenz, K., 1937. "The Companion in the Bird's World." *Auk,* 54:245–273.
69. Lorimer, F., 1929. *The Growth of Reason.* New York: Harcourt.
70. McDougall, W., 1911. *Body and Mind.* New York: Macmillan.
71. McDougall, W., 1929. *Modern Materialism and Emergent Evolution.* New York: Van Nostrand.
72. McGill, V. J., 1945. "The Mind-Body Problem in the Light of Recent Psychology." *Sci. and Soc.,* 9:335–361 (No. 4).
73. Maier, N. R. F., 1929. *Reasoning in White Rats* (Comp. Psychol. Monographs, Vol. 6). Baltimore: Johns Hopkins.
74. Maier, N. R. F., and T. C. Schneirla, 1942. "Mechanisms in Conditioning." *Psychol. Rev.,* 49:117–134.
75. Maier, N. R. F., and T. C. Schneirla, 1935. *Principles of Animal Psychology.* New York: McGraw-Hill.

76. Marshall, A. J., 1944. "Display and Bower-Building in Bower-Birds." *Nature,* 153:685.
77. Mast, S. O., and L. Pusch, 1924. "Modification of Response in Amoeba." *Biol. Bull.,* 46:55–59.
78. Mayr, E., 1942. *Systematics and the Origin of Species.* New York: Columbia Univ. Press.
79. Mead, Margaret, ed., 1937. *Cooperation and Competition Among Primitive Peoples.* New York: McGraw-Hill.
80. Moore, T. V., 1941. "Human and Animal Intelligence" (Chap. III, pp. 95–158, of *Scientific Aspects of the Race Problem*). New York: Longmans.
81. Moss, F. A., ed., 1942. *Comparative Psychology.* New York: Prentice-Hall.
82. Munn, N. L., 1933. *An Introduction to Animal Psychology: The Behavior of the Rat.* Boston: Houghton.
83. Needham, J., 1929. *The Sceptical Biologist.* London: Chatto.
84. Newcomb, T., ed., 1947. *Readings in Social Psychology.* New York: Holt.
85. Novikoff, A., 1945. "The Concept of Integrative Levels and Biology." *Science,* 101:209–215.
86. Pear, T. H., 1937. "The Place of Imagery in Mental Processes." *Bull. John Rylands Libr.,* 21:3–24.
87. Pratt, K. C., 1934. "Generalization and Specificity of the Plantar Response in Newborn Infants: The Reflexogenous Zone: I . . . ," *J. Genet. Psychol.,* 44:265–300; II . . . ," *Ibid.,* 45, 22–38.
88. Pycraft, W. P., 1914. *The Courtship of Animals.* London, Hutchinson.
89. Révész G., 1944. "The Language of Animals." *J. Gen. Psychol.,* 30:117–147.
90. Richardson, Helen M., 1932. "The Growth of Adaptive Behavior in Infants: An Experimental Study at Seven Age Levels." *Genet. Psychol. Monographs,* 12:195–359.
91. Rosenfield, Leonora D., 1941. *From Beast-Machine to Man-Machine: Animal Soul in French Letters from Descartes to La Mettrie.* New York: Oxford Univ. Press.
92. Russell, E. S., 1938. *The Behaviour of Animals.* London: Edward Arnold.
93. Schjelderup-Ebbe, T., 1922. "Beiträge zur Sozialpsychologie des Haushuhns." *Ztschr. Psychol.,* 88:225–252.
94. Schneirla, T. C., 1945. "Ant Learning as a Problem in Comparative Psychology" (pp. 266–305 in *Twentieth Century Psychology,* ed. P. L. Harriman and others). New York: Philosophical Library.
95. Schneirla, T. C., 1946. "Problems in the Biopsychology of Social Organization." *J. Abnorm. Soc. Psychol.,* 41:385–402.
96. Schneirla, T. C., 1944. "The Reproductive Functions of the Army-Ant Queen as Pace-Maker of the Group Behavior Pattern." *J. N. Y. Entom. Soc.,* 52:153–192.
97. Schneirla, T. C., 1941. "Social Organization in Insects, as Related to Individual Function." *Psychol. Rev.,* 48:465–486.
98. Schneirla, T. C., 1939. "A Theoretical Consideration of the Basis for Approach-Withdrawal Adjustments in Behavior." *Psychol. Bull.,* 37:501–502.
99. Schneirla, T. C., 1938. "A Theory of Army-Ant Behavior Based upon the Analysis of Activities in a Representative Species." *J. Comp. Psychol.,* 25:51–90.

100. Shaffer, L. F., 1936. *The Psychology of Adjustment: An Objective Approach to Mental Hygiene.* Boston: Houghton.
101. Shepard, J. F., and F. S. Breed, 1913. "Maturation and Use in the Development of an Instinct." *J. Anim. Behav.,* 3:274–285.
102. Sherman, M., 1927. "The Differentiation of Emotional Responses in Infants: (I) Judgments of Emotional Responses from Motion Picture Views and from Actual Observation." *J. Comp. Psychol.,* 7:265–284.
103. Sherman, M., and Irene C., 1925. "Sensorimotor Responses in Infants." *J. Comp. Psychol.,* 5:53–68.
104. Sherrington, C. S., 1906. *The Integrative Action of the Nervous System.* New Haven: Yale Univ. Press.
105. Sloane, E. H., 1945. "Reductionism." *Psychol. Rev.,* 52:214–223.
106. Stratton, G. M., 1928. "Excitement as an Undifferentiated Emotion" (Chap. 17, pp. 215–221 in *Feelings and Emotions,* ed. C. Murchison and M. L. Reymert). Worcester, Mass.: Clark Univ. Press.
107. Thorndike, E. L., 1911. *Animal Intelligence.* New York: Macmillan.
108. Thorpe, W. H., 1943. "Types of Learning in Insects and Other Arthropods." *Brit. J. Psychol.* (Gen.), 33:220-234; 34:20–31, 66–76.
109. Tinklepaugh, O., 1931. "Fur-Picking in Monkeys as an Act of Adornment." *J. Mammal.,* 12:430–431.
110. Titchener, E. B., 1909. *Lectures on the Experimental Psychology of the Thought Processes.* New York: Macmillan.
111. Tolman, E. C., 1932. *Purposive Behavior in Animals and Men.* New York: Appleton-Century.
112. Uexküll, J. v., 1900. "Die Physiologie des Seeigelstachels." *Ztschr. Biol.,* 39:73–112.
113. Warden, C. J., T. N. Jenkins, and L. H. Warner, 1935. *Comparative Psychology: A Comprehensive Treatise* (3 vols.). New York: Ronald Press.
114. Warren, H. C., 1930. "The Organic World and the Causal Principle." *Science,* 71:204–208.
115. Washburn, Margaret F., 1926. *The Animal Mind,* 3rd ed. New York: Macmillan.
116. Watson, J. B., 1919. *Psychology from the Standpoint of a Behaviorist.* Philadelphia: Lippincott.
117. Werner, H., 1940. *Comparative Psychology of Mental Development.* New York: Harper.
118. Wheeler, W. M., 1928. *The Social Insects.* New York: Harcourt.
119. Wolf, E., 1933. "Das Verhalten der Bienen gegenüber flimmernden Feldern und bewegten Objekten." *Ztschr. vergl. Physiol.,* 20:151–161.
120. Wolfe, J. B., 1936. "Effectiveness of Token-Rewards for Chimpanzees." *Comp. Psychol. Monographs,* 13:1–72 (No. 60).
121. Yerkes, R. M., 1912. "The Intelligence of Earthworms." *J. Anim. Behav.,* 2:332–352.
122. Yerkes, R. M. and A. W., 1929. *The Great Apes.* New Haven: Yale Univ. Press.

A PSYCHOLOGICAL APPROACH TO PERSONALITY

by

V. J. McGILL

V. J. McGill is Associate Professor of Psychology and Philosophy, Hunter College, New York City; Ph.D. Harvard, 1925. Studied under Sheldon Fellowship (Harvard University) 1925–1926, at Cambridge and Freiburg. He is the author of biographical studies of Strindberg and Schopenhauer and of a book of philosophical-literary essays; has written numerous articles on philosophy and some on psychology. He is an editor of *Science and Society* and Secretary-Treasurer, International Phenomenological Society.

THERE are two main approaches to personality. The social sciences tend to represent personality as the product of history and social institutions, while psychology, conversely, generally interprets social institutions as the product of personality. Both approaches are necessary and, as research becomes more concrete and adequate, are seen to be inseparable. That is, the process in which history forms personality is also the process in which personality makes history. Recent rapprochement between psychologists and social scientists is therefore an auspicious sign. The sociological view has the advantage that, if a man's place in history and social affiliations are known, we can predict far more of his characteristics than from any other set of facts. But the social institutions which determine the individual are neither good nor bad but valuing makes them so. Values, conflicts, defeats, and resolution in world history are located in personality and can be comprehended finally only in the process and circumstances of its development. Here lies the advantage of the psychological approach.

The fifty definitions of personality listed by Allport [1] provide a variety to suit every taste. There are omnibus definitions like that of Morton Prince which identify personality with "the sum-total of innate dispositions, impulses, tendencies, appetites, and instincts of the individual, and the acquired dispositions and tendencies—acquired by experience"; and there are narrower definitions which stress thinking, self-consciousness, or social effectiveness.

MacKinnon [2] contends that the most important distinction among the many definitions offered is that some identify personality with the outward superficial appearance, whereas others fix upon "the inner essential nature of man." These two types of definition present a contrast; but to describe them as "antithetical" and "basically opposed" seems to obscure the interdependence of the outer and inner man. MacKinnon is right, of course, in stressing the importance of potentialities and the subjective aspect of personality.

Guthrie's [3] distinction between conceptions of personality which merely catalogue traits and dispositions, or present a cross-section of the person, and those which represent personality as the product of learning, is more helpful. Cross-sectional analysis is preevolutionary, often merely logical or taxonomical, gives the impression that types and characters are fixed features of the universe, and turns aside from causal explanation. It therefore fails to take into account the potentialities of persons and societies, and overlooks changes and improvements in man and his environment which are ensuing, or can be brought about. Genetic explanation, on the other hand, is in the main stream of evolutionary, experimental science, and meliorism.

We shall define "personality" as the organization of needs, abilities, and potentialities of an individual. The study of personality is primarily an investigation of the learning process and the conditions in which personality is formed.

Needs and Abilities

Needs are the internal conditions which sensitize the organism, or lower difference thresholds, to certain stimuli. They are the disposition to respond to certain stimuli repeatedly and persistently, and to "prefer" these responses to others. That a hungry dog "prefers" food means that it is more inclined to respond to food than to other things. A need is *active* when internal stimuli arising from the tissues or organs involved evoke characteristic responses which tend to satisfy this need; and it is *latent* when these stimuli are absent or subliminal. The response which satisfies the need is usually called the consummatory response. If satisfaction of a need is delayed, preparatory responses occur which lead to, or at least in the general direction of, consummation. These preparatory responses are persistent, often varied, alternative and resourceful. When obstacles are put in the way of the goal, a rat or chimpanzee tends to circumvent them either by the sheer abundance of varied responses or by cumulative sequences of reactions—and the chimpanzee by the use of instruments. Once the goal—i.e., the food, water, or mate—is reached, these preparatory reactions give way to the consummatory response which, as Sherrington pointed out, has the right of way in the nervous system. Continued preparatory reactions are incompatible with the occurrence of the consummatory response, and the stimuli which initiated them have ceased to operate. That is, the animal cannot run about here and there while eating food, and as the gastric secretions begin to flow, it is no longer stimulated to do so.

It is to be noted, however, that some needs are not climactic but continuously active, and typically homeostatic. The organism requires oxygen incessantly and rest and movement at long intervals, and there is nothing climactic about these satisfactions. Each gasp of air and every random step we take, so to speak, pays for itself. These non-climactic needs are especially important on the human level, where, for example, the continuous need for aesthetic activity determines the pattern of behavior. Although not goal-directed, these needs conform to our definition: when deprived of oxygen and movement the animal will "prefer" them to other things. When the eyes of a man are bandaged, or he is kept in a dark room or bare cell he will prefer seeing, as long as life needs are satisfied, to anything else.

Ability, the second component of personality, is the disposition to "prefer" successful preparatory responses. The animal possessing an ability selects responses which lead to, or facilitate, the consummation of a need. If it lacks the ability it performs many unsuccessful preparatory responses—i.e., responses which do not bring about consummation, but would if the conditions were somewhat changed. Abilities not only facilitate satisfaction of needs, but may themselves become needs. This is demonstrated in the laboratory when an animal continues to exercise an ability, in lieu of other activities, even when it no longer facilitates the satisfaction of the original need. Through reinforcement many responses that were at first only preparatory become needs as well. Thus a man who plays the piano or teaches for a living, may continue to play or teach beyond hours without pay, though other activities are available to him. That the abilities by which we satisfy our needs should also become needs which are satisfied in the process, is regarded as the human ideal.

But there are also abilities, especially on the human level, which subserve not climactic but continuous needs. Stories of wolf-children indicate that if a child is deprived of human intercourse in the formative years, normal intelligence does not develop, that there is therefore a need for human society. The corresponding ability is the capacity to satisfy this need continuously without too much disruption by inhibition or internal conflict. The need to be free from excessive conflict is notable on the human plane, but is demonstrable even on infrahuman levels, where an experimental animal presented with confused and conflicting signals cannot be brought to react in the situation, but instead cowers in the corner, maintains a rigid posture, or dashes about wildly, and refuses food, though half starved.[4] When the same animal, however, was previously subjected to an experimental routine where signals were regularized and conflictful factors were absent, it reacted to the situation readily, learned its lesson, and got its food. The need for social activity among the higher animals can be confirmed in the same way. In human beings concrete social and rational needs are admittedly decisive in forming personality. What is important to emphasize is that these needs and the abilities which satisfy them are not ready-made endowments, but hard-won acquisitions.

Potentialities are also a part of human nature. They are the needs and abilities which develop when new stimuli are presented. That potentialities are the most important aspect of personality is recognized in the case of children; but when factory hands or subject peoples are in question, especially when they become 'unreasonable', it is commonly forgotten. Potentialities are also largely neglected by psychological laboratories, clinics, personnel and employment bureaus, I.Q. tests, and production records. Yet there is much evidence to support William James's contention that in the ordinary conduct of life a man utilizes only a tenth part of his energies.[5]

Needs, as we understand them, are either tissue needs or acquired, i.e. learned.[6] The distinction, though important, is not absolute, since tissue needs themselves undergo socialization and acculturation. Thirst, hunger, temperature maintenance, sex, and movement are universal tissue needs; but the manner in which they are satisfied is learned, and varies widely from one society to another.

As tissue needs become subordinated within various cultural patterns of expression, they are also transformed. That visceral organs properly connected with sense organ and brain can learn, adapting to new conditions, is well established. Pavlov's early experiments showed that a parotid gland can learn to secrete at a signal. The pupillary response was successfully conditioned by Cason in 1922. Other experiments [7] seem to prove that pain and temperature sensations can be conditioned, at least under special conditions; and there is a strong suspicion that regular meals can routinize the need for food. Pavlov's laboratory has recently established conditioning in the stomach, kidney, and spleen,[8] and psychosomatic medicine is accumulating a great deal of supporting evidence. W. H. Gantt has recommended the hypothesis that psychoneurosis is largely a matter of organic conditioning.[9] The organs of the body not only respond to stimuli but adapt themselves to conditions. Apparently visceral learning is determined in part by the individual's career of social learning, of which it becomes a part; but the converse is no less true.

Acquired needs differ from tissue needs in a number of respects. The latter can be observed directly, but also indirectly, through the behavior that results. Thus when a dog is fed bismuth we can observe its hunger contractions, but also witness its search for food. The case is similar with human beings. Acquired needs, on the other hand, though they cannot be directly observed, can be measured indirectly. Investigation of consumer needs and medical requirements shows what can be done. Prices and purchases in the market also afford an index of needs, but only to the extent that the goods offered for sale are sufficiently plentiful and varied, and within the means of different income groups. Even so, a purchase may not measure a need for the article bought, but only a tendency to believe artificial and misleading claims of advertisers. Othmar Spann's conclusion that great industrialists are more "spiritual" because they spend more of their income on cultural objects, and the workers more "sensual" because almost all of their money goes for material goods, is a ludicrous example of trusting the market index too far. Reports by government agencies and scientific institutions,[10] or the sales response to objective description of commodities on radio programs or in the press, could offer more reliable indices of needs.

Acquired needs, as we have pointed out, are also far more varied, labile, and modifiable than tissue needs. While the food requirements for individuals in different societies measured in terms of carbohydrates, proteins, and fats are fairly uniform, the diversity of acquired needs is enormous, and potentially even greater; for, as the time and pains necessary to satisfy tissue needs decrease, the diversity of acquired needs within a family or society increases.

Acquired needs develop in association with tissue needs, in accordance with conditions and practices in a given environment. Just as a dog acquires a disposition to follow a new master at all times, so a baby learns to cherish its bottle even though it is empty and its hunger has been appeased. The bottle, and even a rubber nipple of a certain shape, become acquired needs in some societies. But where breast feeding is the rule the contours of the mother become the object of attachment permitting no substitute unless, as in Bali, the child is nursed by different women.

Many studies have shown how the child in the course of satisfying its tissue needs hits upon successful adaptations, i.e. reactions which terminate painful stimulation or are rewarded. When the stimulations playing upon a newborn infant are removed or held constant, by placing it in a soundproof room or a stabilimeter, its spontaneous movements can be observed. These spontaneous movements, stimulated by muscle-need or other metabolic processes, encounter obstacles or bring satisfaction—for example, by facilitating new movements. When maturation permits, infants learn to creep; but the concrete circumstances surrounding the first attempts are not the same for different individuals. One learns to creep on his stomach, another on his hands and knees. In other words, infants acquire needs for different styles of locomotion, which will probably be carried over subsequently to new performances.[11] The child which crawled on hands and feet on a level will later climb stairs in this fashion.

One way in which acquired needs are learned is illustrated, with classic simplicity, by Pavlov's experiments. When the bell has been synchronized sufficiently with food, the dog acquires a need to respond to the bell. In the same way a child develops an attachment to a dirty old rag doll, whose disreputable appearance and unhygienic possibilities dismay the parents. The disreputable doll has been associated with too many gratifications to be given up, however many glamorous new dolls are offered in substitute. The adult case is not too different. A hungry man, for example, on several occasions chances upon olives, which are new in his experience. In satisfying his hunger, olive eating is reinforced. Finally, olives come to be preferred to other food, and are eaten for their own sake, after hunger has been appeased. There seems to be no question that the man in this prosaic example has acquired a new need over and above his tissue need, for the food need can be satisfied without eating olives, and zealous olive-eating takes place without hunger.

Acquired needs play a more executive role on the human level and can attain far more independence of tissue needs than in animals. Thus the need for a type of business or professional activity, or for certain kinds of art or music, or the devotion to a certain woman or cause may dominate a life and defy tissue needs within wide limits.[12] The dominating need or grand passion provides the clues to the biographer and novelist, whose delineations are as rich and abounding as the psychologist's are methodical and schematic. Acquired needs in human beings not only achieve extensive autonomy, they also transform tissue needs—the most consequential ones. Strictly speaking, there is no such thing as pure hunger or sex except *in extremis*. All societies, groups, individuals acquire specific needs which restrict indiscriminate satisfaction. In the marginal case, death is preferred to the wrong food, or mate. Tissue needs are "basic" in the sense that if they are not satisfied all needs disappear; but they are not basic in the sense that they account for concrete human behavior.

We have argued that learning establishes new needs, which in great measure dominate and direct tissue needs. The proof of this would be found in *a*) the persistence of learned patterns of behavior which are not reinforced by tissue needs and often prevent their satisfaction, *b*) the mushrooming of intricate proclivities, customs, and amenities precisely at a time when the constant tissue needs are well satisfied and secure, and *c*) the relative success with which individual behavior is explained by social formations in which it occurs.

Status Quo and Genetic Analysis

Although materialism as we understand it emphasizes genetic explanation, it does not disregard the value of phenomenological description. Accurate descriptions, which are not reducible to causal statements, are required at every stage of analysis. If analysis is not to be impeded, however, phenomenological ascriptions must be regarded as provisional, not final. The inferential element [13] or interpretation [14] involved in all judgments of perception, and the notorious ambiguity of psychological terms, put the careful investigator on his guard. If a boy is classified as aggressive because he is seen to push, abuse, pick quarrels, or snatch toys, the significance and remedy of the case depends on how it is interpreted. Is the boy frustrated by his lack of skill in the particular game being played, has he carried over aggressiveness from other groups to which he belongs, has he been rewarded for militancy by adults in situations somewhat different, or is he simply more active and vigorous than other children of the same age? Here is another boy who is cited more often than others for aggressive behavior, but also for sympathy and cooperativeness. The facts do not speak for themselves. Children have been classified as suggestible because, after learning a routine in which a wire, first cold, turns warm, they finally declare the wire to be warm when it is not. But it may be that the routine has only *conditioned* the child's reaction, or that the habit of giving the response that the teacher or authority expects has prevailed.[15] Or again, college students will frequently change their rating of prose passages when new and approved authorship is ascribed to them. Does this mean that they thoughtlessly succumb to prestige suggestion, or that they reinterpret the passages in the light of what they know about the authors? [16]

In all these cases the immediate situation is indecisive. In the field of personality, genetic explanation is always crucial, and not only in exceptional cases. If one child in a group unexpectedly cries at a turn in a story which is being read, we must trace the cause to the past experience of this child; but the same is true with regard to the non-crying of the other children. In personality studies the necessity of giving a genetic explanation of the typical, as well as the atypical, is frequently recognized when primitive societies or alien social formations are under examination. But the normal in one's own society is often regarded as normal, and self-explained.

A far-flung illustration of the limitations of purely cross-sectional analysis is furnished by the extensive literature of "characters" and types of men. Beginning with the "Characters" of Theophrastus in the fourth century B.C., and ending with the types of Spranger, Jaspers, Jung, McDougall, Kempf, Jaensch, and other modern writers, hundreds of depictions of human traits, temperaments, and personalities have been published. Although the tradition takes many different forms, it is consistent in detaching the characteristics of the individual or type from their causal conditions. Theophrastus wrote thirty incisive sketches of characters, such as the Flatterer, the Dissimulator, the Chatterer, the Loquacious Man, and the Unscrupulous Man, characters which were to be found in the Greece of his century. Though his master Aristotle had shown in *Politics* that men behave differently under different governments, Theophrastus made no effort to account for his characters in terms of formative social conditions, or in any other terms, and did not question the norms of his time. The numerous followers of Theophrastus, such as La Bruyère, Vauvenargues, and the English character writers, preserved the same literary form,[17] stopping short with deft description and ignoring causal factors.

Characterology and the psychology of temperaments and types remained through the centuries at the collecting and classificatory stage, and criteria permitting a decision between the different classifications were usually lacking. Instinct theory—i.e., the theory that there are innate patterns of behavior—though it rightly emphasized biological conditions and motivation, did not really break with this tradition, for psychologists began to vie with one another in inventing original lists of instincts, new methods of classifying behavior. When people's behavior did not fit, a list of instincts could be changed to accommodate, or it could be assumed that individuals or societies have different instinctive endowments. Thus McDougall[18] explained the lack of rivalry among a group of Papuan-Melanesians with whom he had lived by averring that they were deficient in the instinct of pugnacity.

The Anglo-Saxon love of competitive games, warlike disposition, and high achievements, he attributed to a more than common share of this same instinct. Historical developments and individual learning, he stated, could have had no part in it.

The lack of causal analysis in the field of personality at present often results from the understandable desire to standardize quick and useful classifications of individuals, whose past history there is no time to explore. A psychograph is a cross-section of personality. A list of traits common to a whole population is selected, including such items as suggestibility, ascendance, persistence, self-sufficiency, and gregariousness. The magnitude of each trait in a given individual is then measured. Factor analysis which attempts to standardize ratings, for mathematical convenience, assumes that the factors or traits are independent of one another; but, as C. Burt points out, the factors are not isolated unitary traits at all, but rather principles of classification which involve "the sum total of the relations between minds and their environment." [19]

Opinion differs as to the value of attitude scales, personality tests, and factor analysis, but it seems pretty clear that if they are to be useful at all they must be constructed and interpreted in the light of biographical facts. The assumption that individuals possess abstract, general traits has been pretty well refuted.[20] One would expect ascendance or selfishness to be generalized from situations in which they have been learned to other situations similar in some degree. But why assume that with motivation and circumstances changed, perhaps completely changed when the biography of a given individual is taken into account, the same trait would still operate, and not some other trait? The temptation to fall into the easy surface language of common sense is very strong: to speak of one man as honest, another as persistent or ascendant, *simpliciter*. But the truth, as Oscar Wilde said, is never simple and seldom pure. Modern psychology has taught us that honesty and dishonesty are devious and tricky in the extreme, often rooted in past commitments and conflicts, almost inaccessible. We also know that persistence could not be generalized indefinitely because persistence in one direction entails lack of persistence in another. Ascendance also varies from one situation to another, as is shown not only in common human experience but by experiments on chimpanzees [21] and children, where the set-up is simpler and more decidable.

The validity of accepting abstract general traits may be questioned, but also its utility. It would seem that evidence that a man has shown persistence or leadership, *in certain situations,* would be more important to an employer than assurance that the applicant has a monotonous compulsion to persist or lead on all occasions. Vocational tests which have a clear objective, that of rating a man's capacity for a given job, and do not pretend to sum up his whole personality have a plain advantage, especially when a job is available and motivation is strong. Even so, the most significant phases of personality may be overlooked; namely, *potential* abilities and needs. Where the typical psychograph tries to measure major traits at the moment, it is perhaps better method to vary conditions, to give the individual the opportunity to show what he can do with a new motivation and training. The Soviet dictum—train while testing as well as test while training—is not a bad guide to personality study. In the United States Air Force of World War II, where there was a serious shortage of trained personnel, and no motive to disqualify applicants by brief tests, it is interesting to note that "train while testing" became the rule.

Perhaps the most revealing aspect of character, without which, as Allport remarks,[22] no psychograph would be complete, is interest. But here again cross-sectional analysis is unsatisfactory. Spranger, for example, distinguishes six types of men, according to the values each esteems most high; namely, the theoretic, the economic, the aesthetic, the political, the social, and the religious. Of all non-historical typologies Spranger's is the most persuasive. Its defects should therefore prove important. In the first place, it assumes that the main motivations of all "economic men" are fundamentally the same: the robber baron and the harassed serf, the Wall Street tycoon, the trade unionist in heavy industry and the fellah of Egypt, all have the same value interest since each of them comes to place chief emphasis on economic matters. It assumes, further, that the motivation of the artist as artist is purely aesthetic; of the religious man, purely religious; of the political man, purely power. It assumes that there is such a thing as interest in theoretical matters, in general, and an abstract passion for art as such, i.e., for self-expression *überhaupt,* overlooking incidentally the fact that art as self-expression is only a late romantic theory. None of these premises of Spranger's is borne out by concrete studies of motivations, which indicate rather that interests are needs learned while adapting to a specific culture.[23]

In another place [24] we have argued that the "consequential" types of men are historical. The great seventeenth century scientist confronted by technology and trade,[25] the English factory owner of the Industrial Revolution,[26] the American New Dealer, business man, the Soviet Stakhanovist, the German big industrialist of the thirties, and the CIO organizer [27] are types that made a difference. Such historical types are accessible to study by questionnaires and public opinion polls, and by intensive Middletown methods. Psychologists have also been employed in research teams with anthropologists, sociologists, and other social scientists.

Antihistoricism, however, seems to be the prevailing tendency in recent personality studies. Kurt Lewin insists upon the importance of the immediate environment of personality as much as anyone could wish, but he completely excludes the influence of past environment, at least from the purview of "dynamic psychology." The reason given is that, since the past does not "exist at the present moment, it cannot have effects at the present. In representing life space therefore we take into account only what is contemporary." [28] It is possible that contemporary events *would* explain personality fully if they were known, and if the brain traces could be detected in some manner; but, since brain traces can only be inferred from past behavior of the individual, Lewin's method appears to be, at best, a remote ideal. In the case of bodies falling on an inclined plane, it was necessary for Galileo to disregard history; in the case of organisms, even the protozoa, as is well known, past behavior is always relevant. Birch has shown that young chimpanzees that are prevented from playing with sticks from birth on do not display the "insight" described by Köhler (i.e., do not suddenly employ the stick to rake in the banana placed beyond reach), whereas an animal that is permitted preliminary play with sticks solves the problem if not with "insight" at least in short order.[29]

Gestalt psychologists of course do not deny the effect of past learning; but they minimize it and try to get away from it. One way is to say that history "as the child experienced it, is also a psychologically essential constituent of the things of the environment," [30] where by environment is meant *"the momentary situation"* of the child or "the chief characteristics of the permanent situation." [31] As a phenomenological description of the consciousness of the child, this is undoubtedly sound. Either history does not count, or it is a constituent of things experienced; viz., either the house next door has always simply been there unchanged, or it is laden with history. The child sees it, for example, as the house where an unfriendly dog lives, or a friendly boy But phenomenological description, though valuable, is not causal explanation.[32] The psychologist still lacks a working knowledge of the contemporary events supposed to determine the child's behavior and, in practice, he must fall back on biographical facts. It is significant that methodological exclusion of genetic factors has not proved a fertile method, and no laws of child behavior have resulted. The difficulty is due, in part, to the use of such abstract terms as "vector," "valence," and "force," which are detached from what is known of the neuromuscular system and maturation and only loosely related to the developing needs and abilities of the child. It is true that a toy placed before a child generally acts as an attractive force, but this is not always so. How explain the negative case without resort to biographical facts? Or, one boy is attracted to one toy, while his companion moves off in the direction of another; one boy avoids a forbidden game, the other takes a chance. And even if two children are attracted to the same doll, the significance of the choice in the two cases may be quite different: Mary may have a doll like that at home, whereas Jane may be attracted because Mary is.

Genetic psychology attempts to trace such differences of behavior and motivation back beyond Lewin's model, momentary situation to differences of past experience. Scrutiny of past behavior of subjects is found necessary even in animal psychology. Pavlov, Gantt, Yerkes, Liddell, Masserman, to name only a few, have recognized the importance of studying experimental animals before and between laboratory sessions. Hebb reports from the Yerkes Laboratories that the past experience of chimpanzees was essential to the interpretation of their momentary behavior. If biographical facts were ignored, emotions could not be identified and motivation became obscured. "In short, the distinction between *shyness, nervousness* and *fear* is impossible without knowing something about the animal; and the term chosen . . . is affected by knowledge of the stimulus, of the response, and of the subject's experience and behavior in the past." [33]

Operationalists, such as Skinner and Pratt,[34] however, exclude most genetic factors systematically, and concentrate upon the "data"—namely, stimulus and response. Like Lewin, they regard the momentary situation as decisive. Thus Skinner argues that the term "try" must be rejected from scientific behavioral language "because it implies the relation of a given sample of behavior to past or future events; but the term 'walk' may be retained because it does not. The term 'see' must be rejected but 'look toward' may be retained because 'see' implies more than turning the eyes toward a source of stimulation or more than the simple reception of stimuli." [35] It may be that "try" and "see" could be excluded in the standardized, elegantly controlled situations in which Skinner's experiments are conducted. But it seems obvious in many other cases that we cannot know that reception of stimuli takes place when an animal looks toward an object, unless we know something about its past behavior. Thus in general practice we should have to employ the terms "look toward without reception" and "look toward with reception"—i.e., "see." Which kind of looking toward occurred would be important, if the question arose whether a rat was "discriminating" [36] floor cues or other cues, or whether chimpanzees were discriminating sticks with respect to some property. In such cases the habits of the species in their natural and laboratory environment could be profitably studied, and descriptive terms linking the laboratory subject to its natural behavior and species would be an advantage. Many phenomena point the same moral. Some writers, for example, have spoken of the "freezing" of animals in the experimental situation due to conditions of life between experiments.[37] Skinner's experiments are a model of precision in hypothetically isolated laboratory situations. If his method were extended as is proposed to psychology as a whole, i.e. if genetic factors as well as physiological facts and mechanisms were excluded from consideration, the range of problems and results in psychology would be drastically limited.[38]

There are also important genetic methods in personality studies. Floyd Allport [39] and E. R. Guthrie [40] certainly explain behavior in terms of past experience. Our view, however, stresses acquired needs, sophisticated spontaneity, the generalization and extrapolation of learning patterns, and insists that wholes, such as populations and organisms, determine their parts, as well as conversely. Psychoanalysis is also a genetic method, but we must leave its evaluation to another article in this volume. Only a few authorities such as Karen Horney, Judd Marmor, and Frederic Wertham, have paid much attention to the social factors involved, and there is no accepted procedure for testing psychoanalytic theory and diagnosis. Clinical psychology, which is closely related to psychoanalysis, has taken steps to overcome this difficulty. Thus H. A. Murray [41] and his group of personality experimentalists and experts, studied a number of subjects in thirty-five one-hour sessions, and then compared notes in a series of councils, argued, and reached agreement as to the rating of ten to forty variables in the case of each subject. The galvanic skin response, attitude scales, Rorschach, the thematic apperception test, were among the diverse psychological techniques employed by experts, who later had to come to terms with experts who had used different techniques. In this way individual bias and caprice were checked.

Other genetic tendencies in personality studies have been mentioned in the text, but we make, of course, no pretense to completeness.

Personality and the Learning Process

Personality is determined by past events, but how far into the past of an individual or society a given study should go is not an *a priori* question. Rank's emphasis on the birth trauma and Freud's insistence on "sexual" experiences of infancy are certainly exaggerations, while attempts to explain personality in terms of constitutional factors have not been very successful even in psychopathology. There is general agreement that personality begins to be formed in earliest childhood; but when its aberrations are learned, is a matter of debate. Theories that personality or its aberrations become fixed at a certain biographical point cannot be proved at the present time, and there is no substitute for careful study of individual variations.

Tests of personality and personality traits, such as intelligence, last a few minutes or hours, but there is a growing conviction that the results require interpretation in the light of biographical facts. In Lorge's extended study, a large group of high-school boys whose I.Q. had been ascertained were retested after the lapse of a few years. The result that some of them showed marked improvement of intelligence, while the others had merely held their ground, was explained by the fact that the former had continued their schooling, whereas the latter had not.[42]

In understanding how personality is learned, the most clearly formulated and well tested theories of learning are probably the best guide. These are association of ideas, classical conditioning, and selective learning. The problem is how far in principle these methods are capable of accounting for the development of needs and abilities. Since the association of ideas is difficult to confirm objectively, we shall use "association" in Guthrie's sense, i.e. spatial temporal contiguity of stimuli, whenever this is feasible. Learning by association is acquiring a response, and a disposition to respond, to stimulus S_2, by virtue of its contiguity with another stimulus S_1. In this sense, association is merely an extension of the principle of classical conditioning. Selective learning is quite a different process. Here the animal is presented with an array of stimuli, which evoke a variety of responses, one or more of which are followed by reward or punishment. If the animal learns selectively, it acquires the ability, the disposition, to select those responses which are rewarded, and to avoid those which are punished.

Although these methods of learning have been well established in experiments with animals, and to some extent with human subjects, the attempt to apply them to complicated human behavior meets with many objections. It often arouses indignation. Yet no one would deny that we have learned a great deal about human disease by the study of animals. The value of explaining the human level, *as far as possible,* in terms of principles which hold for other animals, is in fact generally admitted. Our next step is therefore to form hypotheses as to how far conditioning and selective learning are applicable to complicated human performance, and to consider objections.

The most common objection is that conditioning experiments neglect the "total situation," confining attention to some artificially isolated segment of it; namely, stimulus-response. This is only partly true. Even Pavlov did not restrict his interest to the food and bell, to a parotid gland, cerebrum, etc. He took care to eliminate noise and other disturbing phenomena from the experimental situation and often accounted for his results by the reaction patterns, or "personality," of his dogs. When it became evident to him that a total experimental situation was producing widespread personality changes in his dogs, he devoted many years to an investigation of this phenomenon. In studies of selective learning, likewise, many components of the total situation are taken into account, and are varied to assess their influence on behavior. The condition, training, and habits of the subjects, the size and shape of the experimental room, the presence of other animals, temperature, noises, feeding routine, and many other factors, can be manipulated. Some psychologists also employ movies to record details of the experimental process, which can later be studied at leisure. Sometimes changes in the "total situation" are found to alter results, and sometimes not, even in Gestalt experiments.

Hull has taken a long step toward satisfying the demands of Gestalt psychologists by adopting the expression "stimulus compound" or "stimulus configuration." He not only recognizes that the life of the organism often depends on reacting to the stimulus compound, rather than to its component stimuli.[43] He also formulates principles specifying conditions in which patterning takes place, and the quantity of it that can be expected. Pavlov himself had demonstrated clearly that a dog could be trained to react differently to the stimulus sequence S_1, S_2, S_3, than to the same stimuli taken singly or in any other order; and that reactions to the stimulus compound, or to its components, could be reinforced differentially with marked differences of behavior resulting. Many conditioning experiments in this country bear out Pavlov's results. There is no question, therefore, as to the importance of configuration. Everyone admits *Gestaltqualitäten.* The problem is rather to measure, if possible, the changes in behavior produced by different types of configuration, or stimulus compounds. Hull's principle that the degree of patterning is "an increasing function of the degree of interaction effects among its components" is supported by much evidence. It does not preclude that these components are a function in turn of the interaction of stimulus compounds. A whole *W* may be determined by the interaction of its parts, while these parts are determined, conversely, by the interaction of *W* with other wholes.

Another objection is that learning, especially in human subjects, is not nearly so mechanical as it is assumed to be in conditioning and selective learning experiments. Trial and error, success and failure, for example, are not purely random and hit-or-miss. Since conditioning and trial-and-error experiments are, in many cases, frankly simplified models of the learning process, such criticism is partly justified. On the other hand, American and Soviet psychologists have increasingly recognized the importance of adjusting the experimental problem to the habits of the species employed. Not all trial-and-error responses are regarded as equally probable or frequent. Response series often have a definite trend, as Rubinstein [44] has pointed out, determined by the adaptive habits of the species and the previous learning of the individual animal.

Although conditioning and selective learning have been definitely established in human beings, the previous learning of the adult human is so immense and incalculable that, in important cases, it is seemingly impossible to control experiments of this kind. The question is whether there is any impossibility *in principle*. When H. A. Ruger gave adults a puzzle to solve which was somewhat new in their experience, "random manipulations played some part, and in many cases a considerable part, in gaining success"; and Koffka comments: "The procedure adopted by human beings in solving these puzzles often very closely paralleled the methods employed by the animals of Thorndike's experiments."[45] Many other experiments point to the same conclusion. When the problem is new, human responses are not unlike those of the rat in a maze, whereas when the problem resembles previous problems to some degree, solutions are directed and expedited. In typical human problem solving, success is a function of pertinent prior training. What the prior training does, for one thing, is to exclude whole ranges of erroneous, i.e., unsuccessful, responses. Every individual, for example, acquires grammatical and logical needs which eliminate dozens of mistakes in a single conversation. On countless occasions in the past, slips of grammar and logic have been ridiculed or frowned upon, while correct responses have been reinforced by approval or by continued attention, as when one is allowed to finish one's sentence without interruption. The persistent needs thus acquired not only exclude erroneous responses, but also provide correct responses which, though they may not be *sufficient*, are *necessary* to problem solving. A third way in which prior training facilitates problem solving is by generalization. Many logical and mathematical solutions, for example, are simply generalizations or applications of rules to new cases. In his discussion of transfer of training, Thorndike paid little attention to the transfer of logical forms from one subject matter to another. Yet there seems to be no doubt that an abstract form such as "If p, then q; but not q and therefore not p" is an example of a component "identical" to different situations or subject matters. That abstract forms, such as "outside" can be generalized to new situations has been proved by Gestalt experiments even in the case of birds. Generalization of abstract forms and relations is an immense aid to learning on the human level where the use of language multiplies the instances by millions. Yet generalization has its limits. In most communities there are areas where the exercise of logical needs is punished, or at least not rewarded, and where the extension of logic has no sufficient motivation. On finding that certain primitive societies persisted in making contradictory judgments about the soul, Tylor concluded that they must be talking about two souls, not one; whereas Lévy-Bruhl accounted for the same phenomenon by assigning primitive people to a prelogical stage of development. More probable that either of these theories, in view of investigations in anthropology and child psychology, is the hypothesis that in many societies the law of non-contradiction is not generalized sufficiently to the areas of politics and religion.

In considering the objection that the conditioning and selective learning processes are too mechanical to account for the facts, it is worth emphasizing again that some things are admittedly easier to learn than others. It is easier, for example, to acquire a need to assent to $12 \times 12 = 144$ than to learn $12 \times 12 = 145$,* because the experience of the individual squares with the former, but conflicts with the latter. If a child is rewarded for assertions or performances which are also rewarded in the course of practical activity, learning is established. When what is rewarded by the teacher is punished in experience, conflict ensues, and learning is disrupted. It is easier to learn some things than others because nature, organisms, and societies have certain structures and characteristics. But do we not also learn by insight or self-evidence? Is it not obvious at a glance that "if *A* is contained in *B*, and *B* in *C*, *A* is contained in *C*"? Although the occurrence of sudden learning is undisputed, it is no less obvious that sudden learning depends upon previous experience. In the above example, one must have learned by perceptual training that "contained in," at least in some situations, is transitive.

Still another objection to conditioning and selective learning is that they fail to account for original or productive thinking. Thus Wertheimer, in discussing the psychological steps in the formation of the General Theory of Relativity, remarks that although "one could imagine that some of the necessary changes occurred to Einstein by chance, in a procedure of trial and error" this would be a mistake. "Scrutiny of

* The experiments of George Katona (*Organizing and Memorizing*, New York, 1940) show that good organization of material favors learning.

Einstein's thought always showed that when a step was taken this happened because it was required. Quite generally, if one knows how Einstein thinks, one knows that any blind and fortuitous procedure is foreign to his mind."[46] This conclusion is plausible. Trial and error in original thinking is not blind and fortuitous, because the blind and fortuitous responses are generally eliminated, as unsuccessful, at an early stage of education. Many reasoned and sophisticated responses also are extinguished on the long road to invention or discovery. The hypotheses that remain at the end may be differently weighted (some more reinforced than others), and the key hypothesis may still be missing. Much has been written about the sudden, inexplicable occurrence of momentous ideas, but two things are fairly clear: men with the best training in a field will be most apt to hit upon good original ideas, because they have eliminated more of the unsuccessful responses, and can concentrate on hypotheses that *might be* true; and, the greater the familiarity with the field, the greater the number of promising associations, the more numerous are the hypotheses that *might be* true. Wertheimer's account of the development of Einstein's thought would have been more adequate if he had compared it to that of other scientists who were also working toward the General Theory, and had indicated the very similar training these men enjoyed.

There is admittedly no such thing as inborn originality or originality *sui generis*. One has to learn to learn, and learn to be original, always in specific fields. Students who desire to do original work are advised to study their subject thoroughly and then attach themselves to men doing original work in it. Laboratories such as that of Rutherford at Cambridge, and the mathematical faculty at Göttingen, became famous for the training they supplied in original thinking, in a given field. Among other things, such training apparently inculcates in the student, by emulation and encouragement, a need to try out new unorthodox methods and ideas, which have not been disproved, or completely disproved, and to test them indefatigably. Such a complex need, once developed, may overshadow all other needs and supply the key to a biography. The formation of such master needs, however, seems to require reinforcement by success and extinction through failure, just as it does in far simpler cases. But trial and error in the higher reaches of problem solving, we have emphasized (only because it is usually forgotten), is frightfully sophisticated. All the more obvious trials which might occur to a layman have long since been eliminated by trials and errors, successes and failures, experienced in a protracted technical education. The same education, especially if it has included training in original methods, has provided an abundance of leads and fertile associations.

The public record of the development of an original idea is in the form of objective responses, but they do not tell the whole story. To account for the phenomenon plausibly, we must reconstruct from these responses the concealed mental processes. If this is not done the behavior series will remain full of gaps and not wholly intelligible. In practice the method of association or recombination of ideas is found indispensable. Original thinking is explained by recombination of ideas in a process of trial and error which is restricted and directed by present stimuli, but only after a long course of technical training in the past. Many psychologists, however, are dissatisfied with genetic theories of learning, and emphasize, instead, a kind of congruence between mental states or hypothetical brain states, on the one hand, and the visual field, on the other. Wertheimer and Köhler, for example, argue that "requiredness" in the momentary situation can determine behavior. This is no doubt true as phenomenological description. The genetic psychologist, however, will insist on knowing why requiredness is felt by some men at some times and in some situations, and not by others.

We have argued that the personality trait, originality, is made up of needs and abilities, which are fairly specific and are always learned. Logical and mathematical forms, and certain other scientific schemata, may be generalized to new subject matters; but to explain behavior we must trace the learning process into a specific past. Originality, genius, reason, benevolence, selfishness, piety, pride, aggressiveness, the desire for profits or social security, are never the cause of anything. Whereas idealism attempts to account for behavior by the interrelation of meanings or ideas, materialist explanation is primarily causal and, in the field of personality, genetic. We have emphasized conditioning and selective learning because they appear to be the best qualified genetic theories. Wertheimer himself states that conditioning and selective learning enter into the developmental process; but he insists that they "function in relation to whole-characteristics," that the learning process is "not of an and-summative aggregation, of a succession of piecemeal, chance happenings," nor arbitrary, but "shows a consistency of development." [47] These qualifications, however, are quite acceptable. If one starts with Thorndike's rats, and gives them a *new* problem, their response is likely to be arbitrary, accidental, and disconnected, though perhaps not so much so as Thorndike thought. The same is true of most conditioning and selective learning experiments, which are specifically designed to exclude the effects of past learning, in order to study the basic phenomenon in a simple, well controlled situation. One would expect the learning to be more mechanical, disjointed, and fortuitous than that which occurs outside the laboratory, and wildly dissimilar to the productive thinking of human beings. Once the individual has learned the thousands of needs and abilities which distinguish his society, family, school, profession, trade union, church, and club from other groups, selective learning has become fairly sensible and rational. Trial and error, relatively blind and mechanical in the case of rats, and even in human infancy, are now determined by a great deal of technical knowledge, and restricted to responses of a *kind* which have proved successful, or have not proved unsuccessful, in the past. One learns by trial and error, for example, to avoid trials which involve logical, mathematical, and physical impossibilities or patent improbabilities.

Needs, as we understand them, take many forms. An emotion, for example, may be defined as the disposition to "prefer" response to stimulus-configurations which have been associated with satisfaction or dissatisfaction of needs in the past. If delight is satisfaction, and distress is dissatisfaction of a need, and "anticipation" is defined in terms of past behavior, we may say that hope is the anticipation of delight; fear, the anticipation of distress. In another place,[48] we have defined a number of basic emotions in behavioral, genetic terms. Anger, for instance, "arises from frustration of needs, or injury, where satisfaction of needs had formerly been encountered, the emotion being directed upon an S [a stimulus-configuration] identified as a responsive dissatisfier or responsive injurer." We have argued that such genetic definitions clarify the nature of emotions, which are not to be understood on the surface, or at the moment, but require a scrutiny of past behavior. It is true that the evoking stimulus is in the present, and so perhaps is the object of the emotion; but the individual reacts not only to the external stimulus, but also to internal stimuli produced in the organism by activation of brain traces. In emotion we "react" to things past as well as present, and these things are fairly specific. When psychologists leave out the object, and past reference of emotion, they are not dealing with emotion but only with "shock," or with "excitement" in Stratton's sense.

Attitudes and beliefs may also be described as needs. An attitude seems to be a persistent preference for certain types of responses to persons, and to institutions and places in so far as changes in them are of human importance. The same is true of emotions as defined above. In fact, we may say that an attitude is nothing but an emotion which is persistent or recurrent, and which is generalized from experienced objects to a whole range of unexperienced objects of the same class. The simplest case is where a man generalizes the *emotion* of anger he feels toward several acquaintances to the group to which they belong, and thus develops an *attitude* of aversion toward a race or nationality. Irrational attitudes are also formed by the daily press. A man who has no time to check newspaper stories is repeatedly angered by reports of the misdoing of a certain nation, with the result that he becomes suspicious or angry whatever that nation does or is reported to do. This disposition is an attitude of hostility. Psychologists have given almost exclusive attention to irrational attitudes, sometimes leaving the impression that there is no other kind. The more complex rational attitudes involve reasoning and accurate information, and require specific training. Attitudes, like emotions, have to be traced to past experience, as every good novel illustrates. It is not surprising that the best information about attitudes comes from genetic studies of one kind or another. Piaget's *The Moral Judgment of the Child,*[49] Thrasher's analysis of gang societies,[50] Bettelheim's account of the transformation of attitudes of prisoners of different social classes in a Nazi concentration camp,[51] are examples.

Beliefs can also be treated as needs, i.e. as dispositions to "prefer" one type of behavior or speech to another. This disposition differs from other needs in that the responses "preferred" have to do only with the truth and falsity of statements. Piaget [52] has described three stages in the child's acceptance of rules, or as he says, three types of rules: the motor rule, which is accepted, believed in, automatically; the coercive rule founded on *unilateral* respect; and the rational rule founded on *mutual* respect. No doubt the love and confidence the child feels for parents always help to form beliefs, although there are considerable differences from one society or class to another, some evidence showing, for example, that children of the proletariat are more self-reliant. The crucial test of the child's belief is its own experience. If what the parents say is opposite to what the child himself learns, there is a conflict of needs.

Conflict of Needs and the Organization of Personality

There is a certain advantage in the procedure we have followed. Instead of treating traits as transparent features of personality, exhibited fully by cross-sectional analysis, we have regarded them as phases of the learning process. We have dealt only with acquired needs and abilities, i.e., with learned dispositions of the individual to make certain types of responses to certain patterns of stimuli, abilities being distinguished from needs by the fact that the individual is not disposed to exercise an ability unless it subserves the satisfaction of some need. Emotions, interests, attitudes, and beliefs have been distinguished as different kinds of needs, and it seems clear that all other traits or features of personality could also be regarded as needs, abilities, or potentialities of various kinds. From this point of view, it is still important to classify behavior—to speak, for example, of health, affectability, ascendance, self-assurance, gregariousness and aesthetic interest; but these features of personality are looked upon as phases or stages of the individual's adaptation, as specific as the learning processes which produced them. Generalization of traits, as by the extrapolation of logical rules from learned situations, is not excluded. But the consistency of a trait, its extension to new experience, is not automatic. Sometimes it occurs, sometimes not. General features common to all personalities are of course, undeniable. It is necessary to distinguish such stages of development as automatism, habit, and intelligent behavior. But though the classification is important, it is obvious that intelligent behavior can include habitual and automatic components, while habit and even automatism may adumbrate and anticipate intelligence. The universality of some traits does not mean that they are uniform and transcendental. Each of Kant's Categories of the Understanding, as is said, has a history. The same is true of Kant's "transcendental unity of apperception." If the "I" must be able to accompany every perception, it is because there are conditions in all societies which the individual must adapt to. Actually the formation of the I, and alienation in pathological cases, have long been studied. The need for a name is also a universal personality acquisition. In South Africa, where the white population deny the natives a name, i.e., refer to them invariably by any trick name that comes to mind, disorganization of personality is plainly observable.[53] Philosophers have rightly insisted upon the essential spontaneity of the self in organizing its experience. But this too has a history, sometimes a decline and fall. It is a history of the learning of needs which provide internal stimuli directing action.

So far, however, we have said nothing of the *organization* of needs, abilities, and potentialities. The most plausible view is that organization of personality is a continuous product of the individual's efforts to resolve contradictions among his needs. A conflict of needs arises when an individual, who has a disposition to give a certain response to a stimulus pattern, acquires a disposition to give another *incompatible* response to it. No conflict ensues, of course, if one of the needs is not active at the moment, but only latent; and the severity of conflict will depend on the duration of the stalemate, and the intensity of the needs. Conflict of needs, mild or intense, is continuous or intermittent,[54] and their avoidance or resolution provides persisting motivation. The mechanics of conflict, the reciprocal relation of the antagonistic skeletal muscles, has been studied extensively by Sherrington [55] and others, and much is known of the opposite action of the thoracico-lumbar and cranio-sacral parts of the vegetative nervous system.[56]

Simple examples of resolution of conflict are furnished by animal experiments. A mother rat cannot reach her offspring-in-nest, for which she has an active need, without crossing an electrically charged grill. Unless the intensity is too great she overcomes her conflict by crossing. A chimpanzee behind a fence who sees a banana beyond his reach takes a different course. Instead of attempting painfully to squeeze himself through the bars of the fence, which he has learned not to do, he finally runs around the fence, and if possible, would go over the top, climb a rope, or use a stick. In other words, the resolution of conflict is simply a successful phase of the learning process which we have been discussing all along. By and large, where there is no conflict there is no motive to learn, and no learning. When learning takes place, the conflict is resolved. Learning of needs is therefore no isolated process. Acquiring a need is adjusting this need to other needs and involves to some degree a reorganization of personality. Thus even in Pavlov's seemingly isolated experiments learning produced great personality changes. A less artificial, more complex, instance is the conflict of a boy on his first day of school. There is the need to go to school with the others, and not to anger his mother; but there is also the need to stay home with his mother, to play with toys, etc. The conflict may be resolved by running away from school, by developing school friends and interests, or by feigning illness. In any case the resolution reorganizes a whole system of needs. It is customary to distinguish different types of resolution or adaptation. In another place,[57] we have distinguished, for example, long range *vs.* short range, and social *vs.* antisocial, adaptation. "The hysteric resolves his conflict but in a fashion unacceptable to the community," [58] whereas other forms of psychoneurosis consist of a failure to resolve conflicting needs in any fashion.[59]

There are three main areas in which the conflict and resolution of needs can be studied—infancy and childhood, psychopathology, and work or economic activity; and the current dispute has to do with the relative value of these approaches. All three are necessary and exceedingly important, and none is independent of the others. Thus the question, Which is the predominant? can hardly be avoided. A present tendency in psychotherapy to explain personality and its deformations in terms of infantile experiences which are largely inferred from speculative theories, and largely unverifiable, seems one-sided and disproportionate. Kardiner,[60] in discussing the place of women in the myths and folklore of the Marquesans, criticizes current psychoanalytic theories. The popular theory that the men's fear "of being eaten up by the women represents a wish to return to the uterus" is, he says, "quite meaningless. Why should they wish to return?" Roheim's explanation that the men turn the woman into a cannibalistic demon when she refuses them is also "tenuous." Kardiner's own theory that the mother is assigned a cannibal role because she frustrates the man throughout his entire life-cycle is more plausible but still quite speculative. Although Kardiner is no strict Freudian, and sometimes explains personality development very effectively in terms of economic changes in different societies, his main tendency is to explain the social structure in terms of infant and childhood frustrations, and to neglect socio-economic determinants. His refusal to discuss the "race-suicide" of the Marquesans and their reaction to imperialism is revealing:

> If we were to attempt any explanation of the "race suicide" of these people, we should expose ourselves to a situation too difficult to solve, and one in which all efforts at empathy must fail. Nor can we trust their rationalization that they do not want their children to be the slaves of the French. We do not understand this culture well enough to appreciate the logical incompatibilities created by the contact with French institutions.[61]

It might be thought that history had given some testimony as to the reactions of people to imperialism, and that concrete study of exploitation on the spot (on the basis of Linton's careful notes) would have been very profitable. But Kardiner evidently believes that childhood frustrations and hostilities, though largely "unconscious," are more accessible to knowledge, and can, in fact, be detected at a distance of thousands of miles by Rorschach methods. Another psychiatrist, Wulf Sachs,[62] in his study of South African natives, made the facts of exploitation his main theme and concern. The incompatibilities between the whites and the natives were no mystery. He saw the stockades for the "blacks" and observed the effect of oppressive regulations. Could not one also find some degree of obvious exploitation in the Marquesas, as in other French colonies?

The Marxian theory of the development of societies and constituent personalities recognizes the role of childhood frustrations, but regards it as secondary. When the economic factors this theory emphasizes are properly understood, it is certainly more ample and resourceful than is usually supposed. According to Venable [63] four general factors determine the main development of any society: the quantity of available labor, its needs, abilities, and education; the social factor, the organization of individuals into socio-economic groups such as families, tribes and nations, trade unions and business associations; raw materials and unwrought economic resources of all kinds; and technology. These four factors are said to determine the main course of history; but which of them predominates in a given stage or sector can be discovered only by concrete historical investigation. Though each factor predominates at one time or another, none is of course independent of the others.

The present essay has been concerned with the psychology of personality, which is only one phase of the first factor; but all four factors, as we have said, are interdependent, and contributions in other fields must supplement our account. The needs and abilities which the majority of men were able to acquire under the slavery and domination of Rome, or the subjugation of feudalism, which at one time stretched across civilized Europe, were niggardly and mean compared to the rich array of wants and capacities realized by our own culture. Yet even today the bulk of men's needs and abilities are incident to earning a living. If the second factor mentioned above, the socio-economic organization of men, can be effectively reformed, so that productive forces are released and nations live in peace, then the horizons can be pushed back indefinitely. Personality would then assume its true stature, and history would be increasingly determined, not by economic necessities, but by developing aesthetic and scientific needs.

References

[1] Gordon W. Allport, *Personality: A Psychological Interpretation* (New York, 1937), pp. 27 ff., especially p. 43.

[2] Donald W. MacKinnon, "The Structure of Personality," in J. M. Hunt, ed., *Personality and Behavior Disorders* (New York, 1944), Vol. I, p. 3.

[3] E. R. Guthrie, "Personality in Terms of Associative Learning," in *ibid.*

[4] There is already an extensive literature on experimental "neurosis" in animals. See especially Jules H. Masserman, *Behavior and Neurosis* (Chicago, 1943).

[5] William James, "The Energies of Men," *Selected Essays on Philosophy* (New York, 1917).

[6] See Livingston Welch, "The Inclusion of Both Physiological and Acquired Needs in a Behavioristic System," *Journal of General Psychology,* 35:87–97 (1946); and V. J. McGill, "The Mind-Body Problem in the Light of Recent Psychology," *Science and Society,* 9:335–362 (1944, No. 4).

[7] Binet, A. "La Suggestibilité," in *L'Année psychologique,* Vol. 5 (1898), and C. J. Leuba, "Images as Conditioned Sensations," *Journal of Experimental Psychology,* 26:345 (1940).

[8] E. Airapetyantz and Bykov, "Physiological Experiments and the Psychology of the Subconscious," *Philosophy and Phenomenological Research,* 5:577–593 (June, 1945).

[9] At a meeting of the American Psychiatric Society, New York City, 1947.

[10] For example, *The National Health Conference, Proceedings,* 1938, and the four Brookings Institution books issued in one volume, *The Distribution of Income in Relation to Economic Progress* (Washington, 1936) is an example. A recent volume on the subject is *Measurement of Consumer Interest,* ed. C. W. Churchman, R. L. Ackoff, and M. Wax (Philadelphia, 1947).

[11] L. B. Ames, "Some Relationships Between Stair Climbing and Prone Progression," *Journal of Genetic Psychology,* 54:313–325 (1939).

[12] Alexander Shand's insistence (*The Foundations of Character,* London, 1915) that dominating "sentiments" explain a biography more fully than temporary emotions and impulses must be accepted and, so far as possible, put in behavioral terms.

[13] Edwin G. Boring, *The Physical Dimensions of Consciousness* (New York, 1933), pp. 3–8.

[14] C. I. Lewis, *Mind and the World-Order* (New York, 1929), p. 26. The same question has been discussed by V. J. McGill, "Subjective and Objective Methods in Philosophy," *Journal of Philosophy,* 41:421–439 (1944).

[15] See Binet, *op. cit.*

[16] In an important series of experiments, still unpublished, S. E. Asch has shown that interpretations of prestige phenomena have often been too simple and mechanical.

[17] Richard Aldington in *A Book of "Characters"* (London, 1924) has compiled a number of these character sketches.

[18] William McDougall, *An Introduction to Social Psychology* (Boston, 1911), pp. 114 f.

[19] Cited by MacKinnon, *op. cit.*, p. 34.

[20] See, for example, H. Hartshorne and M. A. May, *Studies in Deceit* (New York, 1928), Allport's criticism (*op. cit.*, pp. 250 f.) of these famous studies seems to be partly right, and to provide suggestions for further work.

[21] R. M. Yerkes, *Chimpanzees: A Laboratory Colony* (New Haven, 1943), chap. v.

[22] *Op. cit.*, p. 427.

[23] M. Sherif and H. Cantril in *The Psychology of Ego-Involvements* (New York, 1947) sum up a great deal of evidence in support of this contention.

[24] V. J. McGill, "Types of Men in Their Relation to Ethics," *Philosophy and Phenomenological Research,* Vol. 3, No. 4 (June, 1943).

[25] See, for example, B. Hessen, "The Social and Economic Roots of Newton's Principia," *Science at the Crossroads* (London, 1931).

[26] See, for example, Paul Mantoux, *The Industrial Revolution in the Eighteenth Century* (New York, 1929).

[27] See, for example, R. R. R. Brooks, *When Labor Organizes* (New Haven, 1937); also, Clinton S. Golden and H. J. Ruttenberg, *The Dynamics of Industrial Democracy* (New York, 1942).

[28] *Principles of Topological Psychology* (New York, 1936), p. 35.

[29] Herbert G. Birch, "The Relation of Previous Experience to Insightful Problem-Solving," *Journal of Comparative Psychology,* Vol. 38, No. 6 (1945).

[30] Kurt Lewin, *A Dynamic Theory of Personality* (New York, 1935), p. 77.

[31] *Ibid.*, p. 71.

[32] This is emphasized by W. Köhler in *The Place of Value in a World of Facts* (New York, 1938). In practice, the distinction is often lost.

[33] D. O. Hebb, "Emotion in Man and Animal: An Analysis of the Intuitive Process of Recognition," *Psychological Rev.*, Vol. 53, No. 2 (1946), p. 91.

[34] Carroll C. Pratt, *The Logic of Modern Psychology* (New York, 1939). See also *Psychological Rev.* where he has modified his extreme view.

[35] B. F. Skinner, *The Behavior of Organisms: An Experimental Analysis* (New York, 1938), pp. 7 f.

[36] *Ibid.*, p. 169.

[37] See, for example, B. F. Riess, "A Possible Explanation of 'Freezing Behavior' in Rats," *Science,* 102:570 f. (Nov. 30, 1945).

[38] Norman R. F. Maier and T. C. Schneirla, "Mechanisms in Conditioning," *Psychological Rev.*, Vol. 49, No. 2 (1942), pp. 117–134. Hudson Hoagland, *Pacemakers in Relation to Aspects of Behavior* (New York, 1935), pp. 3–5, also argues against the exclusion of physiological mechanisms.

[39] Floyd H. Allport, *Social Psychology* (Boston, 1924).

[40] E. R. Guthrie, *op. cit.* See also his *The Psychology of Human Conflict* (New York, 1938).

[41] H. A. Murray and others, *Explorations in Personality* (New York, 1938).

[42] Irving Lorge, "Schooling Makes a Difference," *Teachers College Record*, 46:483 (May, 1945).

[43] C. L. Hull, *Principles of Behavior: An Introduction to Behavior Theory*, (New York, 1943), p. 376.

[44] S. L. Rubinstein, *Fundamentals of General Psychology* (Moscow, 1940), pp. 91–93 (in Russian).

[45] K. Koffka, *The Growth of the Mind* (New York, 1924), p. 194.

[46] Max Wertheimer, *Productive Thinking* (New York, 1945), p. 188.

[47] *Ibid.*, p. 190.

[48] V. J. McGill and Livingston Welch, "A Behaviorist Analysis of Emotions," *Philosophy of Science*, 13:100–122 (1946).

[49] J. Piaget, *The Moral Judgment of the Child* (New York, 1932).

[50] F. M. Thrasher, *The Gang* (Chicago, 1927).

[51] B. Bettelheim, "Individual and Mass Behavior in Extreme Situations," *Journal of Abnormal and Social Psychology* 38:417–452 (1943).

[52] *Op. cit.*, p. 92.

[53] Reported by Wulf Sachs, "Psychotherapy Among South African Natives," paper read before the Association for the Advancement of Psychotherapy, New York, May 23, 1946.

[54] Cf. O. H. Mowrer and Clyde Kluckhohn, "Dynamic Theory of Personality," in J. M. Hunt, ed., *op. cit.*, pp. 69 f.

[55] C. S. Sherrington, *The Integrative Action of the Nervous System* (New York, 1906).

[56] M. B. Arnold reviews some of the literature in "Physiological Differentiation of Emotional States," *Psychological Rev.*, Vol. 52, No. 1 (1945).

[57] V. J. McGill and Livingston Welch, *op. cit.*, pp. 118 f.

[58] V. J. McGill and Livingston Welch, "Hysteria as a Conditioning Process," *American Journal of Psychotherapy*, 1:253–278 (1947).

[59] Among recent writers taking this view are F. Alexander and T. M. French, *Psychoanalytic Therapy* (New York, 1946), p. 4; K. Horney, *The Neurotic Personality of Our Time* (New York, 1937); and Jules H. Masserman, *Principles of Dynamic Psychiatry* (Philadelphia, 1946), pp. 286 f.

[60] Abram Kardiner, *The Individual and His Society* (New York, 1939), p. 215. See also his *Psychological Frontiers of Society* (New York, 1945).

[61] *Ibid.*, p. 199.

[62] *Op. cit.* See also Sachs's *Black Hamlet* (Boston, 1947).

[63] Vernon Venable, *Human Nature: The Marxian View* (New York, 1945), pp. 88 f.

PSYCHOANALYSIS

by

JUDD

MARMOR, M.D.

Judd Marmor, M.D. in Beverly Hills, California, is a practicing psychoanalyst, member of the American Psychoanalytic Association, and Fellow of the American Psychiatric Association. Visiting Associate Professor of Psychology, University of Southern California; Senior Consultant in Neuropsychiatry, U.S. Veterans Administration; formerly Associate in Neurology, College of Physicians and Surgeons, Columbia University; Lecturer in Psychiatry, New York Medical College; Lecturer, New School for Social Research; author of numerous articles on psychiatry and neurology.

OVER the years the influence of psychoanalysis has slowly spread, and has left its mark not only upon psychology and medicine, but also upon anthropology, sociology, and every phase of art and literature. In America it has recently begun to find its way into the curricula of the hitherto hostile medical schools, some of which are for the first time now offering full postgraduate psychoanalytic training courses; and the autonomous psychoanalytic institutes are besieged as never before by constantly growing numbers of young psychiatrists, eager for specialized instruction.

Criticisms of psychoanalysis, however, although perhaps less widespread than formerly, are persistent. In recent years, a growing group of scientifically oriented thinkers has criticized the theoretical concepts of classical psychoanalysis as being at variance with the concepts of modern materialism. This criticism cannot lightly be charged to ignorance, bias, or inner "resistance" in the critics. Much in classical psychoanalytic theory is open to objection on such grounds. It is the contention of this writer, however, that psychoanalysis, stripped of its debatable superstructure and reduced to its *basic concepts* is fully in accord with the principles of modern materialism; that its instinctivistic and mechanistic aspects are subject to increasing criticism within its own ranks; and that psychoanalytic theory, no less than the theory of any of the other basic social sciences, reflects its historical and socio-economic milieu, and is consequently changing and adapting itself to the progress of scientific knowledge.

Contrary to popular belief, there is no close unity among psychoanalysts today either in theory or in practice. For a long time there was a considerable tendency among the more classical followers of Freud to insist on such unity among professed psychoanalysts; but as Ernest Jones, dean of British psychoanalysts and one of Freud's earliest followers, said in a recent speech:

> The impossibility of this ideal is being recognized and it is being replaced by the more practicable, though difficult enough, endeavor to distinguish between what constitute the essential characteristics of psychoanalysis and what are superimposed and more varying features. Here we cannot do better than follow Freud's own definition. Psychoanalysis is simply the study of mental processes of which we are unaware, of what for the sake of brevity we call the unconscious. The psychoanalytic method of carrying out this study is that characterized by the free association technique of analyzing the observable phenomena of transference and resistance. As Freud himself said, anyone following this path is practicing psychoanalysis even if he comes to conclusions different from Freud's . . . and it is plain that we should be forsaking the sphere of science for that of theology were we to regard these conclusions . . . as being sacrosanct and eternal.[1]

Let us examine the elements upon which this basic definition of psychoanalysis as given by Freud rests. They are, "the study of mental processes of which we are unaware," "the free association technique," and "the phenomena of transference and resistance." These elements are by no means separate and distinct from one another. Historically and practically they are closely interrelated and form a unified, dynamic concept of certain aspects of mental activity which is the cornerstone of all psychoanalytic theory and practice, regardless of the extent to which this theory and practice may vary in other respects among analysts.

That mental processes of which we are unaware exist is no longer a debatable matter. One may properly question, as some critics do, the validity of designating such processes in terms of a particular "area" of the mind known as "the unconscious," but the reality of the processes has been conclusively demonstrated not only clinically but experimentally. The experimental evidence is crucial, for out of it, as we shall see, comes the confirmation also of the validity of the free association technique and of the concepts of repression and resistance. Let us first, however, briefly review the historical development of these basic concepts.

Prior to Freud, not only was psychiatry itself static and purely descriptive, but also experimental investigations of human personality, will and emotion, without an adequate guiding theory, were largely fruitless. Freud started his practice in 1886 utilizing electrotherapy, suggestion, and hypnosis, the accepted therapeutic methods of the day. But he learned very early that these tools were unsatisfactory. In all severe cases, he saw "the suggestions which had been applied crumble away again; and then the disease or some substitute for it returned." [2] Some years before an older colleague, Dr. Breuer, had told Freud of his discovery that under hypnosis a "widening of consciousness" seemed to take place, which enabled his patient (the famous Anna O.) to recall many experiences which were not accessible to her in a normal state. Recalling this, Freud began to use hypnosis in investigating the historical antecedents of his patients' neurotic illnesses, and confirmed Breuer's finding that memories, thoughts, and impulses which had previously dropped out of consciousness could thus be brought out, revealing significant connections between the recollections and the character of the symptoms.

Freud next asked himself why it was so difficult to bring to consciousness these dynamically charged ideas and emotions. It seemed logical to assume that they could not become conscious because a certain force was operating in opposition to them. He became acutely aware of this when his inability to hypnotize many of his patients compelled him to seek other means of widening the sphere of their awareness. No amount of direct questioning or urging achieved this desired result. Finally he evolved the method of asking his patients to tell him everything that came to their minds without rejecting anything, and regardless of whether the material seemed relevant or not. By this technique, to which he gave the name of "free association," Freud discovered that patients were actually able to recover many thoughts, impulses, and memories which had hitherto been accessible only through hypnosis. This represented an important technical advance, of which he wrote, "The history of psychoanalysis proper . . . begins with the new technique that dispenses with hypnosis."[3] But while by this technique patients were able to bring previously unconscious ideas into consciousness, Freud observed that they succeeded only in the face of considerable inner resistance. The reluctance of the patient to express certain thoughts, the slips of the tongue, the significant gaps in memory, the "accidental" omissions and inaccuracies all pointed unmistakably to the existence of emotional conflict. It seemed apparent that the impulses and ideas which were unconscious had become so because they were incompatible with other aspects of the patient's personality, and that they had been kept out of awareness as an economical measure to protect the personality from the pain of persistent conscious conflict. Out of this clinical observation Freud developed the concept of repressions, which

> is the foundation stone on which the structure of psychoanalysis rests, the most essential part of it, and yet it is nothing but a theoretical formulation of a phenomenon which may be observed to recur as often as one undertakes an analysis of a neurotic without resorting to hypnosis.[4]

It is worth noting that the free associational technique which led to this theoretical advance rests upon a basic assumption which is thoroughly in accord with modern scientific thinking—the assumption that all psychic phenomena, far from being accidental and haphazard, are strictly determined. This is the concept of *psychic determination*—that cause and effect relationships hold true for psychological phenomena as for all other phenomena. There must be, Freud assumed, a rational explanation for even the minutest psychological event or process, whether it be a dream, fantasy, slip of the tongue, lapse of memory, or merely the sequence in which one thought follows another. He took as his working basis the assumption that the patient's thoughts were not haphazard but were influenced by his repressed attitudes and impulses, and to a certain extent were derived from them.*

* It was this assumption which laid the groundwork for Freud's monumental discoveries about the nature of dreams. It is worth noting that no system of psychology, other than the psychoanalytic, has offered a rational explanation of dream material. While individual analysts, depending upon their theoretical orientation, often differ as to the meaning of certain dream patterns, all analysts accept and utilize Freud's brilliant concepts of the *mechanisms* involved in the formation of dreams—the so-called "dream work" of symbolization, condensation, displacement, etc. These discoveries of Freud have taken dreams once and for all out of the realm of mysticism and related them to the world of reality.

The earliest confirmation of this assumption—"the first bridge between experimental psychology and psychoanalysis"[5]—was in the word association test which Jung adapted from Wundt. In this test Jung showed that, whenever the response to a word stimulus was greatly retarded or was otherwise unusual in character, it could be demonstrated that the word stimulus was associated in the subject's mind with some repressed complex. The experiments, however, could not in themselves be considered decisive, since the complex itself, being unknown to both subject and experimenter, could not be adequately controlled during the experiment. Luria observes:

> The psychologist, as compared with the physicist and the chemist, finds himself in a very unfavorable position; even with the best possible experimentation he usually has to admit regretfully that a great many of the facts he analyses are beyond his control, not capable of being recorded . . .
>
> The ideal for the psychological experimenter has become the possibility to reconstruct artificially the phenomenon under examination, because only this enables one to keep it entirely under control . . .
>
> It is quite comprehensible, therefore, that only an artificial insertion of an affective complex into the psyche of the subject, which complex is known in all details, can create for the psychologist a situation where it would be easier for him to record all the factors forming the affective reaction.

This decisive experiment was performed by Luria himself in 1924–1925:

> We suggested to the person under test, while in a sufficiently deep hypnotic state, a certain situation . . . in which he was playing a rôle irreconcilable with his habits and contrary to his usual behavior. We made those suggestions imperatively, and forced the person under hypnotism to feel the situation suggested with sufficient painfulness; we thus obtained an actual and rather sharply expressed acute affect. After awakening the person under test . . . we had a subject who was "loaded" with certain definite affective complexes, which mostly remained unknown to himself, but which were recorded by us in almost all important details.
>
> [The patients] all were subjected to the following standard operation: the person under test was put to sleep, and a traumatic situation previously prepared was suggested to him. After the suggestion was made, an amnesia was suggested to the person (in control cases the

amnesia was not suggested and we observed a natural post-hypnotic amnesia) and he was awakened. Before the hypnosis, we used a number of word-stimuli—a part of them having a direct bearing on the complex which later was suggested to him; and we obtained the usual series of associated answers with connected motor reactions.* Simultaneously we recorded a free number of chain associations, † which were connected with the respective motor pressures. That operation was repeated a second time after the suggestion was made to the person in his post-hypnotic states; after this the subject was again put to sleep and the suggestion made was countermanded. After his second awakening, he was tested again in the same way.

Luria was impressed by "the entire elimination from the consciousness of what had occurred" and by the fact that "only a few signs, like a heavy feeling, a general anxiousness, etc., remain as symptoms of the fact that in the subject's past there is concealed some severe trauma . . . A strong emotion is hidden here in the past . . . removed from consciousness, though apparently it is still active."

He then went on to test the word associations and connected motor reactions of his subjects, and found that "every time the subject responds to the words connected with the complex with distinct retardation and shows a curve of pressure reaching almost to the limit." But even more striking were the free associational word reactions. In these he noticed that "the subject reconstructs quite unintentionally the [suggested] situation . . . in the chain series, not knowing why that situation has come to her mind, and not being able to explain its contents." His conclusion is identical with Freud's assumption: *"The affective complex constructed by us, though not yet being conscious, creates an affective state and determines the flow of the free associative series."*

These decisive experiments by a noted materialist psychologist—repeated, confirmed, and extended by Erickson in the United States [6]

* "Motor reactions" refers to Luria's method of recording motor responses in his subjects during the word association test. At the instant of response the subject must press a bulb with the fingers of his right hand, a motion which is recorded as a curve on a chart. Normally the curve is regular and occurs simultaneously with the word-response. In the presence of emotional disturbances the curve becomes stronger, irregular, or rises and falls before and after the word-response. Luria also recorded the breathing responses of his subjects, and noted similar irregularities in the breathing pattern when emotional disturbances occurred.

† That is, free associational word-chains.

—thus confirm in the laboratory the facts which Freud noted clinically: that psychic conflict could result in the development of "affective complexes" * which, though concealed from the consciousness of the individual by some defensive functional mechanism, nevertheless continued to exert a significant effect upon his thoughts and actions. The repressive mechanism, says Luria, "seems to be the mechanism which saves the personality from the over-excitement and from the disorganisation connected with an open appearance of the conflict." [7] The existence of conflict, repression, resistance, unconscious mental activity, and the validity of the free association technique are all confirmed in these experiments.

There remains but one other basic assumption of psychoanalysis to consider at this point—the phenomenon of transference. Transference was not "invented" by Freud. It is merely a term which he applied to an incontrovertible clinical fact; namely, that neurotic patients frequently react to the therapist in an irrational fashion, inconsistent with the reality situation. The more neurotic the patient, the more marked is such a reaction apt to be. Unfortunately the concept of transference is often used loosely to include all attitudes that a patient has towards his therapist. If the patient likes the therapist, that is a "positive transference." If he dislikes him, that is a "negative transference." Such a use of the concept leaves no room for rational judgment on the part of the patient and becomes meaningless. If a patient likes a therapist who is friendly and warm, and dislikes one who is surly or uninterested, this is not necessarily a transference reaction. It may be, and often is, a perfectly valid and realistic judgment on the part of the patient. It would probably be better to use the terms "rapport" and "lack of rapport" for such realistic reactions. Freud himself specifically restricted "transference" to irrational attitudes on the part of the patient. His explanation of these attitudes was that the patient was reacting to the analyst with an identical repetition of behavior that had previously been manifested to an emotionally significant figure in the patient's infantile past, e.g., father, mother or sibling; that he was in effect "trans-

* There has been considerable difference of opinion among progressive analysts in recent years as to whether affects are ever actually subject to repression. Some contend that only memories, thoughts, and ideas can be repressed, but that affects themselves are always appropriate to the way in which the individual sees reality. Full discussion of the pros and cons of the problem, however, would take us beyond the limitations of this paper

ferring" to the analyst these attitudes as though the analyst actually represented this emotionally charged figure.

This explanation is considered overly mechanistic by progressive psychoanalysts; but the observations themselves are indisputable and of the greatest significance. The modern tendency is to regard the transference phenomenon not as a mechanical "repetition-compulsion" of earlier attitudes, but as a dynamic expression of certain attitudes, faulty perceptions, or distorted "frames of reference" which have their roots, it is true, in earlier experiences but are not identical with them. Thus a neurotic patient who in early life has been severely traumatized by parental rejection may develop a belief that he is unlovable; and his subsequent relations with people, being colored by this conviction, will be dominated by an unrealistic suspiciousness, hostility, and withdrawal from them. These unrealistic attitudes are also manifested in relation to the analyst to whom he comes for help. From a practical therapeutic standpoint it may at times be of minor importance whether one states that the patient "sees the analyst as the rejecting parent" or whether one states that the patient has developed out of his early experiences a conviction that he is unlovable with consequent attitudes that manifest themselves in all of his significant interpersonal relationships. To some patients both statements may be equally meaningful and useful. From the philosophical standpoint, however, the first statement is a mechanist one, while the second is dialectical and has a wider field of reference.

Another basic idea which is implicit in the concept of transference is that of the historical origin of neurotic difficulties. This parallels in the psychological field the concept of historical materialism in the field of sociology and economics. It is "the historical principle as applied to the development of human consciousness." [8] It rests on the assumption that what an individual is at any given moment (i.e., his character structure) is determined by the interaction of his biological inheritance with the sum total of his past experience. For this reason psychoanalysis, like historical materialism, has been frequently attacked by philosophical idealists as denying the existence of "free will." In so far as psychoanalysis affirms that man's behavior is not mystically independent of his environment, the charge is true. But the affirmation is often corrupted by its critics to mean that psychoanalysis therefore denies the possibility of man's being free to alter his behavior. This is a corruption of psychoanalysis just as the corresponding charge against historical materialism is a corruption of the latter. Like the latter, psychoanalysis affirms that the more men understand about themselves and the world in which they live, the freer they can be in dealing with their environment. This assumption in fact is the rationale behind the very existence of psychoanalytic therapy. Hegel's phrase that "necessity is blind only in so far as it is not understood" may be paraphrased to say that "human impulses are blind only in so far as they are not understood."

Now it will be remembered that one of the distinguishing characteristics of psychoanalysis is that it not only recognizes the phenomenon of transference but utilizes it in the therapeutic process itself. A full discussion of how this is done would require an article in itself; but very briefly we may say that transference manifestations may be utilized in a psychotherapeutic relationship in one of two main ways. One method aims at cure by making the patient aware of his unrealistic attitudes and helping him to study the mode and circumstances of their operation, their relationship to external events, and the consequences of their activity, so that they eventually become modified through insight. This is the method of psychoanalysis. The other method is to use the unrealistic authority with which the patient endows the therapist to influence the patient to better forms of behavior; this essentially is the operational basis for most forms of non-analytic psychotherapy—suggestion, guidance, etc. Contrary to the misconceptions of some critics [9] the psychoanalytic technique is not a prelude to action on the part of the patient, but is closely integrated with what goes on in the patient's daily life. "A change in the activity of the patient is an inevitable accompaniment of any successful psychoanalytic therapy, and an integral part of it." [10]

So much then for the basic assumptions of psychoanalysis: the concept of unconscious mental activity, with its corollary concepts of conflict, repression, and resistance; the concept of psychic determinism, with its corollary assumption of the validity of free association and the significance of dreams; and finally, the concept of transference with its corollary recognition of the historical determination of behavior. All these are functional dynamic concepts, and none is at variance with modern scientific materialism. In so far as they represent correct observations of psychological reality, any theory of human behavior which goes beyond restating them in other terms * to negate them must of necessity be incomplete or inaccurate.

Now we come to the problem of examining that considerable superstructure of psychoanalytic theory which constitutes Freud's theory of instincts and its numerous derivatives. At the very outset, however, we are faced with a manifest difficulty. When dealing with a collection of writings as voluminous as Freud's, it is possible, as with the Bible, to lift individual sentences out of context and thereby demonstrate almost anything one is seeking to prove. It has not been at all difficult, for example, for some exponents of Freud [13] to "prove" by repeated isolated quotations from his works that he was a thoroughgoing dialectical materialist. If we are to evaluate Freud's thinking properly from the philosophical standpoint, however, we cannot lay undue emphasis on such isolated statements, but must be guided by the main currents of it, by the overwhelming preponderance of its direction. If we do this we cannot escape the conclusion that the theoretical superstructure which Freud erected upon the scientific nucleus already discussed represents a combination of mechanical materialistic with entelechistic * thinking. In justice to Freud, however, it should be pointed out that although he emphatically insisted upon the validity of his concept of repression and resistance as "a theoretic inference legitimately drawn from innumerable observations" [14] he made no such claim for his theory of the instincts, which he characterized as the "mythology" [15] of psychoanalysis. Further evidence of his inner uncertainty about this aspect of his work is furnished by the fact that throughout his lifetime he constantly struggled with it, making repeated revisions in it in an

* McGill and Welch,[11] for example, have made an effort to explain many psychoanalytic concepts in purely behavioral terms. While such efforts are both valuable and useful, they do not, in my opinion, negate the validity and predictive value of these basic psychoanalytic concepts. As McGill himself has said in another connection: "What is not always appreciated is that inferences enter into the interpretation of all the data of science. The only question is whether the inferences are valid and whether they facilitate prediction." [12] One of the difficulties attendant upon a purely behavioral approach to mental disorder is that often the disorder finds its chief mode of expression in disturbances of thought—e.g., schizophrenic thinking—which can be dealt with adequately only at a conceptual level. Similarly, no purely behavioral approach, so far as the writer knows, has been able to cope effectively with the problem of dream interpretation.

* "Entelechy" and "entelechism," as used in this article, refer to Freud's concept of instincts as having an autonomous character, which is fundamentally unalterable by the environment.

effort to make it more effectively fit the observable phenomena of human behavior.

For Freud the human being was first and foremost a biological organism, and in following man's vicissitudes he was primarily interested in what happened to man's biological needs in the course of his growth and development. All of his subsequent needs were conceived of as outgrowths, reflections, or "sublimations" of these basic biological "instinctual" drives. Although Freud did not ignore the significance of cultural institutions in influencing the drives, the basic, major determinant in his opinion was the Oedipus complex which arose out of the child's attraction to the parent of the opposite sex and the fear of retribution from the parent of the same sex. Freud regarded this conflict as essentially biological in origin and hence universal to all human beings. "This probably holds true," he felt, "not only in the life of individuals but also in the history of the human species as a whole."[16] Moreover, he considered the "reactions against the instinctual demands of the Oedipus complex" as the prime source of human achievement and the chief basis for the development of the social institutions in every culture—religion, morality, art, literature, etc.

In some respects Freud's thinking is strikingly similar to Hobbes's. Like Hobbes, he believed that man's "innate" tendencies were essentially selfish, animalistic, and antisocial. The chief function of society (and education) was to "inhibit, forbid, and suppress" these impulses which would otherwise destroy it. For this reason Freud was pessimistic about the possibility of success of any cooperative commonwealth, because it would be contrary to "human nature" to expect human beings to be anything but selfishly individualistic. In his concept of human nature as something fixed and ineradicable, which social influences could modify or conceal but never genuinely alter,* Freud clearly dis-

* Ludwig Jekels, one of Freud's early pupils and associates, presents this concept dramatically when, in disputing the thesis that the nature of man can change, he says: "This being, prostrate by the burden of heredity and constitution, driven either by his urges or by tormenting anxiety, nailed to his ego by his narcissism . . . seems unlikely to promise such changeability, and there is little chance for him to become the demiurge of an entirely new world."[17] Note the similarity of this concept to the doctrine of original sin. It is of interest to note also a recent remark of A. A. Brill, dean of classical American analysts, quoted in the *New York Times* of July 23, 1947: "We admit with the Bible that the imagination of the human heart is evil from the beginning, but we do not blame the child for its feelings and actions. We feel it is born that way."

closes both his entelechism and his mechanistic materialism. Like parts of a machine the individual and society impinge upon each other, and changes take place at the periphery; but the basic character of man remains unaltered, to emerge in pristine ugliness in time of war or other stress. This unalterable "essential nature" of man, however, is an entelechistic concept.*

Fenichel, Osborn, and other upholders of Freud's instinct theory have often claimed that it is a misinterpretation of Freud's views to state that he overemphasized the significance of biological forces in man's adaptation to his environment.

> Man [says Fenichel] is guided by certain basic biological drives which are not at all rigid patterns but are formed and developed according to satisfying and frustrating experiences, which means through social forces. . . . According to Freud the human being becomes a human being (an "ego") by entering into "interrelations" with other human beings. . . . Social relations can only "form individuals" because of a certain biological structure of man; and the study of this biological basis and of what happens to this basis under different social

* Bartlett in his essay on Freud [18] has ably elaborated upon the similarity of the Freudian Id to the "isolated individual" or "natural man" of Hobbes and Rousseau, and shown the relationship of all three concepts to the productive relations which exist in contemporary capitalist society. However, he seems to me to make a serious error in interpreting Freud's use of entelechies as idealism. Strictly speaking, "the fundamental principle of idealism is that matter, the actual material world we find ourselves a part of, is not the final reality." [19] If there is any one thread that may be said to run consistently through all of Freud's writings it is his oft asserted conviction that all of man's mental and emotional life was firmly rooted in material, biological origins. The "instincts" as conceived of by Freud are strictly materialistic phenomena with somatic sources. The fact that they are entelechistic concepts does not warrant characterizing them as idealistic. An entelechy may be either an idealistic or a mechanical materialistic concept. That Freud's entelechistic thinking is an outgrowth of his mechanistic materialism and has nothing to do with philosophic idealism is amply demonstrated by the preponderant weight of evidence in his writings. Bartlett's efforts to "prove" Freud's idealism by lifting an occasional sentence out of context are as manifestly lacking in objectivity as the contrary efforts to "prove" him to be a dialectical materialist. On the other hand, there is no denying that the derivations of entelechistic thinking often lead to conceptions of society which *serve the interests* of the philosophic idealists. This is true, for example, of Freud's conception of a fixed "human nature" and of his explanation of social institutions as instinct derivatives. To classify him on this basis as an idealist, however, is incorrect. Freud's theoretical limitations, as we shall see, flow not from any tendency to idealism, but from the fact that his materialism was mechanistic instead of dialectical.

circumstances . . . makes it understandable how social relations form individuals. . . . The statement that a biological substratum is molded by institutions does in no way imply an underestimation of the influence of the institutions.[20]

These statements of Fenichel deserve careful analysis, not only because he was one of the most erudite and brilliant exponents of Freud's classical theories, but also because he was aware of the importance of social forces and of the contradictions within our modern capitalist economy. Yet his comments illustrate one of the basic fallacies of classical Freudian thinking. It is not that Freud (or Fenichel and others) ignores or necessarily underestimates the significance of social influences upon the individual, but that he interprets this influence *mechanistically* instead of *dialectically*. The Freudian view is that man is a biological animal "molded" by his environment, but that the basic "biological substratum" in the form of the reservoir of "instinctual" impulses remains essentially unaltered; their *external manifestations* are, it is true, transformed by social influences, but their basic *inner nature* remains unaltered—compare Fenichel's statement almost in the same breath as his previous one, that "character traits . . . are not at all adaptations made by the ego, but things which happen to the ego against its will by instinctual forces which return from the repressed." [21] The modern dialectical view, however, is that out of the interrelationship between man's biological inheritance and his social environment a new *unity* is formed, a fusion in which *the biological as such no longer exists in man's psychological expressions*; it cannot any longer be separated from the social. The development of the human cortex, with its language and association functions, represents the physiological expression of this unity. A human body without a human brain is no longer human; it is something else but no longer "man." The needs of man can consequently no longer be expressed in simple biological terms; even the basic needs of hunger and sex cannot be isolated from the social influence of the cerebral cortex.

This conception is expressed on a physiological level in the holistic concept of brain activity. Few modern neurophysiologists would assert that subcortical structures have an activity of their own, independent of the activity of the cortex. The living brain functions as a unit; no cortical or subcortical activity takes place that is not at every moment relative to and dependent on the activity of the rest of the nervous system. One could, it is true, study the activity of the isolated subcortex by decorticating the brain; but then one would be dealing with a different unit which could not be validly compared with the subcortex which is integrated in a total living brain. In short, it would no longer be a "human" subcortex. By the same token one might conceivably study the sexual drive or hunger drive in a person who had been totally isolated from social contacts all his life, but then one would not be studying man as we know him but something totally different. What we call "human nature" grows out of man's social relationships and cannot be separated therefrom.[22]

This viewpoint is not, as some classical Freudians insist, an antibiological one, or an overemphasis on environment, or a denial of the great importance of man's biological needs. It is merely a dialectical conception of how these needs operate in contrast to a mechanistic one. I have elsewhere stated the problem as follows:

> The old conflicts of heredity *versus* environment, or biology *versus* culture become meaningless when viewed from the organismic approach of modern psychology. Even in the lower forms of animal life, the organism is immersed in an environment from the very beginning of the life cycle. Each stage of development is determined by the cooperation of heredity and environmental forces. Since the earlier stages influence the character of the development of the later stages, the hereditary and environmental factors become more and more interpenetrated as development proceeds. Nowhere is this more true than in humans, where the cultural factors become indissolubly interrelated with organic processes through the laying down of language patterns in the association centers of the cortex. Thus there develops a new unity which is qualitatively unique in the animal world—a sociobiological unity—called human nature. This interpenetration is so complex and so complete that one cannot separate the hereditary from the environmental factors in man without destroying the specific quality which constitutes the nature of man, just as water cannot be separated into hydrogen and oxygen without destroying that quality which constitutes water.[23]

It is around this same problem that the modern critics of Freud's emphasis upon sexuality rest their arguments. It is not necessary to deny the great importance of the sexual drives, or to question the existence of infantile sexuality, in order to take issue with Freud on this point. The tremendous part which sexual needs play in the life of every person is a phenomenon which any honest student of the human personality can find for himself if he does not close his mind to the observable facts; the same is true of the existence of infantile sexuality. But to assume, as Freud does, that these sexual needs are the prime determinants of character is quite another matter, and one which the modern materialists correctly criticize as one-sided. It is not being "antibiological" to see the sexual needs of human beings as but one vector in the complex series of forces which determine human behavior. Certainly the modes of production whereby men live, their social and economic status, and their security needs for sustenance and shelter all play equally significant roles in the molding of personality. Modern anthropological researches [24] have thoroughly exploded the fiction of the universality of the Oedipus complex and have effectively demonstrated that "human nature" differs significantly in different cultures. The personality of man in our western culture differs sharply from that of the Zuñi Indian, for example, not primarily because of the difference in the fate of their sexual impulses, but because of the total difference in their respective socio-economic organizations and institutions, which themselves are responsible for the difference in sexual attitudes.[25]

Consider further Freud's concept of instinctual aggression. Few doctrines are so thoroughly ingrained in classical psychoanalytic thinking as this theory. It is a particularly persuasive doctrine, for who can look about him in our western culture without finding apparent evidence of its universal existence, from childhood to the grave? The question, however, whether this apparently universal aggression is instinctive and a primary inherited expression of "human nature" in all cultures and in all times, or whether it constitutes secondary or derived behavior is crucial both scientifically and philosophically; for much of the pessimism of Freud and of some of his classical followers concerning the potentialities of man derives from this concept. Moreover it has been used repeatedly by political defenders of the status quo to justify many of the inequities of our economic order as being inevitable reflections of "human nature." The chief arguments marshaled by the classical Freudian in the defense of this thesis are: its apparent universality; the fact that animals are apparently innately aggressive; the apparently universal selfishness and destructiveness of young children; and the predominance of aggression in "primitive" tribes (which Freud considered to be the phylogenetic precursors of our own civilization).

Maslow has summarized the modern evidence against these arguments as follows:

a) Not only are not all animals aggressive but even among those which are, the higher one rises in the phyletic scale, the more one finds

> that aggression becomes less and less primary and more and more derived, more and more functional, more and more a reasonable understandable reaction to a totality of motivation. . . . The chimpanzee, that animal of all animals which is closest to the human being [is] actually more cooperative, more friendly and less aggressive than the average human being.

b) Studies of children show them to be as frequently generous and cooperative as they are hostile and destructive:

> The child who is insecure, . . . thwarted or threatened in his needs for safety, love, belongingness and self-esteem, is the child who will show more selfishness, hatred, aggression and destructiveness.

c) Studies of comparative cultures show great variations in the degree of aggressiveness and hostility displayed, and not a few so-called primitive tribes are remarkable for the almost complete absence of these traits among their people.[26]

Despite these facts the classical Freudian is apt to argue that aggression is instinctual nevertheless, and that its apparent absence in some children or some cultures merely means that it is repressed. The very statement of the problem in these terms, however, discloses the two important errors which are inherent in all aspects of the instinct theory. The first is the tendency to abstract qualities which are observed in human beings in our culture and time, and to assume that they are true for the human species as a whole. The second is the assumption that any aspect of human behavior can be explained on the basis of a single determinant such as an autochthonous instinct. In contrast to this, modern dialectical materialism asserts that human behavior is not unilaterally determined in any of its aspects but can be understood correctly only as a resultant of a complex interrelationship of forces of which the needs of the organism are but a single, often subordinate part. Thus even so basic a biological factor as the rate of growth is never determined by genetic factors alone, but is a resultant of interaction with environmental factors. Even the basic sexual and hunger needs do not operate independently of environmental forces. The sex drive will disappear under conditions of extreme malnutrition or life-threatening danger; hunger will cease to manifest itself in the presence of overwhelming infection or certain emotional stress. This whole formulation has found recent expression in the development of the psychosomatic concept in modern medicine, which recognizes that "psyche" and "soma" in man are not separable entities but constitute a dynamic unit.

The modern materialist does not therefore expect to find an adequate explanation of the phenomenon of aggression in any such single determinant as an "instinct." He seeks instead to discover what are the forces which determine its intensity and direction. If it be charged that such an approach does away with autonomous instincts altogether, the scientist can only answer in the classic words of Laplace, who, when charged with omitting God in his theory of the evolution of the solar system, replied, "I had no need of that hypothesis." [27]

Applying this approach to the problem of aggression, we find ourselves, instead of postulating a purely hypothetical repressed aggressive instinct in cultures relatively free from manifestations of aggression, asking why it is that aggression is so prevalent in our own culture and so relatively lacking in these others. As soon as we do this it becomes apparent that the widespread hostilities in our society spring basically from the insecurities and rivalries engendered by the individualistic competitive economic system under which we live; and different degrees or manifestations of aggression in other cultures become equally understandable in the light of their own socio-economic organizations.*

* This fact is convincingly demonstrated by Kardiner, who in his psychological analyses of various cultures has made one of the major contributions in psychoanalysis towards conclusively disproving the theory of instincts. "One must believe," he writes, "that either the destructiveness must be identified in forces unleashed by external realities which confront man, or that it is unrelated to realities and determined by an autochthonous death instinct. The first view can be clinically verifiable, the second cannot. The first view can be established either by the study of comparative sociology or by a historical study of the same society. The second must remain a matter of belief. . . . In Tanala-Betsilao culture it was clearly demonstrated that both aggressive and masochistic forms of destructiveness . . . increased when there was a scarcity created in subsistence op-

Let us consider, finally, Freud's concepts of feminine psychology. Here too the problem is not whether his *observations* were correct. There is no doubt of the widespread existence in our society of the phenomenon which Freud described as "penis-envy" (although whether it is as universal even in our culture as Freud believed is open to doubt). The modern materialist's criticism of this concept springs from a questioning, not of its existence, but of Freud's interpretation of its significance. Here again Freud the biologist assumed that it sprang essentially from the anatomical difference between the sexes ("anatomy is fate" [29]) and from the woman's envy of the supposed inherently superior value of the penis as compared to the vagina. Now it would be unrealistic to deny that these anatomical differences, as well as the physiological facts of menstruation, childbirth, and menopause, must and do play a role in conditioning the consciousness of women. But the organic factor is but one of many determinants, and its significance in the total pattern of forces depends on its relationship to the other elements involved. Being a woman will have one significance in an androcentric culture, a totally different significance in a gynecocentric one, and still another in a society where the sexes have complete equality of opportunity socially, economically, and culturally. To assume from the facts of our culture that "penis-envy" is a basic aspect of woman's "nature" is but another example of the methodological error upon which we have already commented.

Space does not permit critical examination of all the other derivatives of the Freudian theory of instincts. They refer to clinical phenomena which indubitably exist. But the theoretical assumptions underlying the classical Freudian interpretation of these phenomena reveal the

---

portunities; prior to this time the compensations for suppression of aggression were adequate to hold this mutual aggression in check. Once these compensations were removed in the form of tangible satisfactions, the aggression broke its encapsulated bounds. This precludes the necessity for any hypothesis about autochthonous death instincts." [28] It is noteworthy, however, that Kardiner is not able to completely free himself from the influence of instinctivistic thinking even as he is engaged in refuting it! For in writing of "suppression of aggression," "holding mutual aggression in check," "aggression breaking its encapsulated bounds," he implies the very thing he is attempting to deny: namely, that aggression is an autochthonous force which must be "suppressed" and "held in check" lest it "break its encapsulated bounds." His statement about the Tanala-Betsilao would have been more accurate had he added: "Prior to this time the compensations for *cooperative relationships* were adequate to make aggression *unnecessary*."

fundamental errors of either mechanistic or entelechistic thinking which are implicit in the whole theory of instincts.

At the beginning of this article I indicated that psychoanalytic theory, far from being static, has been undergoing significant development and change. The evidence for this is unmistakable if one attempts even a brief survey of the psychoanalytic literature of the past fifteen years. Freud himself laid the groundwork for a significant reorientation of psychoanalytic theory when in 1926 he revised his concept of anxiety as arising from frustration of instinctual impulses, and recognized instead that it was a defense against outward dangers and a manifestation of the "ego." [30] In 1933 Wilhelm Reich took up the problem and called to the attention of psychoanalysts the importance of studying the character structure of the patient, rather than the vicissitudes of the "instincts." [31] This important turning point in psychoanalysis marked a major shift in emphasis which has characterized it ever since, a shift to "ego-psychology." A period of great ferment in psychoanalytic thinking ensued in the following years. Much discussion and earnest questioning of basic psychoanalytic doctrine began to take place in a way that had never before occurred.* Ernest Jones's comment, quoted at the beginning of this article, is significant of a changing viewpoint to which even Freud's oldest and most loyal followers must sooner or later begin to give cognizance.

* A few of the leaders in this process in America were Alexander, Fromm, Horney, Kardiner, David Levy, Rado, Schilder, and Sullivan. Within the space of a few years there appeared Horney's *Neurotic Personality of Our Time* (1937) and *New Ways in Psychoanalysis* (1939), Kardiner's *The Individual and His Society* (1939) and *Traumatic Neuroses of War* (1941), Rado's *Developments in the Psychoanalytic Conception and Treatment of the Neuroses* (1939); Sullivan's *Conceptions of Modern Psychiatry* (1940), and Fromm's *Escape from Freedom* (1941), all of which made significant revisions in classical psychoanalytical theory and brought it closer to modern materialistic concepts. More recently, the publication of Alexander and French's *Psychoanalytic Therapy* (1946) has stimulated a revaluation of some of the procedural techniques of psychoanalysis. In addition there have been countless articles by other analysts, too numerous to mention, which also have been adding gradually to the momentum of change in psychoanalytic thinking. It should be noted also that even among the ranks of the classical analysts there have been articles questioning one or another aspect of Freudian theory.[32] The task still remains, however, for a psychoanalyst thoroughly grounded in the principles of historical and dialectical materialism to integrate all the positive contributions of psychoanalysis in the light of these principles, into a comprehensive, definitive study of human behavior.

What then are the positive concepts of the most advanced theoretical viewpoint in psychoanalysis today? In the space which remains we can only briefly indicate a few of the outstanding ones. The advanced psychoanalytic view sees the relationship between the individual and society as a dialectical one and denies that any basic conflict of interests inevitably exists between them. It affirms that the human personality is neither innately "evil" nor innately "good," and that man's potentialities in either direction depend on the incentives offered by the society in which he develops. It recognizes that human consciousness is a unique resultant of the interaction between the human organism and the social influences to which it is exposed from the moment of birth onward. It asserts that the particular medium in which this interrelationship first takes place in our society is, for most individuals, the family. In order to understand fully, therefore, how the consciousness of any individual in our society has evolved, it is important to study his relationships within his family group. In this group the influence of the parents, or parent-substitutes, is preeminent, since the parents are in most instances the "chief purveyors and reflectors to the growing child of the contradictory patterns in our culture." This does not deny the tremendous influence which school, church, the street, books, newspapers, radio, movies, etc. have upon the thought processes of every individual in our culture; and full cognizance is taken of these factors. Nor does the insistence upon the historical importance of childhood relationships in the development of personality in any way deny the potentiality of change throughout the life of the individual. Psychoanalysts affirm, however, that childhood experiences have a particular significance because it is in the formative years of childhood that basic character patterns are set down which tend to become the frame of reference in relation to later experiences. Concepts, for example, such as "I am loved (and therefore feel secure) only when I am submissive," or "I am not loved regardless of how I behave," strongly reenforced by repeated childhood experiences, acquire a dynamic importance which profoundly influences all the subsequent life relationships. Being painful in character, they tend to become repressed to protect the personality from persistent conscious conflict. Then, as unconscious "affective complexes" (Luria), they continue to exert a decisive influence upon the subsequent thought and behavior of the individual. Thus, a person who suffers from a deep conviction that he is unlovable withdraws into a defensive shell; by so doing he actually prevents people from loving him and so constantly reenforces his basic neurotic conviction through a vicious cycle.

In considering the interaction of the child with his environment, the progressive psychoanalyst does not, however, conceive of the child as a mere passive recipient or *tabula rasa*. He recognizes that man is born with important affirmative biological needs for food, sexual gratification, and protection from the elements, which are active factors in the dynamic interrelationship with his environment; but he insists that these biological needs "*condition* his development but do not *predetermine* it."[33] The progressive psychoanalyst therefore equally rejects any effort to explain man's behavior entelechistically in terms of autonomous instincts, or mechanistically, in terms of man being simply a "product of his environment." Only out of the recognition of the active and complex interrelationship between man's biological inheritance and his social environment can a truly dialectical and materialistic conception of human nature envolve.

Which brings us to our final point. The progressive psychoanalyst of today recognizes that the forms of production and distribution in our society, and the contradictions between the prevailing Christian ethics of brotherhood and justice, and an economic order which stresses rugged individualism and rewards aggression and deceit, inevitably leave their impress on the personality of every person in our culture. These influences of our society vary in their effects upon the different sociological classes, and the varying effects can be recognized in general in the members of each class. But it does not mean that the behavior of any individual can be deduced from his class relationships alone. Regardless of class similarity, there are wide variations of individual behavior within every class which are understandable only in the light of the specific life experiences of that individual. Historical materialism can explain the general character of any given society or class, but only a dynamic psychology of the individual can fully explain the specific variants in any individual within that society or class. And since circumstances are changed by men as much as men are changed by circumstances, only a combination of these two scientific methods can give us a complete understanding of both "the forest and the trees" in the social world in which we live.

References

[1] Ernest Jones, "A Valedictory Address," *Internatl. Jour. of Psycho-Analysis,* Vol. 27 (1946).

[2] Sigmund Freud, *Collected Papers* (London, 1924), 1:254.

[3] *Ibid.,* p. 298.

[4] *Ibid.,* pp. 297–298.

[5] *Ibid.,* p. 311.

[6] Milton H. Erickson, "A Study of Hypnotically Induced Complexes by Means of the Luria Technique," *Jour. Genetic Psychol.,* Vol. 30 (1934); "Experimental Demonstration of the Psychopathology of Everyday Life," *Psychoan. Quart.,* Vol. 8 (1939); and numerous other papers.

[7] A. R. Luria, *The Nature of Human Conflicts* (New York, 1932), pp. 128–131, 133, 142, 155, 157, 159.

[8] S. L. Rubinstein, "Soviet Psychology in War Time," *Philosophy and Phenomenological Research,* 5:183 (1944).

[9] Joseph Wortis, "Freudianism and the Psychoanalytic Tradition," *Amer. Jour. Psychiat.,* Vol. 25 (1945); and Francis Bartlett, "Recent Trends in Psychoanalysis," *Science and Society,* Vol. 9 (1945).

[10] Judson T. Stone, "Theory and Practice of Psychoanalysis," *Science and Society,* Vol. 10 (1946). This article contains a more detailed exposition of modern psychoanalytic technique, for the reader who may be interested.

[11] V. J. McGill and L. Welch, "A Behaviorist Analysis of Emotions," *Philosophy of Science,* Vol. 13 (1946); and "Hysteria as a Conditioning Process," *Amer. Jour. of Psychotherapy,* Vol. 1 (1947).

[12] V. J. McGill, "The Mind-Body Problem in the Light of Recent Psychology," *Science and Society,* 9:342 (1945).

[13] Reuben Osborn (i.e., Osbert), *Freud and Marx* (London, 1937); Jack Rapaport, "Marxism and Psychoanalysis," *Science and Society,* Vol. 5 (1941); Burrill Freedman and Walton Van Clute, "Dialectical Aspects of Psychoanalysis Misunderstood," *Psychoan. Review,* Vol. 31 (1944).

[14] Sigmund Freud, *op. cit.,* pp. 298–299.

[15] Sigmund Freud, *New Introductory Lectures on Psychoanalysis* (New York, 1933), p. 131.

[16] Sigmund Freud, "Psychoanalysis: Freudian School," *Encyclopaedia Britannica,* 14th ed., 18:674.

[17] Ludwig Jekels, "Psychoanalysis and Dialectic," *Psychoan. Review,* 28:228 (1941).

[18] Francis H. Bartlett, *Sigmund Freud* (London, 1938).

[19] Howard Selsam, *What Is Philosophy?* (New York, 1938), p. 45.

[20] Otto Fenichel, "Psychoanalytic Remarks on Fromm's Book, *Escape from Freedom,*" *Psychoan. Review,* 31:138–140 (1944).

[21] *Ibid.,* p. 140.

[22] Kingsley Davis, "Extreme Social Isolation of a Child," *Amer. Jour. Sociol.,* Vol. 45 (1940).

[23] J. Marmor, "The Role of Instinct in Human Behavior," *Psychiatry* 5:515–516 (1942).

[24] Ruth Benedict, *Patterns of Culture* (Boston, 1934); Margaret Mead, *From the South Seas* (New York, 1939); Abram Kardiner, *The Individual and His*

Society (New York, 1939), and *The Psychological Frontiers of Society* (New York, 1945).

[25] Abram Kardiner, *The Individual and His Society,* p. 111.

[26] A. H. Maslow, "A Comparative Approach to the Problem of Destructiveness," *Psychiatry,* Vol. 5 (1942).

[27] Quoted by Selsam, *op. cit.,* p. 65.

[28] Kardiner, *op. cit.,* pp. 402–403.

[29] Sigmund Freud, "Some Psychological Consequences of the Anatomical Distinction Between the Sexes," *Internat. Jour. Psychoan.,* Vol. 8 (1927).

[30] Sigmund Freud, *The Problem of Anxiety* (New York, 1936).

[31] Wilhelm Reich, *Charakteranalyse* (Vienna, 1933); in English translation, *Character-Analysis* (New York, 1945).

[32] Two examples are: Lawrence Kubie, "A Critical Analysis of the Conception of a Repetition Compulsion," *Internatl. Jour. of Psychoan.,* Vol. 20 (1939); and Gregory Zilboorg, "Masculine and Feminine," *Psychiatry,* Vol. 7 (1944).

[33] S. L. Rubinstein, "Consciousness in the Light of Dialectical Materialism," *Science and Society,* 10:260 (1946).

SOME ASPECTS OF HISTORICAL MATERIALISM

by

BERNHARD J. STERN

Bernhard J. Stern, Lecturer in Sociology at Columbia University, and in Anthropology at the New School for Social Research, was formerly Visiting Professor of Sociology at Yale University, and Assistant Editor of the *Encyclopaedia of the Social Sciences.* He has written extensively in sociology and in anthropology. Among his recent books are *Society and Medical Progress* (1941), *American Medical Practice in the Perspectives of a Century* (1945), *Outlines of Anthropology* (with Melville Jacobs, 1947), *When Peoples Meet: A Study in Race and Culture Contact* (with Alain Locke, 1937). He is an editor of the quarterly *Science and Society.*

THE doctrine of integrative levels is either tacitly or explicitly accepted by many sociologists and anthropologists. Its underlying hypothesis that every level of organization of phenomena has its own regularities and principles not reducible to those appropriate to lower levels of organization is implicit in their use of the concept of culture. Most social scientists acknowledge that there is a sharp and distinct cleavage between the mechanisms of biological inheritance, which transmit physical and physiological characteristics of the human species, and man's cultural traditions that are historically transmitted. Cultural change is now generally recognized as occurring independently of change in biologically inherited traits, and as having its own underlying processes and laws. Racial and physiographic determinist explanations of human behavior have been discredited as the significance of the culture concept has come to be appreciated. There has likewise been a recognition of the fact that human group life and forms of association are patterned by a historically derived cultural tradition rather than by the genetic transmission of behavior patterns as among the social insects.

That cultural phenomena require analysis on a level distinct from the psychological was noted by Marx as early as 1859 in his preface to *A Contribution to the Critique of Political Economy*. It has been advocated repeatedly in different contexts and with varying degrees of explicitness since Tylor's *Primitive Culture* (1871), Durkheim's *Les Règles de la méthode sociologique* (1894), and by Kroeber and other anthropologists in their formation of the "superorganic" in the first decades of the twentieth century. Nevertheless, controversy on the nature of the relation between cultural and psychological processes in human behavior has persisted, and has recently mounted in intensity as interest in personality studies has grown. In 1916 Wissler stated more sharply than most of his contemporaries the limitations of psychological interpretations of culture:

> When we are dealing with phenomena that belong to original nature we are quite right in using psychological and biological methods; but the moment we step over into cultural phenomena we must recognize its historical nature. . . . We often read that if cultural phenomena can be reduced to terms of association of ideas, motor elements, etc., there remains but to apply psychological principles to it to reveal its causes. This is a vain hope. All the knowledge of the mechanism of association in the world will not tell us why any particular association is made by a particular individual, will not explain the invention of the bow, the origin of exogamy, or of any other trait of culture except in terms that are equally applicable to all.[1]

This quotation hits upon what is significant in the doctrine of integrative levels. It does not negate the importance of the psychological processes underlying all cultural phenomena just as biological processes underlie all psychological phenomena. However, it stresses the fact that reduction to a psychological level cannot explain any specific aspect or pattern of culture, for each is a historical product; and that, to interpret properly the forms and functions of culture as they condition the behavior of humans, one must understand their historical backgrounds. Few contemporary sociologists now deny the correlative generalization that, once humans invented culture, a process with its own distinctive characteristics came into being which is not organic, however intimate may be the reciprocal relations between the organic, the psychic, and the cultural.

Some social scientists who are preoccupied with psychological, and especially psychoanalytic, studies have, however, focused on the fact that, since man is the active functioning agent in culture, cultural change consists, in the last analysis, of changes in the attitudes and habits of the individuals who compose society. They have thus tended to conceive of culture merely as a methodological abstraction, and to regard study of the psychological processes of the individuals and group carriers of culture as the crucially important area of study. While a few social scientists have discussed culture schematically, ignoring the fact that it is always the possession of individual human beings interacting in groups in society, the critics of such formalistic analysis, who would confine their studies to the behavior of individuals, have sometimes negated the concept of culture by seeking to reduce all cultural behavior merely to psychological processes.

There has been considerable unrewarding controversy, therefore, around the contrast of culture as a thing in itself, and culture as an activity of persons participating in it. Actually both approaches are valid, and are required to supplement each other for a rounded understanding of cultural behavior. It is necessary to renounce both a reduction of culture to the level of psychology and an overdrawn demarcation between the psychological and cultural-historical sciences. There is special danger that the social psychologist in his studies of the processes in the growth of personality and in interpersonal interactions will lose sight of the fact that the cultural media in which these take place—that is, the cultural patterns which condition individual and group behavior—are historical products. On the other hand, when culture is conceived to be something entirely unrelated to the participation of people who manipulate it with varying degrees of creativeness, and who respond diversely to the inventions and innovations of others, it can be composed of nothing but empty, formal categories. Some of the studies of the distribution of culture traits merit such criticism.

Marett long ago warned that the study of culture might result in a "bloodless typology." In urging that the methods used in the social sciences conform to the subject matter, rather than the subject matter to method, he argued cogently that the respective methods of geology and human history must needs be poles asunder because the earth is dead while man is alive. He went on to say:

> It is quite legitimate to regard culture, or social tradition, in an abstract way as a tissue of externalities, as a robe of many colors woven on the loom of time. . . . Moreover, for certain purposes, which in their entirety may be called sociological, it is actually convenient thus to concentrate on the outer garb. In this case, indeed, the garb may well at first sight seem to count for everything, for certainly a man naked of all culture would be no better than a forked radish. . . . Human history (nevertheless) is no Madame Tussaud's show of decorated dummies. It is instinct with purposive movement through and through. . . .
>
> According to the needs of the work lying nearest to our hand, let us play the sociologist or the psychologist, without prejudice as regards ultimate explanations. On one point only I would insist, namely that the living must be studied on its own right and not by means of methods borrowed from the study of the lifeless. If a purely sociological treatment contemplates man as if there were no life in him, there will likewise be no life in it. The nemesis of a deterministic attitude towards history is a deadly dullness.[2]

This is similar to the argument of historical materialism in its attack upon mechanists who deal with formal abstractions rather than with concrete life situations in all their complex manifestations. Historical materialists urge careful consideration of the reciprocal interaction between man and his cultural-historical and group environment, and note that man serves as an active agent in the historical process within the broad limits of the specific culture in which he lives. Man possesses psychological capacities unique to *Homo sapiens* which enable him to respond to environmental stimuli both overtly and symbolically. Capable of being motivated by goals and stimulated by natural needs and acquired interests, he introduces changes in historical situations in his effort to control and to manipulate the environment to his own advantage. This reciprocal process of interaction between culture and individual personalities and group relations results in the creative recasting of culture and the consequent transformation of personality and of group patterns. Marxists thus not only recognize the historical nature of culture but also insistently take account of man as a dynamic agent in culture. They decry all efforts of mechanists to depict the cultural process as automatic and humans as passive automatons.

Engels declared, for example: "In the history of society . . . the actors are all endowed with consciousness, are men working with deliberation or passion, working toward definite goals. . . . Men make their own history." He then speaks of "investigating the driving forces which—consciously or unconsciously, and indeed very often unconsciously—lie behind the motives of men in their historical actions." [3]

Lenin particularly stressed this purposefulness of human activity as the basis of the revolutionary dynamic. For persons to wait passively for cultural change to occur within the class structure of society, he regarded as a shallow depreciation of the power of men to influence the direction of cultural development. It is for this reason that he underscored the importance of leadership and organization in the struggle for power.[4]

Faith in the ability of human beings to influence the course of history, to plan the direction of cultural change, distinguishes historical materialists sharply from such American sociologists as Sumner and Keller, who have been very influential particularly through their concept of the mores. To them, the mores make up a superorganic system of relations, conventions, and institutional arrangements, which are by origin chance products of a long series of minute trial-and-error adjustments to physical, social, and supernatural environments, dictated by needs and motivated by hunger, sex, passion, vanity, and fear. The mores are conceived as functioning through individuals without possible coordination by any formal authority. The effect of this concept upon sociologists of the Sumner and Keller school is best exemplified in the editorial preface to a volume of studies dedicated to Keller, which states:

> That societal adjustment is achieved in the main automatically through the operation of massive impersonal forces of which the individuals concerned are rarely more than dimly aware, is perhaps the major single contribution of Professor Keller. Social movements spring from the blind reactions of men in the mass to largely unanalyzed economic and emotional incentives. The individual can do little to thwart, direct, or accelerate such movements.

Consequent to this is the generalization:

> To the practical sociologist, awareness of the automatic character of the adjustment process proves an invaluable aid. It stimulates

him to study, rather than to advocate schemes for human betterment.[5]

A comparable position is taken by the neo-positivists in sociology, such as Lundberg who proposes a social physics and declares sententiously, "The social sciences are concerned with the behavior of those electro-proton configurations called societal groups, principally human groups." [6] He advocates that sociologists analyze their data in terms of the symbolic techniques of mathematics and scorns what he derisively designates a "mentalistic" type of analysis. The result is that Lundberg's emphasis has been on quantification rather than on thinking and acting. He would even make a cipher of the social scientists, for he suggests that they should be "non-moral" and should be ready to serve any political regime that happens to be in power: "The services of *real* social scientists would be as indispensable to Fascists as to Communists and Democrats, just as are the services of physicists and physicians." [7] He would thus make scientists the passive tools of interest groups rather than active policy makers. The same result was achieved by the conventional, oft reiterated device in sociological circles of contending that the sociologist must abjure value judgments. Such a procedure if conscientiously adhered to would make the sociologist a passive sieve through which data would drain, rather than the interpretive integrator and creative reformulator of knowledge on which action can be based.

Historical materialism, by combining the concept of integrative levels with the recognition of the dynamic power of the individual agent, has avoided the pitfalls of mechanistic sociology. Contentions to the contrary show both ignorance of Marxist literature and failure to grasp the theoretical significance of the activistic role of Marxist parties in the making of recent history. Such distortion is exemplified in Goldenweiser's statement: "To them [the Marxists] culture is objective, social, historical, cumulative, dynamic, deterministic. To culture the chariot of history is harnessed. The individual is fleeting, passive, epiphenomenal, causally irrelevant." [8] This charge cannot be reconciled with Engels's famous forecast that when history passes under the control of men themselves so that they "will fashion their own history," it will mark "humanity's leap from the realm of necessity to the realm of freedom." [9] It is likewise alien to Marx's much-quoted maxim, "The philosophers have *interpreted* the world in various ways, the point, however, is to *change* it."[10]

The recognition of the reality of culture as a distinctive level of phenomena for scientific inquiry is but the first step for the historical materialist. Culture is too nebulous and omnibus a concept to be an entirely adequate tool of research. What is required is a weighting of the relative importance of its constituent elements, and an understanding of the interrelationships between these elements. Sociologists and anthropologists were long indifferent to inquiries along these lines. Little progress could be made as long as anthropologists argued that inventions were the products of fortuitous combinations of individual incentive and creativeness, favorable geographical opportunities, and the element of pure chance. Since inventions and their diffusion were regarded as unpredictable, cultures were viewed as mere assemblages of "culture traits," with causal relationships between them of little significance.

The functionalists, on the contrary, have assumed that cultures are fully integrated and self-consistent configurations, the functions of the various parts of which can be determined by direct analysis without reference to the history of a culture or its parts. Their studies have been, therefore, merely cross-sectional and have lacked historical perspectives which illuminate causation. In line with their assumption of actual cultural integration, they have argued that everything in a culture that functions has value to that culture and is thus justifiable. No attempt is made to conceive of the possibility of alternative, more effective modes of meeting prevailing psychological and cultural needs. This is illustrated by Malinowski's argument:

> The substance of all religion is thus deeply rooted in human life; it grows out of the necessities of life. In other words, religion fulfills a definite cultural function in every human society. This is not a platitude. It contains a scientific refutation of the repeated attacks upon religion by the less enlightened rationalists.[10]

The functionalists have generally, in a like manner, failed to evaluate what is strategic or essential in the functioning of any culture and what is incidental or peripheral. Radcliffe-Brown, for example, has conveyed the impression that the interrelationship of the clans and the kinship systems with other features of social organization is more significant for an understanding of the functioning of a culture than food collecting, agricultural or pastoral work. Similarly obscure are the sociological proponents of multiple causation who make a fetish of complexity and evade the responsibility of untangling causal interrelationships. For example, Gunnar Myrdal blandly declares, "In an interdependent system of dynamic causation there can be no 'primary cause' but everything is cause to everything else." [12]

Historical materialists on the other hand have taken a decisive stand on the weighing of the importance of different aspects of cultures. One of the most relevant passages in Marxist literature on this point is the comment of Engels in 1890: "We make our own history, but in the first place under definite presuppositions and conditions. Among these the economic ones are finally decisive." This was in a letter in which he vigorously rebuked economic determinists, stating:

> If therefore somebody twists this into the statement that the economic element is the only determining one, he transforms it into a meaningless, abstract and absurd phrase. The economic situation is the basis, but the various elements of the superstructure—political forms of the class struggle and its consequences, constitutions established by the victorious class after a successful battle, etc.—forms of law—and then even the reflexes of all these actual struggles in the brains of the combatants: political, legal, philosophical theories, religious ideas and their further development into systems of dogma—also exercise their influence upon the course of historical struggles and in many cases preponderate in determining their *form*. There is endless interaction of all these elements, in which, amid all their endless *host* of accidents (i.e. of things and events whose inner connection is so remote or so impossible to prove that we regard it as absent and can neglect it) the economic movement finally asserts itself as necessary.[13]

Much controversy has arisen over whether Engels was justified in making the economic factor the decisive variable in culture, while not denying the causative role of other aspects of culture in the process of change. Some of this arises from a misinterpretation of the meaning of the word "economic." It is clear from the context of the quoted letter and from other consistent formulations of Marx and Engels that the term is not used in the sense of economic motivations, or the "acquisitive instincts" of an individual, a postulated economic man. Their analysis is in terms of the interrelations of aspects of culture and only secondarily in terms of the derived forms of individual behavior.

The economic factor has reference to the modes of production by which people acquire their means of subsistence, and the contention of historical materialism is that other forms of social relations and cultural patterns are basically dependent upon such economic activities. This is effectively stated in a passage written by Engels in 1878:

> The materialist conception of history starts from the principle that production, and with production the exchange of its products, is the basis of every social order; that in every society which has appeared in history the distribution of its products, and with it the division of society into classes and estates, is determined by what is produced and how it is produced and how the product is exchanged. According to this conception, the ultimate causes of all social changes and political revolutions are to be sought, not in the minds of men, in their increasing insight into eternal truths and justice, but in the changes in the mode of production and exchange; they are to be sought not in the *philosophy* but in the economics of the epoch concerned.[14]

Available evidence validates this principle for primitive societies. Comparative studies of culture substantiate the fact that the forms of social relationships, the religious and political institutions and practices, the arts and the techniques clearly tend to be correlated with the types of economic life of primitive peoples. The crucial factor found to determine the nature and rate of development of cultures is the presence or absence of surpluses, and these depend upon the mode of production.

The characteristics of the mode of production affect the density of the population, the size of the community, the social organization, the division of labor, the degree of specialization, and status and class relationships. The correlations shown in the accompanying table[15] of changes in populations and other cultural relations with changes in the amount of surplus derived from food production, are too consistent to be accidental, and give striking proof of the validity of the Marxian thesis that the economic factor is the decisive variable. It will be seen from the table that when primitive economics are more advanced the population is denser, the village communities larger, the social organization changes its structure, specialization increases, products become more unequally distributed, ownership of strategic resources passes from the community to private hands, and inequalities in the ownership of wealth develop.

The principle that the mode of production is ultimately the determining factor is substantiated by a consideration of the basic social conditions required for the development of arts and crafts and elaborations of social organizational forms. In simple food-gathering economies the activity of every member of the small community is required for the common task of acquiring sufficient food for survival. There is no opportunity for the cultivation of skills, because the energies of all are directed toward maintaining life. Only when food surpluses are available can persons be released to develop the more complicated techniques of the arts and crafts. Similarly, social gatherings and religious ceremonials can flourish only with leisure; hence, complexity of social organization and cultural activities is positively correlated with increases in surpluses derived from economic activities. Ritualistic behavior associated with the public transfer of property involving future obligations of the recipient—e.g., African marriages, the potlatch in Northwest America and the Kula Ring of the Trobriands—depend upon the presence of property surpluses.

The mode of production also determines in a large measure the type of discoveries and inventions made by a society. The concentration of attention upon a specific economic occupation leads to new achievements in the field, although it does not determine the specific form of those achievements. For example, the sea-hunting Eskimo has developed his boats and his weapons because his life has been centered upon procuring sea mammals for food and for heat. Similarly, cattle breeders and agriculturists have made their technical inventions in the fields upon which their energies have been focused through their economic activities. Man's knowledge of the habits of animals and of the uses of plants have been preponderantly derived from his interest in them as sources of food. The regular movements of the sun and moon have been observed and recorded and calendar systems have been developed because of their relevance to seasonal occupations. Measures of space and time become more elaborate, the more extensive is their use in technical occupations and in the regulation of daily occupations. Religious ceremonies also reflect the context of the economy in which they function; e.g., salmon-fishing peoples have first-salmon ceremonies, and agricultural peoples have fertility rites and harvest festivals.

The nature of the economy further determines whether a people

CORRELATION OF MODES OF PRODUCTION TO OTHER ASPECTS OF CULTURE

	Simple Food-Gathering Economies (*Hunting, fishing societies without exchangeable surpluses*)	*Advanced Food-Gathering Economies* (*Hunting, fishing societies with small exchangeable surpluses*)	*Simple Agricultural Economies* (*Primitive societies lacking pastoralism, with small surpluses*)	*Advanced Agricultural Economies* (*Societies with or without pastoralism, that had large surpluses*)
Density of population	Sparse (except in California).	Many times denser than Simple Food-Gathering Economies.	About same as Simple Food-Gathering Economies.	Mostly denser.
Communities	Bands of 40–80. Temporary greater assemblages brief.	Village community 40–50. Market villages as high as 1,500–2,000.	Villages of scores or hundreds of persons. Rarely as large as 2,000.	Villages, towns, and cities numbering many thousands of persons.
Method of obtaining strategic food supply	Democratically conducted work bands of either sex. Entire community moved seasonally to obtain major food. supply.	Work parties recruited, organized and led by headmen or women who could control incidental or individualistic production too. Village maintained year round, only part of population migrating.	Garden work carried on by individuals. Sometimes community joined in harvesting and other farm work. Democratic work parties for hunting and fishing.	Work carried on by individuals or by slave labor owned by chiefs or monarchs. Production for market by specialists or specialized villages.
Specializations	Simple sexual division of labor, and no other.	Some specialization in addition to sexual division of labor. Carvers, weavers, canoe makers. Beginnings of village and district specialization.	Leisure released many individuals for specialized work or craftsmanship in pottery, basketry, weaving, carving, and ceremonial interests.	Specialization increased.

Distribution of products	Economically strategic products potentially shared.	Distribution of work party products unequal. Hereditarily wealthy received better and larger products.	Garden produce kept by individual producer — shared only in time of community need.	Unequal. Owners of lands and herds and slaves received most. Tribute exacted.
Disposal of surplus products	No economically significant surplus; no money, commerce, trade, or markets. Exchange confined to gifts.	A few products sold. Trading by sea-shell money.	Economically significant surplus bartered or presented from community to community. True money absent or coming into use. No true markets.	Commodities sold in market towns. Trade facilitated by money.
Strategic resources	Ownership by entire band or community, not by individuals or lineage. Generally could be used by any member of community.	Some fishing sites and hunting districts owned by lineage headmen who were wealthy through heredity. Used only by permission of owner.	Owned by community. Cultivated land assigned democratically for long terms to lineages or individuals from which private property tended to emerge.	Agricultural lands, herds, subject persons, slaves privately owned by nobility and well-to-do upper classes.
Ownership of wealth	No significant inequalities; wide differences in ownership of personal effects, of minor social significance.	Hereditary class strata based on inequalities in ownership of productive resources. Nobles receive tribute from relatives, fellow clansmen, and villagers. Predatory raids for wealth.	Because there are no economically important inequalities in ownership, there are no notable inequalities of wealth status. Ownership of personal effects. No hereditary leader. No taxation or tribute.	Inequalities of ownership led to development of classes and castes. Wealthy rulers increased their wealth by taxes, tributes, and fines, and by waging war.

is migratory or has a stable habitat, and this in turn has significant influence upon all aspects of culture. In the case of simple food-gathering peoples, the roving life required in order to follow the game or visit the favorite root-gathering spots according to season makes permanent dwellings impossible and precludes any but very limited possessions. On the other hand, the stable habitat of agricultural peoples provides favorable opportunity for accumulating property resources, and lays the basis for a less grim struggle for survival. While the seasonal movement of food-gathering peoples militates against the formation of large, well organized social units, the conditions are favorable for the development of social and political complexity in an agricultural community occupying a relatively small territory. The small size of the simple food-gathering communities limits the maturing of culture, for there are, as a result, fewer social contacts and thus less interstimulation of persons than in the larger agricultural communities. The sparsity of the technological base, and relatively scant margin of safety which permits few risks, the conformity demanded within closely related groups, the absence of division of labor other than along lines of sex, which diminishes the possibility of experimentation and specialization, and the isolation which limits horizons and experiences and permits few collisions with novel concepts from without, all slow the rate of change in food-gathering as compared to the more advanced agricultural societies.

Changes in the mode of production which lead to property surpluses influence the division of labor between the sexes and bring about marked change in the power and status relations between the sexes in society and in the family. In food-gathering societies, because the bearing and nursing of children impede the movement of women in the hunting of animals, they usually perform the more sedentary tasks. While men generally are busy with the hunting of large and swift animals, women gather berries and roots and other foods within reach of the camps. Although a roughly approximate equality between the sexes prevails, these societies tend to be superficially patriarchal in character because of the relative backwardness of women's knowledge and skills as compared to those of men, and hence women's lesser economic importance. The elaboration of the authority of the mother is especially characteristic of agricultural peoples, for the domestication of plants was a product of women's work, an outgrowth of their food-gathering activities. As a consequence of the development of agriculture by women, economic power and hence social importance shifted relatively in favor of women, so that many, although not all, agricultural peoples are matrilineal. The domestication of animals, on the other hand, was achieved by men as an extension of their hunting activities. When this was combined with agriculture through the use of the animal-drawn plow, and in some areas also through the specialized development of pastoralism, ever larger surpluses became possible. Women then receded in economic importance, relative to men, and patrilineal descent became preponderant.[16]

The findings of V. Gordon Childe on what he calls the Second or Urban Revolution in Europe[17] bear out the correlations between economic changes and those of other aspects of culture demonstrated in the pages above for primitive societies. He shows that the bronze ax presupposes a complex economic and social structure, for "the casting of bronze is too difficult a process to be carried out by anyone in the intervals of growing or catching his food or minding her babies." Moreover, because copper and tin, the constituents of bronze, are rare and seldom occur together, they need to be imported; and this is possible only if communications and trade have been established and there is a surplus of some local product to barter for the metals. In the Near East the so-called Bronze Age is marked by populous cities in which a large number of specialized craftsmen, merchants, transport workers, and also officials, clerks, soldiers, and priests are supported by the surplus foodstuffs produced by cultivators, herdsmen, and hunters. A substantial proportion of the community is withdrawn from the primary task of getting food to engage in the manufacture of tools, in transportation, commerce, and administration. The change from self-sufficient food production to an economy based in addition upon specialized manufacture and external trade promoted a further marked increase in the density of the population. Social organization became increasingly complex, and the number of slaves was augmented. Sedentary life facilitated improved housing accommodations and paved the way for brick and stone architecture and the development of the arch. Artificial irrigation using canals and ditches, the sailing boat, wheeled vehicles, orchard husbandry, and the production and use of copper—important innovations of this period—all involved the application of science to production, and in turn encouraged the development of the abstract sciences. With the development of writing, social organization became further complicated by the fact that society divided into a laboring and an administrative class. The practitioners of the arts and crafts responsible for the surplus which had made urban civilization possible gradually came to form the lower strata of society. In the class division of urban society, scribes belonged to the upper classes, in contrast to the working artisans and farmers. The scribe as the adjunct to the administrator looked with contempt upon manual labor; and as the smith, the potter, and the peasant sank lower in the social scale, their unwritten lore was likewise despised. Only that which was written was esteemed, with the result that there was a separation of the theoretical and practical sciences that long had deleterious effects upon the development of the sciences and society.[18]

Sociological studies in the history of science for later periods have demonstrated that the development of science is controlled and directed by its economic milieu. A few illustrations will suffice to indicate the nature of these findings. Farrington has shown the relation of Greek philosophy to socio-economic changes:

> Milesian philosophy . . . arose in the course of a great wave of economic and political progress, and its essential character, as I shall argue, was that it applied ideas derived from the techniques of production to the interpretation of the phenomena of the universe. . . . If early Greek philosophy was interested in the process of change, it was not simply because nature is so changeable (that has always been true), but because man himself has never before been so active and independent an agent of change. The men who built the cities of Ionia were a new type of men, who had effected an outstanding enlargement of man's control over nature![19]

Similarly the influential anatomical work of Vesalius was a characteristic product of an age which combined humanistic intellectual activity with the new naturalist Renaissance art, fostered by a benevolent autocracy of the merchant princes.[20] The spurt in experimental science of seventeenth century England was inspired largely by the new needs of commercial enterprise of the middle class for more adequate means of transportation and communication, especially in navigation. The prevailing interest in the mechanics of the pump for waterworks and for the drainage of mines, led Harvey to think of the heart as a pump, and to explain the circulation of the blood in terms of its functioning.[21]

With this underscoring of the evidence that the economic factor is the developmental variable in history, there is no attempt to underestimate the unevenness of development in different aspects of culture, because of which there is no complete correspondence of political, religious, and other superstructural institutions at different economic levels. Each social institution has its own internal historical development which plays an important role in determining its functions. Patterns of behavior are tenacious, and forms of social relationships and ideas that grow out of the needs of one economy tend to carry over and persist although they may have little functional significance in the setting of the new economy. When economic changes occur, the readjustments of other aspects of culture are by no means automatic and require considerable time to be effectuated, with the result that there are "cultural lags," incongruities, and contradictions. Since society is always in flux, real equilibrium within the social structure is never attained. What can be observed, however, is a tendency toward integration, a strain toward consistency. A culture is never a mere assemblage of shreds and patches nor an aggregate of culture elements or complexes. The psychological tendency of individuals to seek to integrate into a consistent whole their various attitudes, beliefs, ideas, and actions lays the basis for cultural integration. So too does the social pressure of groups to exact conformity upon their members. But, just as few individuals attain complete integration, and few groups complete conformity, cultures too are incompletely integrated because of the disparate origin and development of their different parts. It is this fact which vitiates not merely the work of the functionalists but also the recent efforts of those who discuss "national character." Such discussion postulates cultural and psychological integration unwarranted by available evidence, and obscures incongruities and variants occasioned by differential adjustments of other aspects of culture to socio-economic changes.

References

[1] Clark Wissler, "Psychological and Historical Interpretations for Culture," *Science,* 43:200–201 (1916).

[2] R. R. Marett, *Psychology and Folklore* (London, 1920), pp. 12–13.

[3] F. Engels, "Ludwig Feuerbach and the Outcome of German Classical Philosophy," in Karl Marx, *Selected Works* (New York, 1936–1937), 1:457–459.

[4] See especially V. I. Lenin, *What Is to Be Done?* (New York, 1929).

[5] George P. Murdock, ed., *Studies in the Science of Society* (New Haven, 1937), pp. xviii, xix.

[6] George A. Lundberg, *Foundations of Sociology* (New York, 1939), p. 204.

[7] George A. Lundberg, *Can Science Save Us?* (New York, 1947), p. 48.

[8] Alexander A. Goldenweiser, *History, Psychology, and Culture* (New York, 1933), pp. 61–62.

[9] Friedrich Engels, *Herr Eugen Dühring's Revolution in Science* (Anti-Dühring) (New York, 1939), pp. 309–310.

[10] Karl Marx, "Theses on Feuerbach" (1885), *Selected Works,* 1:473.

[11] B. Malinowski, *The Foundations of Faith and Morals* (London, 1936), p. 59.

[12] Gunnar Myrdal and others, *An American Dilemma* (New York, 1944), p. 78.

[13] Letter to J. Bloch, London, Sept. 21, 1890, in Karl Marx and Friedrich Engels, *Correspondence, 1846–1895* (New York, 1934), p. 475.

[14] Friedrich Engels, *Herr Eugen Dühring's Revolution in Science,* p. 300.

[15] Based on data given in Melville Jacobs and Bernhard J. Stern, *Outlines of Anthropology* (New York, 1947), pp. 125–134. I am indebted to Melville Jacobs for assistance in formulating these correlations.

[16] This is discussed in considerable detail in Bernhard J. Stern, "Engels on the Family," *Science and Society,* Vol. 12 (1948), pp. 42–64.

[17] The earlier domestication of plants and animals in Europe is designated by him as "the Neolithic Revolution." V. Gordon Childe, *Man Makes Himself* (London, 1936), pp. 9, 40–41.

[18] *Ibid.,* pp. 211–213; Benjamin Farrington, *Head and Hand in Ancient Greece* (London, 1947), pp. 28–54.

[19] Farrington, *op. cit.,* pp. 20–21.

[20] Charles J. Singer, *Evolution of Anatomy* (London, 1925), pp. 111, 117–119.

[21] H. T. Pledge, *Science Since 1500* (New York, 1947), p. 29; Robert K. Merton, "Science and the Economy of Seventeenth Century England," *Science and Society,* 3:3–27 (1939); B. Hessen, "The Social and Economic Roots of Newton's Principia," *Science at the Crossroads* (London, 1931). See also Bernhard J. Stern, *Society and Medical Progress* (Princeton, 1941).

ETHNOLOGICAL THEORY

by

LESLIE A. WHITE

Leslie A. White, Ph.D., University of Chicago, 1927, is Professor of Anthropology and Chairman of the Department of Anthropology, University of Michigan. He has lectured at the University of Buffalo, University of Chicago, Yenching University (Peiping), and at Yale. Formerly Curator of Anthropology, Buffalo Museum of Science. In the fields of his major interest—ethnological theory, Pueblo Indian ethnology—he has published a number of studies and articles.

WE have had two major types of interpretation of culture as well as of physical and biological phenomena. In one, events are explained by recourse to a mind, spirit, or idea which moves the things of the world of sense. In the other, it is assumed that the things in the world of sense experience have properties of their own, and that they behave in terms of these properties. The former view has been called spiritualistic, idealistic, or vitalistic; the latter, mechanistic, materialistic.

Prior to the emergence of anthropology as a science, cultural phenomena were explained theologically in the West, as in the mythologies of primitive peoples: they were the work of spirits, good and bad. Since the rise of anthropology, idealistic, and even spiritualistic, interpretations of culture have continued in use; but the materialistic interpretation has been introduced and is gaining ground—not, however, without considerable opposition.

Christian theological conceptions permeate one of the contemporary schools of ethnology; namely, the so-called *Kulturkreis,* or Culture Historical School. Although founded by laymen—Graebner, Foy, Ankermann—it has been taken over by Roman Catholic priests, under the leadership of Father Wilhelm Schmidt.[1] It is not surprising, therefore, to find traditional conceptions of Christian theology in the writings of this group. Thus, Father Schmidt's American disciples Sylvester A. Sieber, S.V.D., and Franz H. Mueller, M.C.S., discussing economics in *The Social Life of Primitive Man*,[2] employ "original sin" (p. 73). The "scarcity of food," they say, "must be considered a punishment for sin" (p. 74). A "fundamental spiritual and religious basis" deep in the "moral consciousness" of the Pygmies gives them "the stamina to maintain an ideal monogamous way of life" (p. 33). They admit that economic factors condition social life but insist that these do not dominate it: since man is "a being endowed with free will" and has "a spiritual soul, he does not allow material principles alone to determine his whole thought and action" (p. 120). They are opposed to evolutionism because it is deterministic and denies free will, and because it has been identified with the "crass materialism of Marx" (p. 119). Father Schmidt in his book, already cited, argues that the "method of the natural sciences," which he identifies with materialism, is a "false way" for ethnology (pp. 4–5).

Outside the priesthood, Dr. David Bidney has recently undertaken to introduce God and free will into ethnological theory: "Man, under God, controls his own cultural destiny and is free to choose and realize the ends he would achieve."[3]

We may note other expressions of the doctrine of free will in recent anthropological literature. John R. Swanton assures us that "all that is needed" to terminate warfare "is the will to do so."[4] Margaret Mead believes that "man should democratically take control of his own destiny and build himself a world that is fit to live in."[5] Ralph Linton believes that "there are none of our current problems which cannot be solved if people will put their minds to them and it is the educator's task to make them willing and able to do this . . . If the educator can establish a particular value system in his pupils he can control the future of his society, not in detail but in gross."[6] And the philosophy of free will is implicit in a resolution, formed by M. F. Ashley Montagu and Margaret Mead and passed by the American Anthropological Association at its annual meeting on December 28, 1945, pledging the association to work on "appropriate social inventions to guard against the dangers" inherent in the use of atomic bombs.[7]

We turn now to another type of non-materialist thinking which may be called metaphysical in the Comtian sense. This consists in invoking "principles" as causative agents in the explanation of cultural phenomena. Thus M. J. Herskovits says it was "the essential democracy of Plains Indian life" that "inhibited the development of economically privileged classes." [8] R. H. Lowie, in discussing Polynesian social organization, observes that, "owing to the separatism of the natives, no large population was ever anciently brought under a common head." [9] Franz Boas explains group solidarity by citing "the will of the members" as "the unifying force." [10] He also states that "the homology of distinguishing marks of social divisions of a tribe is a proof that they are due to a classificatory tendency." [11] A. R. Radcliffe-Brown explains institutions such as the levirate (where a man customarily marries his deceased brother's widow) as the "result of the action of a sociological principle." [12]

To explain cultural phenomena in terms of "essential democracy—or aristocracy," "wills" as "unifying forces," the "action of principles," "tendencies," etc. is, of course, to offer no explanation at all; it is sterile metaphysics or empty verbalism or both.

Idealist interpretations of war are not uncommon in American ethnological theory. As a general principle, Franz Boas declared that "a more profound teaching of history" would attempt to "elucidate the dominant ideas that have determined the actions of states, churches and peoples." [13] Ruth Benedict asserted that World War II was "a war between two ideologies about the way to set up human societies." [14] Herskovits tells us that "anthropologists, perhaps more than those of any other scientific discipline, had cause to understand the nature of the war that was being fought [World War II]—a war of ideologies." [15] To B. W. Aginsky, World War II was "a war of social philosophies. It is what brought the war about." [16] Boas, explaining war in general, says that "it is not any rational cause that forms opposing groups, but solely the emotional value of an idea." [17] Similarly, he attributes the conflicts between racial groups to a "tendency in the human mind." [18]

The central and basic concept of cultural anthropology is, of course, the concept of *culture*. Culture is the name given to an organization of objects (tools, utensils, etc.), acts (patterns of behavior, customs, codes, institutions, etc.), ideas (belief, knowledge, lore, etc.), and sentiments (attitudes such as an aversion for eating pork, "horror of incest," avoidance of mother-in-law, etc.) that is dependent upon the use of symbols.[19] As such it is confined to the human species. Culture is a specific and concrete mechanism employed by a particular animal organism in adjusting to its environment. It is the mechanism that articulates man with the earth and cosmos. It is therefore something describable in zoological, material, mechanical terms. Yet we have only to browse through the literature to discover how often it is conceived otherwise.

A few decades ago, culture was very real, tangible, and observable to anthropologists. They went out to preliterate peoples, saw and collected tools, clothing, ceremonial paraphernalia, utensils, and ornaments; they observed people *doing* things—grinding seeds, practicing circumcision, burying prayersticks, chewing betel; they observed expressions of conventional sentiments—a loathing of milk, respect for the mother's brother, a fear of ghosts; they discovered the knowledge and belief of the people. All of this was once as real and tangible to the ethnologist as to the native himself. In recent years, however, for reasons which we shall not seek here, culture has become an abstraction, intangible, imperceptible, and all but unreal to many anthropologists.

Thus the anthropologists in Kluckhohn's and Kelly's imaginary symposium [20] continually assert that culture is an abstraction. Furthermore, it is invisible. "You can see the individuals who make up a society," they say, "while you never see 'culture.' " Culture is an abstraction also to Robert Redfield,[21] Radcliffe-Brown,[22] M. J. Herskovits,[23] and Ralph Linton.[24] Even A. L. Kroeber has recently taken this point of view.[25]

To Linton, culture "is something which lies entirely outside the range of physical phenomena. The form, the content and even the existence of cultures can only be deduced from the behavior to which they give rise . . . Culture itself is intangible and cannot be directly apprehended even by the individuals who participate in it." [26] Herskovits [27] also finds that culture is intangible. Culture, according to Linton's conception, seems to be something in the mind that makes peoples behave in their respective conventional ways. Thus he speaks of culture "patterns which control the activities of individuals" and "ideal patterns which direct and control social interactions." [28] Father Schmidt holds the same view. "Culture," he says, "is something immanent, something entirely internal and as such not directly subject to external observation . . . Culture from its deepest nature consists in the inner formation of the human mind . . ." "The proper and deepest culture is the formation of the soul itself," which "engenders within it a vital force which urges on to external actualization . . ." "Culture always and everywhere, also in the so-called material culture, is nothing else than either a passive manifestation of the spirit . . . or an active manifestation . . ."[29]

Thus we see, in the course of ethnological theory, that culture was once tangible and observable; then it became intangible and invisible; finally an abstraction. Linton has taken the last remaining step and has seriously questioned the *reality* of culture. Herskovits grants culture patterns "the reality of any abstraction,"[30] but Linton questions whether culture actually exists.[31] What was once a distinct class of real, observable, tangible phenomena, the subject matter of a special science, has now been conjured almost out of existence!

We turn now to materialist interpretations of culture. One of the best as well as one of the earliest expositions of this point of view is to be found in the work of the American anthropologist, Lewis Henry Morgan (1818–1881), especially in his *Ancient Society.*[32] Here we find man depicted as an animal species evolving biologically from anthropoid to modern forms. Like all other species, he is engaged in a struggle for existence and survival. On the one hand he has his natural habitat to contend with, and on the other he is occupied with competitive rivalry within his own species, in warfare between tribes and nations. But the basis of his existence, both as an animal and as a human being, is the mode of subsistence. Life is made secure only by establishing control over the food resources of the habitat, and culture advances as this control is extended. Let us quote Morgan on this point:[33]

"The important fact that mankind commenced at the bottom of the scale and worked up, is revealed in an expressive manner by their successive arts of subsistence. Upon their skill in this direction, the whole question of human supremacy on the earth depended. Mankind are the only beings who may be said to have gained an absolute control over the production of food; which at the outset they did not possess above other animals. Without enlarging the basis of subsistence, mankind could not have propagated themselves into other areas not possessing the same kinds of food, and ultimately over the whole surface of the earth; and lastly, without obtaining an absolute control over both its variety and amount, they could not have multiplied into populous nations.[34] It is accordingly probable that the great epochs of human progress have been identified, more or less directly, with the enlargement of the sources of subsistence."

Food being man's most important requirement, the tools with which he achieves control over subsistence acquire an importance second only to that of food itself. The invention of the bow and arrow, for example, "must have given a powerful upward influence to ancient society" (p. 22).[35] He likens the bow and arrow of savagery to the iron sword of barbarism and to the firearms of civilization. The domestication of animals enabled certain peoples "to secure for themselves a permanent supply of animal food, including milk; the healthful and invigorating influence of which upon the race, and especially upon children, was undoubtedly remarkable." Moreover, in "supplementing human muscle with animal power," it "contributed a new factor of the highest value" (pp. 25, 26). "When the great discovery was made that the wild horse, cow, sheep, ass, sow and goat might be tamed and, when produced in flocks and herds, become a source of permanent subsistence, it must have given a powerful impulse to human progress" (p. 534). But it was the cultivation of plants, especially the cereals, first in gardens, or horticulture, then in field agriculture, that gave man his greatest control over his food supply. The "acquisition of farinaceous food by cultivation," said Morgan, "must be regarded as one of the greatest events in human experience" (p. 42).

Man's control over nature is effected by technological means. Society advances as this control is increased. Social evolution is therefore a function of technological evolution. The domestication of animals "introduced a new mode of life, the pastoral" (p. 25). Horticulture "led to localization and to village life" (p. 24). "From the increased abundance of subsistence through field agriculture, nations began to develop, numbering many thousands under one government, where before they would be reckoned by a few thousands" (p. 540).

Morgan (p. 43) regarded the production of iron as "the event of events in human experience, without a parallel, and without an equal, beside which all other inventions and discoveries were inconsiderable, or at least subordinate . . . The want of iron tools arrested the progress of mankind in barbarism. There they would have remained to the present hour, had they failed to bridge the chasm."

There is a close connection between technology, property, and social organization. "The systematical cultivation of the earth . . . tended to identify the family with the soil and render it a property-making organization" (p. 543). The institution of slavery originated as a means of accelerating the production of wealth; it became obsolete when a common freeman became "a better property-making machine" than a man in bondage (p. 505). Customs of tenure and inheritance of property have profoundly influenced the structure of society at numerous points: "property became sufficiently powerful in its influence to touch the organic structure of society" (p. 389). Morgan believed that the growing influence of property was the chief cause of the change of descent from matrilineal to patrilineal, and of the emergence of monogamous marriage from earlier forms. His conclusions on these two points have been shown to be unwarranted; we merely cite them as examples of reasoning from materialist premises. "Governments, institutions and laws," he wrote, "are simply contrivances for the creation and protection of property." Business, he remarked in a passage upon the spirit animating—and dominating—London, "is the chief concern of mankind as civilization now goes . . . the Age of Commerce has now been reached through the previous ages of Stone, of Bronze, of Iron, of Agriculture, and of the Mechanic Arts." The trend of social evolution toward larger political units is motivated by commercial considerations: "It is so plainly in the interests of agriculture, manufactures and commerce to form great nations that the inevitable tendency must be in that direction." [36] It "is impossible to overestimate the influence of property in the civilization of mankind" (p. 505—see also p. 552).

The production and accumulation of wealth through increased technological control over nature tends to provoke international conflicts as well as peaceful commercial relations. "The localization of tribes in fixed areas and in fortified cities, with the increase of the numbers of the people, intensified the struggle for the possession of the most desirable territories" and "tended to advance the art of war" (p. 540).[37]

As we have already indicated, Morgan had an idealist interpretation of cultural evolution as well as a materialist one. Institutions are expressions of ideas, of germs of thought implanted in the human mind.

But it is interesting to note that the operation of this principle, the growth of these ideas, is dependent upon material conditions, specifically upon technological advance. The various forms of the family could not incubate and come forth of themselves. They could appear only at the proper "ethnic stages," and these were determined by the technological control over subsistence. Property is influential in affectting social organization at many points, in relation to government and laws as well as customs of inheritance. But here again the production and accumulation of wealth is technologically determined. Thus, although Morgan may give the impression in some passages that institutions are but the expression of certain germs of thought, unfolding logically in the human mind, he makes it clear elsewhere that the growth of these ideas is dependent upon the underlying conditions of subsistence and technology. He makes it plain also that progress is not inevitable either in the social sphere or in the realm of technology. As we have already noted, Morgan argued that civilization could not have been achieved without the use of iron. "The most advanced portion of the human race were halted, so to express it, at certain stages of progress, until some great invention or discovery, such as the domestication of animals, or the smelting of iron ore, gave a new and powerful impulse forward"(pp. 39–40).

The materialist interpretation of culture receives ample expression also in the writings of the eminent English anthropologist Edward Burnett Tylor (1832–1917). Man's first need, according to Tylor, is to get his daily food.[38] He distinguished stages in the development of culture in terms of control over food supply. Like Morgan, he termed the lowest stage, in which man subsisted wholly upon wild foods, "savagery"; and the stage in which animals were domesticated, or plants cultivated, "barbarism." A pastoral economy, he wrote, is more advanced than one based upon hunting and gathering, but is less advanced than an agricultural system. A combination of animal husbandry and agriculture is superior to either by itself (pp. 24, 220). Again like Morgan, Tylor regarded the cultivation of cereals as of fundamental importance in the development of culture. "Those edible grasses," he writes, "which have been raised by cultivation into the cereals, such as wheat, barley, rye, and by their regular and plentiful supply have become the mainstay of human life and *the great moving power of civilization*" (p. 215—emphasis ours). Thus man makes his life secure by technological control over the plants and animals of nature and by defending himself from his enemies with weapons.

Social evolution progresses as the means of technological control are improved and multiplied. "With the certain supply of food" from agriculture "which can be stored till next harvest, settled village and town life is established, with immense results in the improvement of arts, knowledge, manners, and government" (p. 24). To this "change of habit" from a wild food economy to agriculture "may be plainly in great part traced the expansion of industrial arts and the creation of higher social and political institutions." [39]

The development of agriculture had great consequences for culture at many points. With the accumulation of wealth, warfare came to be practiced for gain rather than "for quarrel or vengeance. . . . As property increases, there appears with it warfare carried on as a business" (p. 225). The institution of slavery came into being as a consequence of this new type of warfare. Instead of killing captives, as in earlier eras and on lower cultural levels, the victors now brought them back as slaves and set them "to till the ground." Slavery in turn reacted upon numerous aspects of culture. "It was through slave labor that agriculture and industry increased, that wealth accumulated, and leisure was given to priests, scribes, poets, philosophers, to raise the level of men's minds" (p. 435). Through warfare and slavery "a new division of society takes place . . . Thus we see how in old times the original equality of men broke up, a nation dividing into an aristocracy of warlike freemen, and an inferior laboring caste" (p. 225). Warfare has still further social consequences, according to Tylor. As a matter of fact, he laid "two of the greatest facts in history" at its door; namely, "the organized army . . . and the confederation of tribes" (pp. 432–433). He traced this trend toward larger political units to his own day, and we can witness it in ours, advancing with accelerated speed and greater force. Thus, social and political evolution is directly articulated with the advance in technological control over nature, specifically in agriculture.

Turning to more advanced cultures, Tylor continued his interest in technology and its significance for society. "It was a great movement in civilization for the water-mill and its companion contrivance the wind-mill to come into use as force-providers, doing all sorts of labor"

(p. 204). He also discussed the harnessing of natural forces in the form of coal, and wondered what man would turn to when this source of energy was exhausted. The use of coal was seen to constitute an advance in cultural development because it increased man's control over nature, his energy resources. "Thus the yearly output of millions of tons of steam-coal in Great Britain alone, furnishes a supply of force in comparison with which what was formerly available from wind-mills and water-mills and the labor of men and beasts was quite small" (p. 272). He compared the England of his day with the earlier agricultural and pastoral periods thus (p. 272):

"It is an interesting problem in political economy to reckon the means of subsistence in our country during the agricultural and pastoral period, and to compare them with the resources we now gain from coal, in doing home-work and manufacturing goods to exchange for foreign produce. Perhaps the best means of realizing what coal is to us, will be to consider, that of three Englishmen now, one at least may be reckoned to live by coal, inasmuch as without it the population would have been so much less."

Tylor took a materialist point of view in his interpretation of certain intellectual aspects of culture, too. Many mathematical concepts have their beginning in sensory experience of the external world. Primitive man (p. 309) "knows much of the properties of matter, how fire burns and water soaks, the heavy sinks and the light floats, what stone will serve for the hatchet and what wood for its handle, which plants are food and which are poison, what are the habits of the animals that he hunts or that may fall upon him. He has notions how to cure, and much better notions how to kill. In a rude way he is a physicist in making fire, a chemist in cooking, a surgeon in binding up wounds, a geographer in knowing his rivers and mountains, a mathematician in counting on his fingers. All this is knowledge, and it was on these foundations that science proper began to be built up."

Counting and measuring, the means through which "scientific methods have come into use," were based upon experience of the senses. The savage counted on the fingers of his hands and the toes of his feet, reckoning, as a consequence, by fives, tens, and twenties. Calculating began as the manipulation of pebbles (*calculi*). Measurements likewise were based upon bodily dimensions: the cubit, hand, foot, pace, ell (el-bow), etc. The origin of the concept of the straight line was discovered in its etymology: stretched linen (string). Geometry began as a practical art of measuring land (pp. 310–319).

Thus we see that in the anthropology of the latter part of the nineteenth century the materialist point of view was very much to the fore.

Cultural anthropology in the United States since the 1890's is not easy to characterize. A great deal of the field work has been conceived and carried out in terms of premises close to the materialist point of view, though they are seldom made explicit. Clark Wissler probably comes closer to a materialist interpretation of culture than most anthropologists of this period. In *The American Indian* [40] and other works, he has correlated types of culture with regional types of habitat and emphasizes the influence of natural resources and the means of exploiting them upon the social, ceremonial, and intellectual aspects of culture. A. L. Kroeber, too, has examined the relationship between the natural, environmental areas and the cultural types of aboriginal North America.[41] And more recently Ralph Linton has advanced the following thesis in his discussion of the culture of a Madagascar tribe: [42]

"The securing of food, shelter, and survival to a society's members is the most basic function of any culture, since without these no society can survive. It is here that culture is in most intimate contact with the hard facts of the material world, facts which cannot be changed, still less ignored. The techniques connected with the satisfaction of these basic biological needs thus become the foundation upon which the whole elaborate superstructure of the culture is reared."

Julian Steward employs the materialist interpretation of culture with good effect in two significant papers, "The Economic and Social Basis of Primitive Bands," [43] and "Ecological Aspects of Southwestern Society."[44]

The so-called Functionalist school has, it seems to me, made little contribution to materialism in cultural anthropology. A. R. Radcliffe-Brown's contribution has, I think, been negligible, and this would apply to most of his disciples if not all.[45] In philosophy I believe he might be characterized as an old-fashioned metaphysician: we have already seen that he explains phenomena in terms of "principles" as causative agents. Some fine expressions of the materialist point of view are found in the writings of Bronislaw Malinowski, but also non- and even anti-materialist views. The whole tribal life of the Trobriand Islanders, he said, "is dominated by agriculture." But he could also assert, "Religion and to a lesser extent magic thus become the very foundations of culture." [46] After all, the Functionalists were primarily concerned with the interrelationship of cultural elements, not with the relation between culture and nature.

In cultural anthropology in America since the 1890's the dominant point of view, if such it can be called, has been that of the school of Franz Boas (1858–1942). It is not easy to characterize the philosophy of this group.[47] Materialism has been implicit in part of its field work, and in the interpretations of Kroeber and Steward and some other members, as we have already seen; but the dominant and explicit notes in the Boasian philosophy are anything but materialist. As a matter of fact, materialism is vigorously opposed at many points.

In addition to being antimaterialist, they are anti-intellectualistic or antiphilosophic—regarding theorizing with contempt [48]—and antievolutionist. [49] In fact, they are opposed to so many things that someone has characterized their philosophy as "eclectic negativism." It has been their mission to demonstrate that there are no laws of significance in ethnology, that there is no rhyme or reason in cultural phenomena, that civilization is—in the words of R. H. Lowie, the foremost exponent of this philosophy—merely a "planless hodge-podge," a "chaotic jumble." [50]

Boas and a number of his disciples have opposed the materialist conception of history.[51] The usual procedure is to identify it with economic determinism and then to refute the latter. By "economic determinism" they mean that all aspects of human behavior, all phases of culture, are dominated by a desire for economic gain, for utilitarian advantage. They refute this proposition with little difficulty, and in this way win an easy, though false, victory over materialism.

"Of the great intellectual events of Boas' lifetime," writes Paul Radin, "assuredly the two most significant were the theory of evolution and the economic interpretation of history. To the first Boas always took a prevailingly antagonistic position. The second he never so much as mentioned until the 1938 edition of *The Mind of Primitive Man*. There he dismisses it in a paragraph as of only secondary importance. He so completely misunderstands it as to say that 'cultural life is always economically conditioned and economics are always culturally conditioned.' Marx and Engels are never referred to." [52]

Alexander Goldenweiser equates the materialist conception of history with economic determinism, which he thereupon rejects: "Far from constituting a law of history, economic determination will some day appear as a disease of a particular epoch, during which man temporarily fell under the spell of a tool . . . invented by himself." [53] Lowie goes to some pains, in *Primitive Society* (pp. 356–357), to refute the theory of economic determinism. He cites the case of a Kwakiutl Indian who "in a paroxysm of vainglory confounds a social rival by destroying a canoe and breaking a copper plate valued at a thousand blankets." The Indian's motive, he says, "is manifestly as far removed from the economic as it can well be." He also claims that the extensive warfare of the Plains tribes was not economically motivated; they fought because it was a "worth-while game." Thus, he concludes, "the utilitarian doctrine completely breaks down."

Herskovits, almost alone among anthropologists, distinguishes between "historical materialism" and "economic determinism." [54] He finds *both* theses expressed, however, in Marx's classic statement of the materialist conception of history in the preface to *Critique of Political Economy,* and—again unlike most anthropologists—quotes it. Then, for reasons which are far from clear, he accepts "historical materialism" with enthusiasm: it is "the expression of those methodological aspirations toward the realization of which all effort" of the social scientist "is being continuously directed." But "economic determinism, on the other hand, must be rejected as must any other simplistic explanation of culture." Like Goldenweiser, he explains "the genesis of this theory" as "the reactions to a culture, our own, wherein the economic factors are actually of primary importance," implying that in other cultures they are not of primary importance.

In view of the Boasian opposition to "economic determinism," it is significant to note that Freud, who in popular conception "attributes everything to sex," declares that "the motivating force of human society is fundamentally economic." [55]

At another important theoretical point—namely, the relationship between social structure and technology—the Boas group has taken an antimaterialist point of view. Boas opposed the view that there is a "correlation between industrial development and social development." [56] Sometimes we find simple, sometimes complex, social organizations associated with crude inventions.[57] This view is not only antimaterialist; it makes *any* rational interpretation [58] of culture impossible. In the first place, it denies the integration of culture—that one part is related to another. It conceals the functions of social systems—or denies that they have any that refer to anything outside themselves. And, finally, it asserts that social systems are independent of the technological means with which its human components are articulated with their natural habitat.

Social organization is exactly what the term implies, the social organization of human endeavor in the business of living. Since subsistence, defense against enemies, and protection from the elements are the basic activities of any species, the organization of society is primarily concerned with them. And, since subsistence and defense-offense are expressed through tools and weapons, the form and content of the correlated social system are determined by the technology employed. Those aspects of culture which are not directly and immediately concerned with the manipulation of technological instruments, such as marriage unions, social clubs, and clans, are indirectly related: they are means of perpetuating the group biologically, of promoting social solidarity, fostering morale, etc., to the end that life may be made secure and continuous.

Members of the Boas group do not take this view of social organization, however. They contend that the significance of social institutions is often obscure, unknown, or even unknowable, and that, therefore, there is no necessary correlation between social systems and their associated technologies; the association is merely fortuitous, or at least without rational basis. Thus, in line with Boas's view that there is no "correlation between industrial development and social development," Lowie argues that "the appraisal of sociological features is *wholly different* from that of technological features of culture. The latter may be rated according to the closeness with which they accomplish known ends; the former *have unknown ends* or ends whose value *is a matter of philosophic doubt,* hence they can be graded *only on subjective grounds* and must scientifically be treated as incommensurable." [59] In another place,[60] he observes that "the purpose of an axe is to fell trees, but what is the purpose of art, communal life, belief, marriage?" Ruth Benedict takes the same view of social and ceremonial organization in her *Patterns of Culture;* one gets the impression here that a people chooses, apparently of its own free will,[61] whatever type of social organization it wishes to have.

As a particular example of the lack of "correlation between industrial development and social development," the Boas group cite the cultures of aboriginal Australia. Here, they contend, one finds great complexity of social organization coupled with a simple and meager material culture.

Thus Boas asserts, "There are people, like the Australians, whose material culture is quite poor, but who have a highly complex social organization." [62] Lowie, Goldenweiser, Herskovits, Radin, and Reichard, all students of Boas, express the same view.[63] Their reason for emphasizing the point may not be at once apparent. Their primary purpose was to refute the theory of cultural evolution which postulated a close correlation between social and technological systems. If it could be shown that the tribes of Australia had highly evolved and complex social systems, together with the crudest of technologies, then evolutionist theory would have been dealt a severe blow, to say the least. Furthermore, this argument furthered the Boas-Lowie thesis that culture is but a "chaotic jumble," without rhyme or reason.

But the social organization of Australian tribes is not complex at all in the sense of being advanced or highly evolved. On the contrary, it is as simple as their technology. "The basic elements of social structure in Australia," says Radcliffe-Brown, perhaps the foremost authority on its cultures, "are (1) the family . . . and (2) the horde, a small group owning and occupying a definite territory." The hordes are independent and autonomous. The tribe is simply an aggregation of local groups, or hordes; it is such a loose and indefinite group that "it is often difficult . . . to say whether a particular recognized local group is a tribe, or a subdivision of a tribe, or whether another group is a tribe or a larger unit consisting of a number of related tribes." The tribe "has usually, if not always, no political unity." The Boasians have confused a certain intricacy of kinship system, manifested by some tribes, with a complex, or highly developed, social organization. But even the kinship system of the Aranda, perhaps the most intricate of all tribes, "is not very complicated," according to Radcliffe-Brown, "when we follow it out in terms of individual relationships . . . *the whole kinship system is based on the family.*" [64] The family, incidentally, is a social grouping so primitive that man shares it with the anthropoids. It might be noted here that Morgan placed the Australians on a very low level of cultural development both sociologically and technologically, as did Emile Durkheim.[65]

Thus, by their interpretation of Australian culture the Boas group struck at the theory of cultural evolution and at the same time supported their philosophy of culture as a planless hodge-podge, a chaotic jumble of culture where social systems exist and function quite independently of the technological means with which the group articulates itself with its habitat.

The influence of Franz Boas upon ethnological theory is fortunately now on the wane, although the recent fashion of interpreting culture in terms of the individual personality, especially as it is shaped during the weaning and toilet training period, can be laid at his door to a certain extent. Boas maintained that "the causal conditions of cultural happenings lie always in the interaction between individual and society." [66] E. Sapir, Ruth Benedict, Margaret Mead, and other students of Boas have developed a psychologic, psychiatric interpretation of culture, which is much like the old idealism in new terminologic garb.[67] It certainly is not a materialist, culturological approach.

In recent years the British anthropologist V. Gordon Childe has been conspicuous for his exposition of historical materialism. This philosophy permeates many of his writings but receives perhaps its most explicit expression in *Man Makes Himself* and in his Huxley Memorial Lecture for 1944, "Archaeological Ages as Technologic Stages." [68] Childe shows how the sociologic and philosophic elements of culture are integrated with, and to a great extent dependent upon, the technologic base. And he has shown in a very vivid manner how the growth of culture as a whole has been due, at bottom, to technologic advance.

Regarding the first point, Childe writes:

"The ship and the tools employed in its production symbolize a whole economic and social system. The canoe . . . also implies an economy, a social organization . . . The bronze axe which replaces [the stone axe] is not only a superior implement, it also presupposes a more complex economic and social structure." [69]

The significance of animal husbandry and agriculture in transforming primitive tribal cultures into great nations is fully appreciated and elucidated by Childe, and he indicates in the following passage the importance for the evolution of culture of harnessing energy in nonhuman forms:

"But the most decisive innovation was that by harnessing the ox man began to control and use a motive power other than that furnished by his own muscular energy. The ox was the first step to the steam engine and gasoline motor." [70]

Professor Childe does not hold consistently to his materialist point of view, however. He says, for example, in *Man Makes Himself*,[71] "Changes in culture and tradition can be initiated, controlled, or delayed by the conscious and deliberate choice of their human authors and executors." The title, striking the note upon which this work ends, likewise connotes at least a nonmaterialist view. On Australian culture, he admits a considerable degree of independence in the technologic base from the social, ceremonial, and philosophic sectors of culture. This view, quite at variance with his general position, may be merely a concession to the forceful argument of the Boas school on the point. On the whole, however, Childe's writings offer perhaps the best example of a materialist interpretation of culture history in anthropological literature.

The present writer also has endeavored to develop the materialist philosophy introduced into ethnology by Morgan, and at the same time to rehabilitate the theory of cultural evolution.[72] The gist of his thesis may be presented as follows:

Man is an animal species and, like all other species, exerts himself to perpetuate his kind, to make his life secure and enduring. Man's primary and fundamental need is for food, for without this there is no life. His second need is for protection from his enemies, both human and nonhuman. In order to live man, like all other species, must come to terms with the external world, for this is at once the source of his food and tools, his enemies, and his weapons and armor. Man employs his sense organs, nerves, glands, and muscles in adjusting himself to the external world. But in addition to this he has another means of adjustment and control, one possessed by man alone. This mechanism is *culture*. Culture, as we have already seen, is an organization of objects (tools, utensils, ritualistic paraphernalia, materials of art, etc.), acts (patterns of behavior, customs, rituals, institutions), ideas (belief, knowledge, lore), and sentiments (feelings, attitudes) that is dependent upon the use of symbols. A symbol is a thing—object, act, color, etc.—whose meaning is determined by those who use it; articulate speech is the most important and characteristic form of symbolic behavior. Man alone is capable of symbolic behavior by virtue of unique properties of his nervous system, which, however, cannot yet be described except in terms of gross anatomy—exceptionally large forebrain, both relatively and absolutely; an increase in quantity of brain has eventuated in a qualitatively new kind of behavior.

Tradition—the nonbiological transmission of behavior patterns from one generation to the next—is found to a limited extent in some of the lower animal species. But in man, thanks particularly to articulate speech, the transmission of experience in the form of material objects, patterns of behavior, ideas, and sentiments or attitudes becomes easy, varied, and extensive; in short, the culture of one generation and age is passed on to the next. And, in addition to this lineal transmission of culture, it is transmitted laterally, by diffusion, to contemporary neighboring groups. Culture is cumulative as well as continuous; new elements are added through invention and discovery. It is also progressive in that more effective means of adjustment with and control over environment are achieved from time to time.

Culture thus becomes a continuum of extrasomatic elements. It moves in accordance with its own principles, its own laws; it is a thing *sui generis*. Its elements interact with one another, forming new combinations and syntheses.[73] New elements are introduced into the stream from time to time, and old elements drop out.

The course of culture parallels that of man, its carrier and substratum. The behavior of man, distinguished *as a human being* from a non-symbol-using animal, is determined by his culture. *Human* behavior is merely the response of the articulate primate organism to cultural stimuli. Human behavior is determined, therefore, by culture. But culture is not determined by man, by his wishes, will, hopes, fears, etc. Man is of course prerequisite to culture; he is, so to speak, the catalyst that makes the interactive culture process possible. But the culture process is *culturally* determined, not biologically or psychologically.[74] The best example of this may perhaps be found in language. Philology is concerned with linguistic elements interacting in a linguistic progress which is studied without reference to bones, nerves, glands, sense organs; in short, without reference to the animal man at all. This being the case, a *science of culture* is required in addition to the science of the behavior of man, individually and collectively; culturology, as well as psychology and sociology. This science has been cultivated to a considerable extent in anthropology.[75] So much for the origin, structure, and function of culture. Let us now turn to its motive power.

Everything in the cosmos can be interpreted in terms of matter and energy,[76] whether it be a star, atom, cell, or man. All life is, of course, an organization of matter-and-energy. Mind, too, is but a form of motion of matter cellularly organized. Culture is merely the name we give to matter-and-energy in symbolic form. Chopping wood, singing a song, breathing a prayer, loathing snakes, hungering after righteousness, all are examples of matter in motion. We may thus distinguish various forms and, in a sense, strata of forms, of energy: cosmic, galactic, organismic, physiological (intraorganismal), psychological (extraorganismal),[77] and cultural (suprasomatic).

According to the Second Law of Thermodynamics, the cosmos as a whole is becoming more and more disorganized and chaotic; energy is becoming more equally distributed. In short, the cosmos is breaking down structurally and running down dynamically. But, although the cosmos as a whole is moving in this direction, a tiny sector within it is moving in the opposite direction. This sector is called "life." In living material systems the movement is toward higher levels of organization and higher concentrations of energy. This does not mean that the Law of Entropy is negated at this point or that it does not apply to living organisms. It means that living material systems are able to sustain themselves only by appropriating free energy from non-living systems. All life is a struggle for free energy. Biological evolution has been, to a great extent, the process in which higher forms of organization and higher concentrations of energy have been achieved in living material systems. This is what "higher forms of life" means.[78]

Culture is merely a special form assumed by this life process. It is a special kind of mechanism employed by a particular animal species to capture and utilize energy to the end that its life be made secure and perpetual. Considering culture as a self-contained system, we may study it as a mechanism for harnessing energy and putting it to work, and observe the changes that take place within culture as the amount of energy harnessed per capita per year varies, and as the ways of expending the energy harnessed vary. First, however, let us observe culture as an energy-harnessing and energy-utilizing machine.

As we have just seen, culture must find energy outside its own system and incorporate it within itself, there to use it in the service of man, or rather, *groups* of human beings; for culture's relation to man in reality is always particular rather than universal. The first source of energy drawn upon by the system that is culture was the human organism itself. The amount obtainable from this source was quite small, approximately one-twentieth of one horsepower per capita. The culture of a people whose only source of energy for culture-building is the human organism will be crude and meager, intellectually, socially, and technologically. We know cultures of this sort directly from our acquaintance with contemporary savages—the aborigines of Australia, for example—and we must infer that all cultures were of this character in the earliest stage of development. We must assume, also, that the cultures of mankind would never have risen above the savage level unless some way had been found to augment the amount of energy harnessed by tapping some new source. Culture develops as the amount of energy harnessed per capita per year increases.

The first significant advance in culture was achieved when animals were brought under domestication, or plants under cultivation, or both. Plants and animals are of course forms and magnitudes of energy; and the arts of agriculture and animal husbandry are means of laying hold of this energy and of putting it to man's use, just as hydroelectric plants are means of harnessing the energy of rivers. Incidentally, man made very little use of running water and wind as sources of energy until agriculture was well developed. And fire did not become an important source of energy until the invention of the steam engine, although primitive peoples made minor uses of it. It might be noted too at this point that agriculture is a more important way of harnessing energy than animal husbandry. A pastoral culture is always limited by the herd's or flock's dependence upon wild plant food; but the extent to which energy may be harnessed through agriculture is almost unlimited. The great civilizations of antiquity—of India, China, Mesopotamia, Egypt, and, in the New World, Mexico, Middle America, and Peru—came into being quickly with the maturation of the agricultural arts, after long periods of slow growth during the Stone Ages.

With the harnessing of fuels, especially coal and oil, in steam and internal combustion engines, civilization took the next great step forward.

And now a new source of energy has been tapped: the nucleus of the atom.[79]

Culture has grown as the amount of energy harnessed per capita per year has been increased. But *amount* of energy is not the only significant factor in cultural development, although it is the most important and fundamental one. The *means* by which the energy is harnessed is also significant. This factor is expressed in the efficiency of tools and machines, and in the social organization of their use. With the amount of energy remaining constant, the amount of need-serving goods and services produced will vary with the efficiency of expenditure of the energy. Improvements in tools and machines resulting from the use of new materials or from changes in design, and improved ways of using the tools, whether through individual skills or through social organization, will therefore tend to increase output of goods and services and consequently to advance the culture. The efficiency of a tool cannot be increased indefinitely, however; each has a point beyond which it cannot go. Therefore, cultural advance through improvement of the means of the expenditure of energy alone must always be limited. When the limit is reached, only additional energy will move civilization forward again.

Degree of cultural development is to be measured in terms of human need-serving goods and services produced per unit of human labor: amount of food, shelter, transportation, communication, defense, and control over disease. Cultures can be measured and evaluated therefore in objective terms:[80] amount of wheat or coal produced, goods transported, messages communicated, etc., per unit of human labor; death rates and life expectancies. These concepts provide us also with an objective definition of "progress" as it applies to culture: culture progresses when it increases the amount of human need-serving goods and services produced per unit of human labor. This increase is made possible by (1) increasing the amount of energy harnessed per capita per year, and (2) improving the efficiency of the means through which this energy is put to work.

As development of culture in general is dependent upon progress in the technological sector, so are the non-technological segments of culture dependent upon the technological segment. This is to say that the type of social organization, art, and philosophy of a given cultural system will be determined in form and in content by the underlying technology—a proposition directly opposed to the views of the Boas group as we have already seen.

The social system of a people is, almost entirely, the way in which it organizes and exerts itself in two basic activities: (1) subsistence, which involves production, distribution, and consumption; and (2) defense-and-offense with reference to enemies who threaten the integrity of the society from without or within. These activities are carried on by means of tools, weapons, and machines, which determine their form and content. Thus a technology characterized by a throwing club for game and a digging stick for plant food will have one type of social system; hoe and garden culture, herds of domestic cattle, ox-drawn plow and mailed and mounted knights, hydroelectric plants and bombing planes each indicate a technology that will have its own type of social system.

In the field of art the relationship to technology is the same; the general form and content of art is a function of the subsistence and military technology. A *coup de poing* technology will have one type of art. Or, more accurately, the art correlated with *coup de poing* technologies will vary within limits set by the technology of which the *coup de poing* is the index. Horticultural, agricultural, pastoral, and industrial technologies will find their respective reflections in corresponding types of art. There is nothing farfetched about this thesis. Art, like technology, is a means of relating man to the cosmos, of organizing his behavior toward it. But since man's relationship is actually determined by the material, mechanical means of his subsistence and military operations, his art has to adapt itself accordingly.

What is true of art is true also of philosophy, the sum total of man's knowledge and belief concerning the world he lives in. Here again we shall find one type of philosophy reflected by a hunting technology, another by a horticultural, pastoral, or industrial technology. To take an extreme example, the philosophy of a *coup de poing* culture cannot be of the same type as that of an ox-drawn plow, or photoelectric cell, culture. Here, as in the case of art, philosophy is a means of relating man to his earth and his cosmos and organizing and directing his behavior toward them. But his immediate world is shaped by his technology as the remote is experienced through it, or the lack of it. Philosophy, therefore, must adapt itself to the world as it finds it.

It should not be necessary to say that this thesis does not give us mastery over details and the particular. To point out that of two bow-and-arrow hunting cultures one holds a belief in two souls per person while the other believes in one, or that one has patrilineal descent while the other reckons descent in both male and female lines, is to miss the whole point of this argument. To argue that two-legged, warm-blooded, feathered animals are *birds* is not to specify which are web-footed or which have yellow tails. We are dealing here with general types, and we are claiming only (1) that cultures are *systems,* i.e., made up of correlated and integrated parts, and therefore the technological, social, artistic, and philosophic segments of culture will be fitted to one another, and (2) that each system as a whole rests upon and is determined by its technology because this is the basic and fundamental means with which human organisms are articulated with the surface of the earth, the means of subsistence and defense, in short, the means of life.

Thus, the conception of man and culture that has been developing in anthropology since Morgan's day is a simple one. It pictures man as an animal species, inhabiting a tiny planet in a vast expanse of cosmos. As an organism, his existence is conditioned by such factors as temperature, pressure, humidity, and velocity. He adjusts himself to his setting with the organic means at his disposal, means developed in the biochemical process called evolution. Being possessed of a faculty unique among animals, the ability *to symbol,* man has a means of adjustment and control shared by no other species: culture. With the birth of culture a new order of events was introduced, a suprasomatic order. Culture has a life of its own, governed by its own principles and its own laws. Flowing down the ages, it embraces the members of each generation at birth and molds them into human beings, equipping them with their beliefs, patterns of behavior, sentiments, and attitudes. Human behavior is but the response of a primate who can symbol to this extrasomatic continuum called culture. Culture is a system that grows by increasing its control over the forces of nature. Social systems, philosophies, and art are functions of an evolving technology. Progress in cultural development is an objective concept; progress can be measured and the measurements can be expressed in mathematical terms.

Progress in culture has now attained a degree of technological control over nature that could provide mankind with an abundance of the necessities and comforts of life. Intellectually, culture is beginning to outgrow spirits, demons, and free will, and to learn something about the nature of the real world. Socially, tribes and clans were outgrown long ago and independent sovereign nations are virtually obsolete today, thanks to the advanced technologies of production, commerce, and war. Social evolution has been moving toward larger political units ever since the first human grouping was established, and the goal of a single world organization embracing the whole planet and the entire human race is now almost in sight. But if it is reached it will not be the work of frock-coated diplomats in a United Nations *opéra bouffe,* or the realization of the mission of a terrestrialized deity in Aramaic—or Anglicized—form. It will be the political culmination of an age-old process of technological evolution. But technology is destructive as well as creative, and at the present moment we are faced with the threat of the destruction or crippling of Western civilization through the new engines of war. The issue may be decided within the next generation: either a world organization and a cessation of warfare, or the crippling of civilization. But whatever the outcome of the next World War, and whatever the fate and future of mankind may be, it will be decided by technology, the foundation upon which civilization and the life of man as a human species rests.

References

[1] Wilhelm Schmidt, *The Culture Historical Method of Ethnology,* transl. Sylvester A. Sieber (New York, 1939), is perhaps the best single statement of this school's theoretical position.

[2] Published under archiepiscopal imprimatur, St. Louis, 1941.

[3] "The Concept of Cultural Crisis," *American Anthropologist*, Vol. XLVIII, pp. 534–552 (1946), especially p. 541.

[4] *Are Wars Inevitable?* (Smithsonian Institution War Background Studies, No. 12, Washington, 1943), p. 33.

[5] Introduction (p. 13), R. M. Brickner, *Is Germany Incurable?* (Philadelphia, 1943). Mead's book, *And Keep Your Powder Dry* (New York, 1942), is permeated with the philosophy of free will.

[6] "Potential Contributions of Cultural Anthropology to Teacher Education," in Linton, Fisher, and Ryan, *Culture and Personality* (American Council on Education, Washington, 1941), pp. 9, 16.

[7] Ashley Montagu's letter in *Science,* Vol. CIII, p. 570 (May 3, 1946), makes clear that this resolution was offered as an antidote to the present writer's paper, "Atomic Energy: An Anthropological Appraisal" (see footnote 84, following).

[8] *The Economic Life of Primitive Peoples* (New York, 1940), p. 393.

[9] *Introduction to Cultural Anthropology* (New York, 1940), p. 293. In an earlier work (*Primitive Society,* New York, 1920, p. 364) he attributes lack of cooperation and inability to enforce decisions in Samoa to "the absence of a sense for centralized government."

[10] *Race and Democratic Society* (New York, 1945), p. 114.

[11] *Race, Language and Culture* (New York, 1940), p. 323.

[12] "The Social Organization of Australian Tribes," *Oceania,* Vol. I, No. 4 (1931), p. 429.

[13] *Race and Democratic Society,* p. 198.

[14] "Primitive Freedom," *Atlantic Monthly,* Vol. CLXIX, pp. 756–763 (June, 1942), especially p. 763.

[15] "Anthropology and the Problems of Human Adjustment," *Scientific Monthly,* Vol. LXI, pp. 389–392 (Nov., 1945), especially p. 390. In "On the Values in Culture," *ibid.,* Vol. LIV, pp. 557–560 (June, 1942), he expresses himself similarly.

[16] "Social Science and the World Situation," *American Anthropologist,* Vol. XLIV, pp. 521–525 (1942), especially p. 525.

[17] *Race and Democratic Society,* p. 101.

[18] *Ibid.,* p. 77.

[19] Cf. Leslie A. White, "The Symbol: The Origin and Basis of Human Behavior," *Philosophy of Science,* Vol. VII, pp. 451–463 (1940), reprinted in *Etc.: A Review of General Semantics,* Vol. I, pp. 229–237 (1944); also, "On the Use of Tools by Primates," *Journal of Comparative Psychology,* Vol. XXXIV, pp. 369–374 (1942).

[20] "The Concept of Culture," in *The Science of Man in the World Crisis,* ed. Ralph Linton (New York, 1945), pp. 79, 80, 93, 96.

[21] *The Folk Culture of Yucatan* (Chicago, 1941), p. 132.

[22] "On Social Structure," *Journal of the Royal Anthropological Institute of Great Britain and Ireland,* Vol. LXX, Pt. 1 (1940), pp. 10–11.

[23] "The Processes of Cultural Change," in *The Science of Man in the World Crisis,* p. 158.

[24] *The Study of Man,* p. 464.

[25] *American Anthropologist,* Vol. XLIX, p. 308 (1947).

[26] *The Study of Man,* pp. 288–289.

[27] "The Processes of Cultural Change," p. 150.

[28] *The Study of Man,* pp. 105, 152.

[29] *The Culture Historical Method of Ethnology,* pp. 138, 252–253, 141.

[30] "The Processes of Culture Change," p. 158.

[31] *The Study of Man,* pp. 288, 363.

[32] Morgan has two theories of cultural development, both set forth in *Ancient Society* (New York, 1877). One is materialistic and technologic; the other is idealistic. In the latter, institutions are explained as expressions of a few germs of thought implanted in man's mind at the very beginning. Subsequent growth of these ideas produces the development of institutions (see pp. vi, 4, 8, 17, 61, 553). Thus, Parts II, III, and IV of *Ancient Society* take up the "growth of the idea" of government, of the family, and of property, respectively.

In presenting this interpretation Morgan gives the impression that social evolution proceeds by and of itself, due only to the logical unfolding of the ideas. But in dealing with the process of social evolution he makes it clear, as we shall see, that the development of institutions is dependent upon and conditioned by technological evolution.

It may be noted here that Morgan in his idea of "germs of thought" was drawing upon a philosophic tradition expressed in the writings of Kant, Bastian, and H. J. S. Maine. His materialist interpretation, however, was new to anthropology.

[33] *Ancient Society,* Holt edition, p. 19.

[34] Contrast this with Lowie's "separatism of the natives" which precluded "large populations . . . under a common head."

[35] All page references in the paragraphs following are to Morgan's *Ancient Society,* Holt edition, unless otherwise indicated.

[36] "Extracts from the European Travel Journal of Lewis H. Morgan," ed. Leslie A. White, Rochester Historical Society *Publications,* Vol. XVI, Pt. 2 (1937), pp. 219–389, especially pp. 269 (cf. also *Ancient Society,* p. 505 and 379).

[37] Contrast this with the Boasian interpretation of war as an ideological phenomenon.

[38] *Anthropology* (London, 1881—the page references here and following are to the New York edition published by Appleton in 1916), p. 206.

[39] E. B. Tylor, "Anthropology," *Encyclopaedia Britannica,* 11th ed., Vol II, pp. 108–119, especially p. 118.

[40] 2nd ed., New York, 1922. See also *An Introduction to Social Anthropology* (New York, 1929) and *The Relation of Nature to Man in Aboriginal America* (New York, 1926).

[41] *Cultural and Natural Areas of Native North America* (Berkeley, Calif., 1939).

[42] *The Study of Man,* p. 356. This thorough-going materialist point of view contrasts sharply with views expressed by Linton in other places. When he philosophizes he is eclectic and not always consistent; he is even self-contradictory at times. As a philosopher he finds culture intangible, unobservable, and even of dubious existence. But as a seasoned field worker he finds culture very real, tangible, and observable, and he deals with it in a realistic and forthright manner.

[43] *Essays in Anthropology, Presented to A. L. Kroeber,* ed. Robert H. Lowie (Berkeley, 1936).

[44] *Anthropos,* Vol. XXXII, pp. 87–104 (1937).

[45] See, e.g., *The Social Anthropology of North American Tribes,* ed. F. Eggan (Chicago, 1937), a volume of essays by Radcliffe-Brown's disciples at the University of Chicago, written in his honor.

[46] "Culture as a Determinant of Behavior," a paper delivered Sept. 7, 1936, at the Harvard Tercentenary Conference of Arts and Sciences and included in the Harvard Tercentenary Publication *Factors Determining Human Behavior* (Cambridge, Mass., 1937), pp. 133–168, especially 149, 162.

[47] "Others, besides myself, have found it difficult to define Boas's position," says Paul Radin, a student of Boas, in *The Method and Theory of Ethnology* (New York, 1933), p. 19. When Kroeber, one of Boas's most eminent students, undertook to "explain" him in "History and Science in Anthropology," *American Anthropologist,* Vol. XXXVII, pp. 539–569 (1935), the master countered with "History and Science: A Reply," *ibid.,* Vol. XXXVIII, pp. 137–141 (1936), disagreeing vigorously with the interpretation.

[48] Cf. my "Kroeber's 'Configurations of Culture Growth,'" *American An-*

thropologist, Vol. XLVIII, pp. 78–93 (1946), and "Evolutionism in Cultural Anthropology: A Rejoinder," *ibid.,* Vol. XLIX, pp. 400–413 (1947).

[49] Cf. my "Diffusion vs. Evolution: An Anti-Evolutionist Fallacy," *American Anthropologist,* Vol. XLVII, pp. 339–356 (1945); also, "History, Evolutionism and Functionalism: Three Types of Interpretation of Culture," *Southwestern Journal of Anthropology,* Vol. I, pp. 221–248 (1945).

[50] Concluding parag.aph of *Primitive Society.*

[51] The Roman Catholic clerical anthropologists laud Boas, Lowie, and Goldenweiser particularly for their attacks upon materialism and evolutionism. In "Evolutionism in Cultural Anthropology" I have made a summary presentation of evidence.

[52] "The Mind of Primitive Man," *New Republic,* Vol. XCVIII, pp. 300–303 (Apr. 19, 1939), especially p. 303.

[53] "Why I Am Not a Marxist," *Modern Monthly,* Vol. IX, pp. 71–76 (Apr., 1935), especially p. 72.

[54] *The Economic Life of Primitive Peoples* (New York, 1940), pp. 458–459.

[55] *A General Introduction to Psychoanalysis* (New York, 1920), p. 269.

[56] *The Mind of Primitive Man* (New York, 1911), pp. 181 ff. See also p. 178 o. the 1938 ed.

[57] "The Aims of Anthropological Research," *Science,* Vol. LXXVI, pp. 605–613 (Dec. 30, 1932), especially p. 611. Cf. also *Race, Language and Culture,* p. 267.

[58] Some members of the Boas school would not consider this as adverse criticism. They would argue: Culture itself is irrational—how therefore can our interpretation be rational? This point of view finds its most adequate expression in the writings of Robert H. Lowie.

[59] *Primitive Society,* p. 439. Emphasis ours.

[60] *An Introduction to Cultural Anthropology* (2nd ed., New York, 1940), p. 373.

[61] Clark Wissler comments upon the view, held by "many" anthropologists, that "the spirit of man is free to do its will" in such sectors of culture as social and ceremonial organization—a view which, incidentally, he does not share (*An Introduction to Social Anthropology,* New York, 1929, p. 326).

[62] *The Mind of Primitive Man* (1938 ed.), p. 197.

[63] Lowie, *An Introduction to Cultural Anthropology* (2nd ed., 1940), p. 419; Goldenweiser, review of Durkheim in *American Anthropologist,* Vol. XVII, p. 723 (1915), and *Early Civilization,* pp. 108, 125, 127, and *Anthropology,* pp. 338, 523; Herskovits, "Man, the Speaking Animal," *Sigma Xi Quarterly,* Vol. XXI, pp. 67–82 (1933), especially p. 69; Radin, *Social Anthropology* (New York, 1932), p. 31; Gladys Reichard, "Social Life," in *General Anthropology,* ed. F. Boas (Boston, 1938), pp. 412–413.

[64] "The Social Organization of Australian Tribes," *Oceania,* Vol. I, Nos. 1–4 (1930–1931), especially pp. 34, 36–37, 450, 436. Emphasis ours.

[65] Morgan, "Australian Kinship," *Proceedings* of the American Academy of Arts and Sciences, Vol. VIII, pp. 412–438 (1872), especially p. 416, and *Ancient Society,* pp. 51, 59; Durkheim, *The Elementary Forms of the Religious Life,* transl. J. W. Swain (London, 1915), pp. 63, 96.

[66] "Aims of Anthropological Research," *Science,* Vol. LXXVI, pp. 605–613 (1932), especially p. 612.

[67] For further treatment of this point, see Betty J. Meggers, "Recent Trends in American Ethnology," *American Anthropologist,* Vol. XLVIII, pp. 176–214

(1946), especially pp. 195–197; White, "Kroeber's 'Configurations of Culture Growth,'" *ibid.*, pp. 78–93, especially pp. 85–87; White, "The Expansion of the Scope of Science," pp. 206–207. *Journal of the Washington Academy of Sciences,* Vol. XXXVII, No. 6, pp. 181–210, June 15, 1947.

[68] Published by the Royal Anthropological Institute of Great Britain and Ireland (London).

[69] *Man Makes Himself* (London, 1936), pp. 7–9.

[70] *What Happened in History* (New York ed., 1946), p. 74.

[71] Page 19.

[72] Cf. "Science is *Sciencing,*" *Philosophy of Science,* Vol. V, pp. 369–389 (1938); "A Problem in Kinship Terminology," *American Anthropologist,* Vol. XLI, pp. 566–573 (1939); "Energy and the Evolution of Culture," *ibid.*, Vol. XLV, pp. 335–356 (1943); "Diffusion vs. Evolution: An Anti-Evolutionist Fallacy," *ibid.*, Vol. XLVII, pp. 339–356 (1945); "History, Evolutionism and Functionalism: Three Types of Interpretation of Culture," *Southwestern Journal of Anthropology,* Vol. I, pp. 221–248 (1945); "Evolutionism in Cultural Anthropology: A Rejoinder," *American Anthropologist,* Vol. XLIX, pp. 400–413 (1947); "Evolutionary Stages, Progress and the Evaluation of Cultures," *Southwestern Journal of Anthropology,* Vol. III, pp. 165–192 (1947); "Evolutionism and Anti-Evolutionism in American Ethnological Theory" (written for the first postwar issue of the Japanese journal. *Ethnological Research,* Tokyo; also in Portuguese translation in *Sociologia,* Vol. X, pp. 1–39 (1948), and in the *Calcutta Review,* Vol. CIV, pp. 147–159; Vol. CV, pp. 29–40, 161–174 (1947) (Calcutta, India). (São Paulo, Brazil, *in press*).

[73] Cf. Leslie A. White, "The Locus of Mathematical Reality," *Philosophy of Science,* Vol. XIV, pp. 289–303, 1947, for an exposition of this interactive process.

[74] Cf. Leslie A. White, "Culturological *vs.* Psychological Interpretations of Human Behavior," *American Sociological Review,* Vol. XII, pp. 686–698, 1947.

[75] Cf. Leslie A. White, "The Expansion of the Scope of Science," *Journal* of the Washington Academy of Sciences, Vol. XXXVII, pp. 181–210 (1947), especially pp. 197 ff.

[76] Matter and energy, according to modern physical theory, are but aspects of a common thing or event. But for our purpose the distinction is useful.

[77] See the writer's "Mind in Minding," *Scientific Monthly,* Vol. XLVIII, pp. 169–171 (Feb. 1939), and "The Expansion of the Scope of Science," pp. 193–194. Spencer, likewise, distinguished between physiology and psychology on the basis of internal and external aspects of an organism's behavior (*The Classification of the Sciences,* 1864, Table 3).

[78] This paragraph, with minor changes, is from "Atomic Energy: An Anthropological Appraisal," a paper by the present writer for the Dec. 28, 1945, meeting of the American Anthropological Association at Philadelphia. It was published in the Baltimore *Sun,* Dec. 29, 1945, the Milwaukee *Journal,* Jan. 10, 1946, and the Norfolk *Virginian-Pilot,* Jan. 13, 1946.

[79] The gist of this thesis was presented in the radio address "Energy and the Development of Civilization," Feb. 16, 1947. It was published in *The Scientists Speak,* ed. Warren Weaver (New York, 1947), and reprinted in *Technocracy Digest,* May, 1947, and the *Great Lakes Technocrat,* May–June, 1947.

[80] Cf. Leslie A. White, "Evolutionary Stages, Progress, and the Evaluation of Cultures," *Southwestern Journal of Anthropology,* Vol. III, pp. 165–192, 1947. The Boas school has contended that progress, applied to cultures, can only be a subjective concept, and that cultures cannot therefore be evaluated scientifically.

ON SOME TENDENCIES IN MODERN ECONOMIC THEORY

by MAURICE DOBB

Maurice H. Dobb, M.A. Cantab., Ph.D., London, is Lecturer in Economics in the University of Cambridge and Director of Studies in Economics, Trinity College, Cambridge. Sometime Visiting Lecturer in Russian Economic Studies at the University of London School of Slavonic Studies (1934–1936). Author of: *Capitalist Enterprise and Social Progress* (1925); *Wages* (1928, rev. ed. 1946); *Political Economy and Capitalism* (1937); *Studies in the Development of Capitalism* (1946); *Soviet Economic Development Since 1917* (1948).

THERE is certainly no easy way of summarizing the present state of economic theory. Recent tendencies have been so numerous and so varied. All one can briefly say is that controversy, which twenty years ago was commonly thought to have been stilled (in those agreed "general principles of thought" in the elements of which "important improvements are becoming rare," to which Lord Keynes referred in the early twenties), has broken out afresh in the past two decades and has developed on a number of fronts. Hitherto an orthodoxy had fastened upon the world of academic economics as rigorous as the J. S. Mill orthodoxy which ruled England in the decades before the so-called "Jevonsian revolution." It can hardly be a coincidence that this rebirth of controversy should have followed the economic crisis of the early thirties. Involved in this quickening of debate has been a requestioning of fundamentals; requestioning of assumptions which previously had been taken for granted or had passed unnoticed. By some this has been regarded as an opportunity for repair and reconstruction of the foundations with more lasting material and to a more modern design. Others have treated it as a veritable crisis of economic theory, from which the firm and rounded limbs of the traditional structure of doctrine are unlikely to emerge again as a consistent whole.

Prominent among recent novelties in the world of economic analysis have been the recasting of price theory in terms of monopoly, in place of the traditional assumptions about perfect competition, and a concentration upon a theory of the forces which determine the level of economic activity of the economic system as a whole (as distinct from the theory of relative prices), with the corollary that equilibrium is possible at various levels of employment or of plant capacity. In close affinity to the latter went a variety of studies in economic fluctuations (macrodynamic studies, as they were sometimes called), according to varying assumptions about time lags and about the movements of various series of economic quantities. Prototype of many of these studies was the so-called "cobweb theorem," which was concerned with the conditions under which price and output, instead of converging rapidly upon a position of stable equilibrium, might fluctuate extensively around such a position. In other words, the notion of stable economic equilibrium was itself called in question.

It is evident that the general effect of these recent developments has been to jettison the traditional basis upon which economic theory in the nineteenth century was built as an elaborate apologetic of Capitalism, which was pictured as a self-adjusting economic mechanism tending (with a few exceptions) constantly to maintain an optimum allocation of resources among various productive uses. Where competition is imperfect or monopoly enters, none of the equilibrium positions of traditional doctrine apply. Firms are not of the most economic size, and even where prices conform to costs the latter are not minimized. The distribution of factors of production among various uses is distorted, and a new type of unproductive expense is created, and generalized—selling expenses designed to cajole the consumer and shift demand. Profit is seen as the creature of, and the motive for, restriction and uneconomic practices. Moreover, the possibility was demonstrated both of extensive fluctuations of economic activity—resulting not simply from "accidental" influences but from factors inherent in the system—and of a chronic state of underutilized resources which the system had no tendency to remedy. Such a chronic state of economic stagnation might well become accentuated as the productivity of the system grew. These conclusions derived largely, of course, from a shift of assumptions—and a shift in the theoretical model which unquestionably brought it nearer to the real world—but also to some extent from logical critique of the older theory which revealed that accepted conclusions did not necessarily follow from the premises of this theory, or only followed by virtue of certain further and previously hidden premises which, once brought to light, could not be seriously maintained.

The more advertised controversies around these shifts of doctrine have tended to conceal some questionings which go deeper into fundamental issues of economic method: issues not unrelated to recent controversy, but comparatively little noted. I refer particularly to the questioning of the scope and nature of the subject of economics itself, and to that of the nature of the theory of value which forms the very texture of economic analysis. Most economists have supposed that controversy over both these issues had long ago been laid to rest. A tradition of accepted doctrine had reigned for nearly half a century which few cared, still fewer dared, to call in question. In recent years there can be detected an undercurrent of doubt (if no more) that these basic matters are as settled as has come to be supposed. At any rate the times seem propitious for reopening them.

The problem of the scope and nature of the subject, and the problem of the proper basis for its theory of value, are more closely connected than might at first seem to be the case. The connection will perhaps be apparent if we start by considering what is involved in the former. The methodology of modern economics (unlike that of classical political economy) has tended to make economics essentially a theory of exchange—a determinate theory of price relationships between things which appear on a market as objects of sale and purchase. True, a department of the subject still appears in economic textbooks under the label of "the theory of production." But this is concerned with little more than determining the size of the firm, as the exchange unit, and hence the number of firms; which is a matter incidental to determining the prices of products in a market (since the number of firms is relevant to the nature and extent of competition in this market and to the effect on price of changes in demand). Of a separate theory of distribution modern economic theory contains even less, whatever label may be used. What is customarily called distribution is nothing more than an extension of the general theory of price relations from products to factors of production, the latter being treated—in complete abstraction from the individuals, and the social relations of those individuals which supply them—simply as productive services which enter the market because there is a demand for them derived from the demand for the final product.[1] In this character as a theory of exchange, economic analysis has been regarded as furnishing principles which hold true of *any* type of exchange society. As such they have a universal significance, fashioned from the common substance of which all exchange societies are made. For economists who stand in the neo-Kantian tradition and derive their methodology from Max Weber, economic laws have the force of "synthetic *a priori* propositions": as Professor Hayek has declared,[2] they are built up from, "not physical facts," but wholes "constituted" out of "familiar categories of our minds," which apply to all economic experience. They are not contingent on historically relative, institutional factors: on the contrary, they embody certain "necessities" which are alleged to constrain the working of any type of economic system. In a phrase of Professor Robbins which has come to enjoy wide currency among English-speaking economists, the economic problem is defined as essentially consisting in "the relationship between given ends and scarce means which have alternative uses."

An inevitable result of this refinement of the scope of economic theory has been to exclude a large tract of economic territory which to any realistic view is of great importance for understanding the economic shape, and especially the large movement, of society. Excluded are such considerations as the ownership of the means of production and the class relations contingent thereon. Excluded is any notion of a distinction between cost payments and a surplus, which formed the crux of the classical approach to questions of distribution. Excluded also is any notion of Capitalism as an economic system with specific differentiae, since such differentiae can be given no meaning within the narrowed circle of economic notions. If meaning can be given at all to a notion such as Capitalism (which is more often than not denied), this is said to be a job for the sociologist, not for the economist. The only "system" which can occupy an economist's attention is the market system—the form of price determination.

It is not, of course, denied that so-called historically relative elements enter into economics. But they do not make their appearance until the second story of the building is reached. They admittedly enter into the particular as distinct from the general theory of price determination. But in doing so they play a very special and subordinate role: they have the character of "data" which fix the particular values of the variables, but do not substantially affect the main equations, defining essential relationships, of which economic theory consists. Such a conception evidently implies that the sphere of exchange is capable of being isolated, so far as its main causal sequences are concerned. It can be treated as constituting in the main causally autonomous territory. In so far as it introduces "sociological" factors as "data," it justifies its method of handling them by the assumption that they are independently determined from an outside sphere, and that any interaction between that sphere and the circle of economic relations proper is too small to impugn the postulated independence of the latter, and can accordingly be ignored.

Reflection soon indicates that such a conception can be sustained only at the cost of a drastic departure from reality. Most obvious of the difficulties under which it has always labored is that it has virtually to take the distribution of income as given, since this affects not only the supply of different productive agents but also the pattern of demand. Yet the prices of factors of production, and hence the incomes of those who supply them, are among the dependent variables of the pricing problem. It is hardly surprising in the circumstances that modern economic theory should have abandoned the attempt to provide a theory of distribution: a problem which Ricardo had regarded as central to economic inquiry. The omission has been justified on the ground that the assumption of income distribution as an independently determined datum is no more drastic than the assumptions which any alternative type of theory would have to make; and that all abstraction, which cuts off a slice or aspect of the real world for the purpose of analysis, must ignore certain types of interaction. Whether this particular simplification is more or less drastic than others depends of course on the view one takes as to what is important, and what is relatively unimportant, in the genesis of economic processes. When we look further, however, it becomes increasingly doubtful whether any propositions of substantial importance can be made about exchange relations without introducing "social" or "institutional" data.[3]

The pretense that market relations constitute a "system" for which general principles can be enunciated seems to derive from a particular view as to where the main determinants of exchange relations are to be found. It apparently derives from the notion that these determinants are to be found in the mental attitudes of consumers: in other words, from some version of the Subjective Theory of Value, according to which "the economic constants depend upon human consciousness" (as Pigou has expressed it—with the added admission that such constants "change under the influence of environment"). The supply of agents of production (land, labor, capital) is independently given by social factors outside the market; while the conditions governing their combination and productivity are similarly given by technical factors. In a formal sense, these can be regarded as the essential determinants of price equilibrium equally with the desires of individual consumers. Yet the whole emphasis of the theory, by virtue of the form in which it is cast, is upon the latter. It is certain uniform characteristics of the relation between individual consumers and the objects of consumption that give to the principles of price determination their alleged generality: justify the claim that general laws of exchange can exist in their own right. When the formal theory of price determination comes to be translated into practical terms, there seems to lie at the heart of the matter some notion of consumers' sovereignty (in one of its variants): that, wherever exchange is free, desires of consumers control the pattern both of prices and of allocation of productive resources to minister to those desires in an optimum fashion (with the implied corollary that the mechanism of a free market is necessary in any economic system if consumers' welfare is to sway production).

How, then, does this differ from the classical approach? The methodology of classical Political Economy was far from clearly formulated, if it was formulated at all. But the picture which it presented was of a quite opposite order of determination. Exchange relationships were regarded as being essentially determined by facts of production; and any claim of universality in economic laws was based on the persistence of certain features of production over large tracts of economic history (in particular, the mobility of labor). In other words, the explanation of exchange relations was sought neither within the circle of those relations nor in the attitudes and behavior of any of the participants in exchange, but in certain real cost relationships between factors of production and the product which emerged therefrom. Thus Marx laid emphasis on the fact that value was a *social* relation and not merely a relation of exchange. In this approach demand was not ignored. But, whereas it was held to be a determinant of the *amounts produced* of different things, and hence of the distribution of labor and other resources among various productive uses, it was regarded as being irrelevant to the *exchange ratios* between commodities. Thus, if the demand for commodity A increased relatively to the demand for commodity B, this would cause more of A to be produced and more labor to be employed in the industry producing it as compared with the labor devoted to the production of B. But the normal exchange value of A in terms of B would remain unaffected because this was determined by the comparative cost relation (i.e., the amount of labor required per unit of product) prevailing in the two cases. Thus abstraction could be made from demand in formulating essential economic principles. It was not the individual wills and attitudes of participants in the market, whether they were buyers or sellers, but objective ratios of production that determined the value relations which constituted the warp and weft of economic law. It was this notion of the *objectivity* of economic laws that attracted the attention of Marx to classical Political Economy. Whatever mystical interpretation may have been given to Adam Smith's metaphor of "the unseen hand," it is clear that the notion of economic law which we find in Smith and Ricardo and their immediate followers has close kinship with Hegel's notion that "out of the actions of men comes something quite different from what they intend and directly know and will." Moreover, the notion had been expressly used by Smith to rebut the previous obsession of economic writers (those of the Mercantilist School) with an autonomous sphere of exchange, and to reveal exchange as the sphere of the apparent and the phenomenal and production as the sphere of the essential and the substantial. This emphasis, again, accorded closely with the conception of historical materialism that the fundamental order of determination was from the "mode of production" (in which were included the "social relations of production") to other levels in the structure of economic relations of society as a whole. Moreover, in defining the three main revenues into which "the whole annual produce of the labor of every country must resolve itself," they rested their definition on actual social classes. The factors of production, land, labor, and capital, were intended explicitly to correspond to the classes of landlords, capitalists, and workers; and the questions which their theory of distribution sought to answer were concerned with the different characters and modes of determination of the revenues of these classes.

The formal requirement which a theory of value must fulfill has been expressed by E. Heimann in his *History of Economic Doctrines* as follows: "The crux of the problem of value in economics consists in this. No sum total of cost factors (land, capital, and the various kinds of labor) can be arrived at unless they are reduced to a common denominator." The classical theory reduced all cost to terms of labor: labor conceived as the expenditure of quanta of human energy. The only two value theories which can lay claim to fulfilling the condition that has just been mentioned are this classical Labor Value Theory of Ricardo and Marx and the modern Utility Theory.[4] They are the only real contestants in the field. Since the so-called "Jevonsian revolution" in economic thought, which followed so close upon the heels of the work with which Marx crowned the classical edifice, the second of these claimants has been accepted almost universally as having unquestioned superiority, by reason of its greater generality and its ability to furnish a theory of price determination both at the macroscopic and at the microscopic level. The classical labor theory (which was admittedly interested above all in answering questions at the macroscopic level) has been held to fail at either level for two main reasons: first, because it cannot deal with a situation where capital is used in differing amounts relatively to labor in different lines of production; secondly, because the cost at which a thing can be produced cannot be given independently of demand but varies with the scale on which the thing is produced, the quantity produced depending on the demand. The cost of production of a commodity is not capable of being given a unique meaning.

The first of these objections really rests on a misconception of the classical theory. This stated, not that exchange ratios (or prices) were *equal* to the ratios of embodied labor (save in special conditions). It stated that exchange ratios were in the last analysis *determined* by the relative quantities of embodied labor in various commodities. The statement which was implied in Ricardo and developed by Marx in his famous theory of "prices of production" was that, where the proportions of capital to labor in different lines of production were different, the price of each commodity depended *both* on the amount of labor required to produce it *and* on the profit which had to be paid on the amount of capital advanced; and that this profit depended on the rate of profit, which was itself determined as the reciprocal of the proportion of the labor force of society which was engaged in producing what is nowadays spoken of as "wage-goods" (or in classical terms, "workers' subsistence").[5] In Marx's words, "prices of production" represent deviations from "values" determined by the extent to which in any industry the "composition of capital" is above or below the average and by the rate of profit; but this rate of profit, which is the quantitative measure of these "deviations," is itself determined in terms of the labor principle of value.

The other objection at first looks more formidable. Is it not a commonplace of elementary economic textbooks that production in nearly all industries is subject to either "increasing returns" or "diminishing returns" as output increases (and sometimes to one at some levels of output and to the other at higher levels of output); and that the condition of "constant returns," where cost is independent of output (and hence of demand), is a rare and special case—a case where opposing tendencies happen to cancel out, or all factors of production, including capital equipment, are supplied in relatively small divisible units? On this whole subject there was a good deal of recondite discussion among economists in the late twenties and early thirties. One conclusion emerging from this discussion, to which surprisingly little attention has been paid, was that a condition of "constant costs" *in the relevant sense* was probably to be regarded as the general rule in many-firm industries under competitive conditions, rather than the exception. Accordingly, the classical assumption that cost had a meaning independently of demand was belatedly justified. This conclusion was explicitly stated in the much-quoted article by P. Sraffa in the *Economic Journal* of December, 1926, which started the discussion; but to the statement and its implications most economists seem to have turned a blind eye. Mr. Sraffa's categorical statement was as follows:

In normal cases the cost of production of commodities produced competitively must be regarded as constant in respect of small variations in the quantity produced. And so, as a simple way of approaching the problem of competitive value, the old and now obsolete theory which makes it dependent on the cost of production alone, appears to hold its own as the best available.

The reason for this statement, so paradoxical to the ear of the modern economist, is as follows. For costs in a many-firm competitive industry to change by reason of a change in scale of that industry (and hence for costs to be a function of the demand for the industry's product), the industry must represent a very substantial part of the use for some particular agent of production which is limited in supply or alternatively indivisible (like many types of industrial place and equipment). It is only as a result of a change in the demand for this agent of production (e.g., land in the case of agriculture, or some subsidiary product in the case of a manufacturing industry), and hence in its price and/or the intensity with which it is used, that the costs of the industry in question are likely to be affected. Such a case is, however, likely to be rare, rather than typical, and to be more rare, the more narrowly an industry is defined.[6]

What, then, can be said of the rival claims of the Subjective Theory, which have for so long been accepted as impeccable and superior? Here, again, certain recent tendencies in economic theory have not been without an effect, even if this implication has for the most part passed unnoticed. So long as the Subjective Theory was rooted in the notion of Utility (in the sense of satisfaction), it could pass at least the formal test for fulfilling the requirements of a theory of value (subject to an exception which will be mentioned below). If one was willing to believe in such an entity as Utility (with the description of human psychology implied therein), and if one was further willing, by an assumption of human rationality, to postulate a fairly close identity between this quantity and human desires (and hence consumers' demand on a market), the theory was at least plausible. In the present century the latter postulate has become difficult, if not impossible, to square with the observed facts of an advertising age: the malleability of consumers' demand, and the dependence of demand on selling expenditure incurred by sellers and on the whole complex of sales devices and sales propaganda. Moreover, the tendency of economists in the present century has been increasingly to drop the notion of Utility altogether as an untenable or at least a needless hypothesis. Instead price determination is made to rest on preferences of consumers as registered by the observed behavior of consumers on a market.

After this drastic operation with Occam's razor, one may well ask whether anything substantial is left on which to erect a theory of price determination. The structure of theory looks impressive; and its elevation is elegant enough with its mathematical streamlining. But what exactly is the base on which it all rests? If one analyzes the propositions about demand which it employs as central determinants, one may well ask whether anything more is being stated than that things sell at certain prices because consumers buy them at those prices. At first sight this may seem a grotesque parody. But further examination will show, I think, that nothing of substantial meaning is really being said by modern price theory beyond this. The Utility theory *was* definitely saying something more substantial (whether one believes such an entity to exist or to be related to demand, is another matter). It was saying something about what lay *behind* consumers' market behavior and was independent of the latter; and it was this something that was held to *determine* consumers' demand and, through demand, market prices. But now that this something-behind-demand has been jettisoned, what have we left other than an explanation of an exchange ratio itself—the act of exchange in its aspect of a purchase?

True, modern price theory gives an *appearance* of saying something more: of explaining an exchange ratio in terms of something outside the exchange transaction itself—namely, a demand curve, or schedule of demand prices. This looks very satisfying on paper. But how many of those who manipulate the geometry and algebra of demand functions have ever given a satisfactory explanation of what the entity represented by a demand curve really is? Is it observed uniformities in consumers' market behavior in varying price situations? Of these there exists no sufficient empirical evidence. Is it an instinctive behavior mechanism in the psychological make-up of individuals, of such a kind as to define their potential reactions to every kind of price situation on the market, whether these situations have ever been directly experienced or not? Can one really believe in anything of the kind, even as an unverified but plausible hypothesis? And if a demand curve is none of these things, what are we left with? Can causal statement go beyond the tautological statement that in any given case a commodity is sold at a certain price because someone has bought it at that price?

If we translate the issue into practical terms, it apparently amounts to this. Have we any warrant for saying that market prices are determined by the attitudes and actions of consumers, rather than that consumers' attitudes are conditioned by the market prices with which they are confronted? When we take account of the part played by conventional elements in molding demand and of the fact that demand for any particular thing depends upon the nature and range of the alternatives which are offered (in the determination of which initiative must come in the main from producers), not to mention the malleability of demand in face of advertising pressure which we have mentioned, there would seem to be at least as much ground for thinking that consumers' actions adapt themselves to the market [7] as for thinking the converse. We seem to be left with the conclusion that modern economic theory has really no theory of value at all.

There is one crucial respect in which the Subjective Theory, in any of its variants, has signally failed to fulfill an essential condition of formal completeness. One might even speak here of a crucial contradiction lying close to the heart of the modern theory. This theory has provided no satisfactory method of measuring capital as a separate factor of production. In the Labor Theory capital (in its quantitative aspect) is regarded as consisting of the labor embodied in the actual products (machines, structures, materials, etc.) of which it is composed. But in the modern theory capital appears merely in the guise of a set of values. Its price (the return on capital) is regarded as being determined by the value of its marginal product. Yet the marginal product (from which its own valuation and measure are treated as being in some manner derived) has to be expressed in relation to a *unit* of capital, and hence can be given no meaning until such a unit has been independently defined. Here is a special point of difficulty which cannot receive adequate discussion within the limits of this essay. It must suffice to state the opinion that no satisfactory solution of this difficulty has been provided by modern theories of capital, including those which have sought to represent capital as a quantity measurable in two dimensions, compounded of labor and time.

What, then, of the theory of monopoly price, to which some of the most notable contributions of economists in the past fifteen years have been made? To the determination of monopoly price the classical Labor Theory admittedly affords no clue: such prices appear as "deviations," due to factors of which the general theory takes no account, and which have to be explained in terms of the special circumstances of particular situations. The fact that modern price theory can explain the monopoly case as well as the competitive case has been regarded as one of its outstanding merits. There can be no doubt that modern theories of monopoly and "monopolistic" or "imperfect" competition have carried generalization about various kinds of monopoly situation further than it has ever been carried before: possibly as far as it can be made to go. At the same time, I think it can scarcely be questioned that no *general* theory of price determination under monopoly has been yielded, in the sense of a determinate theory of the *total* price situation. As Dr. Paul Sweezy has well said:

> When the power of limiting supply is in the hands of producers, so also is the power of setting prices, and to determine theoretically, and with a useful degree of generality, at what point prices will be set is impossible; too many diverse factors enter into the determination of a given price to permit the construction of a precise theory with any but the most limited applicability. This is fully proved by the attempts of orthodox economic theory in recent years to establish objective laws of price under conditions of total or partial monopoly. Aside from a few empty propositions such as that price will be set where profit is maximized, monopolistic price theory rapidly turns into a catalogue of special cases, each with its own particular solution. No reasonably general laws of monopoly price have been discovered because none exist.[8]

Admittedly a theory of value expressed in terms of cost relations (i.e., in terms of labor) can afford an explanation of actual price phenomena only with a degree of approximation sufficient to interpret the larger movements of economic society and to focus attention upon the most important influences governing the prices of individual commodities. This needs to be supplemented by special studies of particular situations: studies which are likely to yield little unless they are inspired more richly than hitherto by empirical investigation (e.g., as to how output decisions are taken and profit margins determined in actual cases). If such studies, and generalizations emerging from them, are set within the wider framework of a value theory of the classical type, the whole would have the advantage of a perspective which is lacking in academic economics today. Study of market phenomena would be reintegrated with those factors (for so long dismissed as extra-economic, "sociological" factors) which constitute the material basis of society: its property institutions, its production relations and productive forces. For questions of economic development—an aspect of their subject about which economists, with rare exceptions, have said little—such reintegration is of outstanding importance. In all questions of this type a notion of the proper *order of determination*—of the true causal-genetic sequence of events—can at once be seen to be of crucial importance. It is true that an important lesson of any study in economic and social interpretation is that oversimplification can be the foe of understanding, and that the complexity of mutual interaction must not be obscured by a too schematic and mechanical view of causal determination. At the same time it must be recognized that the study of economic change, whether in the past or in the present, is increasingly demonstrating the primacy of what Marx termed the "mode of production" of the epoch; and if this is so, theoretical "models" of the economic system which obscure, instead of illuminating, the fact are in essence obscurantist.

In conclusion, to avoid misunderstanding, one should, perhaps, add this comment about economic method. The significance of a theory of value has to be looked at, I believe, not as a premise from which all else in economics is deducible *a priori,* but rather as a *method* of analysis: a conceptual framework for focusing our attention upon causal sequences and economic mechanisms which are the important ones for understanding the real world and for acting upon it. Any theory of value is, of course, making a general statement about the real world—about the way it is constructed. This is to say that it makes a qualitative statement about the world in the act of postulating a quantitative relationship. It is presumably true that the notion of property income as surplus value (requiring special explanation to account for its emergence and the specific form of its appropriation) is implicit in the Labor Theory of value; just as the notion that consumers' welfare is maximized and that all factor groups get paid their value contribution (marginal) is deducible from the Utility Theory of value, once the postulate of free competition has been added to it and appropriately defined. But is this not because in each case a language is provided in which such questions can be discussed (while other questions at the same time are excluded as meaningless), rather than because it is a matter of deducing a series of categories from an initial one, within which, like Chinese boxes, all the rest are contained? Is not the proper way of regarding the matter that a constructional principle is provided for building a model of the economic system in which questions such as this (and also answers to them) are implied in the *modus operandi* of the model? The crucial consideration is: Which type of model gives the truer representation of economic actuality, especially in its change and movement?

References

[1] In other words, the pricing of factors of production is treated as a constituent part of the general theory of price determination—determination simultaneously of factor prices and product prices. In a recent collection entitled *Readings in the Theory of Income Distribution,* scarcely any attention is paid to influences affecting the supply of different productive agents, still less to their social and institutional roots, or to income distribution between individuals and social classes. "Distribution" is virtually identified with the theory of marginal productivity, which is simply the theory of price in a particular application. So far as profits are concerned, as Mrs. Joan Robinson has shown, modern economics contains no satisfactory theory of profits at all.

[2] *Ethics,* Oct., 1943, pp. 11 f.

[3] Cf. some remarks of the present writer in his *Studies in the Development of Capitalism,* pp. 29–31.

[4] In the Utility Theory all cost factors are equated in terms of their *values;* and the latter are treated as derived (on the marginal productivity principle) from the values of final products, which in turn are derived from utility.

[5] This can be seen to be given by the productivity of labor in terms of commodities in general and the level of wages. It is the same thing as saying that the amount of profit (and given the stock of capital, the rate of profit) depends upon the ratio of the amount of labor time required on the average to produce a worker's subsistence (i.e., to produce the equivalent of his real wage) over a given period and the labor time worked by the worker over that period.

[6] So far as economies arising from division of labor and specialization are concerned: those internal to a firm will (according to a familiar principle of the modern theory of the firm) have been eliminated before the equilibrium size of the firm has been reached (provided that the industry remains a many-firm and competitive industry); and specialization dependent on the multiplication of products or of product types has properly to be treated as part of the general development of industry, and is expressible as a function of the development of industry in general and not of the size of a single industry alone.

[7] We are speaking here, of course, of adaptation in a more fundamental sense than the mere fact that each individual consumer takes the market price as given and adapts his purchases accordingly. This fact is allowed for in the ordinary theory, and indeed occupies an important place in it: what Prof. Oskar Lange has called the "parametric function of prices" in this theory. But the point is that here the adaptations which each consumer makes are regarded as being circumscribed by his individual "demand schedule," so that in the final analysis the totality of these schedules (and the individual actions conditioned by them) is held to determine the structure of market prices.

[8] *The Theory of Capitalist Development* (New York, 1942), pp. 270–271.

SCIENCE, INVENTION, AND SOCIAL APPLICATIONS OF TECHNOLOGY

by

J. D.

BERNAL

J. D. Bernal is Professor of Physics at Birkbeck College, London. Fellow of the Royal Society in 1937, he was awarded the Society's Royal Medal in 1945. His chief scientific work has related to the structure of carbons, metals, water, but also vitamins, hormones, proteins, viruses and cementive materials, and this research has been reported in many articles. His two books are *The World, the Flesh and the Devil* (1929) and *The Social Function of Science* (1939). In 1945 he was Chairman of the Scientific Advisory Committee to the Ministry of Works, and since then he has been a member of the Road Research Board and the Building Research Board of the Department of Scientific and Industrial Research, and of the Executive Committee of the National Physical Laboratory.

Interactions Between Science and Technology

THE relations between science and technology have in the present century passed through a revolution of importance greater even than occurred with the first impact of modern science on technology in the eighteenth century. What has effectively happened is that the scientific method, and with it the instruments and techniques, developed in the first place for laboratory purposes and aimed at discovering the fundamental laws of the behavior of material systems, are now rapidly permeating the whole technical and industrial field. This is in a sense a complete reversal of the process which occurred at the beginning of modern science in the Renaissance. Whether the early scientists were examining nature or the works of man, they had to use both the equipment and the ideas which were then current in technology. That is, they made use of the whole compendium of practical recipes and equipment of the household, the farm, and the craftsman's shop. The prime organizational discovery which lies at the base of modern science is the experiment, and the experiment or trial is simply the carrying out of a technical process on a small scale. The apparatus of the assayer, as explicitly illustrated by Agricola, is simply that of the smelter on a small scale. In fact the whole of chemical analysis with its use of the balance and measuring glass is a miniature reproduction of industrial chemical operations. In physics with the terrella of Gilbert the scale was so reduced that the whole earth could be represented in a small ball.

It was nevertheless a long time before experimental science had any serious practical effect on technics. Only in specialized fields such as astronomy was it possible by the new philosophical methods to do notably better than could be by traditional rule of thumb. It is true that the scientists of early times—from Roger Bacon if not before—had glimpsed at the ideal of the lightening of men's work through the application of the sciences; but the gap between this ideal and its realization was far greater than they imagined. The first big break was with the invention of the steam engine, which was admitted from the start to be a pure gift of science, a philosophical engine based on the elucidation of the nature of a vacuum and of the pressure of the air. Here in the history of a simple mechanical and pneumatical system is typified the whole cycle of the transformation from technics to science and back again, for it was the scientific study of the practical failure of the suction pump to lift water over thirty feet that had led to the discovery of the vacuum.

Except in this crucial particular the industrial revolution was a technical and organizational rather than a scientific revolution. Its main weapon for advance was the use of multiple, power-driven machinery in the textile industry. This development called on practical ingenuity rather than science and in fact was made possible only because the birth of capitalist enterprise provided favorable economic conditions. New masters were prepared to undertake manufacture and hands were to be found in abundance from the families of dispossessed peasants. It is interesting to reflect that even the steam engine, once it passed out of the hands of its philosophical inventors—Watt himself was the first notable example of a scientific instrument maker turned engineer—came into those of purely technical men. Its early use created the tribe of steam engineers, men like Trevithick and Stephenson, who thought intuitively rather than scientifically about the power of steam and the resistance of iron. The reason for this is not difficult to find: the exploiters of a new idea in early capitalist times had to pay their way. The handling of early machines gave them all the practical experience they needed, and in any case facilities for higher scientific education on an adequate scale simply did not exist. On the other side the scientists themselves, with notable exceptions, tended to leave the field of practical devices once the new principle had been established. Merely to improve the action of a steam engine was not the kind of activity that would bring credit in the scientific world.

The Birth of Scientific Industries

As, however, the nineteenth century passed, the breaches made by science in accepted technical tradition multiplied, and the proportional importance of the engineer and the scientist began to alter. The first new big gaps were provided by the electrical and chemical industries. Faraday's discoveries of electromagnetism found practical application first in the telegraph and then in electric light and power; but, although again a new genus of technician—the electrical engineer—was created, he required for the mere understanding of the processes involved not only a far wider knowledge of mathematics and physics, but also an outlook which was divorced from the start from the old technical tradition. Very much the same happened in the development of industrial chemical processes such as the manufacture of dyes and soda, where the industrial chemists and chemical engineers formed other sections of technicians whose activities were largely based on modern science. It is noticeable even today that, of all industries, the electrical and chemical devote the largest proportion of money to research; research is regarded in them as an essential part of production, and the gap between them and the other industries in this respect is so large as to mark them off as a separate group of *scientific* industries.

The Transformation of Traditional Industries

Meanwhile, though much more slowly, scientific methods were penetrating the older *traditional* industries, where they acted as modifiers of existing practices rather than creators of new. A steady infiltration of science into the older industries has been going on for nearly two centuries. Mr. Thrale, Dr. Johnson's patron, was the first to use the thermometer in a brewery—thus introducing instrumentation, nearly always the first stage of the scientific integration of an industry.

There were usually two reasons for the slowness with which science entered the older industries. In the first place, they had come into existence often thousands of years ago, in response to basic and unchanged human needs—for food, clothing, or simple tools. They had progressed step by step with small improvements and modifications, responding to slowly changing needs and slowly changing technical possibilities. Even such major transitions as that from bronze to iron had taken many centuries to effect. In this way the old techniques always had remained near to equilibrium with demand; they gave satisfaction, and any alteration in them was almost bound to be an alteration for the worse.

The other reason was that the old techniques had been learned by hard practice, guided by the old universally accepted system of thought, one that reasoned by analogy and sympathy, as in magic and primitive religion. Paradoxically this form of thinking had, to start with, an enormous advantage over abstract reason. It made people dare to do things with systems which we now know they could not possibly have understood, but which they believed they did. Most often they must have failed; but failure did not discourage them because, according to their theory, it could always be explained as due to the action of evil forces. Where they succeeded, there was a net gain; and the new methods thus divinely revealed sooner or later became securely preserved in a continuous tradition. The earliest of all existing techniques, for example, is that of food preparation; and it is still most unscientific—we are now only beginning to understand the elaborate enzyme reactions that occur in preserving and cooking food. Yet in most cultures a rich and satisfying art of cookery has evolved. There is accordingly little demand for science and much actual hostility to its introduction.

The forces that broke up this organic evolutionary and balanced development of techniques were the same that led to the development of science. They were predominantly economic—generated by the increasing demands of a developing society reacting against severe limitations presented by lack of materials and man power. The sixteenth century was predominantly a century of high prices and great demands on materials, particularly for war material and imports from distant countries. Deep mining and oceanic navigation had to develop rapidly without adequate tradition. In the eighteenth century the demand for primary consumption goods, of which cloth is typical, had the same effect in the mechanization of cottage industry. With increased demands and limited supplies, older methods break down and there is real scope for ingenuity; and this is particularly so when labor is short. The older methods of doing things were livelihoods; there were always enough people for all the tasks of the village. It is only if men cannot be found for profitable jobs that machines have to be invoked.

It was not necessary that the new demands affect all commodities for them to have a shattering effect on the traditional way of making things. Let the demand at any one level in the productive chain evoke a new mechanism, this was sufficient to distort the whole of the technical system. Invention and improvement generally started at some bottleneck where there was the greatest discrepancy between demand and supply, and where the biggest profits could be made most quickly. Thus spinning was, to start with, the bottleneck in cloth production; but, once inventions for speeding it up had got into operation, weaving became the bottleneck; and, later still, the production of chemicals to wash, bleach, and dye the vast quantities of new textiles produced by the mechanization of the earlier stages. Once the old system cracked at one point the crack ran all through the whole order.

Demand and Supply in the Growth of Science

Radically new kinds of *demands* only began to make themselves felt towards the end of the nineteenth century—in relatively unessential fields such as communication by telegraph and telephone, and rapid personal transport by railway and motor car. Even today, over most of the field of consumption, demand is not essentially different from what it was in civilized countries six thousand years ago. We all want cooked foods prepared from domesticated plants and animals; clothing prepared from animal or vegetable fibers or close imitations of them; more or less warm and light houses with songs, dances, and spectacles for recreation. What has altered is the means for achieving those demands and not the demands themselves. The applications of science throughout the nineteenth century, and indeed until very recently, have always been towards finding some short cut in carrying out an accepted traditional procedure: a tractor to pull the plow instead of oxen; a combine thresher to do the job of human reapers and threshers. To solve such problems a limited amount of physics and chemistry is all that is necessary; and in fact until the twentieth century physics and chemistry, which started under the technical impulse of the early industrial revolution, went under their own steam far ahead of their then possible applications.

The processes by which science transformed industry in the nineteenth century, however conscious in detail and vaguely sensed as general mechanical and technical *progress,* were not effectively understood at the time; and in any case no attempt could have been made then to direct or control them. The whole feeling of the competitive era would have been against any direction or planning. The result was, of course, that an industrial civilization developed fast enough to produce enormous social and material disharmony, unemployment, malnutrition, disease, smoky and hideous towns. Yet at the same time its rate of growth was far slower than it might have been with the knowledge and ability available. The time lags in the application of inventions in the nineteenth century could not be justified on any technical grounds. Faraday made a prototype dynamo that gave current in 1831—the first successful power distribution system did not come till 1889. The sixty years between were full of uneven development depending largely on individual inventors and scientists. A fraction of 1 per cent of the capital available for investment in manufactures and railways would have ensured the speeding up of that development by many times. This lack of rational approach has continued into more recent times; internal combustion engines, for instance, had been used some forty years before there was any serious study of the basic chemistry of combustion of their cylinders. The development of fluorescent lighting, first demonstrated as far back as 1904, is only beginning to come in on a large scale; and serious developmental research was not started until 1934.

Science Under Monopoly

These conditions, however, are now rapidly changing. The basically scientific industries, as they have grown, have had an increasing influence on the older industries. At the same time the economic and social conditions of our time are already far from those of early competitive capitalism. The characteristic feature of the mid-twentieth century has been the parallel development of large industrial monopolies, and large-scale state patronage of science. The industrial laboratory of today has itself become a factory; and indeed, in the United States at least, industrial research has itself become a commodity, and many successful firms have no other function than to produce research for sale. As a consequence of these recent developments science has become far more concentrated and more ordered than it was in the nineteenth century; but this by itself is no guarantee of any increased contribution of human welfare.

The concentration of industrial research in monopoly undertakings in the twentieth century has produced conflicting factors that make an exact analysis a baffling problem. The large research laboratories of the present day are undoubtedly possible only under monopoly or government sponsorship. The mere existence of a laboratory with large staff and expensive apparatus does not, however, guarantee a corresponding contribution to scientific development. The charge is often made that monopolies suppress scientific ideas and inventions; usually the wicked trust is pictured as burning or locking in its safe the brilliant ideas of the individual inventor. The fact that it is extremely hard to substantiate such assertions and relatively easy to disprove them has blinded the public to the entirely different but far more serious way in which monopolies restrict and distort scientific and industrial development. In the first place by concentrating a very large proportion—probably between 80 and 90 per cent—of the available scientific and engineering development talent in their laboratories they can sterilize creative thought at its very source. Nor is this effect limited to the scientists actually working for monopolies. Every university scientist is in fact dependent on the monopolists for the grants which make his academic research possible and for the successful employment of the students on which his teaching reputation rests. In fact the hold of monopolies over physical and chemical science is fairly complete; their only competitors in this field are government agencies which often represent the same monopolies in a different form or at least show no disposition to work against them.

This hold expresses itself in the general direction of research towards preserving the right to exploit the public, which is the *raison d'être* of the monopolies. The actual methods of securing this end are comparatively unimportant. Secret processes, control of patents, agreements to limit developments causing obsolescence, provide employment for an increasing number of scientificolegal experts; but these, although representing a serious wastage of intelligent man power, are only a symptom of the general control of the whole mechanism of science for limited private purposes. That the public may benefit occasionally from some new device or some cheapening of an old one is no justification for an institution that is intrinsically incapable of providing a genuine public service. What is produced has to be measured against what might have been produced if science had been consciously directed towards human welfare in the ways indicated in the latter part of this article. Inevitably, however, because of their monopoly of knowledge, the precise balance sheet can never be known, even to the trusts themselves.

The Dangers of Secrecy

Another aspect of the effect of monopoly on science is growing very much in importance. Until recent years the body of information collected by scientists was available freely to all. Now with the growth of large industrial research laboratories the results of investigations are carefully screened, and only those aspects of the work are published which are thought unlikely to affect the monopoly position of the firm. The judgment as to what material might or might not have this effect varies from firm to firm; some firms publish hardly anything, others almost as fully as university departments. Even by a free scientific community their information cannot be effectively followed up in any desired direction but only in those not deemed to be injurious. For instance, the properties of materials are described without adequate and relevant information as to their mode of manufacture. It is often claimed that all purely scientific information is published. Unfortunately, as experience in the war showed, much material of critical scientific importance may be buried in technical detail without the knowledge of the industrial scientists. If this tendency is not reversed in a few years, the bulk of detailed scientific information is likely to be found locked away in the internal information service of a few dozen big firms. Scientists both inside and outside industry will often be wasting their time discovering things already known.

Even worse than this form of industrial secrecy is the tendency to State secrecy which grew to such overwhelming proportions during the late war. The more important science is considered to be for national military purposes, the more it is endangered by the web of secrecy thrown over it. One of the most vital fields of present-day science, nuclear physics, is already more or less fatally compromised, and others, such as bacteriology, are threatened. Added to this is the withdrawing of thousands of scientists and technical workers from open intercourse with their fellows under secrecy regulations. This, apart from the loss to science in general, destroys their own effectiveness inside the services which depends largely on free interchange of experience and opinion. The fact that in two important countries of the world, the United States and England, the official expenditure on military science is between half and three-quarters of all official expenditure on science indicates the enormous bias towards promoting works of destruction, but it at the same time measures what could be achieved if all science were devoted openly to constructive purposes.

The Economics of Scientific Progress

In view of all these facts there is now an urgent need to examine the essential social and economic functions of scientific research and to use that knowledge in the public interest for controlling both science and industry. It is characteristic of our economic system that even the beginning of such a study has hardly yet been made. This is partly because those whose concern it is to analyze economic and political variables have been divorced from those who operate with scientific and technical ones. It has never been deemed the concern of the scientist or engineer to examine the relation of his work to the total economic and political set-up of the community: he has neither the training nor the time to do it. What is more surprising is that the economists on their side have not made the attempt, considering that it is practically universally admitted that the development of technology is the major new and significant factor which creates both the main problem of our times and the means for solving it.

Economists have, it is true, discussed the impact of technical changes on economic factors. If a technical innovation leads to a large drop in real costs the effect on the general price structure can be measured; so can the effect on the labor market of the introduction of labor-saving machinery. Economists can indeed go further and estimate rather less accurately the capital expenditure which would justify any particular reduction of costs in production. But all this is to treat the technical changes and the scientific discoveries as if they were acts of God. Occasionally economists join the cohorts of politicians and religious leaders who would like to simplify the problem by suppressing invention and technical progress altogether. What they do not do is to examine the economic and political factors which fix the rate of introduction of new techniques and, at one further remove, the rate of discovery which may lead to these new techniques.

The history of the development of industrial science furnishes all the materials necessary for such a study: not only the applications of science but the whole development of branches of fundamental knowledge can be shown to follow definite economic trends, though the details of the interaction between science and economics are often very complicated. Take, for example, the study of the transmission and reproduction of sound. It was the economic need for communication—initially, business communication—that led to the development of the telephone, while the demand for cheap production of music pushed that of the gramophone. Scientific interest in sound, however, remained at a comparatively low level until it became linked with further electronic and optical developments in the radio and cinema. It was the vast new entertainment industry based on broadcasting and talking films that, through its demands on ever improving technique, multiplied by many times our knowledge of sound transmission and reproduction, and even of the physiology of hearing.

Science in the New Industrial Revolution

The characteristic pattern of these developments is analogous to that of the origin of the industrial revolution, already referred to. The awareness of the need for a scientific device in some limited field leads sooner or later to the development of the necessary device. Often it may only be necessary to apply existing principles, but in recent times it has become more and more a matter of studying the problem scientifically, exploring the sciences that underlie it and actually discovering the principles by which the device must work. Once the device is successful and in production, it is usually found to have far wider applications than were originally envisaged. A new, entirely scientific industry springs up, and with it a new group of specialized engineers. As an example we may take the development of domestic refrigeration, well described in Bichowsky's classical and somewhat cynical work.[1]

Here the need to satisfy an anticipated market led to the application on one side of formal thermodynamics and on the other to the discovery of a whole range of new chemical compounds, the freons, created so to speak to order, for their physical roles. As a result the whole science of heating and refrigeration engineering is being transformed, leading in turn to the development of deep freezing and air conditioning. These mark the beginning of an enormous inroad into the traditional ways of food preservation and domestic comfort, and though their use is at present confined to the more luxurious homes of North America they will in the end become major factors in transforming the miserable life of the majority of the human race that live in the tropics.

The new industrial revolution based on science is not, however, merely a reproduction of the old, where the detailed technique of the scientific research laboratory with its teams of workers of all grades takes the place of the workshop of the solitary inventor, and where the ordered knowledge accumulated by the science of past centuries replaces the stock of techniques inherited from thousands of years of slow development. It contains in itself something radically new—an approach which, though often unconsciously accepted, effectively undermines the whole of the economic and political structure which belongs to the era of the older industrial revolution. The essential feature of the new approach is that of planning development and production in relation to scientifically assessed needs, which takes the place of attempting anywhere and everywhere to secure a profit by guessing what people can be persuaded to pay. In essence the new

[1] *Industrial Research* (Brooklyn, N.Y.: Chemical Publishing Co., 1942).

tendency is simply that of introducing the scientific method into the study of the ends of production and not merely of the means, and by doing so to show the arbitrariness of the distinction hitherto imagined to exist between production and needs.

The Planning of Science

It is, of course, in essence by no means a new method. It was consciously the ideal of the founders of Socialism in the nineteenth century, such as Fourier and Owen; but they treated it as an ideal to be aimed at. Marx first showed that it was the natural and logical development of the economic processes of production that had brought about the first industrial revolution. The actual embodiment of these ideas in practice had to wait for the Russian Revolution. There, on the basis of prerevolutionary science, stunted as it was by Tsarist suspicion and indifference, Lenin built up a pattern of scientific research integrally connected with the industrial and agricultural development of the country, the pattern which has been followed to a greater or lesser extent by capitalist countries in the last thirty years. The governments who initiated the planned utilization of science in the national interest were not following Marxist inspiration from choice; the measures that have been taken were forced on them by the necessities of international competition and war.

The objectives towards which science is now planned in capitalist countries are necessarily the objectives of the trusts which hold the dominating positions in these countries; but even these are obliged for their very survival to achieve a degree of economic integration which has in it at any rate the elements of a rational and scientific approach to the problems of production. Inevitably also, the more production becomes scientific the more it runs into the contradictions involved in trying to retain the profit motive as a basis for human activities. For the internal logic of the new scientific revolution shows that it is impossible to redesign the physical and technical aspects of production without at the same time profoundly modifying its economic, social, and human aspects.

Stated in scientific terms, the new objective is the achievement of the current optimum satisfaction of human physical and social needs. In this the first task is the scientific measurement of needs; and here we have already, on a national and even on a world scale, moved far from the old view that this could be left to the chance of the market. In the Food and Agricultural Organization for years now the basic food needs of the world have been assessed, and at least some efforts have been made to see that the food supplies of the world are distributed so as to minimize actual human famine, though the feeding of grain to animals in North America is still considered more important than feeding it to human beings in Europe and Asia. What can be done on a world scale can equally be done in detail over the whole range of production and consumption.

The Pattern of a Scientific Industry: The Assessment of Needs

The characteristic pattern of the new industry is one in which the idea of scientific analysis and control permeates the whole structure. Each particular industry, like industry as a whole, now tends to be considered as a cyclical process of continual satisfaction of continually modified needs. The first phase in the cycle is the scientific assessment of the needs, the greatest satisfaction that can be given by the general type of production in question. Assessment of needs is becoming a science in its own right, a kind of hybrid between the work of the social scientist, that of the market researcher, and that of the operational research worker of war years.

The study of needs is by no means simple, for it takes on a new aspect once the needs of the community instead of the possibilities of profitable sale become the determining factor. In the normal case where a product or service already exists, the result of such enquiry may be simply to indicate the directions in which improvement of performance is most badly needed. It may also indicate that a modification which can be produced at a much lower cost would lead to the opening of an entirely new market. The really difficult case in conditions of free enterprise is where the study of needs leads to the discovery that they can be met most easily by an entirely different kind of product, possibly an existing product of a rival manufacturer, or by one requiring an entirely new plant.

Another characteristic feature of a genuinely scientific study of need, which is apt to have as inconvenient results, is the discovery of the interrelatedness of needs. Research in Britain on the standard of housing needs, beginning with the actual structure and planning of houses, showed that in a house giving maximum satisfaction not only did the furniture, fittings, and equipment have to be designed in relation to the house and vice versa, but many of the consumable goods purchased required some standardization of shape. Another research in Denmark showed that furniture was designed and made without relation to the form and posture of the human body or to the space available in the rooms where it was used. The mere study of the integration of needs, however, can at best produce only first approximations to the means for satisfying them. It is necessary to add experiment to observation before the mutual reactions of different patterns of need satisfaction can be assessed. In Britain at the moment, for instance, we are building and using a large number of experimental houses in which different conditions are tried out and a range of variables are combined together in all possible ways as in an agricultural experiment. Only after such practical need analysis can the directions of modification of production be safely assessed.

Research, Development, and Design

The second phase in the new scientific industry occurs in the transition between assessed need and the technical forms necessary to satisfy it. This is the function of research, design, and development, teamed together to take the place of the individual inventor of the past. The old inventor had at the same time to sense a need and to use his ingenuity to find a new combination to satisfy it. He might, of course, invent the device without sensing the need, and then try to find some use for it. By and large his success was a product of ingenuity and luck and, if he was to profit by it himself, of business sense in addition. The progress took place by a kind of natural selection of inventions. Those that, by luck or skill, hit the target of contemporary needs succeeded; the others disappeared. In that struggle many of the failures were undeserved; and much can be gained even now by looking over failed inventions to see whether, with new knowledge and new techniques, they cannot be made to work. The individual inventor, however, had limitations which would put him out of the running today. He worked without an adequate knowledge of the materials and processes which he used, and with only a very limited knowledge of the demand which he was to serve.

The modern research department makes up for these limitations; it can at least ensure that the solution to demand problems makes use of the best available knowledge and is able to create new knowledge if this appears insufficient. This of course is only a necessary preliminary; the real job of a research department is to find solutions to problems, and, except for unimportant improvements, this makes as much call on ingenuity as it did in the past, or more. If the individual inventor has not disappeared, he is, or should be, found in the research departments of modern industry; and if he works in some other department he should find there ready acceptance of his ideas. Real creative ingenuity is such a rare and valuable gift that, wherever it occurs, it needs the most careful fostering. Solutions of problems, however, are rarely unique; there is a wide range of permissible variation which makes possible and indeed necessary another function of production, that of design—the apparently arbitrary but essentially aesthetic function of choosing among equally functional forms the one which will be most humanly effective because it is pleasing.

There remains one other absolutely dominating factor which has to be taken into account at all stages of design and development: the expectation of cost. Here again the modern research department, with its ties to production and in many cases its possession of pilot plant, is able to work continuously within a framework of what is possible economically. Even in wartime, when victory and not financial cost was the prime consideration, the scientific workers soon learned that the practicability of a new device depended not only on its efficiency and on the technical possibility of its construction, but on whether the man-hours employed in producing it would yield the maximum return as compared with some other and possibly less efficient device. The introduction of the criterion of cost into scientific thinking is not a degradation of science, as many pure scientists have felt, but rather provides for a higher degree of ingenuity and scientific analysis than a simple solution of technical problems involves. The research and development departments of modern industry represent the growing points and active centers of the new industrial revolution. The war enormously increased the experience and effective confidence of research departments in finding the answers to any demand problem and in getting it into production in a time which may be half to one-twentieth as long as it would have taken before the war. We now realize that most of the lag between ideas and realizations was of vested interest and stupidity and was not a limitation of intelligence or of the problem of surmounting physical difficulties.

Science in Production, Instrumentation, and Control

The third stage is production itself, and here the field traditionally reserved for the practical engineer is now coming more and more into the scientific orbit. The first developments of mass production were a logical engineer's answer to a problem put out by businessmen. In solving this problem the engineers created unwittingly many others, particularly the danger of surplus capacity and total loss in slumps, as well as the danger of overcapitalization and the consequent obsolescence of expensive plant. The new scientific engineers are at least aware of these problems. It is not beyond the wit of man to develop production machinery that is as flexible as it is economic in operation, meeting the problem of obsolescence not by hanging on till the last moment and then letting go with a bang, but by continuous intelligent modification of the processes in anticipation of changes.

As in the war, science enters the production level in the first place through instrumentation, now very largely electronic. The instrumentation develops from that of earlier phases in that it is positively linked to control. More and more the actual operations of the factory have ceased to be crudely automatic—as a matter of gears, belts and levers capable only of repeating the same operation without variation—and have become sensitively automatic, capable of adjusting themselves to variations and dealing at any rate with minor dislocations. But the next stage is the reorganization of the total production process in the light of these instrumentation possibilities, and this will mean as big a revolution in productive methods as the introduction of mass production itself. This may lead soon to completely automatic production of series goods. It will certainly include a complete scientific operational and statistical check-up—probably electronically operated—of all production.

The social effect of the general introduction of instrumentation and control is likely to be enormous and will produce changes at least as great as those of the original industrial revolution. What the introduction of machines meant in the reduction of sheer repetitive manual labor—beating with hammers or turning cranks—the new electronic devices mean for such repetitive mental labor as checking of figures or inspection of parts. The first industrial revolution reduced enormously the amount of heavy work; but it increased to an even greater proportion the amount of monotonous light work that had to be performed. The disappearance of such work will permit an enormous liberation of human mental capacity.

The Abolition of Work

The transition, however, if it is not carefully watched, may mean as much hardship to the white-collar workers as the industrial revolution meant to the hand-loom weavers of the eighteenth century. The workers of the next phase will tend to direct themselves on the one hand towards scientific and technical analysis and design, and on the other to increasing concern with human problems, particularly with the achieving of harmonious social and personal relations. In a word, this change will mean the end of *work*. Work has been so much a part of the human tradition that we are apt to forget that it is not a necessity in itself, but a means to an end. Animals do not work, unless men make them; and men work only because most of them cannot get what they like unless they submit for a greater or smaller part of their lives to doing what they do not like. We are more and more tending to understand, as we seek an even higher productivity, that the more people like what they do, the better they will do it. Production designed for the satisfaction of those engaged in it will, in not too distant a future, become the prevailing social pattern.

Industrial and Society Integration

The fourth stage reaches out beyond production to the fate of the product or the service. This is again a scientific study of a social and technical kind linking with the first stage of need determination and thus completing the cycle. However, the essential, characteristic feature of the new industrial revolution is not the fact that all the stages of production are becoming scientific, but rather the integration of all these stages into one coherent effort. Looked at in another way, this marks a return on a vastly increased scale of effort and complexity to the single craftsman of the preindustrial age who carried out and integrated all these functions in his own head. He assessed the needs of his customers, decided what he would make and how he would make it, made it, and saw that it gave satisfaction. The atomization of all these functions was in its time a stage in advance; but their reconstruction and integration is the only way of ensuring a stable and progressive functioning in the face of the dangers of uneven development, which we have all experienced. Such a change in separate industries would be worthless without a corresponding change in the whole industrial, economic, and political organization of each country and ultimately of the world. Success in detail can be and has been completely negated through producing conflicts and disasters on larger scales.

The Responsibility of the Scientist

The war and the present tragic division of the world are indications of the danger of stopping part way to the goal; but the effort to reach anything like a scientific service to humanity as a whole is bound to be a hard one. All those who are concerned with preserving the old state of affairs—and they are in control over most of the world—have a vested interest in limiting science to the abstract and technical fields and keeping it effectively out of the social field. We have just had one of the crudest examples of how this can be done in Nazi Germany, where social ideas proudly acclaimed by the Nazis as barbarian were running parallel with the most refined devices of physical science. The contradiction between those two aspects brought Germany down, as it will bring down any other civilization that tries to preserve in its ideas and social structure a system that is intellectually untenable and is bound to conflict with the very science on which its material development depends.

The sterilization and corruption of the social sciences may provide a temporary defense for general reaction; but, without the understanding that only a genuine social science can give, the ultimate danger of conflict or collapse cannot be avoided. A social science that has any right to its title must, like the physical and biological sciences, experiment. But experimental social science is equivalent to operational research with the possibility of varying the conditions of human societies, factories, towns, etc., and this cannot be made compatible with the sacredness of existing rights and institutions. It can exist only if people have learned the same open acceptance of experience in the social field as the industrial revolution gave them in the physical. We can look forward to a time when the serious divisions which exist today between employer and worker, between work and leisure seem as meaningless anachronisms as the human sacrifices for rain making that once were thought an absolute necessity for practical agriculture. We shall not, however, reach this state unless at least the scientifically trained members of the community take the trouble to follow out the logical implications of what they know, and stand up and fight for it once they have found it.

CONTEXT AND CONTENT IN THE THEORY OF IDEAS

by

ABRAHAM EDEL

Abraham Edel is Assistant Professor of Philosophy, College of the City of New York. Author, *Aristotle's Theory of the Infinite* (1934) and *The Theory and Practice of Philosophy* (1946); contributor to *Naturalism and the Human Spirit* (ed. Y. H. Krikorian, 1944), *The Philosophy of G. E. Moore* (ed. P. A. Schilpp, 1943), the *Journal of Philosophy*, and other philosophical periodicals. Guggenheim Fellow, 1944–1945.

THE central and unique contribution of a materialist theory in the analysis of ideas has been to relate ideas to the material and sociohistorical context in which they arise, take shape, and exert what influence they may. Other elements in the materialist treatment of ideas—an empirical stress in opposition to a Platonic intuitionism, a readiness to regard and explore thinking as a natural phenomenon—are shared in varying degrees by other philosophical outlooks such as pragmatism or positivism. For this reason, attention will be fastened in this paper primarily upon exploring the meaning, scope, and limits of the sociohistorical analysis of ideas.* Some corollaries will be drawn for the relation of theory and practice and the role of ideas in history.

* The ideas worked out in this part of the paper were suggested in much less developed form in two previous papers: "Levels of Meaning and the History of Ideas," *Journal of the History of Ideas,* Vol. VII, No. 3 (June, 1946), and "Coordinates of Criticism in Ethical Theory," *Philosophy and Phenomenological Research,* Vol. VII, No. 4 (June, 1947), especially pp. 554–559.

I

The view that exploration of sociohistorical context yields a fuller understanding of ideas contains a number of distinct theses. One is the view that ideas have sociohistorical causes or are sociohistorical products. A second view is that ideas have sociohistorical functions or roles. A third—and much more difficult notion—is the view that ideas have sociohistorical content. In discussing these different theses, illustration will be taken primarily from philosophical ideas, and the question of possible limits of the thesis, e.g., in application to scientific ideas, will be raised subsequently.

1. *The causes of an idea.* It is commonly agreed that ideas must have causes. As parts of nature they have physical causes, and as qualities of organic bodies they have physiological causes. As growing out of human experience they probably have determinate psychological causes. In historical writing there is usually very little reference to physical and physiological causes of ideas. Occasionally there are references to the psychological properties of thinkers as causally relevant. Thus Kant's moral rigorism is sometimes associated with anecdotes about his methodical habits, with the suggestion that his categorical imperative was produced by a personal order obsession. Schopenhauer's pessimism is often treated in similar fashion.

Materialist theory in its earlier forms stressed the physical and physiological phases of thinking. In ancient times Democritus identified ideas with the movement of special fine round atoms. Seventeenth century Hobbesian mechanism reduced ideas ultimately, through sensation, to the meeting of external and internal (bodily) motions. Eighteenth century French materialism, when it did not, with Cabanis, reduce thought to a secretion of the brain, fitted man's mental life into a world described in the language of mechanics and physiology, supplemented by the language of introspective psychology. Marxian dialectical materialism in the nineteenth century, treating ideas as reflections of the material world, both physical and social, first proposed a systematic theory of social causation of the development and career of ideas.

The general view that ideas do not grow merely out of previous ideas, but stem from and change in response to changing human needs, is so widely established in historical and social investigation today as to seem almost commonplace. Even where ideas develop simply as part of reflective inquiry by curious minds, there are causes to be sought for this comparatively rare phenomenon itself, the disinterested pursuit of truth. And whether these causes are best described in the psychological terms of a surplus allotment of wonder or curiosity in some temperaments, or the social terms of scientists caught up in the movement of a class whose material interests are closely bound to the discovery of truth in special areas, is entirely an empirical matter upon which a disinterested sociology is not without evidence today. While there is no unanimity on the social coordinates to be used for the analysis—whether economic, narrowly technological, political, or simply diffusion from other cultures—there does seem to be dominant agreement that there are social causes.

The dissenting opinion comes chiefly from those circles in liberal sociological theory that tend to deny all determinate causality in social affairs. Taking their inspiration from Max Weber, they end up with loosely related multiple factors, or even, going to an extreme, with nothing but parallels. Thus, the growth of the Protestant ethic parallels the growth of the rationalizing spirit of capitalism; hierarchical philosophic conceptions parallel hierarchical social structure; mechanistic conceptions line up alongside the spread of machine industry; individualistic morals keep pace with the growth of the open market. These are regarded as either parallels or interwoven factors, but no judgment of primacy or causal direction is permitted. On a purely common-sense level it would appear very difficult sometimes to avoid causal judgments. For example, during a great part of the nineteenth century there was a shift in the southern states of America from regarding slavery as an unnecessary evil to justifying it as a positive good. This parallels the expansion of the cotton market as the invention of machines for the textile industry and the tremendous growth of its trade created a veritable hunger for cotton. T. V. Smith, summarizing the process,[1] has no compunction in concluding: "Economic advantage begot cultural compensations. Cultural compensations conjured up humanitarian mitigations. Logical justification followed. And a certain spiritual sanctification crowned the whole." Can there really be much doubt that such arguments as "Slavery is good for the slave," "It brings Africans to missionaries rather than missionaries to Africa," "The Negro really has no soul," [2] had their social causes?

In such judgments of causality there is no special problem for the theory of ideas. Whatever interpretation of causality be taken in speaking of the causes of war, or the emergence of an institution, can likewise be used in posing the problem of the causes of an idea, its emergence, and its development. This is not, of course, the place to enter into the over-all problem of the legitimacy of causal judgments in social science. It should be noted, however, that the denial of such causality leaves the phenomena of parallelism we have noted unexplained. As a consequence it almost invites such theories as "preestablished harmony" or "spirit of an age."

2. *The functions of an idea.* It is generally recognized today that ideas have not merely causes but also functions or uses, that they are or can be weapons. The meaning of such an approach varies. Sometimes it points to the emotional role of ideas. Ideas, over and above their ideational content, give expression to or are associated with emotions, so that the use of the idea gives satisfaction to or is a way of controlling the emotion in oneself or others. William James, for example, classified philosophers as tender-minded (rationalistic, idealistic, free-willist, etc.) and tough-minded (empiricist, materialistic, fatalistic, etc.).[3] Carnap holds to a somewhat similar view: monism expresses an even and harmonious life; dualism, life felt as an eternal struggle; realism, the extroverted constitution; idealism, the introverted type.[4] Since, however, Carnap regards metaphysical propositions as having no factual content, this expressive function constitutes, so to speak, the whole of the idea.

Such a treatment, suggesting that certain ideas are only instruments for achieving emotional effects, has attained to some prominence in political theory. It is easy enough to point to Mussolini's letter to Bianchi demanding that a philosophy be produced for fascism in two months, for "Italian Fascism now requires, under pain of death, or worse, of suicide, to provide itself with a body of doctrine," or to Hitler's reassuring explanation to an industrial leader that he was using socialist slogans because nationalist slogans alone would no longer attract German workmen.[5] Karl Mannheim points out the way in which what he calls "the particular conception of ideology" operates with a psychology of interests and first finds itself by unmasking doctrines to reveal the private interests that they serve.[6] Thurman Arnold in his *Folklore of Capitalism* has popularized the view that abstract ideas operating in political and social life may serve ritual or emotional functions and hinder the satisfaction of concrete human needs. Writers like Lasswell, James Marshall, Burnham tend to regard abstract ideas and ideals largely as propaganda symbols.[7]

The Marxian view that the dominant ideas of an age express the interests of the dominant class may also be taken in this sense, that the ideas serve as weapons for the dominant class. But the theory also admits of other emphases as well. It may be a causal analysis pointing to class elements in the genesis of ideas. It may be a complicated thesis of social selection analogous to natural selection: all sorts of ideas arise, but those congenial to the dominant class achieve prominence. This analysis is most effective when it can predict the intellectual trend. An interesting example is Hilferding's prediction in 1910, on economic grounds, of the role of racial ideologies.[8] Finance capital requires a powerful political state, the regimentation of independent individual capitalists at home, protection for the home market and conquest of foreign markets. This expansive force revolutionizes the Weltanschauung of the bourgeoisie, condemns liberal humanitarian elements, free trade, the ideal of peace, and substitutes the might of the state. It alters the national idea:

> The economic advantage of monopoly is mirrored in the favored place which must be ascribed to one's own nation. The latter appears as chosen above all others . . . Thus in racial ideology there emerges a scientifically-cloaked foundation for the power lust of finance capital, which in this way demonstrates the cause and necessity of its operations.[9]

In addition to such combinations of causal and instrumental analysis of ideas, the Marxian theory may also, as we shall see, be a thesis concerning the content of ideas.

The pragmatist philosophies elaborate the instrumental function of ideas most systematically. In Charles Peirce's initial formulation, ideas were regarded as rules of action,[10] which, in itself, might point to a content analysis (that is what ideas *really are*) as well as an instrumental one. In Dewey, however, the latter phase is dominant; ideas are instruments functioning in the resolution of problem situations. Portions of experience assume an ideational character by the role that they play: "Ideas are anticipated consequences (forecasts) of what will happen when certain operations are executed under and with respect to observed conditions."[11] And he attacks the traditional view of ideas as copies of perceptions for ignoring "the prospective and anticipatory character that defines *being* an idea." The opposition to this broad operationalism comes largely, in the materialist-naturalist tradition, from a realism which insists on a correspondence in some sense or other between experience and existence, in short, an essentially representative role for experience rather than merely a prospective role.

3. *The content of an idea.* All treatments of ideas recognize, in one fashion or another, the existential aspect and the referential aspect of an idea. The latter—which is our present concern—has been referred to in many ways. Some use the omnibus term "meaning"; others more technically speak of the "referent" or the "designatum." Some narrow it to the "mode of verification" of the proposed statement in which the idea occurs; others prefer a more material treatment and speak of "the aspects of existence represented." Logicians commonly refer to the "connotation" of the term. We shall here without further refinement speak of the "content of an idea" as quite literally what it contains or what is rendered clear in its analysis.[12] The central question, however, is what kind of analysis; and the issues at stake in controversies on this question are largely problems of how the analysis of ideas is to be carried out.

It is at this point especially that we find a marked difference within the materialist-naturalist tradition today. It is best seen, perhaps, in the contrast of the positivist logical analysis and the Marxian historical analysis of an idea.[13] In the former, the study of ideas is transformed into the study of language and its uses. Instead of analyzing ideas it analyzes terms, the rules for their combination, their transformation into other terms, and their application. A logical analysis thus yields the factual or scientific content of an idea, which is often regarded as the sense-perceptions with the prediction of which the analysis terminates.[14] Everything else is relegated either to an expressive or pragmatic function in the use of a symbol,[15] or else to a causal examination of the situation in which the symbol is used.

The common philosophic conception of an idea's content does, in fact, tend to draw sharply the distinction between content and context. The career of an idea, and the existential conditions underlying its development, tend to be regarded as external to the idea itself. This is the domain of causality or natural history—the story of how ideas are grasped, their influence over men when they are clearly understood. The studies of the social history of ideas are thus regarded as purely separable scientific ventures, irrelevant to the philosophical analysis of the ideas. History is thus intrinsically irrelevant to ideas, except where it is an inner history of their unfolding, or where the idea happens to be specifically about historical matters. There is even a standard fallacy—the "genetic fallacy"—to connote the confusion of the causal and ideational orders and the attempt to assess the content of an idea by the way it happened to come into existence. Hence the search into the context of philosophical ideas is often dismissed as irrelevant "psychologizing" or "sociologizing."

In the Marxian analysis, on the other hand, the exploration of sociohistorical context is relevant to the exhibition of the idea's content. For example, Marx and Engels say of philosophic ideas, in *The German Ideology:*

> All epoch-making systems have as their real content the needs of the time in which they arise. Each one of them is based on the whole of the antecedent development of a nation, on the historical growth of its class relations with their political, moral, philosophical and other consequences.[16]

On the face of it, such a thesis has innumerable difficulties to overcome. In what sense, when Kant is discussing the *a priori,* Bentham the meaning of pleasure, Plato the immortality of the soul, and Aristotle the law of contradiction, can they be said to be talking *also and in an important sense about the needs of their time?* Is it possible to carry sociohistorical coordinates into the very inner sanctum of ideas? Does not the logical analysis of the ideas give us sufficient content to proceed to judgments of truth or intellectual adequacy? Why should the analysis of content be expanded in new directions?

The general thesis that an examination of sociohistorical context tells us more fully what ideas "are about" was perhaps implicit in the idealist conception of objective mind. Marx and Engels gave it a materialist formulation and also offered a special theory of the kinds of sociohistorical factors pertinent. Since their time the general thesis has become the property of much practicing sociology, anthropology, and history, in so far as ideas are regularly dealt with by these studies in a social matrix. Mannheim, in attempting to found a sociology of knowledge, gave the thesis a specialized and at times almost predominantly political form. Dewey at times employs such a thesis in generalized form, when he explains philosophical dualisms in terms of social cleavages and looks for the meaning of philosophical ideas in terms of the social practices in which they are embedded.

It is quite clear, however, that materialist philosophy cannot hold to this thesis in an unrestricted fashion. For materialism operates with an epistemology in which true ideas are regarded as accurate reflections of the world, and it must therefore allow of some purely physical assertions. Engels sometimes, in fact, speaks almost as if the sociohistorical content of ideas were that part in virtue of which ideas deviate from truth: "Indeed the materialistic outlook on nature means no more than simply conceiving nature just as it exists without any foreign admixture." [17] This phase of the materialist writings leads Mannheim to regard the Maxian contribution as negative, merely directed to unmasking opponents and unconscious of its own similar character. Actually, however, once we distinguish, in using sociohistorical context, the three separate elements of causality, function, and content, then there is no inconsistency in holding that all ideas have sociohistorical causes, that most ideas have sociohistorical functions, that many more ideas than we think have sociohistorical content, that the truth or falsity of ideas is a thoroughly objective question not to be confused with the preceding propositions, and that the holding of true ideas has sociohistorical causes.

In order to come to grips with the problems thus raised, and especially to determine the scope and limits of the thesis concerning sociohistorical content of ideas, it is necessary to explore the wider question of the extension of content as well as the specific one of extension to include sociohistorical content.

4. *The extension of content in the analysis of ideas.* The first identification of an idea is at most tentative. A statement about the content of an idea is an hypothesis for an inquiry whose terminus may very well be a stipulation. The inquiry is in the first place directed to the intentions of a man or group of men as expressed in action, speech, writings. In this sense the ideas we investigate for content are qualities of natural events over periods of time, which we call men thinking. The inquiry may be addressed to ourselves as well as to others. We may examine our own ideas in any field with the intention of exploring and articulating them. We may similarly examine other people's ideas

or the ideas of another age. Evidence and analysis are required to determine where the content of the idea begins and ends. The examination of one's own ideas has this distinctive mark, that the person himself is examining them; therefore the creative element is stronger, and examination may mean growth or alteration. If I discover discrepancies in my idea of "content," for example, I alter the idea. If I discover such elements in Aristotle's notion of "nature," I can only report that they are there and try to see them on a wider canvas in his writings.

This example itself suggests one way in which content may become broadened beyond the initial elements identified, that is, when one is led on in the analysis by gaps and discrepancies. It need not be this alone. One may simply note relationships that suggest a demand for further specification, or even try out some theory of interpretation to see what light it sheds.

In principle, the problem is the same in imagination, in perception, in art, in thought—that of drawing a line between data and interpretation; and what I am suggesting is that no sharp line can be drawn. Suppose a man reports a dream and comes to interpret it in the psychoanalytic process in a given way. Why should the particular form of his first report determine in privileged fashion the content of the dream and everything else be regarded as *its* interpretation? In one sense, it is true, he dreamed (let us say) about a certain friend. He comes to see that the friend in the dream represented his father. Is it purely a verbal matter to say that his father was part of the content of the dream, or even that it was "really" his father he was dreaming about? Actually seeing the friend as the father may give a systematic character to the happenings of the dream which otherwise they would not have. The case is even clearer if we deal not with a person but an emotion. Erich Fromm, for example, says of faith:

> Psychologically, faith has two entirely different meanings. It can be the expression of an inner relatedness to mankind and affirmation of life; or it can be a reaction formation against a fundamental feeling of doubt, rooted in the isolation of the individual and his negative attitude toward life.[18]

Presumably differential qualities of feeling would be involved which the individual, if sufficiently discriminating, might detect. But whether he did or not, if the psychological interpretation in a given case is correct, then the interpretation may be regarded as broadening the *content,* rather than as simply giving a causal explanation of it.

On the other hand, both in these cases and in ordinary perception, it is possible to pursue the opposite policy and insist on narrowing the content. The dream was not of the friend, but of certain color and shape patterns; similarly, what you now see is not a man running a race, nor even a man running, but certain successive color and shape patterns. The feeling is not faith, but something much narrower—hope or anxiety. The various entities are either constructs out of feeling and sensation or, if you wish to be a realist, existing objects and attitudes which *cause* these feelings and sensations. The sole content of thought would turn out on analysis to be some type of sense data—a view found in a number of the forms of positivism.[19]

Let us take a further example from the field of art theory. A painting before you shows certain color and shape patterns. Or it shows a mother and child. Or it shows Mary and the Christ child. What is the content of the picture—sense patterns, familial relations with their emotional implications, a particular religious complex? Even if we are concerned with aesthetic content, any *a priori* limitation really presents a valuation. For example, defining the content as the one the artist intended is a stress on communication as central value; even then, the question of what is expressed by the artist would allow a fresh range of selection, from motives and feelings to patterns of the age of whose broader contours the artist may have been personally unaware.

If the same analysis holds for the content of ideas, any attempt to limit the content to abstract or structural elements, to sensory elements or individual psychological elements, can only be regarded as valuational in character. The desire for a full elaboration of content, as against partial analysis, is likewise, of course, valuational, but the values it embodies are those of the fullest or most systematic description of the world. Hence its intent is scientific understanding.

5. *The sociohistorical content of philosophical ideas.* So far we have merely insisted on the right to look for sociohistorical content. It remains now to see whether and to what extent such content is really discoverable in philosophical ideas, and to what extent it is required in the analysis of an idea.

Perhaps the simplest way to make the point is to examine a few ideas briefly. Take ethical ideas of an abstract order, such as justice or equality. Can we really understand them by such definitions as "Justice is giving each man his due" or such distinctions as Aristotle makes between arithmetic equality (everyone the same) and proportionate equality (to each what he deserves)? Either the notions must be so refined as to be almost purely mathematical propositions, or else the meanings of "due," "same," "desert" require amplification. Aristotle pointed out that what a man deserves is reckoned differently in an aristocracy, an oligarchy, and a democracy.

Once the Platonic approach to pure ideas is abandoned, there is no reason to see the abstract formula as *the idea* and the interpretations as *applications* of the preexistent idea. Justice will mean simply the fundamental principles that systematize the operations of an existing legal system—e.g., its particular assumptions about property structure, responsibility structure, etc. Universal justice will mean any discoverable invariant elements in such systems, or else the fundamental elements of a projected ideal system—where "ideal" refers to existent patterns of striving, with the aims of man seen in sociohistorical terms. Similarly, if we look at Engels's treatment of equality as a moral ideal in his *Anti-Dühring,* we can see that he is not so much exploring causes or describing instruments as showing that the very idea of equality has had different meanings at different stages of man's history. Among the Greeks and Romans it could not mean human equality, embracing slaves. In early Christianity it meant that all were equally born in original sin, the ideational expression of the status of slavery and oppression. Among the bourgeoisie it means the demand for removal of class privileges; while for the proletariat it means the demand for the abolition of classes themselves.

> The idea of equality, therefore, both in its bourgeois and in its proletarian form, is itself a historical product, the creation of which required definite historical conditions which in turn themselves presuppose a long previous historical development.[20]

The conclusion of such an analysis is not merely that, without reference to sociohistorical content, the idea is vague and confusing. This normative proposition is often asserted today in one or another fashion when a demand is made for specification of a term in observationally verifiable consequences, or in the semantic insistence that we speak of $equality_1$, $equality_2$, $equality_3$. The significance of the analysis lies in the hypothesis, over and above the assertions about good usage of terms, that the sociohistorical content is in fact present even where the terms are abstractly used. In short, it is the hypothesis that further analysis of text or context, in dealing with philosophical ideas, will reveal sociohistorical content to complete the idea; that, without it, the idea is fragmentary.

I should like to illustrate the thesis at this point from two philosophical ideas which seem to me to be immeasurably clearer when so regarded. Since they are well worn ideas from the philosophical stock, often treated and the center of many interpretations, whatever success is attained with them may be indicative of what may be achieved with other philosophical ideas. One is the Aristotelian idea of the mean; the other, the Benthamite idea of pleasure.

As is well known, Aristotle uses the idea of the mean to identify virtuous conduct and the states of character which are virtues. If we ask ourselves, however, what after all is the idea of the mean, and explore the Aristotelian texts and the Greek cultural contexts, many phases of content arise as candidates. Abstractly regarded, the mean appears sometimes as the exactly right, measured out to the correct point, with a rejection of too much and too little. This is the artist's or craftsman's concept of due proportion. It also appears as a synthesis of opposing forces which do not disappear but are balanced in the resultant. It appears again as the cultural prohibition of "hybris"—a specific type of arrogance or ambition which, by aiming at what is more than one's mortal lot, invites the envy of the gods. And in Aristotle's *Politics* it appears quite definitely and explicitly as the compromise between oligarchy and democracy, a kind of middle-class rule to avoid the disorder attendant on the strife of rich and poor. The first temptation, from the point of view of traditional philosophical habits, is to call the abstract content *the* idea, and to speak of the others as applications. But such selection of the abstract elements for a central and identifying role appears arbitrary, once the full range is exhibited. A second way out is to start with a plurality, and speak of $mean_1$, $mean_2$, $mean_3$, and $mean_4$. But this may beg the question by stipulating that they are distinct and unrelated. Of course they may be; but this is a hypothesis about Aristotle's writings and ideas which requires testing. Perhaps the fairest approach is to recognize that identification of the idea may start with any phase, that many phases of content may be discovered, that whether they are to be regarded as phases or as the content of distinct ideas is itself to be decided by what degree of unity one actually discovers in the analysis. This implies that criteria of unity can themselves be worked out in the systematic study of ideas. One of these, in the case of a single writer such as Aristotle, would be, no doubt, the degree to which he intends his various treatments to be dealing with the "same" idea; others would be the degree to which they are bound together by common procedures or central purposes. Without entering at this point into the fuller investigation of relation of phases of content, it is clear at any rate that, once a minimum of unity is established, we may speak of the one idea and its various phases of content. And if the analysis is correct, clearly the substantial political and cultural content in the idea of the mean cannot be ignored.

The case of pleasure in Bentham's ethics shows this even more clearly. The questions of the meaning of "pleasure" in Bentham's use, whether it has the additive properties he assigns to it, how one can speak of a whole of pleasure when it is a fleeting feeling, why every man should be regarded as the best judge of his own pleasures, and numerous other issues, are familiar enough in the controversies over the logic of hedonism. Now there is no doubt that one phase of the content of the idea of pleasure is the psychological one: it refers to a type of feeling with which we are introspectively familiar. But the feeling as we so discover it scarcely seems to have the properties Bentham assigns to pleasure either explicitly or implicity in the way the idea appears in his ethical, legal, and political writings. The furthest we can get, if we limit our analysis to the psychological content, is to criticize factually Bentham's psychology and to wonder why he made such obvious blunders. Or we can try to save him by arguing that even if pleasure is not an extensive magnitude a revised Benthamism can get along with it as an intensive magnitude. If, however, we pay attention to the sociohistorical phase of content, much becomes clear that before was puzzling. Bentham turns out to have his eye not on subjective feelings, not on behavioristic description of patterns of preference, but upon the acquisition of wealth as a typical and dominant goal of his time. The properties he assigns to pleasure are the properties of money, and the reduction of all specific value qualities to pleasure is, in effect, the reduction of all aspects of human activity to the test of yielding wealth.[21] If this is so—and the evidence seems to me to support it—can one really understand the ethics of hedonism, both in the origin of modern Utilitarianism and in its various historical expressions, without embracing the sociohistorical elements—institutional, cultural, and specifically historical—as part of the very content of the idea of pleasure?

At this point let us state the view in its minimal terms: philosophical ideas have different phases of content, among which sociohistorical content may often be found. In the examples of the mean and pleasure we recognized abstract, psychological, general cultural, and specifically sociohistorical phases. There is, of course, no *a priori* limit to the types of phases there may be, just as we saw before that there was no *a priori* limit to the expansion of content.

6. *Relation of phases of content.* The next problem that naturally arises is whether the various phases are to be regarded as independent, a simple plurality, or whether their relations are to be construed in a special way. All sorts of metaphors are sometimes used to suggest a relationship. For example, one phase may be said to be the "garb" or "cloak" for a second, to "reflect" or "express" or "represent" it. Obviously these problems reproduce with respect to ideas the problems of the relations between economic, political, religious, intellectual, and other phenomena. A full examination of the question would involve analysis of the reflection or expression relation in much greater detail and with greater specificity than the distinction of causality, instrumentality, and content, made above. Although the metaphor in "reflection" is that of mirror image, involving correspondence of outline, this need not be the sole relationship involved. Just as the meaning of "representation" varies in each of the arts, even though in a general sense art may be representative, so the ways in which some phenomena reflect others may be quite diverse. The ways in which a charred scene reflects the fire that preceded it, an action reflects a purpose, an ideal reflects a need, a dream reflects a wish, an instrument reflects a purpose, are quite different. There may also be secondary senses: A may reflect B because central parts of A reflect B, or because A is constructed by procedures that were developed in the construction of B, and so forth. A critical analysis of such relationships in the light of scientific results in the relation of phenomena would provide the conceptual tools for connecting the phases of content in an idea.

The relation of phases of content may be studied at a particular time or over a period of time. The relation of primacy in content, for example, may sometimes refer to stability; thus ritual may be primary in comparison to myth in the content of a single religious complex, in the sense that it remains the same while explanatory myths associated with it may shift. Or judgments of primacy may refer to causal relations. Or they may refer to purposes, as when one compares a political platform to the interests to which it "gives expression."

To examine more carefully the problem of relationship, let us look at another old philosophical illustration, the question raised by J. S. Mill whether there are qualities of pleasure. Bentham said that, provided the amount of pleasure is the same, pushpin is as good as poetry to those who prefer it. Mill was unwilling to have the superiority of pleasures of the intellect over those of the body lie merely in "greater permanency, safety, uncostliness, etc." He claimed an intrinsic qualitative difference.

> If I am asked, what I mean by difference of qualities in pleasures, or what makes one pleasure more valuable than another, merely as a pleasure, except its being greater in amount, there is but one possible answer. Of two pleasures, if there be one to which all or almost all who have experience of both give a decided preference, irrespective of any feeling of moral obligation to prefer it, that is the more desirable pleasure.

And his defense of the view concludes:

> It is better to be a human being dissatisfied than a pig satisfied; better to be Socrates dissatisfied than a fool satisfied. And if the fool, or the pig, are of a different opinion, it is because they only know their own side of the question. The other party to the comparison knows both sides.[22]

On its face, this argument (like the original Benthamite hedonism) appears to concern what may be found on introspection; namely, qualitative distinctions in the feeling of pleasure. In fact, however, an important political potential readily appears on analysis. Bentham took every man to count as one and gave him permission to decide for himself about his own values. Mill not merely appealed to discriminating persons and made their decision concerning what is good for the "fool" decisive, but even risked the general equalitarian assumption, since a "wise man" might claim more recognition for his qualitatively higher desires than the "fool" for his.

What other phases of content can be discovered in this idea of differences of qualities in pleasure? One is tempted to look for a personal psychological phase in an overintellectualized man of sensitive spirit. Perhaps this is so; certainly a marked preference for intellectual over bodily pleasures is part of the very content of the idea. But a careful study of Mill's other writings expands the content much further. One is struck by the formulation of the central problem in *Liberty*: the assumption that democratic government is as good as established, and that therefore the chief theoretical task is to set a limit to what majorities may do to minorities. His *Representative Government,* moreover, indicates a mistrust of the people at large, in a number of ways. Recognizing the major divergent directions of interest as laborers and employers, he thinks that both interests ought to be equally represented in influence in Parliament,

> since, assuming that the majority of each class, in any difference between them, would be mainly governed by their class interests, there would be a minority of each in whom that consideration would be subordinate to reason, justice, and the good of the whole; and this minority of either, joining with the whole of the other, would turn the scale against any demands of their own majority which were not such as ought to prevail.[23]

He thinks that only those who pay taxes should elect those who vote the taxes, that those on relief should be disqualified from voting. He thinks that intelligence and virtue entitle a man to more weight in voting, but he adds that it is "entirely inadmissible, unless as a temporary makeshift, that the superiority of influence should be conferred in consideration of property." This is only because higher education is presumed in the wealthier; thus, too, the liberal professions entitle a man to plural votes. The poorest man, however, should have a right to present himself for examination to prove his higher worth.[24]

It is clear from such materials, which can be multiplied, that what separates Mill from the earlier utilitarian attitude—epitomized in the Benthamite insistence that all pleasure differences are purely quantitative and the postulate that every man counts as one—is not an issue in introspective psychology but the beginning of a contractionist attitude towards the expansion of democracy. Mill's father, James, had complete faith in the acceptance of middle-class leadership by the mass of men. But by the middle of the nineteenth century the struggle deepened; the socialist and communist movements arose. The revolutions of 1848 showed the depth of the cleavage between middle class and workers. The development of industrialism did not spread the benefits to the degree promised, but brought the misery that necessitated Factory Acts and subsequent social legislation. Mill, in the very act of fighting for the extension of the franchise, in struggling for the wider spread of benefits, found within himself, in spite of his humanitarian outlook, a growing mistrust of the people, and wanted them kept from full power. This is the sociohistorical content of the idea of qualitative differences in pleasures. One can find it by careful examination of Mill's texts. One can also see it in the fuller study of political theory of the nineteenth century. Mill told as much in his *Autobiography,* when he confessed that he had begun as a laissez faire advocate and a democrat, and was ending as a kind of socialist but less a democrat.

If, in this example, we ask what is the relation of the phases of content, we can see that the sociohistorical aspect stands out prominently. It tells us what the idea is essentially about. The other phases do not disappear, but they fall into place tied together and systematized by the sociohistorical content. Looking back at the examples given above, we can see that only by focusing on the successively broadening demands for removal of discriminations, class privileges, and classes is the idea of equality fully clarified; only by seeing that we are faced with the demand of a middle class for political power, and a middle-class ethic cast in the categories of craftsmanship, do we fully grasp the Aristotelian idea of the mean; only by keeping our eye on the process of accumulating wealth in the typical amassing of profit in the period of the industrial revolution do we get to the heart of Bentham's idea of pleasure. For only in such ways do the actual ideas, with all the properties they are assigned in the original texts and all the functions they serve in the contexts, really "make sense."

The sociohistorical content, where it is found, thus rounds out the idea and brings fuller understanding. It does this not merely in the psychological or phenomenological sense of completing what stands out as incomplete and calls for completion, but in the logical sense in which a wider picture provides elements that systematize disparate fragments and reconcile apparent discrepancies. How far this proves to be generally the case, or in what areas of thought sociohistorical content where present may play a subsidiary rather than a unifying role, can only be discovered by careful specific historical and philosophical analysis. That materialists have been conscious of the immense labor required in such analysis may be seen from the remark of Engels:

> The development of the materialist conception even in regard to a single historical example was a scientific work which would have demanded years of tranquil study, for it is obvious that nothing can be done here with mere phrases, that only a mass of critically viewed, completely mastered historical material can enable one to solve such a task.[25]

But the light shed by such an approach in the last century of philosophy would seem to be sufficient warrant for regarding the general hypothesis of sociohistorical content in philosophical ideas at least as a promising heuristic principle.

7. *Summary and formulation of the sociohistorical context hypothesis.* The general hypothesis that an analysis of sociohistorical context is relevant to analysis of ideas may be summarized briefly at this point, putting together the various elements we separated for exploration. It constitutes in the first place a recommendation that in beginning the investigation of ideas one set up first the specific sociohistorical coordinates of the situation in which the ideas—at least the philosophical ideas—occur. It then predicts that causal elements, functional elements, and (with limitations to be discussed below) content elements—all sociohistorical in character—are discoverable, and where discovered will be found to play a central rather than a subsidiary role. The exact meaning of "central" varies, of course, according to the type of inquiry. The three elements we have distinguished may themselves be related or independent. For example, in the case of Mill discussed above, it is probably true that the historical situation of the nineteenth century was a great part of the cause of his attitude to the people. But the sociohistorical content of his view would still be the same (provided that he had written the same books) even if his attitude had been caused by an earlier devotion to Plato, or even if it had been caused by an intense emotional attachment to someone who held that attitude. Again, the ideas, whether they have or have not a social content, may have social causes and serve social purposes. Thus Mill makes clear in Chapter III of his *Autobiography* that his attempt to build an in-

ductive logic was, in effect, a revolt against an autocratic or authoritarian mode of reasoning.

The hypothesis of the relevance of sociohistorical context to the analysis of ideas thus constitutes a composite picture whose various elements may be united in a general theory of the evolutionary development of human consciousness. As Marx and Engels put it in the *Communist Manifesto:*

> Does it require deep intuition to comprehend that man's ideas, views, and conceptions, in one word, man's consciousness, changes with every change in the conditions of his material existence, in his social relations and in his social life? What else does the history of ideas prove than that intellectual production changes its character in proportion as material production is changed? [26]

It follows also that we must distinguish between the general or minimum thesis that sociohistorical coordinates are integral to the analysis of ideas, and the specific thesis that these coordinates are of a definite sort. The general thesis seems already to be involved in much of the treatment of ideas in the social sciences. When an anthropologist, for example, investigates a myth, he may find it expressive of the history of the people, or the typical repressions associated with the familial pattern, or almost any phase of cultural life. The understanding of the myth or of a folk tale requires completion by the fuller picture. Even philosophical ideas, when studied by the social historian, are commonly seen as soaked in history, and changing in response to needs and circumstances.

A specific thesis that the sociohistorical coordinates are of a definite sort rests upon establishing a theory of social phenomena in general, therefore including ideas. Such theories of history have involved such specific coordinates as technology, struggle for power, and mode of production.

8. *Sociohistorical context and mathematical and logical ideas.* Controversies about the sociohistorical context of mathematical and logical ideas are considerably clarified by a distinction of the different phases of the context hypothesis. It is clear that the history of mathematics as part of human history is considerably enriched by causal and functional accounts—the land-measuring origins of geometry, the practical origins of counting, the rhetorical-political as well as the scientific origins of logic, the ethical and political use of mathematical eternity,

the relation of specific branches of mathematics to industrial and technical needs of their day. It is equally clear, however, that such historical analyses are not substitutes for content analyses nor for assertions about the content of mathematical ideas. The question to what degree mathematical and logical ideas may be developed independently of existential assertions, and to what degree these existential assertions, being scientific, have sociohistorical phases of content, can be resolved only by mathematical and scientific analysis and investigation.

Whatever the outcome, one need not, of course, assume a metaphysical domain of mathematical or logical ideas-as-such. The ideas are someone's ideas (individual or group) and have to be investigated as such. Thus, if part of Plato's idea of mathematical ideas is that they are forms grasped by the soul as distinct from the body, then there is clearly some psychological and probably considerable social content in his mathematical ideas. On the other hand, modern logicians often claim to have purged $2 + 2 = 4$ and $a = a$ of all material, not merely ideological content. Their propositions are taken to be analytic truths; their definitions, simply nominal equation of sets of marks; their postulates, sentential functions constituting complex nominal definitions. No vestige of psychological content remains: not-p is neither vehement nor mild in its rejection of p. The purest mathematics becomes, as Russell is fond of pointing out, an idea of nothing in particular. If, in fact, a pure mathematics of such a character is an accomplished fact—and this is a mathematical and logical problem—and if no assumptions about our world are smuggled in, in the process of its development,[27] then the sociohistorical context hypothesis may be satisfied with expounding causes and functions.

If, however, logical ideas are regarded as metaphysical, or as ontologically grounded, as some have been prone to regard them in the history of philosophy, then they gain the widest content; and it is not surprising that part of this content, even apart from cause and function or role, should be sociohistorical in character. For example, the laws of contradiction and excluded middle, in Aristotle, are more than purely tautological assertions capable of exhibition by the truth tables. They express the concept of a fixed order of nature, and are therefore an integral part of his teleological world outlook. In their denial, as Aristotle explicitly says,[28] "those who talk like this do away with substance and essence, for they are compelled to assert that all things are accidents, and that there is no such thing as 'being essentially man' or 'animal.' " And to do away with substance means, in various fields, to deny natures or immanent designs in things. The laws of logic in Aristotle have many phases of content: instantaneous substantival change, for one thing, in physical theory, as well as fixed motions and places for physical elements; fixed species in biology; fixed human nature and fixed goals in ethical theory; fixed social places in political theory (natural slaves and natural subordination of women), etc.[29]

It is not surprising, therefore, that when Engels comes to attack the proposition that $a = a$ he deals with it as fundamentally the problem of permanence and change.[30] With reservations, he allows its use in mathematics, where he regards it as tautological, and its everyday application to small-scale conditions or brief periods of time. But he rejects it for nature, arguing that the individual changes, the species change, the laws change. He takes the old laws of logic, therefore, to be false. There is a real issue between Engels and Aristotle; but it is a question of science, not of tautologies.[31]

9. *Sociohistorical context and science.* There are, of course, many aspects of science as an enterprise or going concern which call for sociohistorical explanation that is causal or instrumental. And this is what is involved in many controversies about the sociohistorical character of science. A materialist sociohistorical approach often explains what aspects of scientific work are stressed or neglected, and why. It shows what problems are set by dominant industries and social issues. It may also explain how, by a kind of overdetermination due to stimulation and direction of human inventive energy, discoveries of one kind or another are matured and hastened. And it likewise often explains why inventions once made are sometimes utilized, sometimes neglected or suppressed. These are problems primarily of the history of the growth of scientific knowledge and its utilization, not its content.

Again, there are aspects closely bound up with the way in which science is conceived, which appear to have a sociohistorical character. The inner texture of scientific theory has often been cast in an ideological mold—for example, when scientific laws are conceived of as inalterable expressions of God's will, or as conventions expressive of human subjectivity. And indeed the full sociohistorical context (including probably content elements) of traditional rationalist and empiricist approaches constitutes a still insufficiently explored segment of western history and philosophy. But all such studies are clearly concerned with the sociohistorical content of specific philosophies of science, rather than with the results of science.

Even when ideological elements and specific or local sociohistorical aims are removed, there remain certain values in the basic aims of the scientific enterprise. Truth is not itself identical with reality or existence; it is a characteristic of some of men's beliefs, assertions, and opinions—in short, a property of the effort by men to see existence as clearly as they can. And this effort contains commitments which are clearly valuational in character. From the old determination to "save the appearances" (i.e., so to frame theories as to neglect none of the phenomena) to the formulation of experiments as questions to nature on which nature, not human wishes, shall give the answer, there is a deliberate harnessing of desire to what we may call a correspondence goal and the prediction and control that it entails. This is recognized by various philosophies in the common formulation that science seeks the dependable features of our world. The pragmatist may interpret this as turning truth into a value; the positivist may take it to be a conventional definition of science; the materialist may regard dependability as a criterion of correspondence. But all can agree on the presence of the value elements in the aims definitive of the scientific enterprise. The question then remains whether a sociohistorical content is to be found in the values themselves.

This problem presents a difficulty only if "sociohistorical" be taken in the narrow sense of class viewpoints or of political perspectives. There are elements in a society which give expression to its mode of production more directly. For example, among the relations of production today there are elements in the organization of work which express the necessities of large-scale technology, closely bound with elements expressing the capitalist control over technology. The whole of the history of practical activity, from the discovery of fire and agriculture through the development of handicrafts and then of machine industry, and so forth, enmeshed as it is by characteristics whose determination is more narrowly political, constitutes the growth of the struggle against nature. And this battle against nature, this growth of effective freedom, constitutes the sociohistorical basis of the widening of the area of prediction and collective control by the clearest presentation of nature's ways.[32] The removal of all ideological elements from science thus frees it of class purposes, but not of basic human aims.

There remains still the central question whether there are sociohistoric elements in the *results* of science, not merely in its genesis, utilization, and basic aims. Certainly in dealing with the social sciences this may well be the case. The hypothesis that the study of man is sociohistorical in some fundamental aspect is a plausible one which has considerable evidence on its behalf. Thus, it would be contrasted with the view that the behavior of men can be scientifically explained in terms of biological factors alone, or in terms of an individualistic psychology, or of moral universals, and so forth. It is strengthened by the degree to which many human characteristics thought to be physiologically grounded turn out to be social products, by the extent to which economics has become infused with historical and institutional content, instead of being constituted by the deductive elaboration of the activity of an abstract "economic man," and so forth.

In some of the sciences of nature, there may be some sociohistorical content in an accidental sense—only to the degree to which the actual phenomena themselves may involve human participation. Thus, the study of the development of animal forms in the last five thousand years certainly involves reference to domestication; and the future of many meteorological and geological phenomena will probably require some reference to control activities of men, the specific character of which will, no doubt, involve sociohistorical components. But there are obvious limits to these components, and in the past certainly their role was less. The question we are considering therefore stands out most clearly on its philosophical side if we ask whether there is any sociohistorical content to the results of the physical sciences, i.e., the accumulating body of scientific laws or truths about the physical world—quite literally, the mathematical equations which together with specified operations yield predictable results.

At this point, certain philosophical approaches may be tempted to seek a persistent human element. For example, it may be said the picture of the results of science at any time will include not merely laws and operations, but a full description of the equipment with which the operations are concerned, plus relevant elements of scientific techniques in construction and utilization of instruments. Can a sociohistorical phase of content be found in this area which bulks large in modern science? It might even seem that the operationalist element in scientific theory would make such techniques and instruments relevant to the full specification of operations and therefore to the content of the science, and not merely limit them to the conditioning effect of technology on the growth of the science. In this sense, a full account of scientific results at any given time, the argument runs, includes some reference to the state of technology of that time. And similar arguments are implicit in the pragmatic effort to see the results of physical science as in some sense an extension of "experience."

As was noted above, such a course of argument is not available to the materialist approach. For it is not ready to resolve science into statements about operations and their relation, and insists that the results of science be taken in some sense as telling us about the world; and it accepts quite literally the scientific view that the world existed before man. Therefore the sociohistorical character of scientific instruments will be taken quite literally to refer to the *instruments* of scientific inquiry rather than the results of scientific inquiry. And such sociohistorical elements could appear in the results of science only as explication of the relative or conditioned element in the result. In short, if the results of science at any time are regarded as "relative truth," the sociohistorical element enters only into the "relative," not into the "truth." [33]

In general, it follows, the materialist approach to ideas is not limited to a sociohistorical approach. In the theory of physical science, the historical element may be relevant to the content of scientific results, since laws are interpreted, roughly speaking, as describing the regularities in the occurrence of material processes *at a particular stage in the development of matter*. But such attention to the change of laws, the emergence of new laws and new levels, and so forth, involves no special reference to the human or the social, and the historical stress is equivalent to a stress on the primacy of change. In short, the sociohistorical represents only one phase of the material-historical.

10. *Sociohistorical context and truth.* In all these various ways in which sociohistorical context enters into science, no one can be interpreted as humanizing truth or rendering it other than "objective." This has, of course, been a central question in such discussions. For example, Mannheim struggles with what appears to be the contradiction of maintaining a social point of view concerning ideas and hold-

ing to an objective theory of truth, and he abandons the latter, at least in historical and political science. He takes Marx to have discovered that there is a class or political view of knowledge and to have revealed the phenomenon of a false consciousness in historical classes.[34] But he believes that Marx used this only against his enemies, insufficiently recognizing that the analysis could be used against his own side. Mannheim distinguishes clearly between treating the sociological analysis as an analysis of motives—a narrowly genetic point of view—and discovering whole outlooks inherent in opposing political groups. In the social process, "Every view should be equated with the social position of the observer. If possible, it should be investigated in every case why the relations appear as they do from every given standpoint." He aims "to distinguish and isolate diverse styles of thinking and to relate them to the groups from which they spring." [35] In some sense or other he takes these thought styles to be integral to the content of the group's thought, and when he comes to problems of validity of ideas, he takes a position in between the irrelevance of group perspective to the establishment of truth and its entire adequacy for determining truth. And he believes that in some way epistemological concepts must be revised to take account of this view. But precisely how the nature of the genesis of an assertion becomes relevant to its truth is not clear, even after much discussion.[36]

Perhaps the nearest approach to it is his statement:

> In certain areas of historical-social knowledge it should be regarded as right and inevitable that a given finding should contain the traces of the position of the knower. . . . The problem is not how we might arrive at a non-perspectivistic picture but how, by juxtaposing the various points of view, each perspective may be recognized as such and thereby a new level of objectivity attained.[37]

It is to be noted in this connection that he has previously adopted the view that all historical knowledge is relative to the position of the observer, that a dynamic synthesis is required, which must be reformulated from time to time.[38] And faced with the question how this can be done by perspective-bound groups, he takes refuge in the intellectuals. For they feel the impact of different classes; they alone are in a position to choose their affiliation; they are capable of carrying out their mission, which is "the discovery of the position from which a total perspective would be possible." [39] Mannheim's questioning here whether "it is desirable to throw overboard all of the opportunities which arise out of their peculiar situation," a situation in which a wider area of choice brings a need for total orientation and synthesis, shows pretty clearly the sociohistorical content of his own approach—the dilemma of the intellectual in our day. But this is the best he can offer in the way of objectivity in social knowledge.

By contrast the Marxian theory is adamant on the objectivity of truth. No one in modern epistemology is more insistent than Lenin in his *Materialism and Empirio-Criticism* on the absolute truth which science, with its relative truth at any time, is constantly approaching. And in the whole of the analysis above we have seen that the sociohistorical context hypothesis is concerned either with the cause and function of an idea (and does not discuss its truth) or with expanding the content of the idea and relating elements of its content (in which case the question of its truth arises only after the content has been expanded, and the answer is a matter of objective inquiry). Of course in the process of expansion the form of the question may change. Instead of asking Mill's question if there are qualities of pleasure, we might ask at the end if in the light of his own high evaluation of individuality his fear of the masses is well grounded. Whether the answer is Yes or No—I should say it is No—the resolution of his question is a scientific matter. Similarly, just as a question may be answered in a rough way prior to analysis, and after analysis may scarcely seem to need an answer, so many questions may tend to disappear on a fuller analysis, not because they are juggled away, but because they are answered on the road to clarification of content. In this respect philosophical materialists tend to the view that questions about personal immortality are not well answered merely by showing that all perceptible consequences that could be deduced from the hypothesis that Mr. A now is a disembodied spirit are not verified or are unverifiable. They are better answered by expanding the content of the idea until it appears as the demand for a richer quality of life in the context of a collective insecurity engendered by lack of control over nature and the conflicts of man against man. Such a transformation has probably answered the question in its analysis of man along the way. And where desired such steps may be rendered explicit.

It need scarcely be added that there is no inherent obstacle to applying the general thesis to itself as an idea, and that there is a sociohistorical context to the very idea that ideas have sociohistorical content. It consists of placing the philosophical and scientific enterprise in the vanguard of the collective effort of mankind to achieve a greater measure of freedom, and thus giving human reason a greater scope in the direction and organization of human affairs.

II

It is perhaps overpresumptuous, after dealing in such small compass with so vast a problem, to try to dispose of two equally broad topics as corollaries of the above analysis. This is by way of apology for the programmatic formulation of what follows on the relation of theory and practice, and on the role of ideas in history.

The thesis of the unity of theory and practice summarizes results and attitudes in metaphysics, epistemology, methodology, and ethics. Its spread may be indicated briefly.

As a metaphysical theory it is primarily antidualistic. If theory be taken as thinking and practice as doing, the unity of the theory and practice is in general form supported by all the philosophies that struggled against the Cartesian dualism, in which thinking was the work of mind or soul and doing the work of body. The view that mind and all its works arose in an evolution of matter and development of the universe thus constitutes the broadest philosophical content of the thesis, and it rests on the results of the sciences in many different fields.

As an epistemological thesis, the view of the unity of theory and practice is often expressed by materialists in the theory that ideas reflect the movement of matter or the properties of existence. In sociohistorical terms this is the theory of causality, instrumentality, and content discussed above. In psychological, physiological, and physical terms it is the familiar scientific attempt to trace the processes of perception, feeling, and thought as qualities of situations of organism and environment interaction. This is all that need be involved in a materialistic *representative* theory of knowledge. Clearly, it is a far cry from the traditional copy theory in the sense which a Lockean dualistic formulation employs.

As a methodological thesis, the unity of theory and practice summarizes a hard-won principle of the psychological and social sciences—a kind of functionalism which is the counterpart of the expansion of content of ideas examined above. Thus a Freudian postulate that there are no chance elements in the mental life becomes, in effect, a demand that some functional role be found in the personality development and expression of the given individual to which the mental element may be related. The historical and anthropological treatment of religion and philosophy as in part emotional security techniques of man in the face of an unknown world, is also a demand for exhibition of the practical side of theory. And conversely, the whole growth of the psychology of personality and of the systematic study of societies lends its weight to the view that human practice is not best regarded as random movement of organic bodies but involves determinable systematic relationships. Such methodological principles and the successes they bring add their weight to the general thesis of the unity of theory and practice.

Perhaps the most difficult aspect of the theory is to be found in the ethical domain. For here it has both descriptive and normative components. It tells a man that, whatever he may say, his theory has a practical side, and at the same time often urges him not to *divorce* theory from practice, which, if the descriptive component is correct, he cannot really do anyhow. The relationships involved obviously call for careful analysis.

The descriptive component represents a methodological principle in the description of a man's values which is as old as Socrates. Socrates contended that no man really knows the good and does evil. Aristotle's treatment of the problem centers about describing the way in which passion blinds a man at the moment of action so that, although in one sense he knows the good, in another he forgets it. The whole of the ethical literature about moral principles and their relation to choice grapples with the same problem. The results may be expressed as a resolution, widely held today, that a man's values are to be described as some function of his choices actually made or his directions of striving, rather than simply in terms of principles preached or even beliefs entertained. Theory is thus formulated initially as a systematic pattern of practice.

The fact that there is a normative element therefore does not deny the relation of theory and practice but points to the added value of its *conscious* recognition. To tell a man not to divorce theory and practice is to warn him not to neglect the practical side of his theory or the theoretical side of his practice. It is also to recognize the way in which consciousness of their relation may modify the subsequent character of both. This raises the problem of the role of ideas in history, at which we shall look below.

If the thesis of the unity of theory and practice has such wide implications and appears to be supported on so many fronts, two tasks are required in its explication. One is an extensive analysis of its meaning and the variety of specific relations in the different fields, and this obviously cannot be undertaken here. The other is some explanation of the appearance of separateness which has characterized theory and practice, and an estimate of what bases there may be for the relative separateness which makes it possible to speak of *their* unity in more than the historical sense of correcting a false dichotomy.

The latter task is not an *a priori* matter. Physiologically, the problem is that of the evolutionary development of the brain and its activity in relation to the motor activity of the rest of the body. Culturally, the problem is that of the growth of language and symbolic systems (from ritual to pure mathematics). Sociologically, the problem is essentially that of the division of labor; it includes the story of the historical separation of "brain" and "brawn," the development of intellectual classes,[40] and the separation and separate functioning of philosophers, scientists, and so forth. The separateness of theory thus reflects the physical and social separation processes; but the content, origin, and reference of theory is existence in all its qualities, on all its levels, and with all its conflicts.

III

If the role of ideas in history has at times seemed an insoluble problem, it is only because the question has been formulated in the premises of an implicit dualism, mechanism, or epiphenomenalism. Ideas taken in a mystical way are with difficulty related to the procession of material events. They either stand apart or are convicted of unreality, or else float helplessly over the flux. From the point of view of a modern materialism, the problem is a thoroughly empirical one, straightforward and without inherent mystery. As in the case of the unity of theory and practice, it has relatively distinct phases.

Physiologically, the question appears as the relation of brain responses to motor responses, and the degree to which—if we may put the matter so loosely—brain patterns at any time determine the form of motor responses, or instead are simply a clearinghouse for original stimuli to the brain itself. This is a thoroughly scientific problem, whose very formulation as well as solution rests with experimental physiology.

Psychologically, the problem is the role of thinking in the life of a man, and its relation to action and feeling. Here again there are no obstacles to a thoroughly empirical study of the role of deliberation in customary activity and in choice. The effectiveness of ideas in this sense is sometimes great, sometimes small, depending on the external circumstances and the given individual. Thus we can distinguish the thinking that is reasoning from the thinking that is "rationalizing," and we can look for the determinants of both types.

Sociologically, the problem takes several different forms. It may be a study of the role of planning in any field of social activity, its scope and effect. Or it may be a study of the degree to which science spreads and becomes the guiding method in human activity in all fields. Or it may be a study of the mode of functioning of intellectuals as a social group.

In the first sense it is clear that ideas not only are practical but have come to have an increasing role in history. A modern war is much more carefully planned than an ancient one; modern industry in its productive aspects is increasingly socialized and rationalized; and so forth.

In the second sense, ideas have likewise come to have a greater role, subject to all sorts of limiting factors. It was Hobbes who said:

> For I doubt not, but if it had been a thing contrary to any mans right of dominion, or to the interest of men that have dominion, *That the three Angles of a Triangle, should be equall to two Angles of a Square;* that doctrine should have been, if not disputed, yet by the burning of all books of Geometry, suppressed, as farre as he whom it concerned was able.[41]

And Nazi racial theory has shown clearly that even today the natural sciences are not immune to external influences. Nevertheless, the physical sciences are too intimately bound to modern industry to lose their effectiveness. The psychological and social sciences are growing apace, although their application lags and ideological elements are frequent. But there is ample reason to believe that, when interest-bound obstructions to clarity are minimized or removed, the social sciences may play as effective a role in social organization as the physical sciences have played in the organization of production.

In the third sense, the role of intellectuals has, of course, been a variable one. For intellectuals have by no means constituted a uniform group. The historical role of medical men is quite different in primitive tribes, in ancient Greece, in modern society; and only at some points is it comparable to that of clergy in the Middle Ages. Clergy, again, vary in the Middle Ages and in modern times. Lawyers have, perhaps, had a more constant role. The role of professors is largely equivalent to that of educational institutions at a given time. In general, the activity of intellectuals has reflected the state of knowledge and the conflict of social classes. Their lot has been assigned to them by the structure of the given society, and they have transcended it at times either by the content of their work (e.g., revolutionary scientific discoveries, whose effectiveness, however, was determined by other factors) or else by their alignment with a rising class (e.g., the French Encyclopedists, Lenin). Therefore there was, for the most part, no special problem of the effectiveness of their ideas. At any time, the ideas of the ruling class are effective enough, while the class is safely in power. The whole problem of the role of intellectuals is transcended in a socialist society that educates the whole of its people and gives full scope for intellectual activity in all phases of its life.

What then remains of the old problem whether ideas necessarily follow practice or lead it? Clearly this formulation is oversimplified, resting on the divorce of theory and practice. If ideas are visions of particular men and groups with differing degrees of clarity and opaqueness, and if, as a problem in the history of ideas, we wish to examine the occurrence of the ideas intellectually formulated, in relation to the social and historical activity of groups of men, then all sorts of relations can be discovered. Ideas can express the past, foreshadow the future, and guide what is coming into being. Ideas can play the part of hardeners, crystallizers, prognosticators, levers for breaking down vested forms, shadows of coming events, organizers. This is seen, for example, in the continual attempts men make to justify the social policies and beliefs which they advance. And we cannot say that only actions count and reasons are unimportant. For the reasons given for action, when fully understood, may indicate the direction of further action; and they will show where the paths of men now acting together may come to diverge. When for example the historian of ideas traces the arguments for the belief in God, with all their variety, or those seeking to justify absolutism, or private property, one can see through them the changing scene to which they respond, and their roles at particular times in crystallizing or sharpening men's attitudes, in covering or clarifying their motives, in comforting or rallying men. But all such functions are served by ideas at any time not as entities separate from practice, but as part of the whole matrix of social life. On its active side, therefore, the theory of the role of ideas is the theory of how policies can and best may be formulated and become effective; in short, it is the theory of leadership as well as that of reflection.

In general, it is patently clear that wrong thinking has momentous results. It is, therefore, equally clear that right thinking can have powerful effects. Once thought is seen in its manifold phases and in its intimate relations with practice, we can understand both its glorification in idealist theory and its crucial role in materialist theory. Aristotle conceived of God as pure thought thinking about itself. This continual rational energizing was the unmoved mover of all that went on in the cosmos. Hegel stretches the process out through time; the Absolute instead of being self-consciousness is realizing self-consciousness in the processes of nature and of history. The materialist philosophy need give self-consciousness no less central a role; but it is a role cast for men, not gods. The evolution of man can be seen as the growth of effective freedom, of man's mastery over nature and over himself. It can thus be seen as the practical growth of a fuller self-consciousness. The active role of thinking in history, so far from being denied, becomes the measure of a society's approach to greater freedom.

References

[1] *The American Philosophy of Equality* (Chicago, 1928), p. 69.

[2] *Ibid.*, p. 178. This argument was used much later when the question of racial equality was seriously advanced.

[3] *Pragmatism*, Lecture I.

[4] *Philosophy and Logical Syntax* (London, 1935), pp. 29–30.

[5] Quoted in Harold Laski, *Where Do We Go f·om Here?* (New York, 1940), pp. 126–227.

[6] *Ideology and Utopia* (London, 1936), pp. 49–53.

[7] H. D. Lasswell, *Politics: Who Gets What, When, How* (New York, 1936);

James Marshall, *Swords and Symbols* (New York, 1939); James Burnham, *The Machiavellians* (New York, 1943). Lasswell, for example, says (p. 156): "From the 'divine right of kings' to the 'rights of man' to the 'proletarian dictatorship'; these have been the principal vocabulary changes in the political history of the modern world. In each case a language of protest, long a utopian hope, became the language of an established order, an ideology. The ruling élite elicited loyalty, blood, and taxes from the populace with new combinations of vowels and consonants."

[8] Rudolf Hilferding, *Das Finanzkapital* (1910), pp. 426–429, as transl. by Paul M. Sweezy, in his *The Theory of Capitalist Development* (New York, 1942), pp. 375–378, under the title "The Ideology of Imperialism."

[9] *Ibid.*, p. 376.

[10] In his famous essay, "How to Make Our Ideas Clear."

[11] John Dewey, *Logic: The Theory of Inquiry* (New York, 1938), p. 109.

[12] Metaphorically, what the idea contains is what we see when we hold it up to the light. If we are thinking of existence, we could speak of the content as what the idea stretches over or covers or mirrors. If we take the notion purely functionally, it is what the idea points to. There is no intention here to minimize the depth of analysis required in these epistemological problems. They are bypassed simply in the belief that the point of the present paper does not require any fuller treatment.

[13] These are, of course, extremes within the materialist-naturalist tradition. Both are united against an idealist or Platonic intuitionist theory of ideas.

[14] Various current approaches derived from the positivist or the instrumentalist analysis or both, show almost a phobia of abstract ideas and insist on translation to discover content into some form of particular experience, whether as with Bridgman (*The Logic of Modern Physics*, New York, 1946) the concept becomes synonymous with the operations performed, or, as in the semanticists, the ultimate reference is to the "un-speakable" or "silent" level.

[15] "Pragmatics" is the study of the relation of signs to interpreters—as distinguished from "syntactics," the relation of signs to one another, and "semantics," the relation of signs to objects. (See C. W. Morris, *Foundations of the Theory of Signs*, Chicago, 1938, and his reformulation of the distinction in *Signs, Language and Behavior*, New York, 1946, pp. 317–320.)

[16] *The German Ideology* (New York: International Publishers, 1939), p. 87.

[17] *Ludwig Feuerbach and the Outcome of Classical German Philosophy*, ed. C. P. Dutt (New York, 1934), Appendix, p. 79. Cf. Part IV of text, especially pp. 64 ff.

[18] *Escape from Freedom* (New York, 1941), p. 78.

[19] I do not pursue here the question whether there are in fact the kinds of sense data mentioned, or whether elements of interpretation are not also relevant.

[20] *Anti-Dühring* (New York 19..), p. 123.

[21] For a presentation of this sociohistorical content in pleasure theory, see my "Coordinates of Criticism in Ethical Theory," *Philosophy and Phenomenological Research*, Vol. VII, No. 4 (June, 1947), pp. 554–559.

[22] *Utilitarianism*, chap. ii.

[23] Chap. vi—in Everyman's Library ed., *Utilitarianism, Liberty, and Representative Government*, p. 255.

[24] *Ibid.*, chap. viii—pp. 279–288.

[25] Engels, in a review of Marx's *Critique of Political Economy* (printed in the Appendix to his *Ludwig Feuerbach, etc.*, New York, 1934), p. 94.

[26] *A Handbook of Marxism,* ed. Emil Burns, p. 44.

[27] See also, for example, the criticism that Russell assumes our world to have the character of simples in the sense required by his logical analysis, in Maurice C. Cornforth, *Science and Idealism* (New York, 1947), chap. viii.

[28] *Metaphysics,* IV, 1007a22 ff. (transl. H. Tredennick, Loeb Classical Lib., Vol. I, p. 171).

[29] It is interesting to note that the atomists, who rejected the Aristotelian concept of nature, took slavery to be an accident; e.g., Lucretius, *On the Nature of Things* (in *The Stoic and Epicurean Philosophers,* ed. W. J. Oates, New York, 1940, p. 77).

[30] *Dialectics of Nature,* pp. 161–163, 182–183.

[31] The propositions about permanence and change, with which Engels is here dealing, themselves constitute an abstract formulation or a boiled-down residue from the original Aristotelian position, which is even richer in sociohistorical content than indicated above. For, in order to understand his whole teleological approach to which his laws of logic belong, we have to take seriously his basic assertion that nature works like the artist; and several of the fundamental discrepancies in his account, will, I believe, become clear by reference to the actual character of the arts or crafts in his time. In this sense, the reference provides content, as well as possible cause or source.

[32] The empirical thesis that scientific results actually grow up in the needs of the battle against nature, whatever specific form it takes in a given society—as against the view that the results of science are gifts of the gods or products of disinterested wonder—is, of course, an essential part of the above view.

[33] I owe this neat formulation to Dr. Stanley Moore.

[34] *Ideology and Utopia,* pp. 110–111, 278.

[35] *Ibid.,* pp. 153, 45.

[36] *Ibid.,* pp. 258 ff.

[37] *Ibid.,* p. 266.

[38] *Ibid.,* pp. 71, 135.

[39] *Ibid.,* p. 143.

[40] See, for example, Farrington's suggestion in his *Greek Science* (1944) that some intellectual fields developed from the administration of men, others from the crafts in their battle with nature.

[41] *Leviathan,* chap. xi.

THE NATURE AND STATUS OF VALUES*

by

JOHN R. REID

John R. Reid is Professor of Philosophy, Stanford University, Ph.D., University of California, 1936; James Sutton Memorial Traveling Fellow in Philosophy, University of California, 1932–1933; Teaching Fellow in Philosophy, 1933–1935; Sterling Research Fellow in Philosophy, Yale University, 1936–1937; John Simon Guggenheim Fellow in Philosophy, 1943–1944. A' Stanford since 1937. Author of *A Theory of Value,* 1938. Contributor of articles to the *Journal of Philosophy, International Journal of Ethics, Philosophical Review, Mind, Philosophy of Science,* and *American Journal of Psychiatry.*

IT IS widely felt (by antimaterialists, anyway) that for materialists the problem of value presents quite special difficulties. Indeed, some critics would go so far as to assert that a solution of the problem is impossible, in "materialist terms," without inconsistency—i.e., impossible. Materialists, it might be generously conceded, can describe and explain (albeit rather crudely) "the facts," but when it comes to values they must call in help from the idealists, who know how to deal with such spiritual things. The truth seems to be, however, that—unless in adopting materialism they have abdicated their intelligence—materialists can describe and explain, or appreciate, values as well as any other kind of philosophers having similar in-

* I wish to thank the Board of Trustees of the Prall Memorial Foundation for their permission to reprint here, with some changes, a large part of the second David Wight Prall Memorial Lecture, which I delivered at Berkeley, Calif., in May, 1946.

terests, gifts, and backgrounds, and if they cannot, it will not be *because* they are materialists—nor, I trust, vice versa.

But this sort of debate is logically hopeless until such terms as "materialism" and "value" are defined. While I hold—with an increasing number of philosophers of all "schools"—that to search for "the true" definition of these or other terms is a confused and misguided undertaking, yet, if our definitions are not to be ignorant and arbitrary, it is necessary to survey the available evidence, which means both looking at a number of facts and looking into various interpretations of them, before deciding what is a "good" (i.e., clear, unambiguous, adequate, and generally useful) definition. As everybody knows, such a definitional inquiry, if circumspect and just to "opponents," is a very lengthy affair. Hence I shall leave materialism to other contributors and concentrate on value—hoping that the acceptability of what I say will not, in any event, be determined by the reader's prior acceptance of *any* ism. Indeed, to speak like a "crass materialist," I should just as lief have it determined by the quantity of gonadotropic hormone secreted by his anterior hypophysis.

To turn at once, then, to a couple of definitions which I hope will prove fairly serviceable in the sequel, I suggest that in the generic and substantive sense of the term, to say that X *is* a value, either positive or negative, is equivalent to saying that X is an *experience* which involves, among its immediate conditions and constituents, *at least* a motor-affective attitude, plus some given *content* towards which this attitude is directed, and to which it is thus *related*. As distinguished from this sense of the term, "value," in its *attributive* sense, may be defined as follows: To say that an object X *has* value is equivalent to saying that X is valuable or—if the jargon be permitted—disvaluable, i.e., that X *tends,* under ordinary circumstances, to evoke recurrently and to sustain for some variable period of time either a positive or a negative motor-affective attitude which is directed towards X itself *or* towards some effect (or partial effect) of X.

Clearly, the only evidence that anything has value in this attributive sense, i.e., that it possesses some value property, is that it is *known* to produce actual values, in the substantive sense of the term—a statement on all fours with the statement that the only evidence that opium has analgesic properties is that when opium is administered, in suitable amounts, we observe (or infer) that it mitigates or completely relieves such-and-such pains. As for actual values, when they are being felt, no evidence is needed to support any statements which merely report their existence, but only the semantical condition that we know what we are talking about and can recognize a case of it when present—which, to be sure, requires, in its indirect way, not a little animal faith.

By way of explaining and justifying the above definitions of "value," let us begin with examining what may be referred to as the value situation. This situation, as I analyze it, is constituted by a value content, a value attitude, a value relation, and some value properties. Such a way of speaking will, I fear, seem both wordy and circular, but I shall try to justify the language by the use to which it is put in what follows. First, some explanations as to its meaning are in order.

By "value content," I designate any content of experience, whether sensory or imaginal, which is the object of a conscious motor-affective attitude. At any moment when we are awake, and at some times even when we are said to be asleep but are dreaming, our attention falls upon some experiential content. If this content is liked or disliked, if we favor it or disfavor it, then this content becomes a *value* content. The content itself may be given to attention through any sensory channels, or it may be largely the product, as we say, of imagination; the perception in which the content is a sensuous ingredient may be classified as veridical or illusory; the content may be relatively simple or complex, and may persist for a long or a short time; but in the language here employed it is a value content if it stands in the relation of being the immediate object of interest, which latter (if positive) may be expressed by saying that the content is liked, enjoyed, found satisfactory, and so on.

Thus whether or not a content is a value content, as distinguished from *any* content, depends upon its status as a term in a functional relation—the other necessary term in which is what I have called an attitude. No content of experience is, intrinsically or absolutely, a value content; but any content is a value content if it is the immediate object of a positive or negative motor-affective attitude. If I am thirsty, the taste and feel of a drink of cool water constitutes a sensory *Gestalt* which is such a value content; so does the view of the pear trees in bloom and the Stanford hills beyond, when I glance up and look out of my study window.

As these examples indicate, I am using the term "value content" so that no restrictions are being implied as to the *degree* that rational mediation is involved. Every content may be ingredient in a perception, and every perception may involve inference, and so be partly a "rational" affair; but still, I am supposing, or, as I think, reporting, that something or other is always present to attention, and one can be liking it or not. If he is, the content is so far good.

Plainly enough, the value of such a content is relative to the interest-conditioned frame of reference in which it occurs. The claim here made is semantically grounded in my inability, which I infer is common, to discover within the nature of any content (essence or datum, if you prefer the latter terms) any marks which might intelligibly be said to constitute the intrinsic value of the content in question. Value may be said to "accrue" to the content, or it may be imputed to it, or to some value property attached to one or more of its causal conditions; but I think that no value can be found within the content itself.

As a usual thing, the value content is complex, and so contains relations, but the relation by virtue of which it is called a value content is external to the content, since it is instituted by a motor-affective act which is not, and could not intelligibly be construed as being, a part of the content valued in the context.

A word about the meaning of the symbol "value attitude." As here used, it refers to what has been variously labeled by different value theorists, "motor-affective attitude," "positive or negative interest," "feeling-attitude," and so on. The label does not matter very much, for the fact is obvious. We react in some degree, positively or negatively, to most of the objects in our experience, if not all. Genetically viewed, it appears to be the case that such a tendency to accept or reject is prior to the formation of any clear and definite notions as to the qualitative nature or causal properties of the object in question—things being good or bad, in this rudimentary and primordial sense, before they are hot or cold, sweet or bitter, red or green, or classified as light or heavy, nourishing or not, and so on. As some plants turn toward a source of light, without knowing, presumably, anything about the "nature" of light, so animals, including men, of course, quite naturally turn away from certain stimuli, and toward others, with such feelings and attitudes as may be inferred, on more or less satisfactory evidence, to accompany their overt behaviors. Such reactions, if relatively simple and if occurring low in the phylogenetic scale, are sometimes called tropisms; and Laird, by analogy, has distinguished a class of human values which he calls values of "natural election."

"Value property," as indicated above, refers to some inferred causal property of a thing—as constrasted with a directly experienced or given value content. Thus, a certain substance in cod-liver oil had a positive value property before chemists isolated and identified it as the particular substance called vitamin A. Plainly, the research of these chemists, in no sense here worth discussing, may in a Pickwickian sense be said to have generated or now to constitute the value property in question, as if one could justifiably assert that cod-liver oil was not good for xerophthalmia before vitamin A was known to exist in it. Such a value property logically differs from a value content in that the latter is by definition a necessary term in a value relation, in the substantive sense of the term, as well as being something of which we are conscious; whereas, we may, or may not, be conscious of a value property, which is integral to value only in the attributive sense of the term, i.e., it causally conditions the occurrence of a value, and so is external to any given value, as such. From this it follows (in the language I am using) that a value property is one kind of *causal* property and is called a *value* property because we believe it stands in the relation of being a cause, or partial cause, of some value.

In the light of these definitions, the symbol "value relation" takes on, or may be usefully given, a dual meaning. Thus the relation holding between a value attitude and value content is one kind of value relation, which I shall call an *intrinsic* value relation, since the relation is logically intrinsic to any case of actual value, in the same sense as a point, called its center, is intrinsic to a circle. On the other hand, it is convenient to refer to the relation between, say, a certain diet and a sense of well-being as a value relation also, though in this type of case the relation in question is *extrinsic* and merely contingent, since what we are saying is that the diet has causal properties which tend to bring about and maintain, in certain organisms, a sense of well-being—this latter phrase designating, I take it, a range of actual values.

Value properties are, of course, relative to value situations, which vary so as to make it, generally, difficult to determine whether or not there is sufficient evidence to justify a value statement through which the claim is expressed that such-and-such an object has, or does not have, such-and-such value properties. But anything having, or not having, a value property is a matter of fact, which to get at, or to make verifiable statements about, requires no special kind of logic or technique of inquiry. The fact that our definition of "value" contains symbols which refer to events private in status does involve us in the familiar difficulties common to using an intersubjective language; but these difficulties are not insurmountable, unless we set up neurotically high standards, and are, in any event, to be preferred, I think, to committing what Mr. C. I. Lewis calls the "fallacy of changing the subject," even though this latter is done in the interest of being operational and "scientific." Thus, to find out whether some new substance has a value property—or, as we should ordinarily express it, is of value, or is valuable—we need only resort to the kind of methods which lead to knowledge when we are conducting inquiries into neutral facts, i.e., facts whose constituent terms do *not* include a value content or value attitude.

Though it may be plausibly argued, if we mean by "belief" something sufficiently primitive and inarticulate, that no values occur except in contexts involving, or in some vague sense expressing, a belief, I suggest that the minimal or necessary logical conditions for applying the term "value" do not include a belief as to the causes of the value experienced. Certainly, values are felt without statements being formulated and asserted about the environmental or intraorganic conditions of the experience, as when I wake up on a spring morning and find myself enjoying what *only later* I infer is the scent of honeysuckle drifting through my open window. Now liking, enjoying, prizing, favoring, and so on, are nonrational attitudes, and, however much mediated and overlaid by thought processes, these attitudes are not judgments which are true or false. Judgments may and inevitably do affect such attitudes, tempering and modifying them in complex ways; and such attitudes, by determining a particular selection of data or bias in interpretation, conversely affect judgment. But still, liking a piece of candy is not the same thing as judging that it is (say) an expensive source of carbohydrates, or that if one is suffering from diabetes, then he ought not to eat it, or that, in the light of relevant gross behaviors and linguistic reports, most persons after going without food for several hours, would like the piece of candy, and so on; for endless judgments can be made about anything.

Both idealists and pragmatists, fearing evidently that a distinction of reason is going to lead to a suppression of its function, have characteristically sought to combine, and have ended up, I think, by confusing, several things in this sort of context. Thus Dewey, in his quest for "warranted assertibility," insists upon either rejecting the simple report of a felt value or transforming it into a causal hypothesis about the sources and effects of the given value—which hypothesis, in turn, is construed as an expression of, and leading to, judgments of practice, whose purpose is to guide and regulate our choice in the problematic situation which provoked inquiry, with the tentative end-result, as he interprets it, that the hypothesis about what "*will* do" also functions as a kind of moral exhortation regarding what, in the context, *ought* to be done. Now this way of talking, confusing though it sounds, no doubt has some pragmatic merits; but it seems to me unnecessary, either for telling the truth or—perhaps something more important—reforming our habits, seeing that all the facts and values Dewey takes into account of can be dealt with in other categories, while maintaining familiar and, I think, useful distinctions between such activities as reporting, inferring, and advising.

Values in some honorific sense, say intellectual values, do, of course, presuppose intellectual activities. Thus if a reader enjoys the *Critique of Pure Reason,* his enjoyment is certainly mediated by many and complex sorts of judgment; and if the reader is incapable of making these judgments, because of a lack of brains or a lack of background, he will surely not enjoy the book, but the opposite. But even in this sort of case, such enjoyment as may occur is not a judgment; nor, on the other hand, is the feeling of boredom, irritation, or frustration, such as might be felt by either a stupid or a very intelligent reader. The conclusion plainly indicated is that, while judgments are a necessary condition of *some* values only, motor-affective reactions are a necessary condition of *all* values.

I have emphasized, what in the context is redundant, that a subject must be aware of value contents, whereas value properties may exist independently of our acquaintance with them, or even inferential knowledge of their existence. Thus a psychiatrist may say that glucose administered intravenously is necessary for a given patient if the latter's brain cells are not to be permanently injured as a result of irreversible changes following upon unduly prolonged hypoglycemic coma due to insulin shock treatment for schizophrenia. The patient, being in a state of coma, is, of course, not aware of any value content, nor is he able to make any inferences as to his need for this or that treatment. But this important type of situation raises no difficulties for our theory. The glucose is good for the patient, whether he likes it or not, because we assume (in saying this) that he will have a better chance for some kind of success, good judgment or happiness if his brain is not affected in certain kinds of ways, although we are trying to alter its functioning by insulin shock in other kinds of ways. But such value terms as "success," "good adjustment," or "happiness," have for at least some of their necessary referents what I have called value contents. So, by a roundabout but yet familiar and rational way, the value judgments made by the psychiatrist—which in turn mediate his "judgments of practice," as Dewey calls them—regarding his schizophrenic patient, fit without undue stretching or distortion into the axiological pattern we are trying to explain and justify.

When we say of something, like insulin or candy, that it "has" certain value properties, we are, I take it, making a factual statement which is true or false—relative to some given context or assumed frame of reference. Such relativity I am inclined to accept as a patent fact of experience; but one still hears—perhaps it is earlier than we think—about the dangers and errors of what is called "relativism." As I see it, values are relative in two senses: (1) That any entity as a value is logically conditioned by and is relative to someone's adoption of a symbolic convention according to which something of this kind falls within the class designated by the term "value." And (2) that any particular object should attract or hold our attention and evoke our liking (or disliking) depends upon, and varies with, the total context. Thus, if we have just eaten a rich dinner followed by a very sweet dessert, we probably shall not like the taste of candy, or will at least like it much less than if we had not eaten for hours, and had just returned from a hike in the hills. Also, we probably shall not like the candy, in spite of a hike in the hills, if it is made of poor-grade chocolate, saccharine, and rancid butter. Similar and quite obvious considerations hold for every kind of food and drink, and everything else to which we respond motor-affectively, including so-called "masterpieces" of art and the intellectual products of even—or should I say particularly?—our greatest minds. Naturally, as animals with similar bodies, living in similar environments, we have similar problems of adjustment in maintaining homeostasis; and similar psychophysical mechanisms are brought into operation, involving such events as nutritious substances, suitable liquids, temperature controls, and muscular adjustments, all tending, in a normally functioning organism, to maintain sufficient constancy in its internal environment, so that it may live and prosper, at least biologically. Any so-called "naturalist" in value theory who exaggerates the differences between human organisms or the variability of their physiological states and resulting motor-affective attitudes and, finally, values is, so far, saying what is false; and *if* he is, then it would be false whether he is a naturalist or not. What the naturalist is emphasizing, and what I do not see how anyone can deny, is that while men's needs are more or less similar, their desires, tastes, and preferences vary, also more or less, but rather more than their needs—though millions like grapefruit and Jane Russell. Two men may be equally in need of food; but the satisfaction they feel in eating it will vary with their personal tastes, which in turn vary with their conditioning, their physical environment, the culture they live in, and so on, indefinitely. To say that all this is "mere" anthropology or physiology or psychology and has no important bearing upon our "real" values seems to me hardly sane, and suggests a mind which feeds almost exclusively upon a diet of words, usually undefined, if not on principle indefinable.

Lest some of you suppose that I am here attacking only straw men, I might cite the case of an Oxford-trained philosopher, to whom I remarked that I was interested in psychiatry, and that I thought it had some important implications for value theory. Controlling his evident astonishment, he merely raised his eyebrows and piped in an epicene voice: "Isn't it curious that you should think that psychiatry has anything to do with value theory!"

That values are relative is no oddity in nature, but is a truth so obvious to the natural scientists I talk with that they can hardly believe that philosophers still argue about it. For the sense in which values are relative is the same sense in which all events are relative to, and vary with, their conditions. The flame is relative to the conditions that support combustion; the amount of a given salt which will go into solution is relative to its kind, the nature of the solvent, and the temperature of the mixture; the rate at which an electric current flows through a conductor is relative to the nature of the conductor, its cross-sectional area, and its temperature; plants require conditions—certain elements in solution at certain ranges of temperature, and so on—which do not vary beyond certain limits, or they will die; and, of course, all animal life depends upon the availability and utilization of various compounds and mixtures of solids, liquids, and gases—which ones, and in what forms and amounts, varying with the species of animal, and even the particular member of the species, a unique individual. In general, A causes and affects B only in a certain kind of context C; and each of these distinguishable factors is reciprocally dependent on the other. So it is hard to see how any philosopher who even occasionally looks into the book of nature can interpret the signs he finds there to any other conclusion than that what is good for man—which, of course, may be different from what he likes at a given moment—is relative to man's nature and his environment, and, strictly speaking, to *this* man in *this* environment. Our similarities may be more important than our differences, but one of our similarities is the desire—and often the need—to have our differences recognized.

Now let us turn to the difficult problem of value judgments. According to a familiar pattern of analysis, when we make a statement we at once express, by means of the structured word-vehicles used, our judgment, and we also semantically characterize at least some possible range of facts. Now if the word "statement" is thus used to refer to a declarative sentence, qua asserted, it being assumed that assertion is expressive, in the way indicated, of an act of judgment, then statements are either true or false—true if what they refer to is the case, and false if not. Statements, so construed, make truth claims—this being so, by definition, whether the statements are about values or about neutral events. Statements may refer, with varying degrees of clarity and descriptive adequacy, to such nonrational acts as liking; but—as we saw above—in the context it is obviously not the liking that is true; rather it is the part of the statement concerned with the occurrence, direction, intensity, object, or other aspects of the liking. To dislike a given picture is no more to fall into error than to dislike oysters or to suffer from indigestion is to fall into error. It may be plausible to argue, in a given case, that one dislikes the picture because he has failed to notice certain facts or to make such-and-such judgments, which, *if* they had been made, would have so altered the motor-affective attitude of the percipient that, instead of disliking the picture, he would have liked it. Also, after eating enough oysters, I may come to like them; and, after being psychoanalyzed, my indigestion may vanish, because I am forced to eat less in order to pay the psychoanalyst. But such changes, however desirable, in organic functions or motor-affective attitudes do not perform the miracle (some theories would require) of transforming these functions or attitudes into statements of which true or false may be significantly predicated.

Logically connected with this problem of value statements and their relation to our value attitudes is the highly controversial problem of the differences between the so-called "descriptive" and "expressive" functions of our value terms. One way of talking is to say that if a symbol describes, it does so because a semantical rule has been set up or accepted, by means of which the necessary and sufficient conditions for class membership within the class designated by the descriptive symbol, say X, have been specified. Hence we can say that, if X is on a given occasion used correctly, then X semantically means such-and-such. For a relatively easy case, take the word "mongrel." It designates, among other things, "a dog of mixed breed." Hence the descriptive function of the term, when so used, is to refer to this *kind* of dog. But we all recognize that to say, "Get that mongrel out of my yard," will produce a different effect upon its owner than to say, "Get that dog of mixed breed out of my yard." In this case, shall we say that substituting the *definiens* for the *definiendum* leaves the descriptive reference of the sentence the same, but alters its expressive meaning? But what does this distinction mean exactly? If we look up "mongrel" in the dictionary, we find that it is a term which is used "disparagingly." Hence, does the word "mongrel" not "say" that the person who uses it correctly does so with intent to disparage the dog? And is this meaning not on all fours with the other part of what the word says in the context, i.e., that the dog in question is one of mixed breed? True, the one reference is back to the attitude of the speaker and the other is forward to certain alleged facts about the dog's ancestry; but an interpreter has a conventional rule, stated in the dictionary, to guide and sanction his interpretation of *both* aspects of the term's meaning in use, and the term, accordingly, "says" something about its user's motor-affective attitude toward the dog, as well as something about the dog's genesis. Either reference may be true or false, but both are equally conventional, and the word-vehicle "mongrel" supports and determines the two interpretations in the same way.

In face-to-face communication, we of course "get at" what a term or sentence means by relying heavily upon the context, having recourse to definitions less often, and in many contexts less profitably, than to observations of the speaker's tone of voice, tempo of utterance, bodily posture and gestures, facial expression, including color of skin, and so on; each and all of these things conditioning our inferences as to the attitude of the speaker. Hence, when we say that a certain set of words expresses an attitude, X, we usually ought to say that the words, plus *n* other things, express X, the other things being in the context, I assume, a necessary part of the grounds of our inference.

Now it would take a long discussion to show adequately the bearing of this brief semiotic analysis upon the meaning of value statements. "Mongrel" is a word of relatively definite meaning, and it behaves in different contexts very simply, indeed, compared with "good" or "value." But I do want to suggest the point that both the descriptive and the expressive aspects of the meaning of the term "good" may be stipulated and governed by definitional rule in the same way. Thus, when we report that "X is good," in the substantive sense of the term, we may be referring both to the nature of X—i.e., what X must be in order properly to be called X—*and* to our attitude toward X, without which X would still be X, but not (in this context) good. For example, the statement, "*Oklahoma* is a very good show," certainly means in part, not only that it is a show, but that (say) the majority of the persons who have seen it have been delighted with it. As to the emotional or behavioral effects of answering some person who asked us, "Is *Oklahoma* a good show?" with "It's a very good show" *or* "The majority of persons who have seen it have been delighted with it," they would vary with all sorts of factors; and I think no useful generalization is here possible. The speaker may or may not side with the majority opinion; he may or may not be expressing his own opinion, or motor-affective attitude, when he says, "It's a very good show"; and the effects on the hearer are so various as to be, in general, unpredictable, without much extra knowledge of the particular situation.

In general, the semiotic point seems justified that a mark or sound describes only when it also expresses, this pragmatical function of the symbol being a presupposition of its semantical function. Of course this does not answer the question *what* is expressed; but we may say, I think, that if the symbol describes, it does so by virtue of acts of reference which are thus mediated through the symbol-vehicle employed. However, such intentional acts of reference relate the mind of its user to the symbol used, and thus institute a pragmatical relation, the psychological term in which is then said to be expressed by the symbol in use. Even if we argue that the semantical reference made by a symbol is not determined by the intention of its user on a given occasion but is the social product of some set of group habits, we still appeal, in case of conflicting interpretations, to a standard user, who knows the language properly, and whose intentions would be expressed if a particular use conformed to the accepted semantical rule governing proper usage, the definitional rule in question thus functioning both as a guide to interpretation and as a norm of correctness.

Expression in this limited sense is logically integral to any process of semiosis. But, of course, the term "expression" is used in another sense, as when we say that a person's facial expression (as the word itself implies) "expresses" something, for example, his feelings. In this case, the feelings said to be expressed are not a logical presupposition of the particular pattern of data observed when we look at the person's face: it is simply that experience of similar cases supports, as we may believe, the inference from one set of data to other data, with the restriction that the latter data, which are said to be expressed, are in a sense internal and private; for where both natural sign and significate are directly accessible, after suitable operations, to the interpreter, we should not use, I think, the term "expression." Thus tenderness and muscular rigidity over the right iliac fossa are *signs* of acute appendicitis, but we should not say that they *expressed* appendicitis; whereas, we should say that the patient's moans or flexed knees expressed his suffering.

This kind of distinction between the sort of relation holding between natural signs and their significates and that between conventional signs and their referents, is, I take it, fundamental. The one sort of relation is "logical" in the sense that it is formally conditioned by definitional rules; and the other is empirical in the sense that it is materially contingent upon how the facts happen to be related. In much of our thinking, these different relations are likely to become confused, since in practice any interpreter of a symbol-vehicle must depend upon causal laws holding in the given case in order to infer correctly that the symbol-vehicle does refer, for its user, to the same class of referents that it does for him, its interpreter. For, obviously, the existence of a definition, even one set forth in a standard dictionary, is no adequate guarantee that any particular user either is familiar with the definition or is on the occasion conforming to it. Our habits in this and other affairs, plus such "insight" as we can muster, are what actually guide us; conventions, whether called logical or merely social, being appealed to for "sanction" and in this way employed as instruments of control.

The relevance of this semiotic analysis to our narrower problem of the interpretation of value statements is, I trust, plain. Thus, if we say that the term "good," when used on a given occasion, expresses but does not describe, we may mean that it is unintelligible to hold that a picture does, or even could, exhibit a referent for the term "good" in the sense in which it might exhibit one for (say) the term "red" or "circular," but that it does furnish evidence, taking "good" now as an empirical mark seen or sound heard, which supports to some extent the inference that the user of the term is in such-and-such an internal state, has such-and-such a motor-affective attitude, and so on. We might add that, on this view, the user of "good" on such an occasion may very well not know what the word does express, its meaning not being given as a referent, but only mediated, through a quite different process of semiosis, by the words he uses, when taken as natural signs. This kind of meaning, conjured with by psychoanalysts, takes conventional symbols and interprets them as members in a causal series, usually so complex and with terms so nearly indistinguishable from one another as to leave utterly baffled, not to say incredulous, all but orthodox interpreters related by direct descent to the Great Interpreter Himself.

It is not my purpose to argue that symbols do not "mean" in this sense. Given a suitable definition of "meaning," obviously they do; the problem being, usually, to find out what. For once we leave members of a class designated through acts of semantical reference and thus, at least to some extent, under our "logical" control, we may, and quite regularly do, lose ourselves in a growing context of relations which, it may be said, are "completed" only in that whole which is never exhibited, but is "necessarily" presupposed by any genuinely significant reference. Of course, pragmatists—as a matter of policy—stop short before symbolically embracing this Context of all contexts; and hence the problem of what a symbol in this loose sense does or does not mean, is only solved (as the pragmatists say) pragmatically.

It appears, from our brief analysis, that the term "expression" is ambiguous in a very confusing way. Thus every symbol in one sense expresses, i.e., it conventionally expresses some mind's intention; otherwise, no reference is made, and the mark or sound in question lapses into mere physical existence, without semantical meaning. On the other hand, every symbol, by virtue of the fact that it has a body or vehicle, is also an event in the causal order of nature. Consequently, through a process of learning, various associations are built up in different minds such that the word-vehicle employed becomes a basis for inference, i.e., comes to function not only as a conventional but also, and often at the same time, as a natural sign, with the result that the word is now both *conventionally* expressive and, if the significate is internal to a mind, also *naturally* expressive. If, as in the case of the word "good," one of the empirical terms in the latter sort of expressive relationship is a motor-affective attitude, then the symbol takes on what may be called emotive meaning, which is, therefore, a subclass of meanings naturally expressed. However, when emotive meanings are so construed, they also may be a part of the semantical referent designated by a symbol, the reference to the attendant emotional process, whether in the mind of the symbol's user or interpreter, being controlled by the definitional rule governing the proper application of the symbol in question.*

If the relational interpretation of the semantical content of "good"

* Critics tell me that there "remains a difference" between expressing an attitude and describing (or designating or mentioning) it. This is of course true, and I have not denied it. What I have done, rather, is to try to say very briefly what this difference is, and what it amounts to in practice. Also I have argued that in some cases—"good" may be so defined as to make it a case in point—the term in use *both* expresses and describes some motor-affective attitude. Granted suitable definitions, "good," for example, might "express" this attitude in several ways: i.e., the term in use might induce or arouse (be a cause of) a motor-affective attitude in its interpreter; it might also be an effect of a similar attitude in the speaker; or it might function as a natural sign so as to make the interpreter *think of* (perhaps also *believe in* the existence of) a motor-affective attitude in the speaker; and finally, "good" might be so defined that in addition to doing any or all of the above things, it also, in *some* usages, logically *designates* the speaker's motor-affective attitude. But these different functions are not incompatible. Hence the same word-vehicle may function, in the same context, as *cause* of an attitude, as *effect* of an attitude, as *natural* sign of an attitude, and as *conventional* sign of an attitude. "Good" does not on every occasion of its use do all these things, but it *may* do all on some occasions *if* the relevant events (or terms) in the context are suitably related by cause-effect, sign-significate, and symbol-referent relations.

is accepted, then how are we to deal with statements such as, "This milk tastes good"? Does this statement not imply that there is before me a fluid, with such-and-such a history, having such-and-such properties, to which I am responding motor-affectively? And hence am I not ascribing a value property to a substance, ordinarily called "milk," as I here-now believe, which is, I also believe, causally conditioning at the time my reaction to it? These implications of conventional language I am, of course, willing to accept. But does it follow, then, that actually every value relation contains more than two terms, because it involves not only an attitude and content, but also some existent, such as this milk or this picture? I think not. True, in some cases, i.e., when we are referring to attributive values, we do make statements whose reference is to more than a dyadic relation between some value content and value attitude; but in other cases it seems to me equally plain that we do not commit ourselves to such outlying claims about the conditions or consequences of some value content but merely report the existence of an intrinsic value relation. Now if, as in this latter sort of case, thought perches—to use James's metaphor—on a given content, whether an aspect which might be referred to some external object, or an imaginal content which is not localized, although it could be dated, we still have only a value content and a value attitude, a two-term relation. But whenever, as usually happens, this content also functions as a sign, thought takes flight, i.e., an act of reference is mediated by the content, which now has meaning, the whole experience being deepened, enriched, and extended. But, in spite of this complexity, value in the substantive sense remains a dyadic relation: it is only when, through predication and inference, we refer to some of the causes or consequences of the value that more terms are logically involved.

If we conclude that in most instances value properties are referred to by value statements, it becomes necessary for purposes of verification to know which ones, at what place-times. Thus, if when I say, "Milk is good," I not only mean that I like the taste of *this* milk here-now and have liked in the past and expect to like in the future the taste of most instances of milk, but infer that many other persons also like milk; and if further I intend to assert that it is a good food, "protective," rich in vitamins and minerals and proteins of high biological value, specifically caseinogen, lactalbumin and lactoglobulin, and that caseinogen particularly contains liberal amounts of the so-called indispensable amino acids, which cannot be synthesized by the organism out of materials ordinarily available at a speed commensurate with the demands for normal growth, and that, further, milk is an economical source of these value properties—if I put all these and other implications into the statement, "Milk is good," then I have indeed *said* a mouthful, and may well feel the need for a glass of milk before making my next value judgment! However, I have no more than scratched the surface of the "meaning" of my statement if I refer, by varying degrees of indirection and through endless unspecified presuppositions, to the whole set of properties conditioning, materially, my value relation to milk. For in milk, as an unconscious symbol of mother-dependence, gastrointestinal fixations, and Œdipus ramifications the Great Father substitute himself only knows of what subtlety and complexity—in milk we have a symbol so rich as to afford the psychoanalysts a field day, and one's whole history, as well as the history of mankind, becomes in some vague sense "relevant."

My remaining space is limited, but I want to say a word about the cant antithesis, subjective versus objective, as applied to value. Man, as Santayana has remarked, has a prejudice against himself—or is it mainly against other men? But, whatever the explanation, many students, to say nothing of their older and presumably wiser teachers, declare that they are profoundly disturbed by what they call the "implications" of the "naturalistic position" on value. For, if value is subjective, then—why, they can do as they please; and, doubtless feeling immoral tendencies within themselves, they are properly horrified by this imagined freedom, and want some rigid and sober doctrine of the objectivity of values to constrain their all-too-natural impulses. Having worked themselves up into this moral lather—their own repressed desires having turned into aggressions against those philosophers who, as they naïvely imagine, would free them, by a species of word magic, from their super-egos, which are riding them hard—these upholders of objectivity are rarely in a frame of mind to stop and inquire what the shouting is all about, few things being so unpopular as a logical analysis of meanings. How much more stirring to declare, in self-confident and ringing tones, "Values are objective" and those who deny this great and eternal truth are shallow, ignorant, and vicious corrupters of youth! All that remains is to bring on the hemlock.

As we have defined the term "value," it is subjective in the sense that it depends upon a subject, a motor-affective attitude being a necessary part of the value relation. But since the other necessary part of the value relation is an object, it is equally plain that value is in this sense objective. Asking whether it is one *or* the other, on the presupposition that it cannot be both, is like asking whether marriage is male *or* female. Plainly, the sense in which values are necessarily objective would hardly satisfy some philosophers; for an object, in this sense, might be perceptual or imaginal, public or private, the only logical requirement being that it be a distinguishable content, simple or complex, and offer a center of interest on which someone can fix his attention. We may call this sort of subjectivity and objectivity "logical," in the sense that it is specified through, and required by, our definitional rule governing the use, in this system, of the term "value."

If we say that values are *perceptually* objective when *one* term in the value relation *appears* to have a locus such that it could be perceived by more than one subject, then at least some values would be perceptually objective. The colors of a picture, as well as the shapes thus made visible, are—for example—in this sense perceptually objective. It may be that both these kinds of visual sense data are conditioned by intraorganic events, with the consequence that the particular sense data, which complete a given value relation, are at least numerically different for different subjects; although assuming sufficient similarity of subjects and stimulus-situations, these sense data would probably be qualitatively similar, whatever the difficulties—and they are notorious—in verifying statements through which such similarity in quality is claimed. However, regardless of our solution of this problem, such data as the white color and rectangular shape of (say) a piece of paper are perceptually objective in the sense specified by our definition, i.e., they *appear* to have a locus in a public space such that they could be perceived by more than one subject, even though, after analysis, we decide that only more or less similar data *are* in fact sensed by different subjects. But if we decide, as I am inclined to do, that a relation should not be called perceptually objective unless *all* of its necessary terms are perceptually objective, then, since one of the terms in the value relation is a motor-affective attitude, which is at least in part not open to the direct observation of more than one subject, it follows that no values are perceptually objective, even though in *some* cases one of its constituent terms is perceptually objective.

A different, but closely related, sense of objectivity may be called "social objectivity." By this I mean that, given outer empirical terms for our value relations, these terms being perceptually objective, we may infer, on the basis of such evidence as the observed similarity of verbal and other perceptually objective responses, that the motor-affective attitudes of different subjects are also similar. But first consider the example of color. If I asked a hundred subjects the color of a piece of paper I hold up before them, I should expect all the subjects —assuming that the illumination, and so on, were held constant—to give the same, i.e., semantically equivalent, answers to my question. The answers might or might not be taken as proof of the identity, or even close similarity, of the color data experienced by these different subjects. It would take a long and technical analysis to do anything with the cluster of difficult problems here involved, and I have no space to go into that matter now. Suffice it to say that the kind of social agreement in response exhibited in my example may serve to explain our definition of social objectivity. In this case, the question being about the color of the paper, *what* the answer of each subject refers to *is* perceptually objective, and since the definition of "white" (let us assume) involves no necessary reference to a subject's reactions, such a color is *not* logically subjective. Furthermore, since we do find, by hypothesis, similarity of verbal responses to the paper, we may say that the property, white, is also socially objective.

The problem now arises, Is the perceptual objectivity of at least one of the terms in the value relation a necessary condition of saying that the value in question is socially objective? In other words, must the value content, the outer term in the relation, be perceptually objective, in order to say that the value is socially objective? If, to this definitional question we answer Yes, as I am inclined to do, then it follows that *some* values cannot be socially objective, for some value relations have terms *neither* of which is perceptually objective. On the other hand, some value relations—one's perception of, and favorable aesthetic response to, a picture on the wall, may be taken as a case in point—do contain empirical terms which are perceptually objective. Hence, assuming that the other necessary condition of social objectivity is fulfilled—namely, agreement in the indicated percipients' relevant overt responses—we have in such cases instances of socially objective values.

"Social objectivity," as here defined, is a matter of degree. Thus, if some artist draws a sketch on this same piece of white paper and we ask the same one hundred subjects to report whether or not they like the sketch, we *may* get the same degree of agreement, i.e., *all* the subjects saying they like it, or exhibiting other behaviors which we might accept as evidence sufficient to support the inference that they like it. But our experience with value judgments makes us expect no such perfect agreement. In short, we expect some to like the sketch and some not to like it. If a large proportion of the subjects asked say that they like the sketch, then we may say (and mean something definite by the saying) that the value of the sketch has, relative to this group of subjects, a high degree of social objectivity. Granted that this group of experimental subjects is representative of any specified larger group of persons, then such a high degree of social objectivity affords empirical grounds for making reliable predictions. Thus, if the sketch in question has the identifiable properties, a b c, then if any other sketch has closely similar properties, a′ b′ c′, we should expect—and not unreasonably—that this other sketch would evoke, i.e., objectively control, or bring about, similar motor-affective reactions, as well as verbal expressions of these reactions, in the such-and-such a proportion of subjects in the larger social group. For a b c, by hypothesis, are properties which, relative to the first group of subjects, were sufficient *in that particular context* to evoke the verbal response "I like the sketch" from (say) three-quarters of the subjects. Hence the inductive inference from this first series of cases to the new series of cases, the members of which are numerically different but are in certain relevant respects fundamentally similar, would have, in general, the same kind of empirical basis which underlies any prediction, even the most exactly formulated and carefully tested.

One other sense of "objectivity" needs, for our purpose, to be distinguished. This we may call "metaphysical" objectivity. It is the sort of objectivity possessed, allegedly, by the atoms of Democritus and the Ideas of Plato, i.e., any entities which exist (or subsist) quite independently of any relations to subjects, whether knowing or valuing or merely existing. Clearly, the definition of value I have been recommending is not logically consistent with the metaphysical objectivity of values; for some value attitude is a necessary term in the value relation. Does this mean that I have "proved" that no values are metaphysically objective? No, plainly not. Our analysis only carried with it the implied challenge that philosophers who speak of metaphysically objective values will have to specify in some intelligible manner what they *mean* by "value," and further that they will have to show, on the basis of evidence, that the referents for "value," so defined, do occupy the metaphysical regions of which they purport to have axiological knowledge. Neither of these conditions has, in my judgment, ever been satisfactorily fulfilled, and I am inclined to say that such a "theory" of value is not really a theory, but rather a pious hope. Of course I have not, in this paper, furnished adequate support for the criticism; and I make it only in the interest of hearer-orientation (not irritation) and do not offer is as either dialectical refutation or empirical disverification.

Summarizing our answers to the question, Are values subjective or objective? we may say, I think, that *all* values are *logically* both subjective and objective; *no* value is *perceptually* objective, even though one of its constituent terms may be, and sometimes is, perceptually objective; while *some* values, among those which contain perceptually objective terms, are *socially* objective.

Do these conclusions, in part analytic to be sure, but resting also, I believe, on relevant factual considerations, jeopardize "true morality"? Does the kind of subjectivity indicated, along with the kind of relativity previously specified, somehow tend to undermine moral integrity, or to divide men, producing conflict—even wars, it has been alleged—because leaving men without an "objective standard" to which they can appeal to settle their differences rationally? These charges are familiar, but they are also hopelessly vague, and in principle unanswerable until their vagueness has been reduced to a tolerable degree and the various ambiguities involved have been eliminated. This task would indeed be Herculean, and would tax, or rather has taxed, the powers of even Morris Cohen, that long famous, but recently publicized, cleaner of Augean classrooms. But, in the absence of clear definitions and more relevant evidence, the criticisms which philosophers of different schools make of one another's systems are hardly more than *ad hominem* pot shots, designed to evoke cheers from the rooters on their side, defenders of the old school team.

With my space used up, I cannot seriously deal with the matter here involved; but I shall try at least to outline the sort of answer which seems to me reasonable, by indicating very roughly a few definitions.

Taking standards to be rules which specify, and thus govern logically, references for the comparative and superlative forms of our value terms, then to say that "B is better than A," if each is some given content, might very well (and does sometimes) mean that B is *liked more* than A, or is *preferred* to A, by at least *some* person. If A and B are physical objects—for example, pictures—then to say that B is better than A means a variety of things, depending upon the particular context of judgment. But in principle it would mean such things as that B has value properties which regularly function, in some specified type of cases, to evoke reactions of preference, where A is reacted to as the competing stimulus-object, the presupposed standard being intensity of liking or direction of preference. An additional standard (what Mr. Perry calls the standard of inclusiveness) is derived from the axiomatic truth that two (or more) positive values are better than one: in short, the more goodness, the better.

So much, in three sentences, for standards. Now let us verbally dispatch, with equal brevity, the problem of value criteria. By "criterion" I mean some natural sign of value, ordinarily with contextual restrictions to some fairly constant and thus reliable sign of an important class of values. A criterion is not intrinsically a value, nor can we infer, merely from a knowledge of the definition of value being used, whether such-and-such a property is a criterion. But when experience shows that such a property is regularly associated with some kind of value attitude, then this property may come to function as a natural sign of value.

Now men, being more or less alike in the structure and function of their organisms, and to some variable extent in their education, it is to be expected—and the event confirms the inference—that they will agree some of the time in their valuations, and sometimes not agree. But no *theory* of value can change these facts. Whatever we *say*, art will have no aesthetic value for those who cannot *feel;* nor will logic have intellectual value for those who cannot *think*. Talking this or that way will not add a cubit to our statures, nor alter a lesion in our diencephalon, which may affect our valuations of "sweet" sleep, temperature changes, and many other things. The responses of animals—including, of course, the human kind—to members of the opposite sex will vary, whether or not moralists approve the fact, with the nature and concentration of various endocrine substances in their blood, thus producing differences in their value judgments, if they make any. And so on. But such well known and, I should suppose, undeniable facts must be accepted by all philosophers who ever expose a suitable receptor outside their ivory towers.

This kind of knowledge at once explains naturally our standards, and grounds empirically our criteria in facts of the sort we need to know if our choices are to be intelligent and if the constancy, as well as the variety, of men's valuations is to be intelligible. Furthermore, when values are seen to be relations within nature, open to scientific inquiry like other facts, ethics and aesthetics do not thereby become impossible; on the contrary, they acquire—if they have not had one previously—a subject matter which can be investigated, about which verifiable statements can be asserted and laws formulated. It is not the truth about the relativity or the subjectivity of values, in the highly qualified senses meant, which divides men. Of course, many things divide men; but some of them, about which philosophers might be able to do something, are various stubborn confusions tied up with linguistic forms which cry out, in diverse contexts, for analysis and clarification. In this way, at least many of our so-called theoretical conflicts could be cleared up and future ones prevented; for, as Heraclitus said, when men are awake they live in a common world.

A MATERIALIST THEORY OF MEASUREMENT

by C. WEST CHURCHMAN

C. West Churchman is Associate Professor of Philosophy, Wayne University; Acting Editor and Secretary-Treasurer, Philosophy of Science Association; author of *Elements of Logic and Formal Science* (1940) and *Theory of Experimental Inference* (1948); member of Board of Directors, Institute of Experimental Method; editor-in-Chief of Bulletin of the Institutes of Experimental Method, consultant, Army Ordnance, the Quartermaster General, Franklin Institute.

IT IS the purpose of this paper to argue that the modern materialist has a new responsibility that differentiates him from the older materialist, not in the purpose which his materialism serves, but in the special kind of issue he must face. The older materialism opposed a prevalent philosophical tendency to place emphasis on the reality of the mind as against the reality of material objects. The antimaterialist tendency was dangerous, I think, because of its social implications. If the reality of the world lies in the mind and its manifestations, then surely it is safe to argue that the major problems of the world also lie in the realm of mind. Hence, the nonmaterialist of the last century was at least implicitly arguing that our major problem is the reformation of mind or spirit and that until this was accomplished we could not hope to advance in a material fashion, i.e., relative to the mode of production. This emphasis on the problem of mind was dangerous, for it diverted attention from the major problem: the reconstruction of the mode of production.

But the older materialist-idealist controversy was couched in terms that have now become hopelessly outworn, and the materialist makes a very bad mistake if he still repeats the old arguments directed to philosophers now dead. The real danger to the modern materialist does not lie in the assertion that the "mind" is real, and matter is not. The hypothesis of idealism was based on the assumption that the content of a person's mind is something he, and he alone, can fully grasp. The psychology of idealism was founded on a theory of conscious mind that is as out of date as the early formulations of the theory of evolution. After all, we do have nearly three-quarters of a century of experimental psychology behind us, in which the problem of mind has been handled in much the same methodological manner as have all the problems of science. Mind has been given an experimental translation, the problems of mind are as conceivably within our grasp as are those of physics, and to talk of "solipsism" and "idealism" is to talk of a problem that science has actually outdated. Of course there are philosophers who still believe the world is essentially mental, or entertain the solipsistic theory seriously. I am merely making the point that those who do, present an outworn controversy of science, and no longer represent a real threat to the materialist. I should suppose that the work in perception theory alone, without the rest of the enormous contribution of modern psychology, was enough to place the old materialist-idealist controversy in the realm of a personality dispute. For perception has become a highly complex problem of modern science, having little or nothing of the early "simplicity," and demanding for its proper study a multitude of other concepts and existences, including material ones. Hence, the statement, "existence lies in being perceived," is naïve today because the determination of whether a thing is perceived demands presuppositions about the material world (racial heritage, other bodies, future states, etc.).

In view of these remarks, it becomes necessary for the materialist to redefine the orientation of his position. The victory of modern materialism over the older idealism does not constitute the settling of the problem, for new issues are bound to arise out of the resolution of the old. The new threat to materialism is essentially a methodological one. The threat is based on the tenet that there are fundamentals in science, in a twofold sense: (1) that certain aspects of scientific inquiry have precedence over others, and (2) that the precedence relieves the scientist of the obligation to investigate them.

This is a threat to close off from investigation certain aspects of the natural world, and to install these aspects in an especially privileged position. Throughout the remainder of this paper I shall refer to this position as "fundamentalism." The paper is designed to attack fundamentalism in one of its most dangerous applications, the theory of measurement. The danger of fundamentalism in this field has consisted in the fundamentalist's attack on the possibility of measurement in psychology and the social sciences. But before considering the nature of the attack, let me first formulate the modern materialist position briefly, so that in the subsequent discussion the alternative to fundamentalism will be clear.

Briefly, the "matter" of the world is taken to be the class of all problems based on human demands, that can be raised about the world. "Dialectics" is taken to be the methodology of question-answering, i.e., scientific method. "Dialectical materialism" is that position which holds that dialectics is capable of answering eventually all the questions about the world; i.e., dialectics imposes no restrictions on the matter of the world.

Much of this may seem obvious, even to a fundamentalist, so that it will be well to point out the intended consequence which differentiates materialism from fundamentalism. The fundamentalist must necessarily close off certain questions from investigation, because to try to answer them threatens his methodology. Hence, the legitimacy of a question for the fundamentalist is prescribed not by the historical demand there may be for an answer, but by the criteria of a rigidly formulated methodology. Familiar examples of this limitation of meaningfulness by method are ethical questions and questions concerning "purely" subjective states of mind. As a less familiar example, the fundamentalist may make the methodological requirement for logical consistency within science. Then he asserts that, when a science can be shown to hold contradictory tenets on a certain issue, the science is in a "bad" way, and it is essential to work toward the removal of the contradiction. Why? Why cannot science live meaningfully with contradictions? The fundamentalist answers that the methodology of science imposes restrictions on the possible things the scientist can do. Is this methodological principle of consistency a sound one? The fundamentalist may answer by pointing out the absurdity of asking the question, or he may employ a purely circular rule such as "If a contradiction is granted, then anything follows—and this, science cannot tolerate," without telling us what "grant" or "follows" means, except in terms of formal consistency or contradiction. But it should be a commonplace that science advances most fruitfully by preserving its contradictions, not removing them. That is, the maintenance of a contradiction, or violent disagreement, is often the basis for our most fruitful progress. Science is progressing toward something far more fruitful than mutual understanding and the absence of contradiction. Hence, in the progress of science, the aim is not to remove contradiction at each stage, but to make gains in man's conquest of nature. Far from obeying a "hard-and-fast" rule of the fundamentalist, we look to the demands of the scientist, or more ultimately to the humanistic demands, to see whether it is advisable to resolve the conflict or to preserve it.

Similar remarks apply, as we shall see in more detail, to the operationist position. Here the fundamentals are direct observation, or concrete operations. The fundamentalist calls a question meaningless if it is so phrased as to exclude its ever being reduced to the terms of direct observation.

Now the modern materialist takes the antifundamentalist position. This is so, because he asserts the right to raise a question on any issue, *including the issue of the correct methodological principles.*[1] Fundamentalists have traditionally raised a smoke screen about this point. "If you start down that road," they say, "you'll soon come to a fork. One sign will say 'Infinite Regress' and the other 'Vicious Circularity.' Now no one in his right [sic!] mind will care to take either fork. Better leave well enough alone and stay on the straight and narrow road dictated by our fundamentals."

This kind of argument is the real threat to modern materialism, for in effect it limits the matter of the world, in the sense that certain questions cannot legitimately be raised. The legitimacy of question-raising, of course, is based on the materialist position that questions come out of human demands, and not out of methodology itself. To permit methodology to impose limitations on question-raising is to put the cart before the horse; we glorify means and make our ends subservient to them.

But to answer the fundamentalist's viewpoint is no easy matter. We are, in effect, forced into a modern theory of the nature of definition in particular, and scientific methodology in general. We must show (1) that science collectively does not have to resort to "primitive terms," fundamental methods, basic axioms; (2) that scientific concepts are all interrelated; (3) that the establishment of complete interrelation *is* the process of definition. In particular, we must show that the adoption of an antifundamentalist position does not play right into the hands of the fundamentalist, by showing that the validity of the materialist's assertion can itself be investigated within science.

The development of this general position is a long story,[2] but the results may be schematized for the sake of this discussion, by picturing science as a spiral with a lattice frame. A certain concept *A*, let us say, is used to define *B*, which in turn is used to define *A*. But when the second operation is performed, i.e., when *B* is used to define *A*, some progress in defining should have occurred; we have a more exact meaning of *A* as a result of the turn of the spiral. The phrase "more exact," and in general the term "progress," give direction to the axis of the spiral; the spiral itself is asymptomatically approaching an ideal limit; i.e., the limit helps define the nature of the spiral, and the spiral helps define the nature of the limit. A circularity of definition is "vicious" only if there is virtually no progress as a result of defining *A* in terms of *B*, and then *B* in terms of *A*. As science advances, the nature of the progressive reciprocal defining becomes more and more complex; what is a vicious circle today, need not always have been so. For an earlier stage of science, the circularity might have revealed relationships which were hidden to the scientists of the day. For present-day science, where the relationships are well known, the circularity becomes vicious. Hence, old defining is apt to appear naïve when we ignore the service it played, and pay attention only to its formal structure.

Of course, the analogue of a lattice spiral for the process of science is not meant to be an exact characterization of the nature of the closed system of scientific concepts but merely an aid to the understanding. The more precise formulation demands a very extensive exposition. The consequence of this, of course, is that scientific defining cannot be taken as a "part-time" job of the scientific specialist. That is, correct definitions are not simple matters that can be handled in the course of everyday experimentation, and given in terms the experimenter expects his readers to understand. Since definitions require the establishment of relationships between all other concepts the scientist uses, what is demanded is a general model of the natural world, a part of which the experimenter intends to investigate. This model is closed, but no materialist would ever assert it was complete. Subsequent investigation will undoubtedly require further generalizations and modifications. The task of model construction of this type is no simple one, and will have to rest in the hands of the experts, just as the many other phases of present-day experimentation require the experience and knowledge of scientific experts. This means that the well designed experiment must turn out to be cooperative; the individual scientist is incapable of handling the many facets of his experimental problem. In the light of this analysis, one might say that the "validity" of traditional rationalism lay in its insistence on a rational or formal process in making a turn of the scientific spiral; empiricism was valid in insisting on the like *necessity* of observations. Both were wrong in attempting to make these functions sufficient, i.e., in not showing how these functions were to be substantiated by other processes in science.

This description of scientific materialism is in direct oppostiion to scientific fundamentalism. There is no denying that the *individual* is often a fundamentalist. He usually begins by assuming certain things to be known and certain propositions and meanings to be self-evident (i.e., evident to himself). But if the "individual" is enlarged enough to include a representation from the major divisions of science, then the fundamentalism begins to disappear. This is the basis of true cooperative effort in the sciences: a group of divergent interests, whose very divergence is the basis of a unified effort that removes the need of fundamentals or elements.[3]

II

The second part of this paper is designed to illustrate the first. The first part has developed the very simple but essential notion that science makes no appeal to fundamentals, if by fundamentals we mean aspects of science that have some epistemological priority. I have suggested that fundamentalism represents a danger to the materialist, and I want to use this second part to illustrate one aspect of this danger: the fundamentalist's attack on the question whether there is such a thing as an exact social science, and in particular whether there are measurements in the psychological and social sciences.

Of course, to phrase the question in this manner is already to have introduced a bias. Apparently, there is no question that an exact physical, or mathematical, science does exist. Therefore, the fundamentalist has only to inquire in an "objective" manner whether the social sciences can lay claim to anything like the precision the physicist has obtained. There is apparently no thought of asking, "What is an exact science?" and then, "Is there *any* exact science?"

This fundamentalist viewpoint, which casts doubt on the findings of the social sciences, has had its impact on the scientific world. The first part of the present century has witnessed enormous strides in the development of techniques of scaling psychological and social phenomena: intelligence tests, aptitude tests, intensity of sensation tests, opinion polls, etc. All this activity has brought the fundamentalists to raise the question concerning one of these scales. The issue is whether the psychological sciences can truly be said to have developed quantitative estimates of sensory events.[4] The British Association for the Advancement of Science appointed a committee of physicists and psychologists to answer the question. Notice, there was no issue as to whether *any* science has developed quantitative estimates; apparently it is taken for granted that the physical sciences have succeeded in this gargantuan project. Almost needless to say, certain physicists came to a negative conclusion concerning the psychologists' success in constructing quantitative estimates. The psychologist is undoubtedly doing something; but, whatever that something is, they believe he is not making *fundamental* measurements. This position has all the snobbish outlook of certain mathematicians who apparently feel that mathematics has attained its objective of ideal precision.

The issue, like all issues, is important, not for setting people's minds to rest on the problem, but for getting on to the next stage. Of course, we as materialists will say the physicists adopted a wrong attitude toward the problem. But they force the methodologist of the social sciences to say what measurement is, and to say it in such a way that one cannot fall into the pitfall the physicists have constructed. It may be ironic that the materialist should have to argue *against* the view that physics is a science more basic and better established than the social sciences, and against the view that all other sciences, to be sciences at all, must look to physics as their guide. But our remarks have shown that materialism should no longer be conceived as adopting the position that all our problems are reducible to problems concerned with the properties of mass points. The prophysicist is asserting a kind of fundamentalism; physical science, he says, is well established, and upon this rock we are supposed to build a social science. The materialist must take the position that there is nothing inherent in a physicist, qua physicist, that makes him a better methodologist than any other scientist. Methodology is neither physics nor sociology, though the verification of methodological principles may come out of either of these, or any other discipline.

In order to make the fundamentalist's attack clearer, let us examine the pro-physicist's reasons for asserting that psychology has not attained quantitative scales. The arch fundamentalist is N. R. Campbell.[5] I don't know how seriously people take Campbell's pronunciamentos now; but at least at the time of the writing of the British report (1938) he still had quite a following. Campbell is of the opinion that there are "fundamental magnitudes." Now it seems reasonable to him "to inquire briefly on what grounds such a class could be based." [6] It is certainly unfortunate that the inquiry is so very brief. Fundamental magnitudes, he says, are magnitudes "the measurement of which does not depend on any other magnitude." [7] This comes as something of a shock to the reader accustomed to the complexities of physical measurement. Where in nature do we find magnitudes that don't depend on other magnitudes for their measurement?

Whatever these magnitudes are, they must, according to Campbell, involve the simplest kind of operation in their determination. The simplest operation for him seems to be one of adding increments. Hence, fundamental scales have an *additive* property. For scales enjoying the additive property, the magnitude x is "the number of standard things or 'units' that have to be combined together in order to produce the thing equal to x in respect to the property." [8] The additive scales, like all scales, are defined for Campbell by a set of operations; these operations must be such that the objects whose magnitude is to be determined are "ordered." In particular, if we say the operation makes A smaller than B ($A < B$), then there must not be any prescribed operation leading to $B < A$.

Now it seems to Campbell that lengths, areas, weights, etc., are additive magnitudes, for they are all based on the choice of a certain standard magnitude; the operations consist of taking parts or multiples of the standard.

But none of this substantiates the claim that the measurements of length, weight, etc., are fundamental in the sense that they do not depend on the measurement of any other magnitudes. The natural question we should like to ask someone weighing objects, is whether the arms of the balance are equal and convection currents absent. And, in general, we want to know what variables must be checked to make sure the balance is behaving properly. But to know the answer to these questions it certainly looks as though the experimenter must take measurements of other magnitudes, and hence the determination of weight is not "fundamental" in Campbell's sense. No, says Campbell, all the experimenter need do is follow through the operations and "discover whether interchange of the contents of the pans affects the balance." [9] As a matter of fact, Campbell thinks the question about all the necessary checks on the balance is "actually dangerous." [10] "For the answer must involve in some form the theory of the balance. . . . We are basing our measurements on theory, rather than our theory on measurement, which is a most dangerous procedure." [11] Dangerous for whom? Campbell does not tell us, but we are led to suppose that the danger is for any good-hearted fundamentalist anxious to get his start somewhere. It is interesting to contrast Brown's dictum: "The discovery of the law makes the possibility of exact and accurate measurement rather than the measurement makes possible the discovery of the law." [12] To refute this position, Campbell argues that to check the process of weighing, we "simply try out" the objects on the pans to see if the operations satisfy the formal conditions of additive magnitudes. Well, how many objects must we try? Who shall try them? On what days? On the critical question of judging a result, Campbell asserts that the determination of lengths, for example, "depends on judgments of the contiguity of parts of lines, which is a relation *instinctively perceived.*" [13] Do all people instinctively perceive alike? Does one person instinctively perceive alike at different times? Of course, I don't know exactly what Campbell means by "instinctively perceived"; but almost any conceivable meaning of the term would lead to a decided negative to the questions. Different observers *do* perceive "instinctively" in different ways, even when the operations are very carefully specified. Further, different observers get significantly different results on different days, in different laboratories, etc.

I think Campbell's position might be tolerated, even in the light of its lack of rigor, if scientific experience indicated that the results of following operations at different times, by different observers, did not differ very widely. As formal methodologists, we could certainly demand an exact experimental proof the claim, and hence show the absurdity of Campbell's insistence that the operations of determining lengths, weights, etc., are fundamental in any sense. But one might feel that these operations are so simple that they are "practically" fundamental, in the sense that it is not critical for experimental science at this time to investigate the minor errors that may occur. This is certainly the position taken by most of the "operationists." They admit that no operations can ever be made absolutely precise, but apparently feel in some cases that the possible lack of precision is small and not critical. Their position is a more sophisticated one, and therefore the more important for the antifundamentalist to oppose. Even if we agree with Bridgman that "the concept of length involves as much as and nothing more than the set of operations by which length is determined,"[14] very little is said. The major task is to determine what an "operation" is, and whether it has been carried through exactly. And that this is a major problem is evidenced by repeated experience in laboratory work. We simply have not found a way of setting up verbal instructions, no matter how simple they may appear in form, which will be carried through in the same way by most if not all observers.

This point has been illustrated over and over again in the so-called "exact" physical sciences. When the same object is made in a number of different places, it is desirable to set up very precise instructions as to the methods of measuring certain of its properties. Now in governmental and industrial practice very carefully worded manuals, together with explanatory illustrations, are given to each laboratory that must make the physical or chemical tests on the product. From time to time it occurs to someone to try a "round-robin" test to determine whether the laboratories agree in the results they obtain by following these "precisely worded" instructions, when all tests are made on the same article. The result has almost always been that laboratories do *not* agree; sometimes they differ by amounts great enough to invalidate the whole process of inspection. Apparently there is something in the individual laboratory's training of its observers which is injected over and above the written instructions, and produces wide differences. For example, in the case of one operation, the very "simple" procedure of counting the grains in a certain well marked area of brass strip led to very significant differences between laboratories. Again, the simple operation of placing an explosive on a steel anvil and dropping a specified weight on it from a specified height, resulted in wide differences. The simple operation of placing a chemical bomb under specified pressure, and observing changes from hour to hour on a dial, led to differences that necessitated a complete revision of the test procedure.

I think it might be a very interesting test to try out Campbell's instructions for ordering and adding lengths on groups of observers, on different days, in different environments, with different motivations, under different supervision. A carefully designed experiment might produce some curious results.

Of course, the obvious answer the fundamentalist can make is that the instructions are usually not made precise or complete enough. But if we want to avoid the tautology that the specified operations be made precise and complete enough to give reliable results, we must show exactly what produces the serious differences we find among observers who are supposedly obeying the same instructions.

One can understand how the physicists, like Campbell and Bridgman, are anxious to push aside the difficult problem of explaining operations to individuals, since this problem lies mainly in the psychological domain. The physicist's inclination is to try to patch things up when the observers become erratic, and to "look around" for the sources of the trouble. I think he is to be "blamed" only when he talks as though there really were no problem; i.e., when he tries to claim that there are "fundamental" magnitudes, and that no other scientist is really needed to help the physicist improve his techniques of measurement. What he should be doing is begging for help from the contemporary psychologist; he should be insisting that physical measurement necessarily involves psychological measurement, in order to determine which operations really are "simple" to the observer, and which are difficult. Degrees of simplicity are certainly as important as any magnitudes to measure in a controlled fashion, and the physicist's analysis shows that the measurement of these degrees is "basic" to all measurement. Physics and psychology should be mutually supporting.

On the bright side, with respect to the physicist's attitude, is an increasing tendency to use the psychologist in the design of instrument panels and dials.[15]

Unfortunately, the psychologists have been slow to appreciate the fact that physical science needs their aid in defining operations. Many of them have been swept along in the operationist stream, with little or no question of its oversimplified belief in the intuitive character of the simple operation. For example, Boring says:

> When a speaker's statement is not clear for the hearer, it is always fair for the hearer to ask the speaker for an operational definition of the terms he has used. Since the operational definition introduces new conceptual terms, a regress is begun, one which may be infinite. This regress is not, however, embarrassing, for it can be terminated as soon as there is mutual understanding between the speaker and the hearer, as soon as there is no further demand for definition.[16]

If this were offered seriously as an operational definition of adequate operations, the practicing scientist might well be puzzled. Learners of scientific techniques as often as not make no further demands for explanation because they are thoroughly confused. But, worse still, conscious feeling of agreement or understanding is apt to have low correlation with future practice. Of course Boring knows all this, but feels that the attainment of a real common agreement is a fairly simple matter. Stevens, too, seems to have the same impression: "The operational regress need be pursued only until agreement is reached." [17] But the amazing thing is that in the face of all the methodological difficulties of opinion polls, attitude tests, etc., two psychologists could think it a "simple" matter to obtain a real common agreement!

III

In this last part I want to formulate a sort of materialist creed to combat the inroads of the fundamentalists. Naturally, the principles enunciated need far more substantiation than can be given here, especially as there is no intention to assert that they are "obvious," or can be formally deduced from fundamentals of scientific method. But I think each materialist should give them careful consideration, since they represent an attempt to escape the autonomy of any one branch of science, and in effect make each branch responsible for the progress of the others.

On the negative side, there are two principles to propose:

1. *We must stop thinking of scientific method as proceeding from the intuitively simple elements to more complex ones.*

Neglect of this principle might be called the Simplicity Fallacy of scientific method. The fallacy seems to have been given its most cogent formulation by John Locke,[18] and I suppose that in Locke's time it was not really fallacious, since he was attempting to fight a progressive battle against the rational intuitionists. But every attempt in experimental science to discover the simple elements has broken down, and many attempts have been made; e.g., "time" has been taken as a simple dimension; "sensation" has been taken as a simple operation; "consciousness" has been assumed to be simple in its form, etc. A review of the history of science's "simples" shows us that there has been a gradual tendency to remove the notion of simplicity from science altogether, and to take simplicity to be a characteristic of personality instead: what an individual takes to be "intuitively obvious," or simple, is a property of his personality, and important in the study of his behavior. But science knows no real simplicities; all problems of science, as they advance, become equally complex. This is so, because science becomes a tightly interwoven system of cross checks, and no problem ever stays long in isolation from all the rest. One might put the principle in the following paradoxical form: to determine what is simple for the scientific worker is one of the most complex problems of science.

2. *Additive Scales are not any more "fundamental" than any other type of scale.*

This principle is a corollary of the first. It may be true, as Nagel says, that the "cleavage between additive or extensive qualities, and non-additive or intensive qualities, is of fundamental importance in the philosophy of physical measurement."[19] But he certainly does not make clear why this cleavage is also a cleavage between "those qualities which are capable of fundamental measurement and those which [are] not."[20] Why use the term "fundamental" in this connection at all? Why not simply say that there are two types of scale (actually many types), and that the experimenter, in order to make clear what he is about, should specify the formal properties of his scales. This absolves the psychologist from any attempt such as that of Reese [21] to defend *his* type of scale, on purely formal grounds. There is no such thing as the Bergmann-Spence "manipulations within a dimension"—those that "do not involve utilization of any of the empirical laws which connect it with other dimensions" [22]—and distinctions of this type are therefore fruitless for the experimental scientist.

The formal problem of scales might be summarized by the following principle:

3. *All exact measurements take place in an idealized environment; the results of an actual experiment are to be regarded as estimates of what* would *happen if ideal conditions could be obtained.*

Let us see how this principle works out in the case of a physical measurement like length. We say that the true length of a line is the length that *would* be obtained if we could place the object beside the standard meter rod, could exactly align the end points with certain markers, could keep the temperature at a specified value, etc. We can't do any of these ideal things; what we actually do is take observations under laboratory conditions. We then make adjustments in the observations in accordance with physical laws, in order to estimate what would have been obtained if idealized conditions had prevailed. In other words, the meaning of true length is given in terms of precise operations in an idealized environment. But estimating what would happen in these idealized conditions requires all the science we have at our disposal; none of the so-called "actual" operations we perform is basic, in the sense that we *infer* concerning the idealized environment from what is "given." The problem of what is actually given is itself only to be estimated; the pure given in experience is again an idealized experiment, just as the determination of a "direct observation" requires setting up idealized conditions. This principle casts some light on the problem of formal measurement in the social and psychological sciences. What do we mean when we ask how much an individual wants something? The present tendency is to grasp the measure directly, by asking the individual. Even though everyone knows that verbal responses are highly unreliable, there does not seem to be any feasible way of adjusting for such errors. But suppose now that we define the degree of want as what would occur under idealized conditions. Let us say that the individual is placed in an environment where he has equai opportunity to pursue any of his objectives, but can pursue only one at a time. Then we might say that the probability of his pursuing one of the objectives in such an idealized environment constitutes the exact measurement of his want. The task of the psychologist is to find a formal system of psychology that is rich enough to provide estimates of what would occur in the idealized want environment.

We turn now to certain general aspects of scales. The materialist tenet, I think, is that we have passed beyond the age when sound principles in science are regarded as such because of some inherent structural condition. This means that we must apply two teleological criteria to scales, as well as to any other aspect of scientific method: the *pragmatic* principle, and the *progressive* principle.

When we apply the pragmatic criterion to scales or metrics, we ask ourselves this type of question: What aspect of the scientist's means in the pursuit of his ends is involved in the scales he uses? Such a question implies that a scale *means* no more for science than the purpose it serves for science. The pragmatic principle, then, reads somewhat as follows:

4. *The scaling of a property of an object provides information as to the most efficient use of that property in any problem-situation.*

This seems to be in accord with Nagel's assertion: "The search for a unified body of principles in terms of which the abrupt, the transitory, the unexpected are to be exhibited and in a measure controlled, is the most conscious guiding principle in the application of numerical science." [23] But the *motive* of control must be made clear; that is, control is not an end-in-itself. Control in measurement is for the sake of treating an object in the most effective manner relative to any problem. For example, let us suppose we know the exact length of an object. Then in any problematic situation in which the property of length is critical, the scaling of the length will provide us with all the information we have to know about the object with respect to its length in order to use it most effectively. This pragmatic notion of the meaning of a scale is based on the principle that science has developed quantitative techniques in order to provide the most complete possible description of an object. And assigning to a property of an object an exact value enables us completely to describe the object with respect to this property. But what does "complete description" mean? It means that the object can be used in the most efficient manner in any situation in which it becomes an instrument or means to an end. It must be understood, of course, that knowing the exact value of a property of an object is not enough for efficient use of the object. We have to have a complete description as well of the other pertinent properties of the object and the environment, and also know the laws governing changes in these properties. But scaling the property should give all the information we need with respect to *that* property.

It is to be feared that far too little heed has been paid to the common sense of the pragmatic principle. Seldom do we know the purposes of scale construction, except for immediate ends in view; thus, length is introduced in physics "in order to determine distances." But this sort of trivial pragmatic analysis is not what the pragmatic principle intends. Rather, it demands a careful evaluation of scientific scales and concepts, from the point of view of their service to any long-run end of science or mankind. For example, two social psychologists construct a scale for measuring "attitudes toward the church." [24] What for? What do the scientists expect to accomplish if they find out what an individual's score is on their test? We should like to say: they want to predict behavior in a certain situation. Well then, what situation, and behavior relative to what? Unfortunately, the answer to this sort of pragmatic demand is usually withheld; instead, we find that "the concept 'attitude' will be used to denote the sum-total of a man's inclinations and feelings, prejudice and bias, preconceived notions, ideas, fears, threat, and convictions about any specific topic." [25] Certainly this "definition" does not make specific what we want to know about the individual's behavior. And the worst of it is that, under the guise of "objective" determination of opinions and attitudes, an opinion poll can play a quite reactionary or conservative role, simply because it does not tell us what the attitude scale is for. We might on the one hand want to obtain an attitude score to see whether the workers will strike if a certain plan is installed; or we may want the score to see what the workers really want. I cannot agree with Guttman that the really critical problem is "to distinguish between . . . scaling and prediction." [26] For it seems that the internal or formal analysis of the scaling operation has meaning only in terms of what we plan to do with the results; there are so many ways we can construct formal criteria, and none of these makes any sense by itself. Viewed as possible ways of obtaining clear-cut objectives, however, the various formal techniques can be evaluated; I prefer to call the whole process, the formalization and the evaluation, a process of "scaling," or "measuring," since these terms have traditionally meant experimental, and not merely formal techniques.

The pragmatic principle requires that the exact value of a property along a scale should enable us to use the property most effectively. But this is a severe requirement. It is clear enough that science can only approximate this sort of ideal. And, as a matter of fact, the more closely science approximates the exact value along the scale, the "better" we take that science to be. This notion of a better science—and, in general, the notion of progress in scientific matters—provides us with the progressive principle concerning scales:

5. *A scale furnishes the experimenter with a technique whereby he can measure the degree of scientific perfection he has attained.*

That is, scales must be so constructed that we can determine how the scientist may improve his knowledge of the properties of objects. This aspect of scale construction is more or less ignored in so-called "operational analysis." The operations by which length is finally determined simply involve the whole history of science, a history of closer and closer approximations to exact measurements. As far as I know, only Singer [27] has made a careful study of all that must be involved in such operations. The story is a complicated one, for we are forced to take a comprehensive attitude toward experimental science. Formal criteria of scales can apparently (but not actually) be worked out very simply without reference to any complicated construct of nature. But the progressive principle, as well as the pragmatic, demands a "closed system" of concepts. We must show the relationship of all the scales of science, in order to have a systematic check on deviations from progressive refinements.

This interrelation of scientific concepts is frequently ignored in an attempt to get some kind of result. An experimenter wishes to see if there is any correlation between two variables, let us say the amount of soot fall and the incidence of tuberculosis, or the amount of steel produced and the salary rate of the steel workers, or blood pressure and temperament. The too common procedure is to set up "scales," in the formal sense, for measuring the variables, to accumulate a good many paired observations, and then to run a correlation analysis. And the results often mean nothing in the pragmatic sense. Suppose the amount of soot fall *is* correlated with the incidence of tuberculosis. What then? What should we do? Is this a sufficient basis for clearing areas of smoky conditions in order to reduce tuberculosis? Not at all. The soot may fall heavily in areas where people are economically poor, and hence poorly nourished. Thus, the soot fall could be reduced, and the incidence of tuberculosis remain unchanged.

All these are typical mistakes that can so readily be made unless we show how the scales we construct are interrelated. Of course we could fix up the tuberculosis experiment; the point is, how do we make sure the same kind of mistake will not be made on a new level? The efficient use of an object, and the improvement of our use of it, can occur only when we see how the property of the object is related to its other properties, and the properties and variables of the environment.

IV

To summarize: I have taken the position that modern materialism faces the crisis of removing fundamentalism from science. "Fundamentalism" is taken to mean the doctrine that certain aspects of scientific method are simpler to manipulate than others, and hence demand less investigation. The pitfalls of fundamentalism in measurement theory have been examined. For the fundamentalist's principles, there have been substituted pragmatic and progressive principles; these are not to be taken as "simpler" to understand than other aspects of science, but as methodological criteria that grow up with science. The evil of fundamentalism is that, by neglecting certain variables, it runs the risk of nullifying the objective of the experiment. And the materialist takes the objectives to supply the matter of all inquiry; neglect of the matter is therefore an insidious type of scientific immaterialism.[28]

References

[1] See T. A. Cowan and C. W. Churchman, "On the Meaningfulness of Questions," *Philosophy of Science,* Vol. XIII, pp. 20–24 (1946).

[2] The "story" has been formulated in many ways; for one such formulation, see E. A. Singer, *Experience and Reflection* (to appear), C. W. Churchman, *Theory of Experimental Inference* (New York, 1948), C. W. Churchman and R. L. Ackoff, *Psychologistics* (U. of Pa., 1947, mimeographed).

[3] See C. W. Churchman and R. L. Ackoff, "Varieties of Unification," *Philosophy of Science,* Vol. XIII, pp. 287–300 (1946).

[4] A. Ferguson *et al.,* "Quantative Estimates of Sensory Events," *Report of the British Association for the Advancement of Science,* No. 108 (1938), and A. Ferguson *et al.,* "Quantitative Estimates of Sensory Events: Final Report," *Advancement of Science,* Vol. II, pp. 331–349 (1940).

[5] N. R. Campbell, *An Account of the Principles of Measurement and Calculation* (New York, 1928). Throughout the rest of the article, this book will be referred to as *MC.*

[6] *MC,* p. 101.

[7] *MC,* p. 101.

[8] "Quantitative Estimates of Sensory Events: Final Report," p. 340.

[9] *MC,* p. 36.

[10] *MC,* p. 36.

[11] *MC,* pp. 36–37.

[12] J. F. Brown, "A Methodological Consideration of the Problem of Psychometrics," *Erkenntnis,* Vol. IV, p. 49 (1934).

[13] *MC,* p. 271, italics mine.

[14] P. W. Bridgman, *The Logic of Modern Physics* (New York, 1927), p. 5, The exact determination of length would involve all the operations there are in science.

[15] M. G. Preston, "Preference and Performance," in *Measurement of Consumer Interest,* ed. Churchman, Ackoff, and Wax (Philadelphia, 1947); pp. 13–16. Preston reports results that indicate a wide difference between an individual's preference for an instrument, and his actual performance. That is, the instrument with which the individual works best is not necessarily the one he thinks he uses most effectively.

[16] E. G. Boring, "The Use of Operational Definitions in Science," *Psychological Review,* Vol. LII, p. 243 (1945).

[17] S. S. Stevens, "The Operational Basis of Psychology," *American Journal of Psychology,* Vol. XLVII, p. 327 (1935).

[18] J. Locke, *An Essay Concerning Human Understanding,* Bk. II.

[19] E. Nagel, "Measurement," *Erkenntnis,* Vol. II, p. 320 (1931).

[20] *Ibid.,* p. 327.

[21] T. W. Reese, *The Application of the Theory of Physical Measurement to the Measurement of Psychological Magnitudes* (Psychological Monographs, Vol. LV, No. 3, 1943).

[22] G. Bergmann and K. W. Spence, "The Logic of Psychophysical Measurement," *Psychological Review,* Vol. LI, p. 9 (1944).

[23] "Measurement," p. 314.

[24] L. L. Thurstone and E. J. Chave, *The Measurement of Attitude* (Chicago, 1929), and *A Scale for Measuring Attitude Toward the Church* (Chicago, 1930).

[25] *The Measurement of Attitude,* pp. 6–7.

[26] L. Guttman, "A Basis for Scaling Qualitative Data," *American Sociological Review,* Vol. XII, p. 148 (1944).

[27] E. A Singer, *Experience and Reflection.*

[28] My thanks are due to R. L. Ackoff, who practically co-authored this paper, and to R. S. Rudner for many helpful comments.

LOGICAL EMPIRICISM

by

MAURICE

CORNFORTH

Maurice Cornforth, who lives in London, first studied philosophy at London and then at Cambridge University. He is the author of *Science and Idealism: An Examination of Pure Empiricism and Modern Logic* (1947), and of several articles and papers on philosophy, and is now at work on a continuation of *Science and Idealism,* dealing with pragmatism and recent theories of semantics and semiotic, and also on a larger book on logic and the theory of knowledge.

How Logicians Announced a Great New Advance in Philosophy

IN 1914 Bertrand Russell, having completed the *Principia Mathematica,* announced that a new way of thinking had "gradually crept into philosophy through the critical scrutiny of mathematics." This type of philosophy, he said, "represents, I believe, the same kind of advance as was introduced into physics by Galileo: the substitution of piecemeal, detailed and verifiable results for large untested generalities recommended only by a certain appeal to the imagination." [1]

The key to this new philosophy was its method, the method of Logical Analysis. Philosophy, said Russell, should not attempt to compete with natural science in working out a theory of the universe, or theories about particular parts of the universe. It was a mistake to suppose "that a-priori reasoning could reveal otherwise undiscoverable secrets about the universe." [2] On the contrary, facts and generalizations about the world, positive knowledge, must be acquired empirically, partly through ordinary perception, partly by the more refined technique of natural science. The task of philosophy was then to subject the propositions established through ordinary perception and by science to a logical analysis. Such an analysis could not establish any new truths. But by making clear the meaning of truths already known it would remove difficulties and confusions and impart a new clarity to our knowledge.

This idea that the task of philosophy is rather to make an analysis of the meaning or reference of empirical knowledge than to establish transcendental truths by a priori reasoning was not in itself anything very new. Already Mach's *Analysis of Sensations,* published in 1885, had set out to make clear the meaning of all scientific propositions by showing how every science was in truth concerned with the order and arrangement of sensations or sense data and with nothing else. And, indeed, the same thing had been put forward more than a century earlier in Berkeley's *Principles of Human Knowledge,* published in 1710.

Russell, therefore, was only restating something which had been common ground amongst empiricists for over two centuries. What he claimed as specifically new was the discovery of a logical technique for restating and refining the traditional method of empiricist philosophy.

Thus in his latest work, *A History of Western Philosophy,* Russell says: "Modern analytic empiricism . . . differs from that of Locke, Berkeley and Hume by its incorporation of mathematics and its development of a powerful logical technique. It is thus able, in regard to certain problems, to achieve definite answers, which have the quality of science rather than of philosophy. It has the advantage," he continues, "as compared with the philosophies of the system-builders, of being able to tackle its problems one at a time, instead of having to invent a block theory of the whole universe. Its methods, in this respect, resemble those of science." [3]

The "powerful logical technique" to which Russell refers is the technique of modern mathematical logic. He had in mind that the methods which had proved successful in mathematical logic and in mathematical analysis could be applied in philosophy.

Mathematicians of the nineteenth century had been able to overcome difficulties in the differential calculus by the definition of infinitesimal quantities in terms of the limit of a series of real numbers. Russell himself believed he had shown in *Principia Mathematica* that the whole of mathematics could be derived from logic by means of Frege's definition of cardinal numbers as "classes of classes similar to a given class." If, then, the nature of numbers, the nature of infinitesimals, and so on had been clarified by a technique of analytic definition, could not the philosophical problems of the nature of the world be likewise solved by a technique of logical analysis, analyzing and defining terms whose meaning was in doubt by an exact logical technique? This would then replace the dubious a-priori theorizing of the builders of philosophical systems.

Science and the Crisis of Philosophical Systems

The use of the method of logical analysis was a reflection of the general state of crisis into which the whole activity of philosophical system building had fallen as a result of the rapid development of natural science.

Already in the nineteenth century the futility of philosophical system building was becoming evident. In terms of eighteenth century science, philosophy could still seem to such thinkers as Leibnitz to have a separate function in interpreting the world, which science by itself could not fulfill. But as Frederick Engels was to point out, the great unifying discoveries of nineteenth century science made such systems once for all unnecessary. The last "great" philosophical system was that of Hegel. More and more has it become obvious that system building and the controversy of systems is barren of results. The systems can no longer satisfy the demands which men put upon them. The tasks of philosophy must be different from the tasks formulated by the builders of systems.

It is worth noting that this issue was already quite squarely put by Marxists some time before it was formulated by anybody else.

"Modern materialism," wrote Engels in *Anti-Dühring* (1878), "no longer needs any philosophy standing above the other sciences. As soon as each separate science is required to get clarity as to its position in the great totality of things and of our knowledge of things, a special science dealing with this totality is superfluous. What still independently survives of all former philosophy is the science of thought and its laws—formal logic and dialectics. Everything else is merged in the positive science of nature and history." [4]

The new formulation which dialectical materialism provided of the tasks of philosophy, and the contribution it made had little influence upon the content of academic philosophy. The official philosophers, the professionals, continued to build their systems. The past hundred years, indeed, have seen the production of many systems, the latest being that of A. N. Whitehead. Sometimes the system builders have tried to use parts of science to bolster up their fantasies—for instance, Bergson, or Whitehead himself. Others, like the English and American "absolute idealists" of fifty years ago, cheerfully ignored science altogether, saying it was concerned merely with "appearances."

But the continuance of this type of philosophy could not but provoke a reaction. It had been challenged by dialectical materialism, and it was again challenged by the representatives of philosophical empiricism. Thus we find that, historically, Russell's announcement that philosophy should concern itself with logical analysis and not with the attempt to "reveal otherwise undiscoverable secrets" by "a-priori reasoning" was flung down as a challenge against the contemporary English "absolute idealists"—Green, Bosanquet, Bradley, and others. He realized clearly enough that their system building could not stand up to scientific criticism, that it was based on confusions and logical fallacies, and that it was wholly useless and undesirable from the point of view of extending scientific knowledge and the application of scientific methods to theoretical problems.

For Russell and those who thought on similar lines, logical analysis, which should in their opinion become the sole concern of philosophy, did not aim at building up its own system of the world, but at interpreting and clarifying the results of science.

Still, such an interpretation of science needed to have some definite content. The theories of formal logic, to which Russell himself made such a great contribution, provided only the bare logical form in which propositions should be stated. But an interpretation that made clear the propositions of science must not only make clear their logical form; it must make clear exactly what sort of things they are about—their content.

It is a noteworthy fact that in seeking the ideas in terms of which the content of science could be clarified Russell and his fellow workers looked backwards, to the results of previous empirical philosophy.

In his three chief works of philosophical analysis—*Our Knowledge of the External World, The Analysis of Matter,* and *The Analysis of Mind*—Russell proceeded on the classical empiricist principle, which he formulated as follows: "It can be laid down quite generally that, in so far as physics or common sense is verifiable, it must be capable of interpretation in terms of actual sense-data alone." [5]

For Russell, mathematical analysis had already made clear the nature of number—what we are talking about when we talk about numbers—in terms of the abstract logical categories of individual things and their properties and relations, as developed in the logical theory of classes. In the same way, he thought, philosophical analysis would make clear the nature of the mind and its relationship to the body, the constitution of the material universe and the existence of the external world—what we are talking about when we talk of mind, body, matter, and so on—in terms of the categories previously employed by philosophical empiricism; namely, impressions, sensations, sense-data.

But this type of interpretation, interpreting all scientific statements in terms of sense-data and so analyzing the objective material world out of existence—"the extrusion of permanent things" was the phrase Russell used [6]—produced a philosophy in essence no different from the sensationism of Mach or the subjective idealism of Berkeley. The "powerful logical technique" was, in fact, nothing but a technique for saying in a new and rather more difficult language what had often been said before.

Thus the renunciation of system building and the path of a Galilean advance in philosophy led, in the hands of the first exponents of the method of logical analysis, to nothing better than a restatement of the old philosophy of subjective idealism. This was duly carried to its logical conclusion in a system of complete solipsism with the publication in 1921 of Wittgenstein's *Tractatus Logico-Philosophicus.*

Logical Empiricism and the Program of Analysis of Language

How to preserve the method of logical analysis without being confronted by the paradoxes of subjectivism and solipsism to which Russell's and Wittgenstein's treatment had led? How to formulate an empirical philosophy which would not be bound by the traditional empiricist ruling that the known world must be constructed out of sense data? These were the problems that faced all those philosophers who followed in the footsteps of Russell. The development of the contemporary school known as logical positivism, or logical or logistic empiricism (the examination of which is the business of the present essay) has been conditioned by precisely these problems.

What was the starting point of this development?

A study of Russell's basic works of philosophical analysis shows that his whole method aimed at the production of some theoretical "construction" of the world. Thus, in *Our Knowledge of the External World* Russell speaks of the task of "discovering what sort of world can be constructed"[7] exclusively out of elements concerning whose existence there can be no possible manner of doubt, i.e., sense-data. He explains that people ordinarily suppose that the world is constructed out of "permanent things." Yet considerable doubt attaches to the existence of such permanent things. Logical analysis, therefore, will "construct the world" out of elements to whose existence no doubt attaches, and these elements are of the nature of sense-data.

For Russell, then, logical analysis was a way of revealing the essential nature of the world, i.e., that the world is constructed out of sense-data, and not out of permanent material things, or spiritual monads, or other dubious kinds of entities to which traditional a-priori philosophy had made reference.

In accordance with this, the analytic philosopher J. T. Wisdom wrote: "The philosopher asks, What is the Self? What is the State? What is Time? . . . The philosopher is asking for a certain kind of definition of the Self, of the State."[8] This definition, provided by the method of logical analysis, will answer the question as to the real ultimate essential nature of things—of the Self, or the State, or Time, as the case may be.

Now it is easy to see that such a conception of the aims of the analytic method can well be criticized from the point of view of a strict empiricism. And it is this criticism which the logical positivists, or logical empiricists, provided. They pointed out that to use a logical-analytic method for "constructing a world," or discovering the ultimate essential nature of things, was merely to repeat in a new way the old errors of the philosophical systems. They claimed that those who professed to be empiricists and to use a logical method should definitely renounce all attempts at metaphysical construction. Their contention was that, while Russell and his associates had begun the criticism of traditional metaphysics, they had not carried it through with nearly sufficient rigor. A still greater transformation of philosophy was required in order to make it truly empirical, scientific, and free from metaphysics.

An important step in this new onslaught against metaphysics was made in the enunciation of the "principle of verifiability" by Moritz Schlick, the founder of the so-called Vienna Circle of empirical philosophers. This principle said that "the meaning of a proposition is its method of verification." A proposition for which no method of empirical verification exists is, then, meaningless. A great many of the propositions of traditional philosophy are in this way to be criticized as nonsensical. And it is asserted that no proposition contains any other element of meaning over and above what is given in its method of empirical verification.

What happens when this principle of verifiability is applied to Russell's analysis of the external world in terms of sense-data? Russell said that the world must be constructed out of sense-data and not out of permanent things. Yet what is the method of verification of this statement? In actual fact, the empiricists now contended, there is no method of verification for the statement that the world is composed of sense-data, if this statement is intended to contradict the statement that the world is composed of permanent things. You can say whichever you like, it makes no essential difference. One mode of expression may be better for one purpose, the other for other purposes. They are merely two different forms of words, two alternative languages for expressing the same facts, and not rival statements of the nature of reality.[9]

The conclusion was drawn that philosophers have been misled by language. Russell himself, in formulating the logical-analytic method, had already remarked upon this. But he was now criticized on the ground that, instead of carrying forward a thorough logical critique of language, he had allowed himself to be diverted into what were essentially metaphysical speculations, whose meaninglessness was revealed in the light of the principle of verifiability. The task of philosophy, however, could not be to construct the world, or discover the real nature of things, by extrascientific methods—whether methods of a-priori system building or methods of logical analysis. The task was represented as a quite different one—namely, "critique of language"; for the past methods of formulating the problems of philosophy had always rested "on the misunderstanding of the logic of our language." [10]

The new conception of the tasks and methods of philosophy which emerged from the principle of verifiability was most clearly and systematically stated by Schlick's associate, Rudolph Carnap.

"A philosophical, i.e., a logical, investigation must be an analysis of language," Carnap wrote.[11]

"The questions dealt with in any theoretical field," he wrote further, ". . . can be roughly divided into object-questions and logical-questions. . . . By object-questions are to be understood those which have to do with the objects of the domain under consideration, such as inquiries regarding their properties and relations. The logical questions, on the other hand, do not refer directly to the objects, but to sentences, terms, theories, and so on, which themselves refer to objects." [12]

Object-questions are only to be answered by the empirical methods of natural science. They cannot be answered by extrascientific philosophical means. Philosophy, as distinct from science, must be exclusively concerned with logical questions, i.e. with questions about the logic of the language in which we express our statements about objects. Philosophers must not inquire into the nature of objects, must not try to analyze the nature of Reality; they must leave that to science. They must confine their inquiries to the study of the logic of language. And this study will do the job which they really want done—it will enable them to reach agreed solutions of philosophical problems, and in particular it will throw a flood of light upon the problems of the philosophy of science.

The school of logical empiricism, then, which arose out of the logical-analytic method of Russell and out of the criticism of this method, may be said to be characterized by two guiding principles:

(1) The repudiation of all "metaphysics," i.e. all doctrines about the world as a whole, the ultimate nature of Reality, and so on, not capable of empirical verification; together with the acceptance of the empirical view that all knowledge is derived from experience and must be verified in experience.

(2) The formulation of the task of philosophy as being the logical analysis of language, and specifically the logical analysis of the language of science.

This means that critically the aim is to destroy "metaphysics." Positively, it is to make clear the significance of science; for the analysis of scientific language will show what science is doing, together with the connections of the sciences in one single universal science.

Despite the fact that rather widely varying views on different questions have been put forward in the give and take of discussion between members of the school—by such writers as Carnap, Neurath, Frank, Tarski, Reichenbach, C. W. Morris, and Popper—the above represents the principles of method and programmatic aim which they all have in common.

In the light of these common principles, the logical empiricists, in the period preceding the recent war, set about organizing international congresses of scientific philosophy and launched the project of an International Encyclopedia of Unified Science. Their aim was to establish a scientific activity of philosophizing on an international scale, which would be comparable with the natural sciences and mathematics in the steady building up of accepted and certifiable theoretical results.

Having now briefly examined the historical background of logical empiricism and its general program, I propose in what follows to discuss the actual content of its critical rejection of metaphysics and of its attempt at an analysis of science, and then its general tendency as a philosophy and whether it serves the interests of the advance of scientific knowledge and of social progress.

Metaphysics and the Theory of Knowledge

In his *Philosophy and Logical Syntax* Carnap says that the function of logical analysis is to analyze all assertions in order to make clear the sense of each and the connections between them. The principal task in this connection is to find out the "method of verification." The assertions of traditional metaphysics are found to admit of no method of verification. Since to be able to find no method of verification is the same as to be able to find no meaning, the metaphysical theories are therefore meaningless, nonsensical. They appear to have a sense only because they arouse emotions. Carnap distinguishes an "expressive" or emotion-arousing use of words from the "representative" use, and says: "Metaphysical propositions are . . . like laughing, lyrics and music, expressive."[13]

The criticism of metaphysics shows in particular, Carnap continues, that all general assertions about the "Reality" of so-and-so are metaphysical and senseless. For example: Is Matter real? Is Mind real? Is there really an External World? All such questions, and the theories purporting to answer them, are senseless.

All this makes it very clear that in Carnap's opinion the traditional problems of philosophy must be ruled out as senseless and as "pseudo-problems." Natural science, on the other hand, being systematic verifiable theory, alone will stand the test.

But with regard to science, philosophy must not ask such questions as: What kind of objects does science deal with? Does science refer to objective external realities, or is it on the contrary a technique for predicting the order of sensations? For, in Carnap's words, "the questions of the kinds of facts and objects referred to by the various languages [of science] are revealed as pseudo-questions." [14] Philosophy deals with the language of science—with its syntactical and semantical rules—and by so doing may hope to clear up the kind of difficulties that receive expression in such "pseudo-questions."

By such arguments as these it is definitely claimed that empiricism has rid itself of the taint of subjectivism. For the view that "only sense-data exist," that the world is to be "constructed out of sense-data," and so on, is rejected as "metaphysical." But the view that "external material things" exist independent of their being perceived—the "realist" view, which is a part of any materialist philosophy—is likewise rejected for precisely the same reason. In this connection, Carnap writes:

"Sometimes the views of the Vienna Circle have been mistaken for a *denial* of the Reality of the physical world. But we make no such denial. It is true we *reject* the thesis of the Reality of the physical world: but we do not reject it as false but *as having no sense,* and its idealistic antithesis is subject to exactly the same rejection. *We neither assert nor deny these theses, we reject the whole question.*" [15]

And again: "We make no assertions as to whether the given is real and the physical world appearance, or vice versa; for logical analysis shows that such assertions belong to the class of unverifiable pseudo-statements." [16]

Is it the case that by this downright "rejection" of all "metaphysics" the method of logical analysis has really succeeded in separating itself from subjectivist trends of philosophy? The view which asserts the existence of the material world independently of its being perceived or thought about, which is generally counterposed to subjective idealism, is not denied, but is rejected. Subjective idealism, too, is rejected, but not denied. The position is a delicate one for the logicians who have thus distinguished rejection from denial. Just what it is that they claim to be rejecting, and where such rejection leads, is worth inquiring into.

"The material world exists"—"The material world does not exist." "The material world contains processes which are reflected in various ways in our perceptions and thought but exist independently of such reflection"—"What we call material things are nothing but complexes of sense-data." Here we have statements which have often been debated by philosophers and continue to be debated, but the controversy between which, we are now told, is without meaning. What is at stake in this controversy? What is at stake is our whole point of view with regard to human knowledge.

Both the upholders and the detractors of the existence of the material world, together with those who say the question is nonsense, may be at one in recognizing that all knowledge is based on experience. This recognition is the common denominator of a wide variety of views —materialists, subjective idealists, and logical empiricists, all share it. The differences arise over the question of the source of our experience itself.

The materialists who affirm the existence of the material world are saying that our perceptions have their source in the interaction between ourselves and our material environment; that this interaction is such that our perceptions reflect or mirror the external reality well enough to serve generally as a trustworthy guide in practice; and that, by the use of scientific methods and logical modes of thinking, our thoughts and theories can likewise be made fairly adequately to reflect various aspects of the material world in which we live.

On the other hand, those who deny this are saying that our sense-experience is ultimate, absolute, an ultimate given datum, into the origin and significance of which there is no sure means of inquiring, but which can at most be a subject of speculation. Thus Berkeley, denying the source of sensation in the external material world, said it must be called forth in our minds by the will of God; Wittgenstein, writing two hundred years after Berkeley, did not mention God (because he thought that would be "nonsense"), but spoke instead about "the mystical." True, these same philosophers recognize the right of science to speak about the way our sensory apparatus is stimulated by impulses originating from the external environment. But, according to them, these very statements of science are themselves to be interpreted as having no other subject matter than sense-data. For Mach, for instance, the brain, like everything else, was nothing but "a complex" of sense-data, so that to say that sensations are aroused by impulses affecting the sensory centers of the brain was only to establish a relationship between two complexes of sense-data, and was not to establish the source of experience itself.

These were the kind of considerations which Lenin evidently had in mind when, explaining and defending materialism, he wrote: "All knowledge comes from experience, from sensation, from perception. That is true. But the question arises, does objective reality belong to perception, i.e., is it the source of perception? If you answer yes, you are a materialist. If you answer no . . . you deny the objective content of experience, the objective truth of your experimental knowledge."[17] "Materialism and idealism differ in their respective answers to the question of the source of our knowledge and of the relation of knowledge . . . to the physical world."[18]

Whether in this connection you "reject" the source of our experience in the material world or whether you "deny" it—whether you deny that our experience has a material basis or reject it as meaningless—does not make a great deal of difference. It is possible to argue about "the meaning of meaning." But at all events the question of the reality of the material world as the source of experience has had enough meaning to divide philosophers into two rival camps according to the way they have answered it, and it still has that meaning. When logical empiricists "reject the thesis of the Reality of the physical world" they thereby reject the objective reference of science, the objectivity of knowledge, the material basis of experience. In this way they place themselves in the same camp as the older empiricists, the subjective idealists, although they protest that they reject subjective idealism as well.

This fact is exemplified in the argument developed by Carnap and others to the effect that it is possible to use either "a physical object language" or "a sense-datum language" at will: the difference between saying that a thing is "a complex of atoms" and saying that it is "a complex of sense-data" is merely a difference in choice of language. If that is so, then the possibility of ever being able to express the dependence of our "sense-data" on the circumstances of our material existence is a-priori ruled out, and every essential point has been conceded to the side of subjective idealism.

Materialists—unlike some of the representatives of what is often called philosophical "realism"—justify their "thesis of the reality of of the physical world" and of the material basis of experience, not by general "metaphysical" arguments a priori, but by appealing to experience itself. The materialist considers that this "thesis" is "verified," not indeed by any particular crucial experiment, but by the whole development of science and technique. And the "thesis" has its basis in the entire structure of a materialist theory of knowledge, which regards knowledge as a social product whose foundations lie in the interactions of men with one another and with their material environment.

From this point of view the essential weakness of the "antimetaphysical" theory of logical empiricism is to be found precisely in its theory of knowledge—or, rather, in its lack of a theory of knowledge. A philosophical formulation of the standpoint of science, embodying the justification of a scientific view of the world and the rejection of a-priori philosophical theorizing, must have as its basis scientific theory of knowledge. No system of formal logic or abstract "principle of verifiability" will serve as a substitute. The very principles of the "logical analysis of language" remain suspended in the air so long as they have no basis in a concrete examination of the actual material social foundations of the thought process which is expressed in language. The "principle of verifiability" itself remains a mere phrase so long as the principles of the actual concrete process of building up knowledge and verifying it are ignored.

Thus the rejection of metaphysics, announced by logical empiricism, is undertaken on a most inadequate basis. This school of philosophy claims to be able to distinguish those propositions which have sense from those which have not, and to single out and reject the propositions of metaphysics as belonging to the latter category. But its apparatus for carrying out this task is defective. It does not proceed from any scientific analysis of the actual process of human knowledge. And in the absence of such an analysis, the upshot of its "antimetaphysical" program is to reject the objectivity of scientific knowledge.

In this respect logical empiricism remains in line with the whole development of empirical philosophy since Berkeley. But Berkeley's open rejection of knowledge of the material world, and the "construction" by Mach or Russell of an alternative "world" out of sense-data, are now replaced by the "logical" explanation that the whole question of the sources and objects of knowledge is to be "rejected."

But you neither solve nor get rid of a crucial question by "rejecting" it.

The Logical Analysis of Science

I said above that logical empiricism had a double aim—critically to destroy metaphysics, positively to make clear the significance of science. How does it proceed with the positive aim?

In the first place, we may consider the results of a simple application of Schlick's principle of verifiability. According to this, the sense or meaning of all propositions of science is given by the "method of verification." The verification of propositions of astronomy, for instance, is given by looking through telescopes, so that the *meaning* of these propositions is to be elucidated in terms of what we see through the telescopes, i.e., in terms of the sense-data of astronomers. Again, the verification of propositions of atomic physics is given by observations off electrical apparatus, so that the *meaning* of these propositions is to be elucidated in terms of what we see when we operate such apparatus, i.e., in terms of such sense-data as flashes on screens, and pointer readings.

In other words, the scientific theories of astronomy and physics, and similarly all other scientific theories, are to be understood as shorthand expressions of what we may expect to observe, or what sense-data we may expect to experience, under various specifiable conditions. That exhausts their meaning. To say, for instance, that the theories of astronomy reflect the stellar universe existing independent of all experience, or that the theories of atomic physics reflect the physical world existing independently of all experience, is to be regarded as senseless metaphysics.

It is not difficult to see that this subjectivist interpretation of science is far from satisfactory. There are parts of science, for instance, which deal with the past history of the earth, with geological periods before the appearance of man and before the existence of any experience. What is the meaning of these particular propositions of science? According to the present interpretation they must be understood simply as predictions of future sense-data—and yet we can recognize that this cannot exhaust the meaning of such propositions. Another difficulty arises in connection with psychological propositions about other people's mental states. Yet another difficulty arises in connection with psychophysical propositions about the dependence of mental upon physiological phenomena.

These difficulties need not be elaborated here, because they are obvious and have often been mentioned by contemporary philosophers of all schools. The logical empiricists themselves soon became aware of such difficulties, and therefore tried to revise the purely subjectivist interpretation of science which was the first result of the application of the principle of verifiability.

In his books *Philosophy and Logical Syntax, The Unity of Science,* and *The Logical Syntax of Language,* Carnap developed the view that previous empiricist studies in the analysis of science had been vitiated by the attempt to explain the *meaning* of scientific propositions. This led to a subjectivist metaphysics which he had to confess was just as bad, in its way, as a "realist" metaphysics.

But on the contrary, he explained, "the logic of science is nothing else than *the logical syntax of the language of science.*" [19] And: "By the logical syntax of a language, we mean the formal theory of the linguistic rules of that language—the systematic statement of the formal rules which govern it, together with the development of the consequences which follow from these rules." [20]

Thus philosophy will not inquire what science means, what scientific propositions are about, since in the light of antimetaphysical criticism "the questions of the kinds of facts and objects referred to by the various languages [of science] are revealed as pseudo-questions." In brief: "The philosophy of a science is the syntactical analysis of the language of that science." [21] By sticking, then, strictly to "syntactical analysis" the difficulties of subjectivist interpretation are to be avoided. Such difficulties just do not arise. It will soon be found, however, that other difficulties arise instead.

Proceeding to the "logical syntax of the language of science," Carnap wrote: "Science is a system of statements based on direct experience and controlled by experimental verification. . . . Verification is based on *protocol statements*." Protocol statements are "statements needing no justification and serving as the foundations for all the remaining statements of science."[22]

Instead, therefore, of trying to interpret the meaning of scientific statements, the task of the logical analysis of science is now to be regarded as being to show how science, the whole system of scientific statements, is derived from protocol statements according to certain formal rules. The protocol statements serve the function of reports on the basic observational data of science and on the observed results of experiments designed to verify scientific theories.

Where, then, does the syntactical analysis lead? It will be found to lead to results no less paradoxical than those of the previous subjectivist analysis. These results were summed up by Neurath as follows:

"Sentences are to be compared with sentences, not with 'experiences,' not with a 'world,' nor with anything else. All these senseless duplications belong to a more or less refined metaphysics, and are therefore to be rejected. Every new sentence is confronted with the totality of sentences which are present and which have been brought into agreement. Then a sentence is called correct if it can be brought into the system. Whatever we cannot systematise is rejected as incorrect. Instead of rejecting the new sentences we can also, wherever we find it generally difficult to make a decision, alter the whole system of sentences until the new sentence can be included. . . . In the present theory we always remain within the realm of speech-thinking."[23]

Neurath here correctly pointed out that, if you adhere to a strictly syntactical analysis, then the only account that can be given of science is that it is a changeable system of sentences which have to be continually "brought into agreement," and the correctness of any scientific theory depends on how it can be fitted into the existing system of scientific sentences, and on nothing else. Even with regard to the basic "protocol," it cannot be said that the protocol is certified because it expresses the ultimate experiential data on which the rest of science is based: this, too, would be a non-syntactical statement, another "senseless duplication" belonging to "a more or less refined metaphysics."

The analysis began by saying that science is "based on direct experience" and "controlled by experimental verification." But no account of such basis and control can be given in terms of a strictly syntactical analysis—these are non-syntactical, non-formal concepts.

Thus if the subjectivist analysis based on a simple application of the principle of verifiability led to a severing of the connection between science and the objective world by making science deal purely with predictions of future sense-data, the new syntactical analysis severs the connection even more completely by ruling out any sort of consideration of what science deals with and making it appear simply as a system of sentences, the correctness of each of which depends solely on whether it can be "brought into the system."

But such an analysis can give no account at all of what science is doing, why it is doing it, what is its value, or why we should prefer it to mysticism or metaphysics. In other words, it is altogether wide of the mark as an analysis of science. Its chief feature is that it continues to "reject" the idea that science reflects the real world and gives us objective truth.

This syntactical analysis is not, however, the last word of logical empiricism. As this type of philosophy is led from one impasse into another it continually produces some new device wherewith to try to extricate itself.

In the first volume of his new *Studies in Semantics* Carnap announces that "the field of theoretical philosophy is no longer restricted to syntax but is regarded as comprehending the whole analysis of language, including syntax and semantics and perhaps also pragmatics." [24]

This reflects the widening out of the logical study of language to include not only logical syntax, but also "semantics" and "pragmatics," already announced in the second number of the International Encyclopedia of Unified Science.[25] According to this improved analysis, the functioning of a linguistic sign—a particular case of what is called "semiosis," or the functioning of signs in general—involves the sign in a threefold relationship; namely, to other signs in the same language, to what it designates, and to the people who use and interpret the sign. Logical syntax studies signs in relation to other signs; semantics studies signs in relation to what they designate; pragmatics studies signs in relation to the people using and interpreting them. The whole logical study of language, which is a part of "semiotic," includes all three special studies. The logical analysis of science, then, is incomplete if it confines itself to the syntactical aspects of science: it must include the semantic aspect, "and perhaps also pragmatics."

Thus logical empiricism starts the analysis all over again, inspired with better hopes of success.

The essential feature of logical syntax is that it studies the formal rules employed in the construction of a given set of statements, i.e., the rules of formation, which determine which statements have sense or are permitted within the system, and the rules of transformation, which determine which statements are formally compatible with which other statements, which are formally incompatible, and how statements can be formally deduced one from another. Semantics, on the other hand, is concerned with the rules determining the truth or falsity of statements, i.e., with the determination of truth conditions for statements.

If we consider any system of statements, such as a science, then the assignment of semantic rules for determining the conditions of the truth and falsity of statements belonging to that system will constitute an "interpretation" of the system. The logical analysis of science is, then, concerned, not only with the syntax of the language of science, but also with the semantic rules employed, i.e., with the mode of determining the truth or falsity of statements belonging to the science, or with the interpretation of the science.

In his contribution to the International Encyclopedia, Carnap indicates the way in which a more complete logical analysis, which includes semantics, can apply to the science of physics. He distinguishes between the "elementary" and the "more abstract" terms employed in physics.

The elementary terms are those which refer to what is directly observed—such as the pointer readings, flashes on screens, tracks in Wilson chambers, and so on. He points out that "singular sentences with elementary terms can be directly tested." In other words, the system of the science includes semantic rules for determining the truth or falsity of all such sentences. The sentence, "The pointer-reading is *n*," is true if and only if the pointer gives the reading *n*.

On the other hand, the theorems of the science expressed in the "more abstract" terms—for example, about light waves, and electrons—can only be indirectly tested. Such indirect test consists in deriving from them singular sentences with elementary terms in accordance with the syntactical rules of the science, and then utilizing the semantic rules to find out whether such singular sentences are in fact true. For example, we test whether an electron has been emitted by observing the track in the Wilson chamber; we test whether an alpha-particle has been emitted by observing the flash on a screen, and so on.

Therefore, Carnap concludes, in the science of physics we need give no interpretation of any of the more abstract terms or theorems. It is enough if the science includes syntactical rules for connecting the more abstract theorems with elementary singular statements, and only the latter need be interpreted.[26]

Much the same conclusion is presented in Hans Reichenbach's recent *Philosophical Foundations of Quantum Mechanics.* There he distinguishes between "phenomena" and "interphenomena"—a distinction which amounts to the same thing as Carnap's elementary and more abstract terms. Statements about phenomena may be determined as true or false, but statements about interphenomena will have the truth-value of "indeterminate." In other words, we need rules for connecting the two sets of statements in the system of the science; but an interpretation as true or false need only be given to the statements about phenomena. Quantum mechanics includes rules for connecting statements about electrons with statements about tracks in Wilson chambers and lines on photographic plates; but the former need be regarded as neither true nor false, truth is to be ascribed only to the latter types of statements.

Here, then, we have an analysis of science of an apparently most elaborate kind, presented with a wealth of logical terminology. What does it all amount to? It is interesting to compare it with the much simpler account of the work of science—or, at least, of physical science—which was given in 1927 in the Gifford Lectures of the late Sir Arthur Eddington, and which earned some notoriety at the time.

Eddington said: "The whole subject-matter of exact science consists of pointer readings and similar indications." [27] As to what the pointers signified, he went on, this was "inscrutable." What difference is there between this simple statement and the logical theory that truth or falsity can only be assigned to "singular sentences with elementary terms" and that the "more abstract" statements of science can be given no interpretation? There is no difference.

Eddington also said: "*Something unknown is doing we don't know what*—that is what our theory amounts to." [28] What difference is there between this simple statement and the logical theory that all statements about "interphenomena" have the truth-value indeterminate? Once again, there is no difference.

Thus having fled from a subjectivist analysis of science into the realms of pure logical syntax, and having then sought the aid of semantics, the logical empiricists find themselves to all intents and purposes again saddled with a subjectivist analysis. They are once again interpreting science in the classical empiricist way in terms of predictions of observations. They are once again saying that scientific theories are to be understood as shorthand expressions for what we may expect to observe, or what sense-data we may expect to experience, under various specifiable conditions. This semantic account of the objects the theories refer to, plus the syntactical account of the formal connection between the elementary and more abstract statements of science, plus the pragmatic account of how scientific statements arouse definite expectations on the part of the people who interpret them, exhausts the meaning of scientific theory.

Limitations of an Analysis of Language

In what does the inadequacy of this whole analysis of science consist?

It consists in its inability to show the source of scientific knowledge as knowledge of the objective world, to show the grounds for confidence in science as knowledge and as guide to action, or to show how we can best organize scientific research in order that it may serve the ends of human progress.

Whence does this inadequacy arise?

It arises from the narrow preoccupation of the logical empiricists with questions of the logical analysis of language.

According to C. W. Morris in the International Encyclopedia of Unified Science, the study of science falls entirely under the study of the language of science, because this includes not only the formal or syntactical structure of scientific theory, but also its relations to the objects designated (semantics) and to the people using it (pragmatics).[29] But in fact, far from the study of the language of science comprehending the whole study of science, it leaves out the most essential features, which nevertheless have to be reckoned with if the work of science is to be properly appreciated.

For an all-round, rather than an abstract and one-sided, understanding of science it is necessary to take into account such facts about science as the following:

Science is a social activity; and the theories of science, set forth in the statements in scientific language, are products of this social activity.

The history of science shows that the problems tackled by science are ultimately connected—though the connection may be far from direct or simple—with the problems set by the development of social production and production technique, and by social organization.

In the case of the physical, and no less the biological, sciences, there is a close relationship between theory and technology. Theories are devised in the light of an experimental technique. Theories about the constitution and laws of various physical or biological systems are founded on the use of a technique for effecting controlled changes in those systems and for recording and measuring the changes produced. In this way the more science finds out about the constitution and laws of motion of material systems, the better the technique that can be devised for finding out more; and the better the technique, the further can scientific theory advance. Advance in theory leads to advance in technology, advance in technology leads to advance in theory, and neither can advance without the other.

It is just these essential considerations about science that are neglected and glossed over in the abstract logical study of the language of science. That such is the case is most glaringly shown in the further contribution of Leonard Bloomfield to the International Encyclopedia.

There an analysis is made of what is called a typical "act of science." Such an "act" is said to consist of the following steps: observation; report on observations; statement of hypotheses; calculation; prediction; testing by further observations. It is then pointed out that all but the first and last steps are "acts of speech." [30]

In the light of such an analysis of the work of science, it is very natural to suppose that we should simply accept the initial and end observations as "given"—as hard facts, so to speak—and that the "study of science" should fall, as Morris suggested, entirely under the study of the language of science. And it is also natural to come to the positivistic conclusion that the objects designated by the language of science consist of the observational data—pointer readings and the like in the case of the physical sciences; and that the pragmatic function of science is to organize expectations of the occurrence of such observational data.

The whole inadequacy of the analysis is contained in the lack of analysis of what is involved in "observation."

If we consider, for example, what is involved in the observation of a pointer reading, then it becomes very clear that the "act of science" is far from beginning with the observation. For in order to get a pointer reading (or a flash on a screen, a black line on a photographic plate, or a track in a Wilson chamber) there is first necessary the technical process of devising and constructing scientific instruments. This is an act of social technique, which consists in the production of a physical system whereby the scientist-technician will be able to control the occurrence of certain processes and record or measure them.

The basic observational data for scientific theory are not "given" but *produced.*

The observation and the record of the observation, which serve as starting point for a further development of scientific theory, are themselves *produced* by the application of a technique; and this technique has its foundation in already established theoretical knowledge, in the light of which it seeks to win further knowledge of and control over physical processes.

The real "act of science" has its basis, then, not in a mere "observation," but in an activity of social technique. The subject matter of scientific theory is by no means the observations—"pointer readings and similar indications," as Eddington said—but the objective material processes to which the technique relates, and which are registered, recorded, measured by means of the observations obtained by the use of the technique. Similarly the theories of science are tested in the further application of technique, and in the success or otherwise of new techniques invented in the light of the theories.

The observations of science are obtained in such a way that they throw light on the actual constitution and laws of physical systems. And scientific theories, if properly understood and used, serve the ends of increasing our all-round understanding of ourselves and the universe, of increasing our power to use natural processes for our own ends and our ability to organize our own social affairs. In this way, it may be added, the test of scientific theories is by no means confined to a laboratory test, but is effected in the whole application of science in social life.

The analysis of science, then, ought to show it as arising out of social life, as both engendered by and engendering social techniques. Such an analysis of science is materialistic. Traditional empiricism regarded science simply as a theory or set of theories whose aim was to sum up the regularities discerned in past observations and predict regularities in future observations. Logical empiricism only restates this in terms of "an analysis of scientific language." Materialism, on the other hand, sees science as a social activity arising in the course of the development of production and of production technique. It sees the observational data of science as obtained in the course of men's struggle to understand and master natural and social forces. It sees scientific theory, therefore, not as a summary and prediction of observations, but as the best account which we are able to give of the world we live in and of our own place in it.[31]

It is clear enough that all scientific results are stated in language, and that, as scientific activity becomes specialized, so a specialized use of language is developed in the statement of scientific theory. The logical empiricists are undoubtedly right in stressing the importance of the logical study of this language. It becomes important not only for the philosophical understanding of science and its significance for us today, but also for the development of science itself, since theoretical difficulties arise which can be shown to be associated precisely with the use of the instrument of language.

But the study of the language of science does not include the whole study of science. On the contrary, the study of language ought itself to proceed on the basis of a study of the social technique of scientific knowledge, which uses language as an instrument.

To propose a merely abstract study of language is to rule out in advance the possibility of showing how the scientific statements whose language it is proposed to analyze express objective knowledge, or are anything more than a means of referring to observational data and organizing expectations of future observational data. And such is, indeed, the outcome of logical empiricism.

Those who wish to preserve and develop what is positive and useful in the logical study of language, but to overcome the shackles of the traditional empiricist standpoint, must seek to do so on the foundations of a materialist theory of knowledge. On the solid basis of the materialist theory of knowledge, achieved in dialectical materialism but still awaiting a fuller development, philosophers may hope to show the sources of our knowledge of the objective world. And when they study the language of science from this point of view, they will study it as the means of expressing such knowledge.

Conclusion

It remains to summarize the principal conclusions that emerge from the criticism of logical empiricist philosophy from the materialist point of view.

Logical empiricism has the central theoretical weakness that it seeks to criticize the traditional philosophical systems, and to analyze and assess the meaning of science, with the help of nothing but an abstract logical theory of language, and ignoring the necessity of a scientific study of the actual process of knowledge. For this reason it is led continually to misrepresent the nature of our knowledge as knowledge of the objective world.

In essentials logical empiricism is nothing but a continuation of the tradition of the subjectivist theories of the older empiricism, which it restates in new forms and with a new terminology. In relation to science, the analysis of which is the central aim of logical empiricism, this tradition consists in ignoring the fact that science enlarges our knowledge of nature and of humanity and our practical control over natural and social forces; instead it represents science as a set of theories summarizing and ordering what is given in observation.

That this whole mode of "analysis" of science is a misrepresentation is evident if a concrete and historical consideration of the actual process of building scientific knowledge is substituted for the abstract preoccupation with the analysis of language. But it is also worth considering some of the broader consequences of this misrepresentation, because this helps to place logical empiricism in its correct perspective in the picture of contemporary ideologies.

The consideration of the character of science as knowledge is connected with the consideration of the part which the development of science plays or can play in modern society. The application and planned development of science can mean abundant food, shelter, health, rest, culture, and happiness for every human being. This demands a social reorganization, which in turn depends on a scientific understanding of the laws of social development and of the conflicting forces operating in contemporary society.

A philosophy which correctly recognizes how the development of modern science is a development of our knowledge of nature and mankind cannot but recognize and stress the above facts, and such a philosophy is an indispensable possession of those who are taking part in the struggle for progress. On the other hand, the misrepresentation of the character of science which is made by logical empiricism is such as to obscure the whole social function of science and to confuse the issues of the fight to realize the progressive potentialities of scientific knowledge. In relation to the task of extending scientific knowledge and securing its development and utilization in the service of human progress, the program of "logical analysis" bears a barren and scholastic character. In this respect it is certainly no "progressive philosophy"—a title which is often claimed for it. Quite the reverse. By rejecting the objectivity of scientific knowledge it obscures the significance of science as a weapon of enlightenment and progress.

The fact should always be borne in mind in discussing philosophy that, though the philosophers may lecture in universities and engage there in learned discussions which are quite incomprehensible to the majority of mankind, nevertheless these universities are factories of ideas which go forth into the world and play a part quite independently of the intentions of their creators. The ideas propagated in the discussions and writings of logical empiricists certainly do not help people to form a scientific picture of the world and man's place and prospects in it, or to understand how science can be utilized in the service of the common man. But this very scholastic negativity, this very failure to present a scientific philosophy comprehensible to the common man, means that the way is left open for the deception of the people by supernatural, idealistic, and antiscientific illusions. If the scientific philosophers put it out that science is concerned with nothing but pointer readings, the common man will agree with Eddington that in that case science does not tell us very much. It is in vain for philosophers to pretend that they are energetically combating idealism and irrationalism and supernaturalism as meaningless metaphysics, when they have nothing to put in their place, and when they just as energetically combat the scientific materialism which is the only practical alternative.

C. W. Morris in his latest work, in which he claims "to lay the basis for a comprehensive and fruitful science of signs," [32] succeeds in carrying linguistic, or rather "semiotic" studies to a new point, where the door is deliberately opened wide for any form of extra-scientific or antiscientific ideology. The new "science" reduces the significance of all signs, from the buzzer which summons experimental dogs to their dinner to the utterances of scientists and philosophers, to their function as organizers of behavior, and the whole process of knowledge consists in building up effective sign systems. A place is readily found for religion as "prescriptive-incitive discourse" which "lays down the pattern of behaviour which is to be made dominant in the total orientation of the personality." As for philosophy, it is "discourse dominated by the systemic use of signs in its greatest comprehensiveness." [33] The worst of it is that C. W. Morris takes no account of the fact that powerful interests antagonistic to progress are in the habit of loudly engaging in "prescriptive-incitive discourse" and "systemic use of signs" for their own ends and in order to deceive and hoodwink people. To expose such activities, to show up their deceptiveness and falsity, and to arm the common people with a scientific view of the world, is an essential task of a progressive philosophy. Such a task, the philosophy we have been considering is utterly unable to fulfil.

Logical empiricism set out to abolish "metaphysics" and to establish the foundations of a new type of scientific philosophy. Yet it succeeds only in continuing in new forms the traditional empiricist philosophy which rejected the material basis of experience and the objective reference of scientific knowledge. And the very latest outcome of the new "science of signs" is to reinstate speculative system-building—not to mention religion—as a "systemic use of signs."

Logical empiricism has failed to make a scientific approach to science itself. We would not deny the positive value of some of the specialized work which has been done in connection with the study of language and signs, nor the technical advance which modern formal and mathematical logic has made over the traditional logic. Here there is no doubt a basis for fruitful discussion between materialists and empiricists. But in estimating the philosophy as a whole, materialists can come to no other conclusion than that it misrepresents the whole character of scientific knowledge.

References

[1] Russell, *Our Knowledge of the External World* (1914), p. 4.
[2] *Ibid.*, p. 5.
[3] Russell, *A History of Western European Philosophy* (1945), p. 862.
[4] Engels, *Anti-Dühring*, p. 32.
[5] Russell, *Our Knowledge of the External World*, p. 81.
[6] *Ibid.*, p. 107.
[7] *Ibid.*, p. 72.
[8] J. T. Wisdom, "Ostentation," in *Psyche*, Vol. XIII.
[9] This is argued at length by A. J. Ayer, *Foundations of Empirical Knowledge* (1940), chap. i.
[10] Wittgenstein, *Tractatus Logico-Philosophicus*, Preface.
[11] Carnap, *The Unity of Science* (London, 1934).
[12] Carnap, *The Logical Syntax of Language* (1937), p. 277.
[13] Carnap, *Philosophy and Logical Syntax* (1935), p. 29.
[14] Carnap, *The Unity of Science*.
[15] Carnap, *Philosophy and Logical Syntax*, p. 20.
[16] Carnap, *The Unity of Science*.
[17] Lenin, *Selected Works*, Vol. XI, p. 19[illegible].
[18] *Ibid.*, p. 316.
[19] Carnap, *The Logical Syntax of Language*, p. xiii.
[20] *Ibid.*, p. 7.
[21] Carnap, *Philosophy and Logical Syntax*, p. 88.
[22] Carnap, *The Unity of Science*.
[23] Neurath, "Sociology in Physicalism," *Erkenntnis*, Vol. II, p. 603.
[24] Carnap, *Studies in Semantics*, Vol. I, "Introduction to Semantics" (1942), § 39.
[25] C. W. Morris, *Foundations of the Theory of Signs*.
[26] Carnap, *Foundations of Logic and Mathematics*, §§ 24, 25.
[27] Eddington, *The Nature of the Physical World*, p. 252.
[28] *Ibid.*, p. 291.
[29] C. W. Morris, *Foundations of the Theory of Signs*, §1.
[30] L. Bloomfield, *Linguistic Aspects of Science*.
[31] A very interesting approximation towards a materialist standpoint is made in Hans Reichenbach's *Experience and Prediction*, in the views he there develops concerning probability. Unfortunately there is not space here to discuss Reichenbach's analysis.
[32] Morris, *Signs, Language and Behavior* (1946), p. v.
[33] *Ibid.*, pp. 146, 234.

PRAGMATISM AND THE PHYSICAL WORLD

by

G. P. CONGER

George Perrigo Conger is Professor and Chairman of the Philosophy Department, University of Minnesota. He studied in Marburg, Berlin, Jena, Heidelberg, the Sorbonne, Union Theological Seminary (B.D., 1910) and Columbia (Ph.D., 1922). His writings include: *Theories of Macrocosms and Microcosms in the History of Philosophy* (1922), *A Course in Philosophy* (1925), *New Views of Evolution* (1929), *A World of Epitomizations* (1931), *The Horizons of Thought* (1933), *The Ideologies of Religion* (1940), and he has published numerous articles—some on the doctrine and criteria of levels.

PRAGMATISM is well known, so that no long introduction is necessary. One hardly needs to say, either, that the better one becomes acquainted with it, the more clearly its ancestral traits appear. Pragmatism is an offspring of idealism—an idealism troubled by the hard facts presented by the physical world and the precarious values engendered in practical affairs. In his early work James did his best to be faithful to the facts of psychology, but indicated that further considerations would lead to idealism.[1] Dewey started as an Hegelian, but found Hegelianism inadequate in the face of social problems.[2] In each case there is a shift of emphasis from the classical idealisms of sensations-perceptions-ideas to an idealism which emphasizes other aspects of experience, such as satisfactions, valuations, activities, and controls, and, with uncounted variations, in principle goes on to identify our satisfactions, valuations, controls, etc., with meaning, knowledge, and truth. In its extreme reaches, this method is expanded into a metaphysics, and made to furnish an account of the world.

II

The history of half a century has shown that it is difficult to argue with a pragmatist, and this for at least four reasons. First, there is the pragmatist's version of the egocentric predicament. From the beginning of its recognition, the egocentric predicament might well have been analyzed or regarded in various aspects. With or without the ego, whatever that is, we are all in the experiocentric predicament. There is no escape from experience; any attempt to escape from it—and as far as we can tell, any escape from it—is just so much more experience. Furthermore, the experiocentric predicament may be variously regarded without any danger of exaggerations. We do not import anything into it if we call it "interegocentric"; the pragmatists may have discovered inquiry, but they did not invent it. Our predicament is also always to some degree satisfactiocentric, volitiocentric, and in a word, pragmatocentric. In this sense we are pragmatists—we are all asking questions, exerting whatever it is that is called "will," and seeking satisfactions. We are all guiding our conduct and our thoughts by satisfactions achieved, anticipated, or desired. The result is that any critic of pragmatism is open to a kind of *tu quoque*, or "Whoever denies this affirms it" rejoinder.

In the second place, pragmatism, because of its initial shift of emphasis away from perceptions and ideas, turns from those functions and processes of mind which yield most clearness, or at least are most readily communicable, to satisfactions, controls, etc., which are more vague and lacking in precision. This vagueness and lack of precision resulted in what might be called the thirteen original pragmatisms [3] and has left a penumbra of indefiniteness around the whole subject. There was, to be sure, in the *Zeitgeist* some justification for lack of precision. Pragmatism arose in a period when both facts and values made change and flux conspicuous and put a premium on dynamism. So the pragmatic emphasis on change led to an emphasis on the anticipated future, and to pragmatism's rather too frequent shifts of position and changes of doctrine. In its attempts to be Herculean it has been Heraclitean, if not Protean. In the early days, sometimes one could hardly step twice into the same argument, and one grasped a point only to find it transformed in one's hand.

In an over-all view, it must be admitted that any broad philosophy either suffers or benefits from some vagueness; the only point for the moment is that pragmatism's peculiar vagueness often makes it difficult to argue.

Once more, pragmatism's insistent emphasis on experience, if it does not open, at least does nothing to close the Pandora's box (or the Portia's casket) of epistemology. And whatever one's estimate of what comes forth in epistemology, it must be said that epistemological arguments are subtle and difficult.

Finally, by its doctrines of truth as satisfaction and the obvious plurality of satisfactions in an individual or a group, pragmatism has tended to pluralism; and pluralism, whatever be its proper status as a philosophy, can evade many an issue by saying both Yes and No.

III

No one should presume to discuss the work of John Dewey without first paying a tribute of admiration for his almost threescore years and ten of productive writing in the field of philosophy; any one of the multitude who have known Dewey must add to professional admiration personal appreciation of his unfailing kindness and helpfulness to younger men.

It is impossible in anything short of a young lifetime to read everything that Dewey has written, or to be sure that any brief treatment will be altogether adequate. In the present connection, however, the main lines of his work appear to be clear, and they may be summarized as follows:

1. If we are forced to answer the question, "Is there a physical world?" the answer is a shaded "Yes." [4] Mind operates in a changing, problematic environmental situation, which is the source and test of our knowledge. Experience contains in a fused union somewhat experienced as well as some processes of experiencing. Mind participates in nature.[5] Things are had and enjoyed; this immediate experience, however, is not cognitive.

2. Mind participates in a knowing way when by inquiry and attack it transforms antecedent conditions into consequences marked by increasing control, organization, and satisfaction.

a. In this process of knowing, objects are, we might say, transitional. An object is that set of connected distinctions or characteristics which emerges as a definite constituent of a resolved situation and is confirmed in continuity of inquiry. There is some finality about an object, but objects are essentially events with meanings. An object is a set of qualities treated as potentialities for certain existential consequences. Sensible qualities do not constitute an object except in virtue of consequences.[6]

b. Our experience with objects is described in propositions. There is an important distinction between (1) generic propositions concerning objects as of a given kind or class and (2) abstract universal propositions. Generic propositions may deal with objects, but an abstract universal if-then law has for its subject matter an interrelation of characters which are integral members of a comprehensive system. Universal propositions are non-existential and necessary. The differences between the two kinds of propositions lead to some careful distinctions. For instance, if the proposition "All Cretans are liars" is merely generic, meaning that a disposition to lie is one of the characteristic traits that mark off Cretans, it does not follow that every Cretan is necessarily a liar.[7]

The validity of a principle is determined by the coherency of consequences produced by the habits which it articulates. If it generally produces conclusions sustained and developed in further inquiry, then it is valid, even though in an occasional case it yields a conclusion that turns out invalid. In such cases the trouble lies in the material dealt with, rather than with the habit or general principle. Invariants are necessary for knowledge, not for existence.[8]

c. Propositions exhibit logical forms; these forms arise within the operations of inquiry and are instances of relations between means and consequents in inquiry which is properly controlled. Logical forms are the conditions which inquiry as inquiry has to meet. For instance, the subject of a judgment is constituted by observed facts which bring a problem to light and provide evidential material for its solution; the predicate is constituted by the conceptual contents which anticipate a possible solution and which direct observational operations.[9]

d. Ideas, statements, or propositions embodying such logical forms are tested by applications to the given situation.

e. As the originally problematic situations are progressively organized and transformed, practical activity transforms experience into knowledge. Knowing, we might say, is know-how.

f. Our knowledge, developing in such a process, is not fixed, but changing; not absolute, but limited; not certain, but progressively warranted.

3. Throughout the argument, there is recurrent emphasis on experience rather than on nature. The problem of the existence of the external world is said to be artificially generated by epistemological premises. When we act and find environing things in stubborn opposition to our desires and efforts, the externality of the environment to the self is a direct constituent of direct experience. Existence is existence, and the test and modification of hypotheses by ascertained fact is a circular movement. But it is a movement within inquiry. Although the discovery of America was a stumbling upon an existence antecedent to the search, there was no discovery in any pregnant intellectual sense until old beliefs had been transformed. The world was transformed, too; the altered maps were part of the world. Changing the meaning of the world effected an existential change.[10]

This emphasis on experience typically takes the form of a biological emphasis. Dewey says that for him the word "subject," if used at all, has the organism for its proper designation; it refers to an agency of doing rather than to a knower, mind, or consciousness.[11] But we should note that doing also belongs to experience. Once Dewey admits nature into his purview: he says that to see the organism in nature, the nervous system in the organism, the brain in the nervous system, the cortex in the brain, is the answer to the problems which haunt philosophy. But again he says that the world is environment only as it enters directly into life function.[12]

4. At least in one work it is maintained that the qualities of our experience belong to nature. The use and enjoyment of things belong to things as well as to us. Stir and thrill in us is as much theirs as is length. Even the utility of things is a quality possessed. Qualities characteristic of sentiency are qualities of cosmic events. That there should be two separate systems, mind and world, in one-one correspondence is the acme of incredibility.[13]

IV

Dewey's theory of scientific knowledge for the most part conforms to the above outline.

1. Scientific knowledge grows out of our immediate experience of situations, but presents problems differing from those of ordinary perception.[14]

2. Scientific knowledge is an extension and elaboration of ordinary knowledge, involving the operational presence of general modes of activity.[15]

a. Science is concerned not with objects, but with data, i.e., subject matter for further interpretation. By comparison, ordinary objects are finalities. Science is concerned not so much with characters as with highly abstract relations, with things as and when they are placed in an extensive ideational or theoretical context. Scientific objects are statistically standardized correlations of existential changes.[16]

b. Scientific laws are arrived at by the help of generic propositions, but are formulated in universal propositions. This distinction is important for Dewey. A generic proposition is one about kinds, and is arrived at by selective discrimination. A universal proposition demands another type of abstraction, the abstraction of relations. A law states a relation of characters, of traits which describe a specified kind; examples are found in our conceptions of mass, time, and length, as well as in the category of causation. The function of a universal proposition must not be taken as if it were part of the structural content of an existential proposition. A scientific law is not about a sequence of events. What recurs is the kind of event; the uniform or constant relation which the law describes is not temporal or sequential.[17]

c. Like the logical forms, mathematical subject matter, so important in science, is an outcome of intrinsic developments within the comprehensive pattern of inquiry. Mathematical discourse, free from the necessity of existential reference, provides the possibility of indefinitely extended reference. Mathematical concepts are to be interpreted in a context of activity or operations. For instance, the postulates of a mathematical system state elements which have functionally the status of data, and ways of operating upon them. Again, within a given system, equivalence is always an end in view or object to be attained. Zero is a symbol for a balance of operations. In mathematics, as in science generally, verification is not a matter of finding an existence which answers to the demands of a theory but is a matter of the systematic ordering of a complex set of data by means of the idea or theory as an instrumentality.[18]

d. Theories and laws are of course tested by experiment.

e. Operations are essential. Laws are instrumentalities determining through operations the ordered sequences into which gross qualitative results are resolved. In particular, the Michelson-Morley experiment is regarded as showing the operational and (*f*) relational character of scientific conceptions. Science is not fixed but changing. Although we are not warranted in making assertions about the universe, there is progressively warranted assertibility as scientific inquiry proceeds in old and new directions.[19]

3. Dewey's emphasis continues to be on experience rather than on nature. This appears, for instance, in his statement that it is as arbitrary to assign complete reality to atoms at the expense of mind as it is to make a rigid separation between here and there in space. It appears also in his interpretation of the work of Heisenberg, that since either position or velocity may be fixed at choice, leaving the element of indeterminacy on the other side, both of them are shown to be conceptual in nature.[20]

His emphasis on experience makes control of experience involve the same principle as control of external events. There are two degrees of control of change which differ practically but are alike in principle. In astronomy, for example, we cannot introduce variation into remote heavenly bodies. But we can deliberately alter the conditions under which we observe them, which is the same thing in principle of logical procedure. By special instruments we modify observed data. In physical and chemical matters closer at hand and capable of more direct manipulation, changes introduced affect the things under inquiry.[21]

The motive for this emphasis on experience appears to be a desire to avoid a transcendent a-prioristic rationalism and to insure some status for values.[22]

4. The extension to nature of the qualities of our experience would, if sustained and developed, amount to a metaphysical idealism. It is

apparently not featured in works subsequent to *Experience and Nature.*

V

Criticisms of Dewey's theories have been legion; to many of them he has replied with characteristic vigor. Some remarks which are important in the present connection may be indicated by following the outline.

1. As regards immediate experience, we need not elaborate the point that the neo-realists, to say nothing of the intuitionists and mystics, have accorded to immediate experience a considerable status as knowledge. By comparison, Dewey's definition of knowledge is restrictive, cautious—or (to go along with the commonly recognized intensive, extensive, and ostensive definitions) *retrotensive.*

2. Granted that at least in much of our experience there is a transformation which yields knowledge, (*a*) Dewey seems to underrate both the extent and the value of correspondence between our minds and the world. We noted that for him the problem of the existence of the external world is an artificial one generated by epistemological presuppositions.[23] But once he has accepted that existence, he seems to presuppose that it can contribute to our knowledge only as it constitutes an exercise ground for our activity. (The presuppositions of pragmatism are worthy of scrutiny; sometimes Dewey appears to assume that only his opponents have any.) In terms of current theories of truth, Dewey recognizes the importance of coherence as well as that of the consequences of our actions; but the emphasis is on consequences. The coherence is a coherence within our experience, and there is little place or time for correspondences. If any correspondences are assumed or achieved, they are straightway plowed back into the business of knowing.

There is of course room for endless debate about correspondences. An idealist will point out that there is no proof of correspondences between mind and world; even the critical realists admit that our interpretations of the correspondences are mediated and indirect. Everyone must grant that scientific objects are in some respects different from ordinary objects; they are constructs, more than ordinary objects are, and the construction is within our experience. But this does not mean that the objects are in our experience; and as soon as the correspondences between our constructs and the objects weaken, the objects, if they do not cease to be scientific, become about as meaningless as anything can be. The fact that there is no logical demonstration of correspondence should not cause us to overlook it. It may well be that for this, as for other epistemological questions, no one has the complete answer. The conviction deepens that epistemology, like Aristotle's ethics, is not an exact discipline. In any case, some correspondences or correlations are indispensable. Copy-theory or no copy-theory, if they are not emphasized and relied upon, man with his values, coherent and satisfactory as these may be, is wandering about in worlds unrealized, and his so-called knowledge is so much shadow boxing.

Pragmatism overemphasizes activity and adventure; there is a kind of restlessness about it. Its watchword is "Excelsior." If pressed, it must admit that there are plateaus in progress, just as Dewey admits that objects as contrasted with data are in a sense finalities. Pragmatism here, as elsewhere, is a strong emphasis which exaggerates its thesis. A degree of repose and security is a more important factor in knowing than pragmatism would lead us to suppose.

b. Again, pragmatism assuredly has no monopoly on doctrines of generalization and the procedures which yield universals and laws. A rather ordinary and chastened empiricism can cover this ground, and where degrees of abstraction and generalization are recognized, (*c*) can account for logical universals, including mathematical theorems, allowing for their full use in (*d*) experimental tests.

Dewey's distinction between generic and universal propositions raises subtle logical problems. Suppose we say that in a generic proposition (actively and for practical purposes, if any one wishes to emphasize the point) we select and group objects of a specific kind, members of a given class, while in a universal proposition we try explicitly to include the entire class, or to sum up the relations or predicates characterizing the members of the entire class as such. Now the mark of a universal proposition (as distinct from a universal, where the latter is held to be anything like a Platonic idea) may be taken to be the presence of the word "all" or some equivalent word. In this sense, a generic proposition, although loosely framed, is already an implicit universal. Dewey says that the difference between generic and universal propositions is that of different orders of abstraction. This, we would say, is true in so far as in the one case members of a class are selected or abstracted, while in the other case characters, properties, relations, or predicates are selected or abstracted. But the essential difference is a difference of logical process, or operation; to group a number of subject terms into a class is one operation, while to attach predicates to a subject term, whether it is a singular term or a class term, is another operation. Often the former operation involves the latter; but this fact should not obliterate the difference between them. Either kind of abstraction passes easily into a generalization. In the former, individuals are abstracted and grouped in classes which are denoted by class terms or general terms; in the latter, such terms serve as subjects for general propositions. Thus, instead of saying "this whale," this "whale," etc., we may say "(the class of) whales." Such a generalization is a rudimentary or implicit universal; unless it is specified, one cannot tell the difference between "whales" and "all whales." Once our class term is arrived at, we may go on to say, "Whales are mammalian," or "Whales are over forty feet long"; again, unless specified, this is indistinguishable from "All whales are mammalian," "All whales are over forty feet long." In each case, the word "all" marks our completion, or alleged or attempted completion, of the "inductive leap."

Sometimes the inductive leap by which we group items or instances inclusively and exhaustively into classes turns out well enough to save us from the risk of another leap whereby we attach predicates to subjects; for example, at least as long as the class term "whales" retains its present meanings, there is no risk in saying, "Whales are mammalian." In such a case, each singular subject term, so to speak, takes the predicate with it into generalization. Obviously the case is different if we say, "All whales are over forty feet long." These examples may be said to illustrate the difference between an analytic and a synthetic proposition. The difference between analytic and synthetic propositions, with or without the psychological and epistemological circumstances as regards who knows what and when he knows it, indicates a property of terms which is parallel in the growth and development of an organism. At any moment an organism, we may say, has certain cells in its constitution, and in selecting food acquires others which are broken down and built into it. Just which cells are which depends upon the moment when the process is studied. Similarly a term (instead of being fixed, as in traditional logic) may have some predicates established while other predicates are being selected or rejected. In the remote abstractions of mathematics, dealing with classes of classes, or with classes of these, the inductive leap has been safeguarded, if not eliminated, by postulates and definitions, so that mathematical propositions are analytical. Such high abstractions tend, as it were, to remain above the battle (or behind the front lines); their certainty or necessity is of an analytical and rarefied kind. Sooner or later, however, they are applied in ordinary experience of the world. This application is often without question or thought of testing them, but they are at least unconsciously and indirectly tested all the time, and some possibility, however slight, always lingers that they may fail or be abrogated in favor of more tractable abstractions. In short, there is nothing sacrosanct about a so-called logical universal or mathematical theorem or law of nature; even if there were something of the kind, it would hardly fall to pragmatism to celebrate the quality.

Any sufficiently alert philosophy can agree that (*e*) as science progressively effects transformations—that is, rearranges the elements of more or less limited environmental situations—we gain increasing confidence. On the other hand, in basic ways the world controls us; it waits there to be found out, and we lose perspective if we take ourselves too seriously.

3. The crux really comes in the emphasis on experience rather than on nature. Pragmatism grew strong in the half-idealistic psychology of James and in the social concern of Dewey; but when it is carried over into a philosophy of nature it shows its limitations as it contracts the universe into the environment. Of course we cannot get out of the experiocentric predicament; but it is equally sure that we cannot get out of the physical world. We must admit that experience has a certain priority; it is psychologically and epistemologically prior, but quite evidently it is not cosmologically prior, and—depending on what is meant by "logic"—it is not necessarily logically prior.

4. The passage from any idealist epistemology to extravagant consequences in metaphysical idealism is a well trodden path which consistent pragmatists in the long run can hardly avoid taking. Idealism is truly a great philosophy, but it would be greater were it not for the physical world, which from the days of Hegel has been its chief

stumbling block. One might say that idealism has always presented a stumbling-block universe.

VI

It might be expected that pragmatism's treatment of the physical world would appear to best advantage in the work of the physicist Bridgman. Since his work is confined to a particular scientific field, it is not to be expected that it will cover as much ground as a full-fledged philosophy. It shows signs, however, of conforming in general to the outline used above.

1. There is the shaded admission of the independence of the physical world. For a physicist, fact is the ultimate thing from which there is no appeal. The fundamental operations are determined by nature.[24] Later, this is modified, as we shall see.

2. Mind may be said to participate in nature. From the operational point of view it is meaningless to try to separate nature from our knowledge of nature.[25]

a. Science deals with relations and objects which are different from ordinary relations and objects. It is possible to analyze nature into correlations without any assumption as to their character. As for the objects of science, we infer that there is a physical reality, e.g., stress, outside our direct experience because it is uniquely connected with other phenomena independent of those by which it is defined.[26]

b. In place of Dewey's distinctions between generic and universal propositions, there are the usual empiricist assumptions about the laws of nature. All experience justifies the expectation that the laws of nature with which we are already familiar hold at least approximately and without violent change in the unexplored regions immediately beyond our present reach. By assuming an unlimited validity for the laws as we now know them, mathematics enables us to penetrate the twilight zone and make predictions which may be later verified. But this must not be carried too far afield.[27]

c. Mathematics was invented to interpret nature.

d. The main point of connection between Bridgman and the pragmatists is in his operationalism. Finding, particularly in the light of Einstein's work, that classical concepts have become inadequate because they take for granted more than experiment can corroborate, Bridgman tries to establish the experimental method, in an essentially operational sense, as a criterion of scientific truth. He aims in this way to make it unnecessary for the sciences of the future again to be subjected to a revision of fundamental attitudes toward nature. He stretches the term "operations" to include mental as well as physical operations. In general we mean by a concept nothing more than a set of operations. If the operations to answer a question cannot exist, the question has no meaning.[28]

e. We may expect by strict adherence to the experimental or operational method to establish a science, but (*f*) experimental knowledge is often hazy. We soon arrive at its limits. We cannot be sure of any scientific statement until the crucial experiments have been performed. Future operations may reveal new experiences, but there is an appalling if not unending series of experiments to be performed.[29]

3. There is recurring emphasis on experience. A kind of absoluteness is secured for operationalism by treating the question in terms of experience. Any necessity of revising our attitude toward nature is avoided by describing nature in terms of experience. In this way there is a correspondence between experience and our description of it. In Bridgman's later work, his discussion is entirely of the contents of consciousness. Things are said to exist because, for one thing, our concepts work in the way we want them to work.[30]

Bridgman's operationalism, shorn of its confused epistemology and its report of scientific findings to date, seems to be no more than a brief for experimental methods as such. But experimental methods ought to be put to work to tell us in matter-of-fact fashion something about the world around us; they are short-circuited and weakened when they are made merely to interpret the content of our consciousness or our experience. The work of Einstein and many another scientist should of course teach us to be cautious and critical in our empiricism, but should not force us to entrench ourselves in subjectivism. Moreover, granted that experiments are crucial in science and that experiments are operations, it is a serious question whether our operations can never do full justice to the facts of nature. Too much has to be taken for granted before any experiment is performed, and before any scientist gets his laboratory or his intellectual equipment. On the one hand, a restrained subjectivism is enough to show this, especially if operations are made to include mental operations.

On the other hand, after all feasible experiments have been completed, too much in the universe has to be left just as it was. Man's operations, after all, are feeble stirrings in the midst of nature.

VII

Lewis, more Kantian and Platonic [31] than Dewey, recognizing that for any of us there are certain antecedent conditions, a categorial and *a priori* factor in knowledge, relies on pragmatism to answer the question how this *a priori* factor applies, if not to answer the question what this *a priori* factor is.

1. For Lewis, also, there is the shaded admission of the reality of an external world. There is such a thing as experience, the content of which we do not invent but merely find. There is a relation which might be called "participation"; mind has entered into the structure of the real world. For Lewis, however, as for Dewey, the givenness of immediate data is not knowledge.[32]

2. Immediate experience is developed into knowledge when a content is assigned to the momentarily given.[33] The process is not as aggressive as is the case with Dewey; the kingdom of knowledge is not taken by assault.

a. Objects tend to be regarded as more nearly final and less as transitional. The given as conceptually interpreted is envisaged as the real object. Mere sensible qualities do not constitute an object except by the aid of abstract concepts and categorial principles. The pragmatic element in truth and knowledge lies between the choice of a conceptual system for application and the assigning of sensuous denotation to the abstract concept. There is some attention to the future. Any thing is a bridge between given experience and predictable change.[34]

b. Lewis uses a distinction recalling Dewey's doctrine of generic and universal propositions, but in a context quite Platonic. He says that there are recognizable qualitative characters of the given which may be repeated in different experiences and are thus a sort of univerals. These he calls "qualia." He distinguishes between (1) empirical generalizations which are universal but not *a priori* and (2) the *a priori* elaboration of purely abstract concepts apart from any question of possible applications and (3) the categorial knowledge of interpretative principles. The categorial principles are not empirical generalizations in the sense that some later experience may prove an exception and thus invalidate them. The fact that pragmatism does not touch the *a priori* truth which is still absolute and eternal is the only thing which saves us from skepticism.[35]

c. He is close to Dewey in his view that logical forms and categorial principles become evident in the course of our purposive activity, or at least our active attitudes. A categorial principle is a sort of purposive attitude taken in the interests of understanding and intelligibility with which we confront the given. The laws of logic make explicit the base principles of all interpretation of our general modes of classification. For instance, the law of excluded middle formulates our decision, declares our purpose to make for every name a complete dichotomy of experience, for simplicity and similar considerations. Concepts and principles reveal themselves as instruments of interpretation; their meaning lies in the empirical consequences of the active attitude. If the categories had no practical consequences the mind would never use them.[36]

d. We may test the significance of any philosophic principle and pave the way for determining its truth if we ask, How would experience be different if the principle should be correct from what it would be if the principle were false?[37]

e. Knowledge accumulates, framed and controlled by the *a priori* categories; but these are themselves significant of our active attitudes, and the reflective method is inevitably pragmatic.

f. For Lewis, as for Dewey, there are conditions and limitations. The interpretation by which the given is referred to a category is always such that it may possibly be erroneous. Its validity can never be known with certainty. Categorial modes of interpretation may be subject to gradual transition and even to fairly abrupt alteration. To the extent that newly discovered empirical evidence may render old principles practically impossible, the old truth was never anything but hypothesis, and is now proved flatly false. Mind may alter the *a priori.* No equipment of categories and concepts which the mind is likely to achieve will enable us to understand experience completely and in every respect.[38]

3. In the work of Lewis there is unmistakable emphasis on mind. The problem of a correctly conceived metaphysics, like logic, is one

to be resolved by attaining to clear and cogent self-consciousness. We can discover mind and what is independently given to it only by an analysis within experience itself. The given is in, not before, experience. Whether the subject-object relation is universal in reality or not, clearly the answer must be compatible with its universality in knowledge. All order which is worthy of the name of law depends eventually on some ordering by mind.[39]

4. For Lewis, apparently the qualities of our experience are not ascribed to nature.[40]

VIII

1. Philosophy for Lewis is not cosmology, but it may be concerned with the broader and more general aspects of problems, the investigation of which belongs principally to natural science. It is especially concerned with the categorial, *a priori* element in scientific knowledge. For example, no experience of the physical can fail to bear those marks, the absence of which would bar the given content of experience from interpretation as physical reality. The formulation of our deliberately taken and consciously adhered to attitude of interpretation constitutes a categorial definition of the physical. This does not limit the content of the given; it forbids nothing in the way of experience.[41]

2. Science substitutes for ordinary things (*a*) things which are conceived in terms of correlations less directly observable.[42]

b. Whatever is of the essence of a thing need not be established by induction or vested in empirical generalization. In the march toward scientific ideals there comes a stage when it is no longer easily possible to say whether concepts are devised and laws discovered to fit phenomenal facts or whether the conceptual system itself rules and facts are reconceived in conformity with it. At least the give and take between the two is on approximately even terms.[43]

c. It may be that the inevitable movement of the exact sciences is in the direction in which mathematics has preceded them. With exact science as with mathematics, a stage is possible, if not already reached, in which the problem of scientific truth can be phrased equally well as the discovery of empirical laws sufficiently comprehensive to constitute a systematic whole, or as the selection of an abstract system which will be applicable to the facts.[44]

d. When the inquiry is about the application of an abstract system the sense-data must necessarily figure; the logical integrity of the abstract system is no guarantee of applicability.[45]

e. As might be expected, operationalism for Lewis is not conclusive but confirming.[46]

f. In the nature of its ideal, the ultimate things of science must be eternal; but any categorial principle is open to change.[47]

3. The emphasis upon experience recurs. For instance, Lewis asks whether, if we reflect upon the history of chemistry, it will not be obvious that the determination of what belongs to the deductive elaboration of concepts and what to empirical generalization from experience depends rather simply upon our modes of conception themselves.[48]

IX

The work of Lewis raises two main questions. First, does it face squarely and do justice to the evident facts of evolutionary psychology and anthropology? He says that the active attitudes of animal life presumably represent the phenomena from which genetically the human type of knowing has arisen. Moreover, men are creatures fundamentally alike in needs, interests, and powers, and they are confronted with a common reality, indicated in sense experience which is comparable. Even the coincidence of categories may be interpreted to mean a necessary psychological coincidence of the formal or relational aspect of experience. Doubtless what is fundamental, as logic is fundamental, has its roots in the nature of the human mind, although not in such wise as to be either self-evident or the only self-consistent possibility.[49]

What, we may ask then, is left to be *a priori*? If categorial principles have their roots in the nature of the human mind which genetically goes back to the animal mind, and if any categorial principle is open to revision, it would seem that what is one man's or one generation's *a priori* is a former man's or generation's *a posteriori*.

This suggests a second point; namely, that if it comes to an actual test and an attempt to say just what principles are *a priori*, Lewis overreaches himself. He says that "Parrots are birds" is *a priori*; any creature which is not a bird cannot be a parrot. "Parrots have a raucous cry" is *a posteriori*; the difference is between the intensional and the extensional "all." [50] But, as we said before, classification, no less than predication or the ascription of properties, etc., has to take the risk involved in the inductive leap; the proposition "Whales are fishes" is intensional and *a priori* enough for amateur taxonomists. We now say, "Whales are mammals"; but we should not try to make future revision of taxonomy impossible. Every attempt to make the *a priori* cover any concrete or existential fact, object, classification, property, or predicate is open to question, and to the possibility (although not the necessity) of future revision. Lewis admits that it is "the principle of the category only" that is *a priori.*[51] This seems to amount to saying that only the form, the syntactical structure, of general and universal propositions is inevitable. This, with or without Plato, is clear so that any one who can abide antecedent realities may call them *a priori.** They are the forms that our experience takes. Just *what* experiences or objects conform to them is left to be found out. We may readily agree with Lewis that some, though not necessarily all, of these facts have to be wrested from their natural matrix by pragmatic methods, rather than by ordinary observation.

X

Pragmatism is a rear-guard action, a Battle of the Bulge on behalf of idealism—a thrust of emphasis on human experience or mind, reinterpreted to bring out its dynamic and practical functions.

Like any reasonable idealism (witness Berkeley, Kant, Bosanquet), pragmatism has to admit some realism. There is no proof for it anywhere; but it is at least natural, if not inevitable, for us to say that experience is experience of something which under other conditions is independent of us.

The question always is, What is the relative contribution of mind and of world to the panorama? Taken in a long-range historical per-

* I may add that it is possible to work out a realistic view according to which the logical forms, while exemplified and persistent or ingredient in mental processes, do not originate there; they are also exemplified in the world of nature. In a logical realism they may be said to be prior to both mind and nature. The problems of intensional and extensional logic, as well as of analytic and synthetic propositions, need to be restated in terms of syntactic structures, freed from their non-essential encumbrances with psychology and epistemology.

spective, idealism may be viewed as a protest against Copernicus with his demoting of the earth, including man, in the cosmos. In this protest Descartes emphasized experience; Locke analyzed it; Hume showed the flaw in Locke's insulation of mind from world; Kant answered Hume with a rejoinder which (curiously and perhaps more significantly than he realized) he called a Copernican revolution; and idealism flowered in Fichte and Hegel and their successors. In much of this development, nature was, so to speak, taxed without being represented; in Hegel, nature was transformed, *aufgehoben*.

Such a tradition exercises a powerful effect on those who were trained in it or near it. Sometimes it woos them so far away from the world of affairs that there is an inner reaction, and idealism becomes heartily practical, as in Dewey. In any case, the laboratory sciences seem cold and inhuman, and are thought to be in need of some epistemological and logical overhauling which will make the human factor more conspicuous there. Traditionally the overhauling sought to construe data as phenomena. More recently there have been attempts to make definitions arbitrary or symbols counters in a game, or experiments illustrations of operational procedures—anything, it would seem, to bolster man's importance.

When one attempts to gain a view inclusive of theory and practice, laboratory and life, man and the world, there seems to be a sliding scale of mind's effectiveness and importance. Experience is a coefficient in any expression for our knowledge, but it is a variable according to the type of knowledge. Epistemology is not an exact science, and we can determine the value of the variable only approximately. Sometimes, as in many practical interests, its value is high; but it tends, perhaps asymptotically, toward 1, so that, as we get further and further and further from our emotional and practical commitments, the coefficient changes the value of the expression only slightly if at all. At that end of the scale, notably in astronomy, nature appears to get on suspiciously well without us. Pragmatism tried to provide a fresh grip on nature for our slipping valuations; but in any large perspective, even if in the future we succeed in artificial rain making or interplanetary migration, the grip is feeble and enthusiasm for it as constituting anything final can hardly be sustained. For a philosophy which aims at a world view rather than at a description of methods and procedure, pragmatism neglects too much. The stupendous mechanism of the stars in their courses, the dance of atoms, the rock-ribbed earth with its seas and mountains and sky, the majestic pageant of extinct and living species of plants and animals, the wonders of metabolism and reproduction, the indescribable complexity of nervous systems, the slow-moving structures and processes of societies are excluded from philosophy, except as they are the content of our experience or the field of our activity.

All this lost world, an adequate and comprehensive naturalism may restore. The pragmatic objection to naturalism is that it provides poor support for human values—as if human values could be better off when left to lift themselves by their own operations in a universe as overwhelming as the sciences show ours to be! A return to nature, however, does not necessarily mean a blank universe. It does not involve the forfeiture of values, as for Dewey, or a lapse into skepticism, as for Lewis. Nature itself, properly approached and adequately understood, is the firmest ground for our values and our surest refuge from skepticism.

Suppose that in a scientific age, with its objectivism, we shift the emphasis from "man and his manners" at least temporarily back to nature; study the world structures and processes empirically, and the life and mind structures and processes in the same way; and find that in detail they all exhibit the same principles. We may then infer that we with our valuations do not intrude into nature, but belong there. It does not follow that the world is a Mind; rather, the mind is a world, and valuations which develop in the little world have a natural ground and sanction in the great one.

In such an enterprise, pragmatism instead of diverting us with half-futile hopes may be one of our best guides. It may fulfill its function of preventing overemphasis on sensations, perceptions, and ideas, without another overemphasis on actions, satisfactions, and controls. What it, as distinct from ordinary empiricism, teaches about stars and atoms and organisms will be negligible. Its field is not so much that of ideas as of ideals. It operates properly in the data of the social sciences rather than those of the physical sciences. The problems of society, of economics, politics, philosophy of history, are too complex for ordinary methods, and for our rational or empirical resources. These resources, so to speak, have to be pooled in the face of our difficulties. Pragmatism offers us a kind of moral statistic, to help us over the sometimes bristling and sometimes elusive single factors in the societal complex; without being able to analyze or appraise them singly, we can attack them *en masse,* and either live them down with our present procedures or change our procedures in the course of the effort. Pragmatism, properly restricted, may teach us to test our valuations in practical adjustments to the world and in rearrangements there, without requiring or implying that we rebuild the world by our testing. In questions about the physical world it is often out of place and sometimes presumptuous; but when we understand the world by other means, then in the great gripping questions, in the life problems of realizing *our place* in the physical world, it can help us to gain assurance when we manage to get on the right track.

Notes

The following abbreviations are used:

AKV C. I. Lewis, *An Analysis of Knowledge and Valuation.* Open Court, 1946.
EN John Dewey, *Experience and Nature.* Open Court, 1926.
LMP P. W. Bridgman, *The Logic of Modern Physics.* Macmillan, 1927.
LTI John Dewey, *Logic: The Theory of Inquiry.* Holt, 1938.
MWO C. I. Lewis, *Mind and the World Order.* Scribner, 1929.
PJD P. A. Schilpp, ed., *The Philosophy of John Dewey.* Northwestern University Press, 1939.
QC John Dewey, *The Quest for Certainty.* Minton, Balch, 1929.

[1] See W. James, *Psychology: Briefer Course,* pp. 7, 466.

[2] J. Dewey, in G. P. Adams and W. P. Montague, eds., *Contemporary American Philosophy* (1930), Vol. II, pp. 16–20.

[3] A. O. Lovejoy, in *Journal of Philosophy, etc.,* Vol. V, pp. 5 ff., 29 ff. (1908).

[4] *LTI,* p. 521.

[5] *PJD,* p. 544.

[6] *QC,* pp. 99, 137, 168; *LTI,* pp. 129 f., 520.

[7] *LTI,* pp. 380, 383, 442 ff., 468.

[8] *LTI,* pp. 13, 390.

[9] *LTI,* pp. 3 f., 11, 14 f., 124.

[10] *EN,* pp. 156 f.; *LTI,* p. 266; *PJD,* p. 542, n. 27.

[11] *PJD,* p. 542.

[12] *EN,* p. 295; *LTI,* p. 133.

[13] *EN,* pp. 108, 267.

[14] *PJD,* pp. 536 ff.

[15] *PJD,* p. 538.

[16] *QC,* p. 99; *LTI,* p. 116; *PJD,* pp. 538, 578.

[17] *LTI,* pp. 441 ff., 450 ff., 468 f.

[18] *LTI,* pp. 394 f., 405 f., 410 ff., 418.

[19] *QC,* p. 127; *LTI,* pp. 454, 475, 531 f.

[20] *QC,* pp. 202 f.; *EN,* p. 110.

[21] *QC,* p. 84.

[22] *PJD,* pp. 538, 541.

[23] *PJD,* p. 542, n. 27.

[24] *LMP,* pp. 2, 29.

[25] *LMP,* p. 62.

[26] *LMP,* pp. 37, 55.

[27] *LMP,* p. 64.

[28] *LMP*, pp. 2, 5, 28.
[29] *LMP*, pp. 3, 10.
[30] *LMP*, p. 6; Bridgman, *The Nature of Physical Theory* (1936), pp. 22, 51.
[31] *MWO*, pp. 29, 58, 272, 307.
[32] *MWO*, pp. 30, 46; *AKV*, pp. 182, 188.
[33] *MWO*, p. 37.
[34] *MWO*, pp. 58, 272, 395.
[35] *MWO*, pp. 13, 121, 273–275.
[36] *MWO*, pp. 31, 228, 246 f.
[37] *MWO*, p. 31.
[38] *MWO*, pp. 224, 228, 233, 265, 271.
[39] *MWO*, pp. 10, 30, 55, 192, 254.
[40] Cf. *AKV*, p. 201.
[41] *MWO*, pp. 13 f., 17; *AKV*, p. 138.
[42] *MWO*, p. 394.
[43] *MWO*, pp. 397–399.
[44] *MWO*, pp. 393, 398.
[45] *MWO*, p. 399.
[46] *AKV*, pp. 196 f.
[47] *MWO*, p. 397; also, pp. 224, 228, 233, 265, 271.
[48] *MWO*, p. 399.
[49] *MWO*, pp. 91 f., 211; *AKV*, p. 10.
[50] *MWO*, p. 434.
[51] *MWO*, pp. 223 f.

ARISTOTELIAN PHILOSOPHIES OF MIND

by

WILFRID SELLARS

Wilfrid Sellars, M.A. (Oxon), is Associate Professor of Philosophy at the University of Minnesota. Rhodes Scholar at Oxford University, 1934–1937, taking First Class Honors in Philosophy, Politics, and Economics, 1936. Author of articles on epistemological topics in *Philosophy and Phenomenological Research,* the *Journal of Philosophy,* and *Philosophy of Science.* Co-editor with Herbert Feigl of *Readings in Philosophical Analysis.*

I PROPOSE in this essay to examine certain concepts and propositions which make up the backbone of the Aristotelian philosophy of mind. Since I do not have the space to develop my argument by way of detailed commentary on texts and quotations, and since isolated quotations are notoriously two-faced and of little scholarly value compared to the space necessary to make them intelligible to the non-technical reader, I shall instead proceed by developing as clearly as possible the assumptions and conclusions which, as I see it, are *typical* of the way in which classical Aristotelianism dealt with problems relating to the nature of thought. By laying bare its logical skeleton, I hope to show how *reasonable* the Aristotelian philosophy was, and that, in so far as it made mistakes, the mistakes were not foolish but sprang from plausibilities and confusions the true character of which could be exposed only with the aid of intellectual tools which were centuries in the future, and are not even yet in general use among philosophers.

Before we turn to this more specific task, however, we must first sketch the general framework of ideas in terms of which this philosophy approaches its problems. The framework is the "hylomorphic" conception of the world; that is to say, its interpretation in terms of the contrast between matter (*hylē*) and form (*morphē*) as these terms are understood in the Aristotelian tradition.[1]

At the level of common sense we interpret our world as consisting of an immense multitude of *things* each of which falls in one or another of a relatively small number of *kinds*. These things work out histories consisting of successive *states*. Though things and states alike come into existence and cease to exist, things are distinguishable from their actual histories. This difference is bound up with the fact that a thing could have behaved otherwise than it actually did. The "capacities" of things are richer than the actual sequence of events in which they participate. Though this water is now liquid, it *could have been* solid; it had it in it to be solid. What a thing has it in it to be is its *nature*. It is the nature of water to freeze and boil; of turnip seeds to grow into turnips. It is with reference to their natures that things are divided into kinds.

Something is clearly lacking in what I have just said. We must say not only that a thing *could* have behaved otherwise than it did, but also that it *would* have behaved differently if the circumstances had been different. Water is not only "capable" of freezing; it would freeze if the temperature were reduced to 32° F. To clarify this fact we must distinguish between the concepts of *capacity* and *dispositional property*.[2] Both involve a reference to laws of nature, but the former is a weaker notion and is essentially negative. To say that a thing is capable of being in a certain state is to say that its being in that state is contrary to no law of nature.[3] On the other hand, to speak of a dispositional property of the thing with respect to that state involves a positive reference to a law associating that state with a certain kind of circumstance. Thus, to say that dispositional property D necessitates the occurrence of state S_i in circumstance C_i must, if true, be true by definition; for D can only be defined as the property of being in state

$$\begin{array}{lcl} S_1 & \text{in circumstances} & C_1 \\ S_2 & & C_2 \\ \cdot & & \cdot \\ \cdot & & \cdot \\ S_n & & C_n \end{array}$$

and, if the statement is true, then S_i and C_i must be among the values included in these lists.

Now while the above indicates the lines along which the concept of a dispositional property and hence of the nature of a thing would have to be analyzed, and already makes it clear that the correct analysis of what a thing has it in it to be involves a reference to causal laws, it is by no means true that one must know this analysis in order to make use of the thing-nature language. It is characteristic of human thought that we are constantly making sensible use of concepts which we are not able, at the time, to explicate.

It follows from what we have been saying that concepts of *kinds of things* are the ways in which common sense crystallizes its experience of the world, and that this crystallization contains the common-sense grasp of natural laws, crude and incomplete though this grasp may be. To the philosopher it is an interesting and important fact that common sense thus formulates its understanding of the world order in terms of a framework which, when correctly analyzed, is seen to be logically more complicated than that of a functional correlation of events.[4] It is not my purpose either to "defend" or to "attack" the thing-nature framework,[5] but rather to show the use to which it was put by a philosophy which was unable to give it a correct analysis.

I conclude, then, that the concept of the nature of a thing, in so far as it is a coherent one, can be analyzed in terms of the concept of a dovetailing set of dispositional properties which specify both the states by which it has responded to its historical circumstances, and the states by which it *would* have responded to other circumstances.

We have spoken of a "dovetailing set of dispositional properties," for it is clear that according to the common-sense framework, a thing not only may, but invariably does have more than one dispositional property. Of the relations between different properties (we shall now use this shorter expression) of one and the same thing, that which most interested the Aristotelians was a relation which we might call "being founded on." Thus, to the Aristotelian, biological properties are founded on physicochemical properties. This relation is not to be confused with that of *being analyzable into,* which is what the mechanist believes to hold in the case of these two kinds of properties.

According to the Aristotelian, the various kinds of things to be found in our part of the universe fall into irreducible levels. The hierarchy consists of (1) merely physical substances, (2) living but not sensate physical substances (the vegetative level), (3) sensate but not rational living physical substances (the brute level), and (4) rational sensate living physical substances. Each thing or substance of a higher level has properties of a kind to be found in things of a lower level.

Thus, vegetables *fall,* animals *take nutriment,* and men *have the power of sensation.*

The Aristotelian also insists that the *lower level properties* of *higher level substances* are not identical with the *lower level properties* of *lower level* substances. This is reasonable, since, for example, what physical events will happen to a higher order substance, e.g. an animal, depends in part on what events of higher order, e.g. sensations and appetites, are going on in that substance.[6] The lower order properties of higher order substances are thus as bound up with the higher order properties of these substances as the higher order properties are bound up with them.

To sum up, the "dovetailing" of the properties of a substance involves (1) the dependence of higher level properties on lower level properties, (2) the connectedness of its lower level properties with the higher level properties founded on them, and (3) the necessary coexistence of such properties as are on the same level. These three modes of connectedness make the nature of a thing a genuine unity. The concept of unity of the nature of a substance plays a key role in one of the arguments we shall be considering below. Needless to say, all these modes of connectedness can be given a correct analysis only in terms of laws of nature.

We are now in a position to characterize the Aristotelian conception of *form.* First, we note that it is only too easy to overlook the fact that a disposition word is properly *defined* in terms of a specific correlation of states and circumstances. One who philosophizes on the basis of the common-sense view of the world has nothing to protect him from thinking of it as standing for an entity wich "generates" or "produces" states $S_1 \ldots S_n$ in circumstances $C_1 \ldots C_n$, from finding here an ontological fruitfulness, an overflow, a necessity which is no mere consequence of a definition.[7] It is equally easy to fall into the similar error of thinking of the unity of the dovetailing properties which make up the nature of a thing or substance as itself a distinguishable entity from which the various properties "follow" in the same "fruitful" way.[8] Such an entity would be an Aristotelian *form,* or, as the Scholastics were to put it, *substantial form,* if the Aristotelians had started out with a reasonably clear-cut notion of a dispositional property and had only blundered in the two ways we have just pointed out. Actually, as we have indicated, they did not have this clear-cut notion. The consequences for the Aristotelian interpretation of nature and science were enormous.

Turning now to the Aristotelian concept of matter, we must be extremely brief, since this concept plays a minimal role in our argument and what must be said can best be said when needed.

We tend today to mean by "matter" a set of *things* which in no sense are made up of other *things,* and of which all the properties are of a sort which we should call "physical," or, at least, would refuse to call "mental" or "vital." In this "thing-language" framework, materialism is the doctrine that all things either are "ground-floor" things of the above sort, or else are "made up" of such things. Materialism takes two forms: (1) *reductive materialism,* according to which all properties of "composite" things are "reducible" to properties of matter—which amounts to saying that except for convenience (abbreviation) an omniscient scientist would need no more non-logical and non-mathematical symbols to describe human organisms than he needs to describe the *behavior* of matter in a mindless universe. I say "behavior" because if dispositional properties are included, the criterion will not distinguish reductive from non-reductive materialism. For if *reductive* materialism be false, one could not describe the dispositional properties of matter in a mindless universe without referring to specifically mental characteristics. (*If* such and such *had* happened, mental events *would have occurred,* and the universe would not have been mindless.) (2) *Emergent materialism* is materialism which denies the "reductionist" claim.

The notion to be found in emergent materialism of things and properties which are "founded" on "lower level things and properties" and ultimately on "ground-floor things and properties," is also to be found in Aristotle;[9] and when he says that matter is *matter for form,* part of what he has in mind is that lower order things are matter for higher order things which, in some sense, include them without being reducible to them. It is only with the further contention that even ground-floor substances consist of matter and form that the Aristotelian conception of matter shows itself to be radically different from that of the emergent materialist. That ground-floor substances involve form is clear; water (which is one of Aristotle's ground-floor substances) has a nature, has properties. But what could the matter for water be? Clearly it cannot be a substance with a nature, for then water would not be on the ground floor. Thus, the "matter" for ground-floor substances must be "indeterminate," that is to say, without a positive nature of its own.

Why did Aristotle think that he needed an indeterminate principle? There are a number of mutually reenforcing considerations, some of which will come out in our later argument. At this point we shall limit ourselves to pointing out that Aristotle, in accordance with what was rapidly becoming the dominant trend in classical philosophy, *refused to think of the actual history of the world as an ultimate fact.* Process must not only *depend on,* it must also somehow be *derived from* factors which are intrinsically immune from change or becoming. (It will be recognized that this assumption underlies many of the metaphysical arguments for the existence of God.) Now, things or substances change; but it does not even make sense (except metaphorically) to say that the natures or forms of things change. Thus, change is impossible unless there is more to things than their forms. This more is matter, *prime* or *first* matter. But not all forms need matter; only those from whose forms "follow" contrary states, only those whose nature involves a reference to states which cannot coexist —only the forms of changing things.

How matter which is completely indeterminate can cooperate with form to "produce" change, or how, indeed, it can perform *any* function, is difficult to see, though we shall have more to say on this subject later on. The inadequacy of form and matter to "account" for change is recognized by Aristotle himself; he finds himself forced to introduce an Unchanging Changer. But it is, of course, no easier to "derive" change from three unchanging factors than from two. The actual history of the universe must be recognized to be an ultimate fact. There may be other aspects of reality on which process *depends,* in the sense that without them it would be impossible; but process cannot derive from that which is not process. This, however, is a story for another occasion.

II

In the Pre-Socratic period of Greek philosophy, philosophers had searched for one or more stuffs of which all things are made. Thus if they spoke of the "common realities" shared by the objects of our sense experience, they meant the ultimate ingredients of which perceptible, ephemeral objects were mixtures. Socrates and Plato, on the other hand, gradually and imperfectly disentangled the different notion of the *common* as *universal.*

When today the philosopher considers the statements, "*This* is a triangle" and "*That* is a triangle," he characterizes them as saying of two *particulars* that they *exemplify* one and the same *universal,* namely *Triangularity,* and he does this irrespective of his views on the "ontological status" of universals. Thus, in interpreting these statements, he characterizes Triangularity as an *identity* which is *common* to the many triangular objects that come and go in the world process.

Now it is clear that it does not make sense to speak of universals as *changing* or *coming into existence* or *ceasing to be.* It is rather to the objects which exemplify universals that these concepts apply. In these respects, universals are like the fundamental stuffs of the Pre-Socratics, for example the atoms of Democritus.[10] If it is pointed out that the latter were not immune from all change, since they formed the world-process by a constant mixing and unmixing, can we not reply that the various universals are related to (exemplified by) different particulars at different times? This point of resemblance between universals and world-stuffs might have been sufficient by itself to lead Socrates and perhaps the younger Plato to hold that universals are ingredients, and, indeed, the most "real" ingredients of the world-process. But there were other and even more convincing considerations.

Every truth (or falsehood, for that matter) involves at least one universal. Thus, "*This* is round" tells us that in *this* we have a case of Roundness, that *this* exemplifies Roundness. Now thoughts, or at least some kinds of thought, are characterizable as either true or false. Therefore thought *has to do with* universals. It is difficult (though, fortunately, not impossible) to avoid the conclusion that this is no metaphor. Surely universals must have a mode of existence such that mind can "grasp" or "apprehend" them.[11]

Thus, universals became to incipient Platonism the most real ingredients of the world-process, which thought could grasp, thus gaining knowledge of existence in so far as it is capable of being known. Furthermore, thought at its best, which, for the Greeks, was the thinking characteristic of geometrical demonstration, not only is concerned with universals (the various *kinds* of geometrical object) but is actually indifferent as to whether or not these universals are exemplified in the "world of becoming." Universals, it was concluded, are the appropriate objects of mind; particulars are the appropriate objects of the senses.[12]

It soon became apparent that the relation of universals to perceptible objects was quite different than that of the atoms or other elemental ingredients discussed by the Pre-Socratics. "Mixing" and "sharing" or "participation" could now be used only in a thoroughly metaphorical sense. Yet that the spatio-temporal world is in some way derived from a domain of universals (perhaps in conjunction with an equally ultimate but amorphous principle), and that knowledge at its best consists in a "vision" or "grasping" of these universals,—these are enduring elements in the Platonic tradition. Just how the relation of universals to particulars was to be understood became a serious problem. Fortunately, the history of this problem does not concern us here.

III

Let us approach the Aristotelian-Thomist theory of mind in terms of the place of the senses in the human cognitive enterprise. We have already pointed out that, for Plato, thought at its best is solely concerned with the Ideas and their mutual relationships and, in this respect at least, is independent of the senses. Yet, even though one holds that thought at its best is not *directed upon* the objects of perception, there is room for maintaining a causal or genetic dependence of even such thought on sense experience and imagination. In other words the shifting progress of thought by which we "grasp" now one universal, now another, may rest, in whole or in part, on the stream of sense and imagery—by which a reciprocal influence is not excluded.

One possible view would be that sense-experience (including the imagination) completely determines the subject matter of thought, in the sense that it "selects" the universals to be "grasped" by thought. Such an approach is completely foreign to Platonism. It is only if one is convinced on *"a priori"* grounds that thought *must* be paralleled by experienced or imagined objects that one finds the courage to populate the imagination with *non-linguistic* counterparts of thought. (To the empirically minded, of course, the only sensuous items which parallel the course of thought so closely that they could with some plausibility be held to be its determinants, are the symbolic or linguistic activities of the imagination which the Platonist, when he notices them at all, takes to be a consequence or "expression" of thought. (It is these symbol activities which the contemporary anti-Platonist *identifies* with thought. They are organic functions of much greater "depth" than the mere occurrence of verbal imagery.) The fact that classical philosophy neglected or minimized the role of symbolizing activities in its interpretation of thought is of vital importance for the argument that follows. We shall not have these activities in mind unless we explicitly mention them. Thus, unless otherwise indicated, they will be excluded from the scope of the terms "sense" and "imagination."

Now, while Aristotle, in common with Plato, rejects the position that the data of the senses and the imagination are the sole cause of the course of thought, he nevertheless insists, and in so doing parts company with Plato, that sense or imagination is a necessary condition of every thought in that *no universal* [13] *can be apprehended unless an instance of that universal is given to sense or imagination.*[14] We shall be concerned to draw out the implications of this position, for we shall discover that the characteristic features of the Aristotelian theory of knowledge, including the puzzling distinction between the "agent intellect" and the "possible intellect," can be traced to Aristotle's adoption of this alternative.

In order to understand the development of the Aristotelian theory of knowledge, one must appreciate the extent to which mathematics and, in particular, geometry dominated the intellectual scene in antiquity. Geometry, it must be borne in mind, was conceived of as a science which begins with infallibly grasped elementary truths about elementary geometrical objects, and proceeds to derive complicated truths concerning complicated geometrical objects. Thus conceived, geometry was a set of apprehended necessary connections between geometrical *kinds* (Point, Line, Triangle, etc.) forming a tight system with a foundation of self-evident first principles. In the absence of systematic empirical science (e.g., physics as we know it) the Greeks tended to draw the boundary between general truths which were *knowledge* or *science,* and general truths which were *educated guesses* (*"mere"* opinion) in such a way that science included only mathematics and such other studies as shared the above characteristics of mathematics. Today, on the other hand, while we should not regard empirical science as identical in either method or the status of its results with pure mathematics, we should include both the boundary which marks off reliable knowledge or science from the rule-of-thumb beliefs of common sense.

One of the characteristic features of classical geometry was the fact that its objects were capable of being given, even if only "imperfectly," a sensuous embodiment. Our visual field, in particular, presents us with geometrical points, lines, planes, and solids as the boundaries of qualitative differences—a line, for example, being a boundary between two adjacent color expanses. Furthermore, mathematicians made use of this fact in developing their proofs; and while it was recognized that the proofs were not *about* the particular lines in the diagram, yet it was believed that scrutiny of the construction was essential to the grasp of the demonstration. That this is not true of properly formulated Euclidian demonstrations (such as now exist), the theorems being logically contained in the premises, is not to the point. The historically significant fact is that there was sufficient misunderstanding of the nature of geometrical argument for it to be believed that scrutiny of diagrams is an essential ingredient in proof.

Turning now to Plato, we find him insisting on the necessity of diagrams for geometrical reasoning.[15] We might, therefore, be prepared to find him insisting that in all scientific thought there must be "illustrative material" to play the role played by diagrams in geometry. However, in the very passage in which he insists that diagrams are necessary to the *geometer's* thinking about geometrical kinds, he points out that the philosopher or *dialectician* has no need of diagrams for *his* thinking about geometrical or other kinds. We do not find in Plato a doctrine to the effect that to grasp an idea we must be acquainted at the time with an experienced exemplification of that idea.[16] On the other hand, whether it is because universals exist only "in" particulars (which is therefore "where" to apprehend them) or because universals are natures of experienced particulars which take on the character of universality *for thought* (so that in the absence of an experienced—or imagined—particular there can be no universal-for-thought), the Aristotelian insists that a universal can be grasped only by a mind which is acquainted at that time with a sensed or imagined exemplification of that universal. This notion, together with an un-Platonic optimism concerning the possibility of a *science* of the "world of becoming" (in the classical sense of "science" which we characterized above), led to the characteristically Aristotelian conception of the sciences of nature and man.

This conception, absorbed by Aquinas, and only gradually questioned by later Thomists under the impact of modern science, can be called the "abstractive theory of scientific knowledge." According to it, a truly scientific understanding of the various kinds of object in the world of nature is achieved by abstracting the forms of these objects from experienced cases, just as (supposedly) a truly scientific understanding of geometrical shapes is achieved by abstracting geometrical natures from experienced cases. Scientific method is that which conduces to the grasping of an ordered manifold of truths about a kind of object, by bringing about the grasping of the substantial form of an object of that kind—which substantial form is, as we saw above (p. 547, see also note 8), the ontological source of these truths. The fundamental role played by sense in this process is that of providing experienced cases from which the form is abstracted.

Aristotle combined his "abstractive" theory of thought with a causal theory of sense-perception. By this I mean that, for him, the contribution of the senses to experience consists in the fruit of the action of external objects on the organs of sense. This action was said, in Scholastic terminology, to "impress" the "sensible species" or "sensible form" of the object (e.g., a lion) on the organs of sense [17]—"sensible form" seeming to mean the states (or powers) of the object to which are due the resulting states of the sense organs affected by the object. The analogy used by the Aristotelians is that of a signet ring impressing its shape on wax. It is the sensible form of an object as "impressed" on the perceiver which is conceived by the Aristotelian to be the basis of an abstractive science of the object, as boundaries in the visual field are the basis of an abstractive geometry of the shapes of physical objects.[18]

Let us now ask the question, "How must the impressed sensible form of a lion be related to the substantial form of the lion if it is to be the basis for an abstractive science of lions?" Clearly, since the abstractive science of lions is the grasping of what flows from the ontological richness of the substantial form, and since the substantial form is abstracted from the perceptions of the senses, this form (called in the context of knowledge the "intelligible form") must be *present* in the impressed sensible form.[19] Here a decisive difficulty arises. Must we not say that for the senses to have impressed on them a character which *includes* the substantial form *Lion,* is for the senses to *exemplify this form, and hence to become or contain a lion?* (So that one who sees a lion would literally have a lion in his eye!)

There would seem to be only two ways out of this difficulty if the notion of an abstractive science of lions is to be retained. (1) The causal theory of perception might be abandoned in favor of a direct realism. Lions are directly apprehended, and the intelligible form is abstracted *from the lion,* and not from the product of the lion's action on the eye. Whatever might be said for or against such a theory, it is not to be found in either ancient or medieval philosophy—while modern direct realism has no truck with the abstractive theory of science. (2) The intelligible form might be held to be in the sense organ, but not by way of *actual* exemplification. Lion would have *existence for sense,* as opposed to *actual existence,* in the impressed sensible form. Two comments can be made on this suggestion which is to be found, for example, in Brennan's *Thomistic Psychology,* p. 117 (see also pp. 113 ff., 135–137; Maritain, *The Degrees of Knowledge,* p. 140). (a) To speak of the "existence for sense" of a lion when a tawny sensation occurs can at best be a misleading way of pointing out that the process of sense perception involves interpretation or thought in addition to mere sensation. Thus, "existence for sense" when it is opposed to "actual existence" is just a special case of "existence for thought." If this is so, then the "presence" of the intelligible form in a perception can hardly be that from which the thought of the intelligible form is derived, *since it is that thought* itself (albeit on an unreflective level). (b) Even should it be insisted that "existence for sense" is to be distinguished from *both* "actual existence" and "existence for thought," the result would merely be that the abstractive theory of thought would be explaining our ability to *think* of something (give it *existence for thought*) in terms of an ability of the same general kind (our ability to give things *existence for sense*) which is taken as ultimate. It is clear that the abstractive theory of thought makes sense only as a theory to the effect that the thought of, say, Triangularity is abstracted from an *actual case* of Triangularity.

The conception of natural science as a matter of abstracting intelligible forms from impressed sensible forms is, of course, of merely historical interest. Before we go on to see what has taken its place in recent Thomistic thought, let us consider for a moment what it was that made this conception plausible. *First,* there is the fact that the common-sense view of natural objects, which, since it is a crystallization in language and action of funded human experience, seems bodily given to us by our senses, was essentially all there was to the science of the day. *Secondly,* there was the complete neglect of linguistic and, in general, symbolic activities and habits in the interpretation of the facts of thought. *Thirdly,* an anti-Platonistic attitude towards universals, combined with the recognition that thought "deals with universals," led to the abstractive theory of thought. *Fourthly,* the Aristotelians, lacking the concept of a law of nature, had no clear theoretical understanding of a *dispositional property.* They did not distinguish it from the weaker notion of a capacity; nor did they have a clear idea of a dispositional property. Consequently, they fell back on pictorial thinking (*although in many contexts their statements about properties are quite reasonable!*), taking the "potential" to be that which is *implicit* in a thing, and the implicit to be that which is *present* in the thing but "obscured by" or "immersed in" matter. *Fifthly,* instead of thinking of the growth of a living thing (e.g., an acorn) as involving the appearance in an irreversible order of new dispositional properties, and of the nature of a thing as involving the higher order dispositional property of having specified lower order dispositional properties in specified circumstances,[20] the confusions mentioned under "fourthly" led them to think of the nature of a thing as an ideal *state* of the object present in it but obscured by matter, and of growth (which was the ultimate model for their conception of all change) as the progressive increase in the "clarity" with which the ideal stands forth. It is in the context of growth that we best understand the Aristotelian identification of matter with potentiality. In general, we must say that the plausibility of the abstractive theory of science rested on the extent to which lack of clarity in the analysis of the nature of a thing was balanced by a lavish use of matter as an objective unclarity of things, as an ontological bog or mire. As soon as the concept of law of nature as a functional correlation of events came on the intellectual scene, the abstractive theory of science was doomed.

Among contemporary Scholastics, those who have made a sincere effort to interpret the methods and results of modern science (Jacques Maritain and Mortimer Adler, to mention two whose writings are available in English), while they still insist that it makes sense to speak of grasping the intelligible forms of substances, admit that human beings cannot arrive at the intelligible forms of natural substances by abstraction *from the perceptions of the senses.*[21] They admit that empirical science works rather by the method of *saving the appearances.* But in their interpretation of this method they swing to the opposite extreme, and make the same mistake as the phenomenalists and positivists.

This mistake consists in hanging on to the fundamental thesis of the abstractive theory of thought, as well as to the idea that the data of the senses are the abstractive base of scientific thought, while recognizing that these data do not "contain" substantial forms to be elicited by thought. Thus, these Neo-Thomists regard scientific concepts and propositions as constructions of which the content consists of universals abstracted from the immediate data of the senses, while the rest is a matter of *logical and mathematical structure*. The importance of "merely symbolic thinking," of language as a calculational device, is discovered and emphasized, though it is insisted that there is also "real thinking" in which the mind is apprehending universals and meanings.[22] These New Schoolmen, then, agree with the positivists that, from the standpoint of the philosopher, scientific activity consists in the logical and mathematical manipulation of expressions which stand for actual or possible observations ("Red flash seen . . ." "Arrow-shaped line coincides with dot . . ."), a manipulation which, when successful, enables us to predict (or postdict) the course of sense experience. Those scientific terms which are neither purely logical nor purely mathematical, and do not stand for observable qualities—in short, those terms which the realistic philosopher of science takes to refer to properties of physical systems—are interpreted as *merely calculational devices,* since it is held, in accordance with the abstractive theory of thought, that only those non-logical and non-mathematical terms which name sense qualities name universals at all, *given that only these universals can be abstracted from the experiences which are the raw material of empirical science.*

Since, after all, these Neo-Thomists are Realists and not Positivists or Phenomenalists, they are led to distinguish between an angelic science which grasps the intelligible forms of things, and human science which builds up, by inductive methods, complex constructions of *practical and predictive value*.[23] Human science, thus, systematizes the appearances beneath which there is a core accessible only to the angels. Scientific laws are not truths about the physical world, but are merely calculational devices for predicting sense-experience. Where the Neo-Thomist does not overlook the fact that properties and, indeed, substantial forms can be defined in the language of empirical science, he is forced to hold that such properties and substantial forms are ontologically bogus, substitutes (with a "foundation" in things) for the "real" article.[24] Since the "real" articles they have in mind are only the common-sense notions of the natures of things, the Neo-Thomists are opposing the crystallizations of pre-scientific experience (which has no privileged source of information, and in which time takes the place of method) to the fruits of the systematic exploitation of the same material which is empirical science. Or can it be that pre-scientific experience has a privileged source of information? For these philosophers, being uneasy about the extent to which they have trodden the road to phenomenalistic skepticism, hasten to insist that, since "man is of all natural things the one with which man is most intimately acquainted, the only one whose specific nature he is able to comprehend fully," we have in the science of man "the *only* body of philosophical knowledge relevant to a species of physical thing." [25] Here alone can abstractive thought with ontological, as opposed to merely phenomenalistic, reach supplement the constructions of empirical science. Man's nature involves physical, vegetative, and animal levels of being. Thus, while man's knowledge of himself cannot replace empirical science, it abstracts a knowledge of these realms from his own being which, though limited, is not of the substitute sort, and thus transcends the limitations of his senses.[25] So the argument goes; but it is, of course, confusion. Its plausibility rests on man's pre-scientific knowledge of himself, just as the pre-scientific knowledge of the physical world (the presence of which in sense-experience makes this so much more than seeing colors or hearing sounds) made plausible the abstractive theory of physical science. In each case, the fruit of the long process of pre-scientific learning is transmogrified into a bogus process of intuitive abstraction. The confusion is bolstered by the fact that such learning, like "intuitive abstraction" is not a matter of systematic and deliberate saving of appearances.

IV

Let us now leave the subject of Neo-Thomist attempts to patch up the Aristotelian theory of knowledge, and return to an examination of the original theory, this time with a view to its bearing on the mind-body problem. We shall restrict our attention to the distinction, vital to the Aristotelian tradition, between the "active" and the "passive" reason.

Before we begin, let us remind ourselves that neither Aristotle nor the Scholastics conceived of soul and body as two changing, interacting substances, as did Plato and Descartes. The Aristotelians define the human soul as the substantial form of the human individual, who consists of matter and form as does any terrestrial substance. With qualifications which will be introduced at the proper place, it is the human individual that acts, that does things, and not the soul; just as it is water that freezes, and not the nature of water.

Let us also remind ourselves that even should it be necessary (which it is not) to recognize the existence of unique acts of "intellection" which are not explainable in terms of psychological laws relating to linguistic activity, this would not by itself force us to adopt a dualism of mind and organism as separate or separable *things*. The recognition would lead us to expand our list of ultimate features of the world, and our list of irreducible laws; and therefore to expand our list of irreducible dispositional properties. But just as we are not led to postulate a new *thing* every time we discover a new property of what we have been taking to be one thing, so the mere recognition of an irreducible set of acts and dispositions relating to thought would not call for a thing-dualism of mind and body.[26] It is only if we could show either that acts of thought are found to occur apart from the acts and dispositions characteristic of biological organisms, or else that they are completely independent of the remaining acts and dispositions of the organism, that we should be justified in arguing either that they belong to a separate thing, or, at least, that they will not be "touched" by the organism's death. The first alternative is that of finding empirical evidence for the existence of disembodied rational spirits. This, of course, can be left in the capable hands of the Psychical Research Society. It is a modified form of the second alternative which we find in Aristotle.

Let us now consider certain implications of the abstractive theory of thought, using as an example the proving of a geometrical theorem with the aid of a complex construction. We shall conceive of the process of proof as the successive grasping of ever more intricate relationships between the geometrical universals involved in the proof, a process culminating in the grasping of the proposition to be proved as necessitated by the relationships apprehended in the earlier stages of the proof.

We remember that, according to the abstractive theory, one cannot grasp a geometrical universal unless an instance of that universal is present to sense or imagination. Again, one cannot think of *a triangle* unless one is grasping the universal Triangularity. Now, suppose that at a certain stage in the argument the inscription of a circle is required by way of construction. It follows directly from the abstractive theory that *one cannot think of constructing a circle in sense or imagination unless one is already aware of a sensed or imagined Circle.* Thus, if we ask, "By what *rational* process is the geometrician led to make a new construction?" the answer must surely be, "None." The construction cannot be caused, even in part, by the thought of the construction, *for the thought of the construction presupposes the construction!*

We can generalize this implication of the strict form of the abstractive theory. It is a necessary consequence of the theory that thought, abstracting the universals which define its subject matter from the data of the senses and imagination, must accept with natural piety what the senses and imagination offer it in the way of material for abstraction. *The coming to have a kind of experience (sense or imagination) cannot have as its cause (in whole or in part) the thought of the kind of experience one comes to have.*

We must hasten to qualify the conclusion of the preceding paragraph, for Aristotle, taking a hint from the Socratic Doctrine of Recollection, worked out a most ingenious theory to avoid this consequence of the abstractive theory. Before giving Aristotle's solution of this problem, let us reformulate the difficulty as accurately and completely as possible.

According to the abstractive theory of thought, the thought of X cannot be a causal factor in one's coming to experience a case of X, since in order to think of X one must already be experiencing a case of X. If this is the case, then sense and imagination yield material for coherent sequences of thought only *per accidens.* For example, imagination *happens,* owing to causes lying outside the intellect, to provide the series of imaginative constructions which make possible the grasping of ever more complicated relationships between geometrical universals which, according to the Aristotelian, is the process of arriving at a proof.

There would seem to be only two ways (within a generally Aristotelian framework) of avoiding this consequence.

The first—relatively modern—consists in distinguishing between "symbolic" or "substitute" thinking (which is characterized as a calculational activity of the imagination, a manipulation of symbols according to learned habits) and "real" thinking (which is a matter of grasping relationships between universals and other meanings). I took this approach myself in an earlier rationalistic stage of my philosophical development. Those who argue in this way insist that "merely symbolic" thinking rests on habits learned in connection with "real" thinking, which is abstractive in character. They seek to avoid the objection we have raised against the abstractive theory by claiming that a temporal process of thought is either a sequence of real thinkings for which the orderly flow of abstractive material is controlled by the rational or calculational habits of the imagination, or else is symbolic thinking through and through.

Concerning this first theory we limit ourselves to two comments. (1) Those who take this course undercut, as we shall see, the ground on which rests the Aristotelian conception of the active intellect. (2) Once systematic and "rational" processes are recognized which are not apprehendings of universals or other types of meanings, then, even though one insists that such apprehendings must exist as the necessary conditions of the existence of "symbolic" thinking, one is open to a line of refutation which argues that "symbolic" thinking can be empirically accounted for without postulating such apprehendings. I have made it clear that in my opinion such a line of refutation would be successful.

The other approach to our difficulty is that taken by Aristotle who, in common with almost all philosophers up to relatively recent times, overlooked the possibility of a psychology of linguistic activity which would interpret it as something other than a means of "expressing" and communicating "real" thinking. (Actually "real" thinking is a ghost of "linguistic" thinking which haunts the rationalist.)

Aristotle [27] realized that unless thought somehow had a hand in the flow of imagination, the occurrence of *the right image at the right time* which is necessary (on the abstractive theory) for systematic temporal processes of thought, would be a mere matter of chance. Unwilling either to admit this or to abandon the abstractive theory, and overlooking the possibility of invoking "symbolic" thinking, he had to find some way of reconciling the abstractive theory of discursive thought with his conviction that *thought* as well as hunger, fear, etc., was a causal factor influencing the human imagination. *Somehow we must be thinking of what we are going to think before we think it.* This "prior" thinking (which, in the nature of the case cannot be the abstractive thinking it is designed to explain) is the active reason or *intellectus agens* (νοῦς ποιητικός). The term "prior" is, of course, misleading, since the active intellect is, for Aristotle, a ceaseless activity of knowing all essences and what they involve. It does not change, since it does not first know one thing, then another, but *always all things.* The active reason is a "part" of the soul of each rational being who is capable of a science of the world; but whether there is one active reason for all, and how the active reason is related to the forms are questions which Aristotle never answered, or to which his answers have been lost.

It is by this conception of the active intellect as a "part" of the human soul that Aristotle is enabled to hold that the flow of our experience is guided by thought—guided *in part,* for clearly thought is not the sole cause of the course of experience; it competes with the appetitive nature of man. It is only by a complete misunderstanding of the requirements of the Aristotelian conception of thought that his active reason has so widely been interpreted as the act of abstracting the universal from the particular.[28] The latter is an essential phase of temporal or passive reason which, "illuminated" by active reason, disengages the universal from the sensuous embodiment which the active reason, by influencing man's imagination in competition with other aspects of his nature, has made available to it. Discursive thought, for Aristotle, is the tenuous product of the impact on the imagination, which man shares with the brutes, of the unchanging and divine activity of pure thought which is the active reason. The latter is, of course, a thinking which is completely independent of sense, imagination, and temporal thought. It is therefore independent of the organism, and is not "touched" by death. It is the immortal "part" of the human soul.

As is well known, it is the impersonal immortality of the Aristotelian active reason which the Thomists have converted, under the pressure of Christian Dogma, and with the aid of the central confusions of the perennial philosophy, into the immortality of the human soul. Their argument can be tersely analyzed into the following steps:

(A) Each substance has only one substantial form. This is a direct consequence of the definition of a substantial form, since, properly understood, the substantial form of a substance is the unity of all the properties characteristic of that kind of substance. The error of maintaining that one substance can have a plurality of substantial forms comes from noting that higher level substances have properties of a kind which is also to be found in lower level substances—the elephant can slide down the grassy slope—while failing to note that these lower level properties of higher level substances take the form they do as bound up with the higher level properties of these substances. (See p. 546–7, above.) For the Scholastic it follows that it is a confusion to think of higher level substances as including lower level substances.[29] It is said that the substantial forms of higher level substances include the substantial forms of lower level substances "virtually" [30] by including their properties modified to fit their higher estate.

(B) Thus, the substantial form of a rational animal is a unity which involves all the properties characteristic of human beings.

(C) But the substantial form of rational animals includes the *intellectus agens* or active reason.

(D) Now the *intellectus agens* is not *just a property* in virtue of which *man* does things. It is not, in our terminology, a dispositional property as is, say, vision. *It does things. It knows*; [31] and knows in a way which is independent of the organism. Therefore the human soul is not just a unity of properties, *it does something; it knows.*

(E) Consequently, the human soul is not only the substantial form of the human individual, *it is also a substance.* For that which acts is a substance.

(F) Since the human soul is a *unity* which is in one aspect immortal, it is immortal as a whole. Therefore the entire human soul with all its dispositional properties, both original and acquired, is an immortal substance.

Now the crucial step in this argument is step C. Unfortunately it is a mistake. It by no means follows from the fact (granted that it is a fact) that human discursive thought could not occur without the influence of the active reason, that the latter is a *part* of the human soul, any more than it follows from the fact that without the sun the earth would not move in an ellipse, that the sun is a part of the earth. It is only because of the complete misunderstanding of the nature of a thing which we have traced in the course of our argument, that the active reason which (1) is not a dispositional property, and (2) is *ex hypothesi* completely independent of the organism, could be conceived of as "part" of the human substantial form. In general, it is only by pictorial thinking of the crudest sort that one can interpret the unity of a substantial form as other than a functional unity of dispositional properties. Indeed, it must not be just any functional involvement of dispositional properties (for, after all, the nature of gold includes the property of dissolving in *aqua regia,* and the nature of *aqua regia* includes that of dissolving gold) but only that sort of involvement which requires us to say that we are dealing with one thing rather than two. As the Averroists saw, what we have in the case of the human reason (again, we are making the contrary-to-fact assumption that it makes sense to speak of an active reason at all) is two things, one of which, *man,* could not perform certain activities, i.e., think, unless the other, *active reason,* were influencing it (illumination).

Another argument from the nature of thought to such an independence of thought from the body as might back up the dogma of the immortality of the soul can be dismissed even more briefly.

This time it is argued that the activities of "real" thought cannot be the acts of any organ (specifically, the brain), because universals are present in acts of organs only by way of *actual exemplification,* whereas in thought universals and other objects of intellect have *being for thought* or "intentional being." The argument continues (I quote from Mortimer Adler's *What Man Has Made of Man,* p. 179) as follows:

". . . (8) Therefore the intellect must receive universal forms. (9) But no form is universal according as it is received in matter. (10) Therefore intellectual reception must be immaterial, which is to say that understanding is not the act of a bodily organ. This last proposition is the capital premise for the conclusion that the soul, having this immaterial mode of operation, must also to that extent have an immaterial mode of being, and hence it is not only the substantial form of the body, but is capable of separate self-subsistence upon the corruption of the composite."

Now even granted that there is such a thing as the intellectual reception of universal forms—in short, "real" thinking—and that this notion is not merely the confused echo (due to the mixing of the psychological and the logical approaches to thought) of symbolizing habits and activities, even granted this, the argument is unsound. Everyone would surely admit that the fact that, *if mechanism in biology be false,* acts of organs are not *acts of chemical elements.* has not the slightest tendency to show that acts of organs are capable of *separate existence* apart from acts of chemical elements, *in view of the dependence of acts of organs on acts of chemical elments.* The situation is exactly the same with respect to the above argument. It must be granted that "intellectual receptions of universals" are not the acts of any bodily organ, *for they are certainly of a different nature from those acts which we class as acts of organs.* But intentional acts of the understanding (if such there be) are related at least as intimately to the biological activities of the nervous system as these biological activities are related to physicochemical activities. They are unique acts of the *man* who, by performing them, shows himself to be a substance of a higher level than the merely "organic" or biological.

The only difference between the case in point and proposed analogy lies in the pictorial dimension. Our imagery for physical and biological activities is robust and colorful; for "thought" it is pale and bloodless. Thus we tend to think of intellectual activities as present only in a ghostly and tenuous way in the physical and biological turmoil; whereas the dependence of the biological on the physical, though no greater, is depicted in terms of a pictorial involvement more adequate to the dependency. Once childish things are put aside (and pictorial thinking is childish) it is clear that from *difference in kind to capacity for separate existence* it is only possible to argue given lack of dependence. (The virtue of the argument from the active intellect was that there such independence was involved in the very argument which "established" the existence of the active intellect.) But given the degree of dependence of discursive thought on brain activity, with particular emphasis on symbolizing habits, which confronts the most casual study of scientific evidence, it is clear that the only acceptable argument for the *possibility* of the separate existence of thought must rest on evidence of the *actual* occurrence of separate thought. ("From actuality to possibility the argument is sound," to quote a Scholastic maxim.)

Thus, here again we are thrown back on the Psychical Research Society, unless an examination of the theological and ethical arguments for survival would prove more convincing. But that is beyond the scope of the essay.

Notes and References

1. The phrase "formal materialism" frequently occurs in contemporary Thomist literature as an alternative to "hylomorphism," particularly when it is a question of wooing intellectuals whose quest for certainty has led them to flirt with "dialectical" materialism, or any other philosophy avowedly materialistic in character, and for whom this phrase might build a bridge to the eternal verities. See Mortimer Adler, *What Man Has Made of Man* (1938), pp. 167 ff., 180. For an elementary statement of Thomistic hylomorphism, see Maritain, *Introduction to Philosophy* (1930), pp. 166 ff.
2. I wish to acknowledge my indebtedness to Prof. C. D. Broad's discussion of dispositional properties and the concept of the nature of a thing in *An Examination of McTaggart's Philosophy* (1933), Vol. I, pp. 142–151, 264–278. See also chap. x of his *The Mind and Its Place in Nature.*
3. Note that the contrast between "state" and "circumstance" belongs to the thing-nature language. Causal laws conceived of as functional correlations of events are not formulated in terms of "states" and "circumstances." The relation of the thing-nature or thing-property language to the event-law language is not the simple one of whole to part. Laws are formulated differently in these two frameworks. See also note 5 below.
4. It is especially significant to the historian of philosophy that the thing-nature framework, though historically prior to and more "natural" than the event-law framework which was to dominate science from the seventeenth century on, could be correctly analyzed only by a philosopher who has a clear con-

ception of a law of nature, and that, although many if not all laws can be formulated in both the event-law and the thing-nature framework, attention is explicitly focused on laws only in the process of research which must make use of the event-law framework. The language of things and properties, states and circumstances, where it is appropriate, sums up what we know. But the scientist doesn't know what kinds of *things* there are until he has arrived at laws which can be translated into the thing language. Thus, the historian infers that one would hardly expect to find a correct analysis of the thing-nature framework until scientists were explicitly looking for causal laws. He also infers that, unless the thing-nature framework is essential to science, it would be discarded by the scientist in favor of the event-law framework, so that the motivation for such an analysis would be lacking at the very time it becomes possible. The history of philosophy bears out both these inferences. On the other hand, the historian would expect that, should it ever become either necessary or convenient to formulate certain areas of knowledge in the language of things and dispositions, philosophers of science would soon reexamine this framework.

5. Whether the elaboration of concepts within the thing-nature framework is anything more than a convenient common-sense dodge, whether it is, in the last analysis, self-consistent, and, indeed, whether this elaboration is possible with anything other than the crudest laws, are questions into which we shall not enter. For a discussion of these and other questions which together make up the philosophical problem of "substance," the reader is referred to Prof. Everett J. Nelson's essay in this volume.
6. Adler, *op. cit.*, pp. 111, 190.
7. Leibnitz was to realize that the necessity with which the states of things occur, given their natures and circumstances, is analytic or tautological, but, owing to a confusion about relations, was to think that a reference to circumstances could not be involved in the definition of the nature of a substance. More accurately, this confusion led him to conceive of the circumstances to which a substance responds by taking on a given state as *other states of the same thing*. For this to be plausible, he had to put the environment of each thing inside the thing. The result was his famous doctrine that each monad or substance mirrors the entire universe.
8. "Essence and power are distinct, but powers flow from essence."—Adler, *Problems for Thomists: The Problem of Species,* p. 182.
9. Aristotle thought that *historically* the higher could not come from the lower, and believed that all natural kinds have existed from eternity, because he confused "coming from" with "reducible to." Contemporary Aristotelians who are aware of the distinction rightly see no incompatibility between "irreducible levels" and "evolution."
10. A. E. Taylor, in his *Varia Socratica,* has shown that by the time of Socrates the term "idea" (εἶδος, ἰδέα), which originally referred to the human form, had become a technical term for the ultimate ingredients which mix and unmix to form the world process. Thus Democritus referred to his atoms as Ideas. Compare the process by which the German word *Gestalt* has become a technical term in psychology, and, indeed, in philosophy.
11. The solution of the problem of universals consists exactly in showing that the following statements are all true: (1) "Universals exist." (2) "Thoughts mean universals." (3) "It is nonsense to speak of any psychological relation-

ship between thought and universals." The solution involves ***first*** a making explicit of the ambiguities of the term "existence," and *second* a distinction between "meaning" as a term belonging to the framework of logical analysis and criticism, and "meaning" as a descriptive term in empirical psychology relating to habits of response to and manipulation of linguistic symbols. The classical conception of mind as apprehending universals and meanings is based on a confusion of the logical with the psychological frame of reference. To deny that universals "exist" *when speaking in the framework of logical analysis* (logical nominalism) is as mistaken as to assert that universals "exist" *when speaking in the framework of the psychological description of thought* (ontological realism or Platonism).

12. Recent logical analysis has made it clear that just as every thought involves a reference to at least one universal, so every thought—even the most "abstract"—involves a reference to at least one particular. Indeed, instead of abstract thoughts referring to *no* particulars, the exact opposite is the case, for they refer to *all* particulars. Thus, "All A is B" says of every item in the universe that if it is an A it is also a B. This line of thought cannot be explored on this occasion. It is sufficient to note that, if sound, it explodes the Platonic contention that universals are more appropriately the objects of thought than are particulars.

13. It is often said that the essential difference between Platonist and Aristotelian is that while both maintain the ontological reality of universals, the Aristotelian holds that they exist only *in* particulars, the Platonist giving them an existence *apart*. One should always be cautious about attributing nonsense to intelligent philosophers; and to say that universals are literally in (or apart from) particulars is nonsense. This interpretation of the difference between Platonist and Aristotelian rests on two mistakes. (1) It overlooks the fact that the "apartness" of the Platonic Ideas is, in large measure, their Olympian self-sufficiency. Plato teaching—except in the *Parmenides?* —that the Ideas would exist even if the "world of becoming" did not. (2) It rests on the assumption that the Aristotelian clearly and unambiguously thinks of his *forms* as "objective" universals, for that the forms of changing things exist only as ingredients of these things for this philosophy is granted. The truth of the matter is that the Aristotelian has a strong bias against the ontological reality of universals, and tends to think of them as contents "abstracted" from sense and imagination, which contents become *universals* only *in and for thought*. The Aristotelian matter can scarcely be a principle of particularity which supplements universals (as it is for the Platonist); otherwise "pure forms" would be universals, which they clearly are not intended to be. Matter makes change possible, and in doing so is a principle of *difference* for objects having like nature; for objects of like *nature* can differ only *in their histories*. Matter is the *principium individuationis* rather than *principium particularitatis*. It must be admitted, however, that the Aristotelian has his Platonizing moments, especially when puzzled about the objectivity of knowledge. Notice that I have been speaking of the Aristotelian tradition rather than of Aristotle himself. A discussion of the extent to which the latter exhibits the characteristic ambivalence of the Aristotelian tradition with respect to the status of universals would take us far beyond the scope of this paper. Fortunately, the argument which follows does not depend on either interpretation of the Aristotelian theory of universals. For a pene-

trating account of Aristotle's difficulties with universals see H. F. Cherniss, *Aristotle's Criticism of Plato and the Academy,* Vol. I (1944), pp. 324–376. For the Thomistic treatment of the problem see Maritain, *Introduction to Philosophy,* pp. 160 ff.; Mortimer Adler, "Solution of the Problem of Species," *Thomist,* Apr., 1941, pp. 303 ff. See also Maritain, *La Philosophie de la nature,* p. 9.

14. *De Anima,* Bk. III, chaps. 7, 8. See W. D. Ross, *Aristotle,* 2nd ed., p. 148; Mortimer Adler, *What Man Has Made of Man,* pp. 162, 175; Maritain, *Introduction to Philosophy,* pp. 170 ff.; R. E. Brennan, *Thomistic Psychology* (1942), pp. 179 ff., 202. Cf. Brennan's discussion of imageless thought on p. 204, where, in his eagerness to reconcile Aquinas with empirical fact, he contradicts not only the entire Aristotelian tradition, but what he has himself just finished saying.
15. *Republic,* VI, pp. 510–511.
16. The Doctrine of Recollection (*Phaedo,* pp. 72–77; *Meno,* pp. 80–86) might be thought, at a hasty glance, to be or entail such a position. Plato's point, however, is that the object of thought can neither be nor be derived from the object of the senses. He also assumes that the objects of thought cannot be directly grasped by an embodied soul (an assumption which Plato himself later abandoned, and with it the Doctrine of Recollection which falls without it). When the object of sense *seems* to be the object of thought it is because it is putting us in mind of the object of thought (of which we must have an innate non-sensuous image or imprint). He argues that what reminds us of an idea need not be like the Idea. While he puts this forward in the *Phaedo* to reconcile recollection with the great difference between sense-objects and Ideas, it is clear that Plato does not intend to restrict the stimulus of recollection to sense-experience alone. Interrogation also can put us in mind of Ideas.
17. Ross, *Aristotle,* 2nd ed., pp. 136–142; Brennan, *Thomistic Psychology,* pp. 11–16, 117–123; Maritain, *The Degrees of Knowledge* (1938), p. 143 n.
18. Note that the science of the geometrical properties of color patches will not be the same as the science of the geometrical properties of physical objects, unless the terms "triangular," "straight," "shape," etc., have the same sense in the context of physical objects as they do in the context of color patches. Now the important thing about the shapes of color patches is that they are directly given to consciousness, so that, if there is a mental activity of abstraction *as conceived of by the Aristotelians,* it will make sense to speak of grasping geometrical universals by abstraction from cases with which the mind is directly acquainted. Furthermore, if the geometrical universals exemplified by physical objects can reasonably be identified with the geometrical universals exemplified by the boundaries of colors, then the science in question would be the science of the shapes of physical objects as well as of the shapes of color patches. If we assume, in Aristotelian style, that the colors we see are in the observer's organism, *then the science of physical shapes would rest on the exemplification in the knower's organism of geometrical universals.* Compare the case of the science of lions in the next paragraph.
19. See, for example, Brennan, *Thomistic Psychology,* pp. 178–184, 189–193.
20. "We must . . . notice that dispositions fall into a hierarchy. A bit of iron which has been put inside a helix in which an electric current circulates acquires the power to attract iron-findings. . . . If we call this magnetic

property a 'first-order disposition,' the power to acquire this property when placed in a helix . . . may be called a 'second-order disposition.'" (Broad, *Examination of McTaggart's Philosophy,* Vol. 1, p. 266.) See also the references listed in note 2 above.

21. Maritain, *La Philosophie de la nature,* pp. 42, 89–93; Maritain, *The Degrees of Knowledge,* p. 249; Brennan, *op. cit.,* p. 170; Adler, *Solution of the Problem of Species,* pp. 399 n., 347 n. Adler has apparently not got around to drawing the implications of his remarks in the latter reference. They contain enough dynamite to force a complete revision of his ontology, *or* epistemology. Is *substantial form* a category in the Kantian sense?
22. Adler, *What Man Has Made of Man,* p. 207; Maritain, *The Degrees of Knowledge,* pp. 77, 168, 216, and *La Philosophie de la nature,* pp. 100, 143.
23. Maritain, *La Philosophie de la nature,* pp. 75–80, and *The Degrees of Knowledge,* p. 249, also pp. 77, 168, 216.
24. Maritain, *La Philosophie de la nature,* pp. 75, 110, 140–143, and *The Degrees of Knowledge,* pp. 168, 216–217.
25. Mortimer Adler, *What Man Has Made of Man,* p. 187. On the value of prescientific experience for philosophy, see Adler's distinction between general and special experience, *op. cit.,* pp. 11, 57, 129, 131; see also Maritain, *La Philosophie de la nature,* pp. 89–93. On the ability of the philosophy of nature to penetrate "behind" phenomena, see also Adler, *op. cit.,* pp. 28, 160. But cf. the reference commented on in note 21 above.
26. The traditional mind-body problem is unnecessarily confused by a careless use of the term "interaction." Properly, this term belongs in the *thing*-language, and denotes a relation between things or substances. However, it is sometimes used by philosophers in such a way that it means only a causal entanglement of two series of events of fundamentally different kinds. The latter use analytically presupposes "qualitative" dualism, and if mental events are "irreducible" there is interaction in this sense. Usually at this stage the ordinary sense of interaction takes over and, presto chango, our philosopher has a dualism of interacting mental and physical *things.* Whether or not the thing-language is anything more than a common-sense dodge, it is important to note that qualitative dualism of events does not, by itself, entail dualism of things. This insight is characteristic of the Aristotelian traditions, as of modern emergentist theories.
27. *De Anima,* Bk. III, chap. 5; see also 413a 3–7, 413624–29 and 42963–4. The basis in what survives of Aristotle's works for a reconstruction of his distinction between active and passive reason is extremely tenuous, amounting to but a few sentences of explicit discussion. The interpretation which I offer is, I believe, not only compatible with what he does say, and with the analogies from other areas stressed by commentaries, but is a reasonable argument, given his premises. For an account of the evidence as well as of the main lines of interpretation see Ross, *Aristotle,* 2nd ed., pp. 148–153, and E. E. Spicer, *Aristotle's Conception of the Soul* (1934), pp. 103–112.
28. "Abstraction, which is the proper task of the active intellect . . ." (Brennan, *Thomistic Psychology,* p. 191.) See Ross's comment on this type of mistake on p. 149 of his *Aristotle.*
29. Except *potentially.* If you kill an elephant, earth, air, fire, and water, which were present in the living elephant only as physical *properties,* come into existence as *substances.* I shall not comment on this theory as it would take

us too far into the analysis of substantiality, and would be irrelevant to the specific confusions involved in the argument for immortality. See Maritain, *The Degrees of Knowledge,* p. 219 n.

30. See Adler, *What Man Has Made of Man,* p. 190.
31. In so far as the Scholastics attributed to active reason the function of abstracting the universal from its sensuous embodiment, a dispositional property is involved which is essentially bound up with organic existence. This property, and hence the act of abstraction, is therefore more properly attributed to the *man* than to the *intellectus agens.* The latter should be restricted to the timeless knowing of all natures.

EXISTENTIALISM

by

GEORG LUKÁCS

Georg Lukács is Professor of Philosophy at the University of Budapest. Besides many articles on literary and philosophical topics, his writings include the following books: *Die Seele und die Formen* (1911); *Die Theorie des Romans: Ein geschichts-philosophischer Versuch über die Formen der grossen Epik* (1920); *Geschichte und Klassenbewusstsein: Studien über den Zusammenhang seiner Gedanken* (1924); *Goethe und seine Zeit* (1947).

(*translated from the German by Henry F. Mins*)

> *Tout se passe comme si le monde, l'homme et l'homme dans le monde n'arrivaient à réaliser qu'un Dieu manqué.*—SARTRE, *L'Etre et le néant*

THERE is no reasonable doubt that existentialism will soon become the predominant philosophical current among bourgeois intellectuals. This state of affairs has been long in the making. Ever since the publication of Heidegger's *Sein und Zeit* the *avant-garde* intellectuals have seen in existentialism the philosophy of our times. In Germany, Jaspers undertook to communicate the principles of the new philosophy to broader sections of the educated public. During the war and since its end, the tide of existentialism rolled over the entire Western cultural field, and the leading German existentialists and their precursor, Husserl, have made great conquests in France and in America—not only in the United States but in Latin America as well. In 1943 the basic work of western existentialism appeared, Sartre's big book cited above; and since then existentialism has been pressing forward irresistibly, through philosophical debates, special periodicals (*Les Temps modernes*), novels, and dramas.

1. *Method as Attitude*

Is all this a passing fad—perhaps one which may last a few years? Or is it really an epoch-making new philosophy? The answer depends on how accurately the new philosophy reflects reality, and how adequately it deals with the crucial human question with which the age is faced.

An epoch-making philosophy has never yet arisen without a really original method. This was so for all the great philosophers of the past, Plato and Aristotle, Descartes and Spinoza, Kant and Hegel. What is the originality of existentialism's method? The question is not settled by referring to the fact that existentialism is an offshoot of Husserl's philosophy. It is important to note that modern phenomenology is one of the numerous philosophical methods which seek to rise above both idealism and materialism by discovering a philosophical "third way," by making intuition the true source of knowledge. From Nietzsche through Mach and Avenarius to Bergson and beyond, the mass of bourgeois philosophy goes this way. Husserl's intuition of essence (*Wesensschau*) is but one strand of the development.

This would not in itself be a decisive argument against the phenomenological method. If we are to arrive at a correct judgment, we must first understand the philosophical and topical significance of the "third way," as well as the place and function of intuition in the knowing process.

Is there any room for a "third way" besides idealism and materialism? If we consider this question seriously, as the great philosophers of the past did, and not with fashionable phrases, there can be only one answer, "No." For when we look at the relations which can exist between being and consciousness we see clearly that only two positions are possible: either being is primary (materialism), or consciousness is primary (idealism). Or, to put it another way, the fundamental principle of materialism is the independence of being from consciousness; of idealism, the dependence of being on consciousness. The fashionable philosophers of today establish a correlation between being and consciousness as a basis for their "third way": there is no being without consciousness and no consciousness without being. But the first assertion produces only a variant of idealism: the acknowledgment of the dependence of being on consciousness.

It was the grim reality of the imperialist period that forced the philosophical "third way" on bourgeois thinking: for only in becalmed, untroubled times can men hold themselves to be thorough-going idealists. When some students broke Fichte's windows over a college quarrel Goethe said, smiling: "This is a very disagreeable way to take cognizance of the reality of the external world." The imperialist epoch gave us such window-breaking on a world-wide scale. Downright philosophical idealism gently faded out. Apart from some minor professorial philosophers, anyone who declares himself an idealist today feels hopeless about applying his philosophy to reality (Valery, Benda, etc.).

The abandonment of the old downright idealism had been anticipated even in the middle of the last century by petty-bourgeois asceticism. Ever since Nietzsche, the body (*Leib*) has played a leading role in bourgeois philosophy. The new philosophy needs formulae which recognize the primary reality of the body and the joys and dangers of bodily existence, without, however, making any concessions to materialism. For at the same time materialism was becoming the world view of the revolutionary proletariat. That made a position such as Gassendi and Hobbes look impossible for bourgeois thinkers. Although the method of idealism had been discredited by the realities of the time, its conclusions were held indispensable. This explains the need for the "third way" in the bourgeois world of the imperialist period.

The phenomenological method, especially after Husserl, believes it has discovered a way of knowing which exhibits the essence of objective reality without going beyond the human or even the individual consciousness. The intuition of essence is a sort of intuitive introspection, but is not psychologically oriented. It inquires rather what sort of objects the thought process posits, and what kind of intentional acts are involved. It was still relatively easy for Husserl to operate with these concepts, because he was concerned exclusively with questions of pure logic, i.e., pure acts and objects of thought. The question became more complex as Scheler took up problems of ethics and sociology, and Heidegger and Sartre broached the ultimate questions of philosophy. The need of the times which drove them in this direction was so compelling that it silenced all gnosiological doubts as to whether the method was adequate to objective reality.

Even when the phenomenologists dealt with crucial questions of social actuality, they put off the theory of knowledge and asserted that the phenomenological method suspends or "brackets" the question whether the intentional objects are real. The method was thus freed from any knowledge of reality. Once during the First World War Scheler visited me in Heidelberg, and we had an informing conversation on this subject. Scheler maintained that phenomenology was a universal method which could have anything for its intentional object. For example, he explained, phenomenological researches could be made about the devil; only the question of the devil's reality would first have to be "bracketed." "Certainly," I answered, "and when you are finished with the phenomenological picture of the devil, you open the brackets—and the devil in person is standing before you." Scheler laughed, shrugged his shoulders, and made no reply.

The arbitrariness of the method is seen especially when the question is raised: Is what phenomenological intuition finds actually real? What right does that intuition have to speak of the reality of its object? For Dilthey's intuition, the colorfulness and the uniqueness of historical situations are the reality; for Bergson's, it is the flow itself, the duration (*durée*), that dissolves the petrified forms of ordinary life; while for Husserl's, the acts in which individual objects are meant constitute "reality"—objects which he treats as isolated units, with hard contours like statuary. Although mutually exclusive, these intuitions were able to dwell together in relative peace.

These interpretations of reality stem from factors even more concrete than the social need for a "third way." It is a general tendency of the imperialist period to regard social relationships as secondary circumstances which do not concern the essence of man. The intuition of essence takes the immediate givenness of inner experience as its starting point, which it regards as unconditioned and primary, never looking into its character and preconditions, and proceeds thence to its final abstract "vision," divorced from reality. Such intuitions, under the social conditions of the time, could easily abstract from all social actuality while keeping the appearance of utter objectivity and rigor. In this way there arose the logical myth of a world (in splendid accord with the attitude of bourgeois intellectuals) independent of consciousness, although its structure and characteristics are said to be determined by the individual consciousness.

It is impossible here to give a detailed critique of the phenomenological method. We shall therefore merely analyze in summary fashion an example of the way it is applied. We have chosen the book of Szilasi, the well known student of Husserl and Heidegger,[1] partly because Szilasi is an earnest thinker who aims at scientific objectivity, not a cynical fabricator of myths like Scheler; and partly because the elementary form of the example is well suited to a brief treatment. Szilasi takes as his instance the co-presence (*Miteinandersein*) at his lecture of his hearers and himself. Describing the essence of the situation, he finds that the hall lies before him, the benches, in a word, the external world: "This space with its variously worked boards is a lecture hall only because we understand this mass of wooden objects as such, and we do understand it so because from the outset we mean it as something presupposed in our common task—namely, lecturing and listening." From which he concludes, "It is the way of being together that determines what the thing is."

Let us consider the result of this intuition of essence from the methodological point of view. First, it is a primitive abstraction when Szilasi speaks of "variously worked boards," and not of desks, benches, etc. But this is methodologically essential, for if he should concede that the lecture hall is equally adapted to holding philological, legal, and other lectures, what would be left of the magical potency of the intentional experience, which is supposed to make the object what it is?

However, what the analysis omits is still more important. The hall is in Zurich, and the time is the 1940's. The fact that Szilasi could deliver a lecture precisely in Zurich has the most diverse social preconditions. For instance, before Hitler's seizure of power Szilasi gave his lectures in Freiburg; after 1933 they were no longer permitted, in fact the lecturer had to leave Germany because his personal safety was threatened. Why is all this missing from the intuition of co-presence? It belongs there at least as much as do the "worked boards."

But let us return to the boards. The fact that boards are used in a certain way to make desks and benches presupposes a certain stage of development of industry and of society. Again, the fact that the boards and the hall as a whole are in a certain condition (is there coal for heating, or glass in the windows?) is inseparably connected with other social events and structures. But phenomenological method, excluding all social elements from its analysis, confronts consciousness with a chaos of things (and men) which only individual subjectivity can articulate and objectify. Here we have the well publicized phenomenological objectivity, the "third way," which turns out to be only a revival of Neo-Kantianism.

Phenomenology and the ontology deriving from it only *seem* to go beyond the gnosiological solipsism of subjective idealism. A formally new formulation of the question reinstates ontological idealism. It is no accident that (just as forty years ago the Machists reproached one another for idealism, each recognizing only himself as the discoverer of the philosophical "third way") today the existentialists make similar accusations against one another. So Sartre complains of Husserl and Heidegger, two men he otherwise prizes highly. Husserl, in his opinion, has not gone beyond Kant; and he criticizes Heidegger as follows: "The character being-together [co-presence, *Mitsein*] introduced by Heidegger is a character of the isolated ego. Hence it does not lead beyond solipsism. Therefore we shall search *Sein und Zeit* in vain for a position beyond both idealism and realism [meaning materialism]." An analysis of Sartre's philosophy will show us that he can be taxed with the offense for which he condemns Husserl and Heidegger. In Heidegger's philosophy existence (*Dasein*) does not mean objective being (*Sein*) proper, but human existence, i.e., a being aware of existence. In some places Sartre, who has more interest than his predecessors in the emotional and practical relation of man to nature, spells out the complete dependence of nature on man's consciousness. When speaking of devastation, he denies that it exists in nature itself, in which only changes take place. "And even this expression is inadequate, for in order that this changing-to-something-else may be posited, a witness is needed who somehow or other preserves the past within himself and is able to compare it with the present in its 'no-longer' form." And in another place he says: "The full moon does not denote the future, except when we observe the waxing moon in the 'world' which reveals itself in human actuality: the future comes into the world by way of human existence."

This purely idealistic tendency is heightened in Sartre by the fact that his way of handling problems compels him to study concrete questions of co-existence (*Mitsein*) even more frequently than Heidegger. He meets the difficulty partly by choosing loosely connected manifestations of co-presence that can be referred with some plausibility to the inner experiences of the ego (a rendezvous at a café, a trip in the subway). But when actual social activity is involved (labor, class consciousness), he makes a methodological *salto mortale* and declares that the experiences of the relevant intuitions of essence are of psychological and not of ontological character. The reason for this is the secret of the initiate, those to whom the intuition of essence is granted. It is therefore no accident that when Sartre tests the relation of man to his fellow man he recognizes only the following relations as ontologically essential, that is, as elements of reality in itself: love, speech, masochism, indifference, longing, hate, and sadism. (Even the order of the categories is Sartre's.) Anything beyond this in *Miteinandersein,* the categories of collective life together, of working together, of fighting in a common cause, is for Sartre, as we have seen, a category of consciousness (psychological) and not a really existent category (ontological).

When all this is applied to actual cases, the result is banal Philistine commonplaces. In his popular book Sartre takes up the question of how far he can have confidence in his freely acting comrades. Answer: "As far as I have immediate personal knowledge of them, to count on the unity and will of the party is just like counting on the streetcar to come on time, and on the train not to jump the tracks. But I cannot count on men that I do not know, banking on human goodness or man's interest in the common good, for it is a given datum that man is free and there is no such thing as a human nature on which I can count." Apart from the involved terminology, any petty bourgeois, shrinking from public affairs, could, and does, say as much.

2. *The Myth of Nothingness*

Il est absurde que nous sommes nés,
il est absurde que nous mourrons.
—SARTRE, *L'Etre et le néant*

It would be an error to assume that such an abstract narrowing of reality, such an idealist distortion of the problem of reality, by intelligent and experienced men is intentional deceit. On the contrary, those inner experiences which constitute the attitude revealed in the intuition of the *Wesensschau,* and its content, are as sincere and spontaneous as possible. But that does not make them objectively correct. Indeed this spontaneity, by betraying its immediate uncritical attitude toward the basic phenomenon, creates the false consciousness: fetishism. Fetishism signifies, in brief, that the relations among human beings which function by means of objects are reflected in human consciousness immediately as things, because of the structure of capitalist economy. They become objects or things, fetishes in which men crystallize their social relationships, as savages do their relationships to nature; and for savages the laws of natural relations are just as impenetrable as the laws of the capitalist system of economy are to the men of the world of today. Like savages, modern men pray to the fetishes they themselves have made, bow down to them, and sacrifice to them (e.g., the fetish of money). Human relations, as Marx says, acquire "a spectral objectivity." The social existence of man becomes a riddle in his immediate experience, even though objectively he is a social being first and foremost, despite all immediate appearances to the contrary.

It is not our aim nor our task to treat of the problem of fetish making: to do so would require a systematic development of the whole structure of capitalist society and the forms of false consciousness arising out of it. I shall merely point out the most important questions which have had decisive influence on the development of existentialism.

The first is life's losing its meaning. Man loses the center, weight, and connectedness of his own life, a fact life itself compels him to realize. The phenomenon has been known for a long time. Ibsen, in *Peer Gynt,* puts it into a striking little scene. The aging Peer Gynt is peeling off the layers of an onion, and playfully compares the single layers with the periods of his life, hoping at the end to come to the core of the onion and the core of his own personality. But layer follows layer, period after period of life; and no core is found.

Every one whom this experience has touched faces the question: How can my life become meaningful? The man who lives in the fetish-making world does not see that every life is rich, full, and meaningful to the extent that it is consciously linked in human relations with other lives. The isolated egoistic man who lives only for himself lives in an impoverished world. His experiences approach threateningly close to the unessential and begin to merge into nothingness the more exclusively they are his alone, and turned solely inward.

The man of the fetishized world, who can cure his disgust with the world only in intoxication, seeks, like the morphine addict, to find a way out by heightening the intensity of the intoxicant rather than by a way of life that has no need of intoxication. He is not aware that the loss of communal life, the degradation and dehumanization of collective work as a result of capitalist division of labor, and the severance of human relations from social activity have stupefied him. He does not see this, and goes further and further along the fatal path, which tends to become a subjective heed. For in capitalist society public life, work, and the system of human relations are under the spell of fetish making, reification and dehumanization. Only revolt against the actual foundations, as we can see in many authors of the time, leads to a clearer appreciation of these foundations, and thence to a new social perspective. Escape into inwardness is a tragi-comical blind alley.

As long as the pillars of capitalist society seemed unshakable, say up to the First World War, the so-called *avant-garde* danced with the fetishes of their inner life. Some writers, it is true, saw the approach of the inevitable catastrophe (Ibsen, Tolstoy, Thomas Mann, etc.). The gaudy carnival, often with a ghastly tone from tragic incidental music, went on uninterrupted. The philosophy of Simmel and Bergson and much of the literature of the time show exactly where things were heading.

Many a good writer and keen thinker saw through the intoxication of carnival to the fact that the fetishized ego had lost its essence. But they went no further than to sketch tragic or tragi-comic perspectives behind the garish whirl. The fetishized bases of life seemed so beyond question that they escaped study, let alone criticism. If there were doubts, they were like the doubt of the Hindu who questioned the accepted doctrine that the world rests on a huge elephant; he asked modestly on what the elephant rested; and when told it rested on a huge tortoise, he went his way contented. Mind was so formed by fetish thinking that when the First World War and the subsequent series of crises called the very possibility of human existence into question, giving a new tinge to every idea, and when the carnival of isolated individualism gave way to its Ash Wednesday, there was still virtually no change in the way that philosophical questions were asked.

Yet the aim and direction of the quest for essence did change. The existentialism of Heidegger and Jaspers is proof. The experience which underlies this philosophy is easily stated: man stands face to face with nothingness or nonbeing. The fundamental relation of man to the world is the situation of *vis-à-vis de rien*. There is nothing particularly original in this. Ever since Poe, perhaps the first to describe the situation and the corresponding attitude, modern literature has dwelt upon the tragic fate which drives a man to the edge of the abyss. As examples we may mention the situation of Raskolnikov after the murder, and the road to suicide of Svidrigaïlov or Stavrogin. What is involved here? A characteristic tragic form of development, arising out of present-day life. A great writer weaves these tragic destinies, which are as vivid and positive as were the tragedies of Oedipus and Hamlet in their day.

The originality of Heidegger is that he takes just such situations as typical and makes them his starting point. With the help of the complicated method of phenomenology, he lodges the entire problem in the fetishized structure of the bourgeois mind, in the dreary hopeless nihilism and pessimism of the intellectuals of the interval between the two world wars. The first fetish is the concept of nothingness. In Heidegger as in Sartre, this is the central problem of reality, of ontology. In Heidegger nothingness is an ontological datum on a level with existence; in Sartre it is only one factor in existence, which nevertheless enters into all the manifestations of being.

A very specialized philosophical dissertation would be required to show the chains of thought, sometimes quite false, sometimes obviously sophistical, by which Sartre seeks to justify his theory of negative judgment. It is true that, for every "No" which expresses a particular judgment, there is a positively existing situation. But it is only idolizing of subjective attitudes that gives nothingness the semblance of reality. When I inquire, for instance, what the laws of the solar system are, I have not posited any negative being, such as Sartre envisages. The meaning of my question is simply that I lack knowledge. The answer may be put in either positive or negative form, but the same positive reality is indicated in either case. Only sophistry could infer the "existence" of nonbeing. The nothingness which fascinates recent philosophers is a myth of declining capitalist society. While previously it was individuals (though socially typical ones) like Stavrogin and Svidrigaïlov that had to face nothingness, today it is a whole system that has reached this chimerical outlook. For Heidegger and Sartre life itself is the state of being cast into nothingness.

Existentialism consistently proclaims that nothing can be known by man. It does not challenge science in general; it does not raise skeptical objections to its practical or technical uses. It merely denies that there is a science which has the right to say anything about the one essential question: the relation of the individual to life. This is the alleged superiority of existentialism to the old philosophy. "Existential philosophy," Jaspers says, "*would be lost immediately if it started believing again that it knew what man is.*" This radical ignorance on principle, which is stressed by Heidegger and Sartre, is one of the main reasons for the overwhelming influence of existentialism. Men who have no prospects themselves find consolation in the doctrine that life in general has no prospects to offer.

Here existentialism flows into the modern current of irrationalism. The phenomenological and ontological method seems, it is true, to stand in bold contrast to the ordinary irrationalist tendencies. Are not the former "rigorously scientific," and was not Husserl a supporter of the most fanatical of logicians, Bolzano and Brentano? But even a superficial study of the method at once discloses its links with the masters of irrationalism, Dilthey and Bergson. And when Heidegger renewed Kierkegaard's efforts, the tie became even closer.

This connection is more than an accidental convergence of two methods. The more phenomenology is transformed into the method of existentialism, the more the underlying irrationality of the individual and of being becomes the central object, and the closer becomes its affinity to irrational currents of the time. Being is meaningless, uncaused, unnecessary. Being is by definition "the originally fortuitous," says Sartre. If nothingness comes to "exist" by the magic of existentialism, existence is made negative. Existence is what man lacks. The human being, says Heidegger, "knows what he is only from 'existence,' i.e., from his own potentialities," whether he becomes the one he "is," or not. Is man's becoming authentic or not? We have seen that in the leading trends of modern philosophy this question has an antisocial character. Using the familiar method, Heidegger subjects man's everyday life to phenomenological analysis. The life of man is a co-existence and at the same time a being-in-the-world. This being also has its fetish; namely, "one." In German, subjectless sentences begin with *man* ("one"): "One writes," "One does." Heidegger, making myths, erects this word into an ontological existent in order to express philosophically what seems to him to be the function of society and social life; viz., to turn man away from himself, to make him unauthentic, to prevent him from being himself. The manifestation of "one" in daily life is chatter, curiosity, ambiguity, "falling." To follow the path of one's own existence, according to Heidegger, one must take the road to death, his own death; one must live in such a way that his death does not come upon him as a brute fact breaking in on him from without, but as his own. Actual existence can find its crowning achievement only in such a personal demise. The complete capriciousness and subjectivism of the ontology, concealed behind a show of objectivity, come to light once more. As a confession of a citizen of the 1920's, Heidegger's way of thinking is not without interest. *Sein und Zeit* is at least as absorbing reading as Céline's novel, *Voyage au bout de la nuit*. But the former, like the latter, is merely a document of the day showing how a class felt and thought, and not an "ontological" disclosure of ultimate truth. It is only because this book is so well suited to the emotional world of today's intellectuals that the arbitrariness of its pseudoargumentation is not exposed. The contrast of abstract death to meaningless life is for many men today an implicit axiom. But it suffices to glance at the mode of thought of older times, before collapse started, to realize that this attitude toward death is not the ontological character of "being" but a transitory phenomenon. Spinoza said: "The free man thinks of anything but his death; his wisdom is not death but pondering on life."

Jaspers and Sartre are less radical than Heidegger in this respect, although their thought is not the less conditioned by time and class. Sartre flatly rejects the concept of specific or personal death as a category of existentialism. In Jaspers, the phantom of "one" does not appear formally in such a radically mystifying form, but only as the totality of the nameless powers ruling life (that is, essentially, social life once more objectivized in a fetish). He contents himself with assigning man, once he has acquired his essence and begun to live his own private existence, strictly to the paths of private life. In Geneva recently Jaspers developed the thesis that nothing good or essential can come of political or social activity: the salvation of man is possible only when every one passionately concerns himself exclusively with his own existence and in relations with other individuals of like persuasion.

Here the labors of the philosophical mountain have only produced a dreary Philistine mouse. Ernst Bloch, the well known German antifascist writer (whose book appeared in 1935), said of Heidegger's death theory (from which Jaspers' personal morality is obtained simply by the addition of water): Taking eternal death as goal makes man's existing social situation a matter of such indifference that it might as well remain capitalistic. The assertion of death as absolute fate and sole destination has the same significance for today's counterrevolution as formerly the consolation of the hereafter had. This keen observation casts light too on the reason why the popularity of existentialism is growing not only among snobs but also among reactionary writers.

3. *Freedom in a Fetishized World and the Fetish of Freedom*

> *Je construis l'universel en me choisissant.*
> —SARTRE: *L'Existentialisme est un humanisme.*

Existentialism is the philosophy not only of death but also of abstract freedom. This is the most important reason for the popularity of Sartre's forms of existentialism; and—although it may sound paradoxical—the reactionary side of existentialism's present influence is here concealed. Heidegger, as we know, saw the way to existence's becoming essential and real only in a life directed toward death; Sartre's shrewd comments put an end to the specious probativeness of Heidegger's exposition. This contradiction between Sartre and Heidegger is an expression not merely of the divergent attitudes of French and German intellectuals toward the central problems of life, but also of the changed times. Heidegger's basic book appeared in 1927, on the eve of the new world crisis, in the oppressed murky atmosphere before the fascist storm; and the effect Bloch described was the general state of intellectuals. We do not know when Sartre's book appeared; the nominal date is 1943—that is, when liberation from fascism was already in sight and when, just because of the decade-long rule of fascism, the longing for freedom was the deepest feeling of the intellectuals of all Europe, especially of countries where they had grown up in democratic traditions. The inner experience—above all, in the western countries—was one of freedom in general, abstractly, without analysis or differentiation, in brief freedom as myth, which precisely because of its formlessness was able to unite under its flag all enemies of fascism, who (whatever their point of view) hated their origin or their goal. Only one thing mattered to these men, to say "No" to fascism. The less specific the "No" was, the better it expressed the feeling of actuality. The abstract "No" and its pendant, abstract freedom, were to many men the exact expression of the "myth" of the resistance. We shall see that Sartre's notion of freedom is most abstract. This enables us to understand why the sense of the time exalted existentialism and yielded to it as adequate philosophy of the day.

However, fascism collapsed, and the construction and reenforcement of democracy and free life engaged the public opinion of every country as its first concern. Every serious argument, from politics to Weltanschauung, revolves now around the question of what the democracy and freedom should be which mankind is building on the ruins of fascist destruction.

Existentialism has kept its popularity under these changed circumstances; indeed, it would seem that it is now for the first time—to be sure, in Sartre's formulation, not Heidegger's—on the road to world conquest. One decisive factor here is the fact that existentialism gives the notion of freedom a central place in its philosophy. But today freedom is no longer a myth. The strivings for freedom have become concrete, more and more concrete every day. Violent disputes over the interpretation of freedom and democracy have split the supporters of the various schools into antagonistic camps. Under such circumstances how is it possible that existentialism, with its rigid, abstract conception of freedom, should become a world-wide trend? Or more precisely, to whom, and how, does existentialism carry conviction as a philosophy of freedom? To answer this central question, we must come to closer grips with Sartre's concept of freedom.

According to him, freedom is a basic fact of human existence. We represent, says Sartre, "freedom which chooses, but we could not choose to be free. We are doomed to freedom." We are thrown into freedom (Heidegger's *Geworfenheit*).

Not choosing, however, is just as much choice as choosing is; avoiding action is action too. Everywhere Sartre stresses this role of freedom, from the most primitive facts of everyday life to the ultimate questions of metaphysics. When I take part in a group excursion, get tired, am weighed down by my pack, and so forth, I am faced with the fact of free choice, and must decide whether I will go on with my companions or throw off my burden and sit down by the roadside. From this problem the way leads to the final, most abstract problems of human existence; in the plans or projects in which man concretizes his free decision and free choice (*projet, projeter* is one of the most important notions of Sartre's theory of freedom) there lies the content of the ultimate ideal, the last "project": God. In Sartre's words: "The basic plan of human reality is best illustrated by the fact that man is the being whose plan it is to become God. . . . Being a man is equivalent to being engaged in becoming God." And the philosophical content of this ideal of God is the attainment of that stage of existence which the old philosophy denoted as *causa sui.*

Sartre's notion of freedom is extremely broad and indeterminate, lacking specific criteria. Choice, the essence of freedom, consists for him in the act of choosing oneself. The constant danger lurking here is that we could become other than we are. And here there is no moral content or moral form which could act as compass or plumb line. For instance, cowardice stems from free choice just as much as courage does. "My fear is free and attests my freedom; I have cast all my freedom into my fear and chosen myself as cowardly in such and such circumstances; in other circumstances I might exist as courageous and put my freedom into courage. With respect to freedom, no ideal has any precedence."

Since for Sartre all human existence is free by definition, his notion of freedom is even more indefinite than that of Heidegger. Heidegger could differentiate between the free and the unfree. For him, that man is free who programmatically lives toward his own death; unfree and unauthentic, he who, forgetting his own death, lives not as a self but in the crowd. Sartre rejects this criterion, as we have seen. He also rejects such a hierarchy of moral values as Scheler had conceived, as well as any connection of free choice with man's past, viz., the principle of continuity and consistency of personality. Finally, he denies the Kantian formal distinction between free and unfree acts.

He seems, it is true, to be somewhat frightened by this indeterminateness. In his popular pamphlet he says, "Nothing can be good for us which is not good for everyone," and in another place: "At the same time that I will my own freedom it is my duty to will the freedom of others. I cannot set my own freedom as goal unless I also set that of others as my goal." This sounds very fine. But in Sartre it is only an eclectic insertion into existentialism, of the moral principles of the Enlightenment and the Kantian philosophy. Kant did not succeed in establishing objective morality by generalizing subjectivity. The young Hegel, in a sharp critique, showed this failure. However, Kant's generalization still stands in intimate connection with the first principles of his social philosophy; in Sartre, this generalization is an eclectic compromise with traditional philosophical opinion, contradicting his ontological position.

In his capital work he does not make these concessions. True to his basic thought, ontological solipism, the content and goal of the free act are meaningful and explicable only from the point of view of the subject. Here Sartre still states a view opposite to that of his popular brochure: "Respect for the freedom of one's fellow man is idle chatter: even if we could so plan that we honored this freedom, such an attitude would be a violation of the freedom which we were so busy respecting." In the same place he illustrates this conception by a very concrete example: "When I bring about tolerance among my fellow men, I have forcibly hurled them into a tolerant world. In so doing I have in principle taken away their free capacity for courageous resistance, for perseverance, for self-testing, which they would have had the opportunity of developing in some world of intolerance."

This cynical view that there are no unfree acts has significant resemblance to the view that there are no free acts. While even Heidegger knew that we can speak of a free act only if man is capable of being coerced as well, Sartre does not know this. Like the determinist, Sartre reduces human phenomena to one level. But determinism is at least a system, verifiable in part, whereas Sartre's free acts are a disconnected, fortuitous conglomeration.

What is the legitimate factor in Sartre? Without question, the emphasis on the individual's decision, whose importance was undervalued alike by bourgeois determinism and by vulgar Marxism. All social activity is made up of the actions of individuals, and no matter how decisive the economic basis may be in these decisions, its effects are felt only "in the long run," as Engels so often stresses. This means that there is always a concrete area of free choice for the individual, which does not conflict with the fact that history has its general and necessary trends of development. The mere existence of political parties proves the reality of this area. The main directions of development can be foreseen; but, as Engels stressed, it would be idle pedantry to try to foretell from the laws of evolution whether in a given case Peter or Paul will individually decide this way or that, vote for this party or the other, and so forth. The necessity of evolution is always effected by means of internal and external contingencies. It would be a service to science to show their significance and study their place and role, if at the same time their methodological meaning in the whole dialectical process were more precisely determined than formerly. In this sense a role which should not be underestimated attaches to moral problems and questions of freedom and individual decision in the total dialectical knowledge of social development.

Sartre, to be sure, does exactly the opposite. We have seen that, as has been fashionable for decades, he denies necessary development and even development itself. Even in the case of individuals he divorces decision situations from the past. He denies any genuine connection of the individual with society. He construes the individual's world as completely different from that of his fellow men. The notion of freedom thus obtained is fatalistic and strained in a mechanical way; it thus loses all meaning. If we look at it a little more closely, it has virtually no connection with the actual moral concept of freedom. It says no more than what Engels said in an occasional remark; namely, that there is no human activity in which individual consciousness could not play a part.

Obviously Sartre himself sees the difficulty of his notion of freedom. But he remains faithful to his method, and busies himself with balancing one overstrained and meaningless conception against another: freedom against responsibility, the latter being for Sartre just as universal and unconditionally valid as the concept of freedom. "If I choose to join the army instead of to die or suffer dishonor, that is equivalent to taking the entire responsibility for this war."

Here again the formal-logical overstraining of a relative truth-factor leads to the theoretical and practical annihilation of the concept in question. For so rigid a formulation of responsibility is identical with complete irresponsibility. We did not need to be politicians or Marxists to see that. A master of the "psychology of depths," Dostoevski, often said that extreme rigid forcing of moral principles and moral decisions generally has no influence on men's actions. They sweep overhead, and the men who act on them have weaker moral guidance than would be the case if they had no principles at all. In the shadow of the rigorous pitiless feeling of responsibility, extending to the point of suicide, it is easy to commit one villainy after another with frivolous cynicism.

Sartre sees something of all this, but without drawing any conclusions from it. So he weaves fetishes and myths around the problem he vaguely discerns, and concludes with the trivial phrase: "Any one who in anguish" (*angoisse* has been a decisive category of existentialism since the Kierkegaardian Reception) "realizes that his condition of life is that of being thrown into a responsibility which leads to complete isolation: that man knows no more remorse, regret, or self-justification." Just as the sublime is but a step from the ridiculous, so a certain kind of moral sublimity is only a step from frivolity and cynicism.

It was necessary for us to elaborate thus sharply on the bankruptcy of the Sartrean concept of freedom because this is precisely the key to the widespread effectiveness of the doctrine in certain circles. Such an abstract, forced, totally vacuous and irrationalized conception of freedom and responsibility, the haughty scorn for social viewpoints and public life used to defend the ontological integrity of the individual—all adequately rounds out the myth of nothingness, especially for the requirements of snobs: for they must be particularly impressed with the mixture of cruelly strict principle with cynical looseness of action and moral nihilism. But in addition this conception of freedom gives a certain section of intellectuals, always inclined toward extreme individualism, an ideological support and justification for refusing the unfolding and building of democracy. There have been writers who, calling themselves democrats, under took to defend the rights of the black market and of the sabotaging and swindling capitalist, all in the name of individual freedom, and who carried the principle so far that room is found for the freedom of reaction and fascism; responsibility has been the slogan in whose name the attempt was first made to block the registration of the new owners' land and later to call for their return. Sartre's abstract and strained conception of freedom and responsibility was just what these forces could use.

Sartre's books do not give us the impression that he exactly desires to be the ideologist of these groups; and certainly there are genuine and sincere democrats among his French supporters. But large-scale fashions pay little heed to the internal intentions of their authors. The various currents of society have their own ideological requirements, and say with Molière, "je prends mon bien où je le trouve." So, not only snobbishness but reaction too manages to cook its broth at the fire of existentialism. This is one more reason for us to point out that the acquisition of existentialism is no Promethean deed, no theft of celestial fire, but rather the commonplace action of using the lighted cigarette of a chance passer-by to light one's own.

This is no accident, but follows from the very nature of the phenomenological method and from the ontology which grows out of it. The method is far from being as original as its apostles would like to believe. For, no matter how arbitrary the transition may be from "bracketed" reality to allegedly genuine objective reality, the mere possibility of the transition still has its philosophical roots, though this point never is consciously formulated by the ontologists. This basis is essentially that of the dominant theory of knowledge in the nineteenth century; namely, the Kantian. Kant's clear formulation had the cogency worthy of a serious philosopher: existence does not signify enrichment of the content of objectivity, and hence not formal enrichment either; the content of the thought-of dollar is exactly the same as that of the real dollar. The existence of the object means neither novelty nor enrichment, whether with respect to content or to structure of the concept. Clearly, therefore, when the ontologists "bracket" the thought-of object and then clear the "brackets," they tacitly assume this Kantian conception.

The notion appears quite obvious; the only thing wrong with it is that it is not true. The Kantian idealism unconsciously borrowed from mechanical materialism the identity of the structure and content of the thought-of and the actual object. The real dialectic of objective reality, however, shows at every step that existence enriches the thought-of object with elements which are conceptually new with respect to content and structure. This consequence follows not only from the virtual infinity of every actual object, as a result of which the most complete thought is only an approximation, i.e. the object of ontology is even in principle richer in content and therefore of richer, more complicated structure than the phenomenological object of mere consciousness. And this is a consequence as well of the extensionally and intensionally infinite *Verflochtenheit* (interrelatedness) of real objects, in which the reciprocal action of their relations changes the objects' functions and then reacts on their objectivity. In this context mere existence, the brute fact, becomes under certain circumstances one of the characters and changes the concept of objectivity, with respect to content and structure. Let us consider the theory of money, to continue with Kant's example. So long as we speak of money as a medium of circulation, we might still assume that thought-of money is identical with real money (although we should be wrong even here). But the very concept of money as a medium of payment implies existence; there is present in this case a conceptual difference between the thought-of dollar and the real one, a difference which constitutes a new category. Only the actual dollar, in one's possession, can be a means of payment. Money in itself is not enough; we must *have* it too.

Modern ontology by-passes these considerations, not unintentionally. The isolating intuition of the isolated individual—in this connection it is immaterial whether his interest is directed toward the object, fixed in its rigidity, or toward the changefulness of thought—lifts every object out of the complex and living fabric of its existence, functions, relations, interactions, etc., dissolving it out of the real, living, moving totality. The "original achievement" of phenomenology and ontology in this field consists merely in the fact that it dogmatically identifies reality with the objectivity it has thus obtained. For them, objectivity and objective reality mean one and the same thing.

References

[1] *Wissenschaft als Philosophie* (Zurich, 1945).

EXPERIENCE AND SUBJECTIVISM

by

MARVIN FARBER

Marvin Farber is Professor of Philosophy and Chairman of the Department, University of Buffalo; S.B., Ph.D., Harvard; awarded traveling fellowship in Philosophy, Harvard, 1922–1924, Guggenheim Foundation fellowship, 1944–1945; President, International Phenomenological Society since 1940; editor, *Philosophical Essays in Memory of Edmund Husserl* (1940); editor of the international quarterly journal, *Philosophy and Phenomenological Research;* author of *The Foundation of Phenomenology* (1943) and of numerous contributions to philosophical publications.

I. THE ANALYSIS OF EXPERIENCE

A. The Historical and Social Character of the Analysis of Experience

THE choice between rival philosophies may be decided on the basis of their treatment of experience. Now the appeal to experience is invariably an appeal to an experience defined in terms of a given theory, to an "interpreted" experience. The "atomic" experience of Locke conforms to the pattern of individualism of his time, and is different from the rationally conditioned experience of Kant, or the socialized experience of more recent date. The very statement of the problem of analyzing experience, in particular the "given" in experience, is thus historically conditioned. In view of the fact that scholars of divergent tendencies appeal to "experience," as well as the fact that all philosophical problems can—and must—be traced back to their locus in experience, this theme is of primary importance.

The "appeal to experience" is ostensibly an appeal to observed facts, and to the use of logical methods. In the wrong hands, especially when made by a philosopher rooted in the tradition of idealism, it proves to be a trap for metaphysical purposes. If one begins with the mind, he rarely gets beyond it. A "great mind" is frequently the outcome. That is because of initial dogmas, or initial assumptions, in the use of the concept of experience. Whose experience is meant? One's own? If one proposes to restrict himself to his own experiences, he has still to take account of other persons, as well as the natural world. The *basic fact* for all philosophizing which aspires to be true to experience is the fact of the natural world and its priority to man; and also the priority of a cultural tradition to each individual man. The latter is what he is because of the tradition which produced him. In other words, no treatment of experience may disregard the fact that experience is an event in the natural world, any more than it can disregard the fact that it is a cultural product.

The question of the nature of experience is far-reaching enough to call forth the familiar alignments of standpoints. The survival and continued activity of the various historical traditions is sufficient to bring that about. It does not matter that the development of science has outmoded many of the traditional views, for in philosophy death is no guarantee of disappearance, and even the unreal may "come to appearance." If one reads philosophy on the surface, taking statements at their apparent face-value, many of the differences of views appear to be trivial or senseless. But philosophy should never be detached from its social-historical context, in terms of which its significance is to be sought. These considerations help to explain why such a seemingly straightforward theme as the analysis of experience is still in a state of dispute.

Finality in the analysis of experience is never to be achieved, unless one operates abstractively with a limited view of experience—limited in its historical extent and with respect to the person making the analysis. If the knower plays a role in experience, and if the cultural group to which he belongs conditions and influences the process of experience; and if, furthermore, there are "meaning-sediments" of past generations, of an intellectual, aesthetic, etc., type—then there can be no finality. That there must be certain "structural" features of experience, in view of man's being what he is and of his relationship to his fellow men and the rest of nature, will be granted, while recognizing the unavoidable openness and incompleteness of experience. It follows that the analysis of experience must be undertaken again and again, in each cultural generation at least. That is always necessary, if only because of the added advantage of the later perspective. There is also the factor of scientific progress; for obviously a number of sciences cooperate in the understanding as well as control of experience. In this sense, the analysis of experience will never disappear as a problem, or as a theme for philosophic inquiry. It is not a matter of a stubborn problem which resists all attempts to solve it, as in the case of the historical "problem of knowledge."

In recent years considerable attention has been devoted to what is "given" in experience. The very expression "the given" is assumptive —as though there were an independent, fixed mind, opposed to the world, so that one could ask what is "given" to it. If one adopts a subjectivistic method in philosophy, or a transcendental method, in conformity to the Kantian tradition, the nature of the "given" is an important problem. That problem may be said to be "methogenic," or to result from the method adopted, in contradistinction to "empiriogenic" problems, which are real in experience. If one views the evidence of experience objectively, he realizes that man, and consequently the mind, is the result of a long process of evolution; that man is a part of the world and of society; and that it is a strange aberration to ask, as Schelling did in his program for transcendental idealism, how the mind comes to present a world. Only a historical account of the social and religious motivation can explain such a fantastic position. The objective point of view in philosophy does not ignore or falsify the established results of the sciences. It is determined by them, guided by them. It seeks to analyze experience and its conditions *within the framework of physical nature.* The *basic fact* of the priority of nature is not construed as something "given" to a mind, and an archaic mind at that. The understanding of man as a part of nature is an accomplished fact, even though it is necessary to recognize a series of levels of existence, from the inanimate to the social and intellectual. Man has been parceled out among the various sciences, and the mind is treated in terms of behavior. It is a quaint matter, then, to ask how nature comes to be presented, in the fashion of the transcendentalists or subjectivists; or indeed, what is "given" to a mind somehow already on hand. The methogenic problem of the "given" is seen in proper perspective by an analysis which is abreast of the scientific development of the present era.

The question of the "given," while an important historical problem, is, strictly speaking, a false one, the result of freezing the mind into a formal agent which somehow conditions experience. The *analysis of experience,* on the other hand, is a real problem, truly "empiriogenic." Now experience is in nature, and not nature in experience. There was a time when there was no experience, meaning human experience; and probably human experience will eventually disappear. The independence of the world, with respect to the knower, is a brute fact which no philosopical arguments can alter. These considerations are commonplace in our time, but they are by no means accepted by all philosophers. Their consequences would make spiritualism impossible in all its forms.

Having made clear the assumptive use of the expression "the given," we shall find it instructive to examine its use in some prominent examples of contemporary philosophy, both non-idealistic and idealistic. In the name of the systematic analysis of knowledge and experience, some philosophers have made the individual thinker the point of departure, and have sought to determine what he "contributes" to experience, and what is "given." But what is "given"? For some, it is a formless, nameless "stuff"; for others, it is a world of things; and for still others, the mind (a "great" mind) does all the "giving"—it gives the "given."

Man constitutes a part of his own environment—a fact which is fully recognized by cultural scientists. To go still further and to speak of constituting the "material" of culture, and the world of nature itself, is to substitute dogma for the recognition of a patent fact. But it is not enough to grant the "constitutive" activity of man in his process of experience. The nature of that activity must be determined truly. It is seen that there is always a "standard equipment" of the mind for a given time and place, and that that equipment changes historically. There are no fixed forms of the mind, any more than there is an unchangeable physical nature. The concepts and explanatory principles are different in ancient India, ancient Greece, and the modern world.

The varied interpretation of the world itself requires an explanation. In part, the differences in interpretation are due to the self-corrective and cumulative efforts of scientists to understand and control the world, and in part, but more fundamentally, they are due to the nature of human activity, to social factors. In a significant passage, Engels has pointed out [1] that the alteration of nature by men—not solely nature as such—is the most essential and immediate basis of human thought. Because of human activity, there is very little left of "nature" as it was in earlier periods. But if one abstracts from such changes, the physical environment may be regarded as a "constant." The "variable" human environment is then seen to condition the intellectual changes; the dominant world-view pattern for a given period is closely related to the leading social interests. The social environment has exercised deciding influences, and has determined the "given" in its most important sense.

For one who is a Catholic, the philosophy and theology of the Church are more potent factors in his "given" than the sun and the seas. The worker who enters a mine daily in order to support himself and his family must surely assign a position of central importance in his "given" to the mine and all that it entails. To the youth who thinks of marriage there are still other facts, organic and social, which are conspicuously "given." In short, experience and its world, in its most comprehensive sense, constitute the "given."

To limit experience to one segment or stratum is justifiable only for a particular purpose, as in the use of a subjectivistic procedure for the analysis of experience. Thus, one may restrict consideration of the "given" to his own conscious processes, to what may be called "methodological solipsism," which is quite different from the absurd position of genuine solipsism. The convinced solipsist, if such there be, and if he is really sincere and wishes to be consistent, is doomed to silence and inactivity. To think or reflect must be perpetually embarrassing to him, because his thought and linguistic system are social in their significance and reference. This does not apply to the "methodological solipsist," who is not "convinced" of solipsism, and who, perhaps, should therefore not be called a solipsist. That is the case with the phenomenological method in its initial "egological" stage, at which the experiences of an individual knower are considered in provisional isolation from all other knowers, but without injecting any assumption concerning the privacy of an individual mind, or the like. That an individual mind can only occur as a member of, or in relation to, a group of minds is an immediate fact that must be accepted by everyone, including the phenomenologist. The recognition of the "intentional" character of experience (meaning that experience refers to an objectivity) alone does not save the phenomenologist from accepting a philosophy of "immanence," which is merely a form of idealism, depending upon the well known assumptions.[2] More must be allowed for in characterizing experience.

It would be better to speak of reflectively viewed experience in its first stage, as limited to an individual, and in its second stage, when extended to comprise social experience. The first stage carries through a "suspension" of beliefs (an "epoché") concerning the world and other knowers as far as possible, and it operates with a highly restricted "given."

B. *Philosophic "Immediacy" and the Point of Departure for Philosophy*

Interest in the "given" is often motivated by the aim of determining an "immediate" fact for philosophical analysis, which could provide a point of departure, basic criteria, and a secure support for the whole structure of philosophy. There can be no question about there being *something* immediately given for any point of view, whether subjective-idealistic or materialistic. Its precise nature is what presents the problem; and the greatest difficulty turns out to be due to the standpoint that has been adopted beforehand. The identification of what is taken as "the immediate fact," for a particular point of view, with the total "given" as such, has been the source of much confusion.

When Whitehead begins the exposition of his "Method of Extensive Abstraction" [3] he takes "Something is going on" as the immediate fact, for his point of departure. But this immediate fact is not taken in isolation. It is included in a "duration," which is a "concrete slab of nature." This applies very well to the present discussion of experience. No individual perception in a specious present can serve as the immediate fact. Every perception involves a past and a future; it retains from the past, and anticipates the future. Furthermore, it involves a physical and a social environment or context, and therewith it takes its place as an event in cultural history. An isolated perception cannot be an ultimate unit of experience, any more than there can be an isolated physical fact. Such units are provided by retrospective analysis.

The immediate facts, for the basic natural attitude, are above all the stubborn, unavoidable or challenging events and conditions so abundantly illustrated in ordinary experience—the joys and sorrows, births and deaths, the cases of hunger and frustration. What Dewey went to pains to emphasize, in *Experience and Nature,* as the "precariousness" of life may serve as a title for some of the foremost immediate facts. In this sense one *participates* in the general process of experience; one is immersed in the world of experience, and can never *really* get outside it. One likes the things to which he has been conditioned—food, clothing, entertainment, etc. Both in feeling and in thinking one is the product of his time, even in his negative reactions against some of its features. In the struggle for survival and mastery over nature, it is not "man against nature"; it is man as a part of nature attempting to adapt the forces of nature to his own ends. It is even less meaningful to suppose that one gets outside his cultural system when criticizing it, however fundamental the criticism may be. And finally, it is if anything still less possible really to get away from or "behind" experience in general. One does not accomplish that feat by calling the latter "natural" experience, which is then to be viewed from another, allegedly superior vantage point. It is simply impossible to remove oneself from his natural and cultural setting, which is the *basic, immediate fact* for philosophy, just as it is for everything else, for all analyses and inquiries in the special sciences.

This general thesis should be borne in mind throughout the discussion. It would be a simple misunderstanding to suppose that one in the process of pure reflection leaves behind the field of experience. It should also be emphasized that an actual experience, or even the stream of experiences, is not regarded as the immediate fact for the natural view of the world. They are immediate in a specially defined sense, within the limits of an explicitly defined, subjectivistic point of view. The *abstractive* treatment in phenomenology of the stream of experiences, with the objects referred to as such, is a stage in the reflective analysis of experience for which there is ample justification. But it should not be confused with the immediate fact for man the organism and man the active knower, finding his way in a hostile world, or in a world of social conflicts. The reflective analysis is intended further to serve that knower, and it is only folly resulting from wishful thinking, aided and abetted by fallacious reasoning, that can bring about the dissolution of the real immediate fact in an idealized pure consciousness.

C. *The Mind as Contributive and the Error of Irrationalism*

No account of experience can be true which does not do justice to the contributing activities of the mind. That the mind is not purely passive in experience was recognized by Locke, who pointed out that the mind is able to perform operations of its own. No better evidence for the contributiveness of thought is needed than the amount of nonsense there is in the world. To what extent thought is contributive is another matter, of course, and there the claims of the idealist must be examined carefully—both the part-idealist for whom something is given to mind and by mind, and the whole-idealist for whom the mind provides all reality, and sometimes more besides.

To point out the fact that the knower (and, indeed, the whole tradition of knowers) "contributes" to experience, is not to suggest that the knower makes anything out of whole cloth. He is a product of his time, and what he does is conditioned by the existing scientific level, the motivation of his social system, and his aptitudes. On the social level, he may seek to transform society; but he does not "constitute" or "create" society. On the cognitive level, he may devise new theories, or new concepts, some of which may radically change past views. The nature and degree of the "creativeness" is determined by conditions beyond the control of any individual thinker. Experience "reflects" the world and cultural tradition, and the nature of that tradition, as well as the existing social system, determines the kinds of innovation which are possible.

The fact that the mind contributes meanings and interpretations to experience can be ascertained descriptively. That does not mean acceptance of the Kantian principle that form is contributed by the mind. The Kantian view can be made workable only with the aid of the "Absolute Mind" that hovers over the Kantian system, giving it the necessary support, and that assumption is itself not supported by evidence. The mind has a history, and there are no demonstrated eternal, fixed forms. To recognize the "contributiveness" of the mind is not to imply that any ideas or conceptual forms can be genetically unrelated to the causal order of experience. The truth that Kant himself recognized, that, in point of time, there is no knowledge before experience, applies generally.

The mind is contributive on the perceptual as well as on the conceptual level.[4] Illustrations of its contributive function on the conceptual level are most readily seen in its idealizations, which are not merely reports of what is found in the natural world. Philosophers in all ages have been tempted to hypostatize the idealizations and to assign them a being of their own. The reflective description of the process of idealization tends to dispel that dogma, and shows that the function of constituting ideal forms, and, indeed, the entire process of ideal identification, of the recognition of sameness is necessary not only for theoretical purposes, but also for the most fundamental activities of experience.

A well known type of question will be suggested at once. If to know is to know meaningfully, and is to apply conceptual forms and schemes, then it will be asked whether it is possible to know "truly," i.e., whether there may not be a falsification of experience due to the employment of a falsifying scheme. In other words, are we placed in a "predicament" by the fact that the mind contributes to experience? The very formulation of this question is assumptive. It disengages the mind from its natural framework, and supposes that the conceptual productions are regarded as substantive, ideal entities which somehow are capable of shutting us out of the correct view of an independently real world. Indeed, the supposed independently real world is assumed to be already interpreted truly, i.e., it is "in itself" the object of a true interpretation which for some reason the mind is forbidden to realize in experience. If one considers the actual function of the process of idealization and the constitution of ideal conceptual systems, he will see that they are proved or disproved in experience, that they are verified or invalidated in practice, so that it is misleading to ask, in static terms, whether it is possible to know reality truly.

The verification of some of our conceptual schemes becomes a mystery, or at best a matter of good fortune, on the view that the mind is a falsifying agency. There cannot be a complete falsification, in view of our practical success in solving our problems. The alleged falsification cannot be more than partial, and it is not to be identified with the cases of false statements or incorrect hypotheses which have to be abandoned. The cure for the latter is more and better knowledge. There is no cure for the alleged evil besetting knowledge essentially, due to the use of static concepts other than use of some other means than the intellect in order to experience reality "truly." Instead of speaking of "truth," it would then be more appropriate to speak of the night in which all cows are black. To look to "intuition," in the sense of Bergson,[5] would be to abandon all hope of objective truth, and to forget the painstakingly acquired lessons of scientifically controlled inquiry.

It would certainly be a strange situation if the mind "falsified" reality by devices proved valuable in practice. But even if there is no necessary falsification there are difficulties in the way of descriptive analysis in reflection. One's vision, reflectively directed, is itself conditioned by the scientific and philosophical level of the time, and also by traditional ideas and schemes. Personal factors may also be of influence. It follows that the desired complete descriptive analysis is an ideal which is largely realized only in the best examples of philosophical analysis, i.e., when care is taken to reflect upon the reflective process, including the investigator and all the conditions that bear upon him.

D. The "Given" Element in Experience According to Lewis

This function of reflection is recognized by Lewis,[6] although he is concerned with the purely epistemological rather than the sociological conditions of experience. In his view, "it is the business of philosophy to analyze and interpret our common experience, and by reflection, to bring to clear and cogent expression those principles which are implicit because they are brought to experience by the mind itself." Philosophy is thus "the study of the *a priori,*" its aim being "to reveal those categorical criteria which the mind applies to what is given to it"; and thus "to define the good, the right, the valid, and the real."

Historical considerations are obviously excluded by this type of analysis. What is here called "our common experience" is already interpreted, and bears the imprint of countless past generations. Then what can be meant by the interpretation of the philosopher, who has the role of interpreting "our common experience"? Can the philosopher do that by means of certain ultimate, intuitively "clarified" concepts? Descriptive analysis without interpretation, i.e., without the use of concepts and explanatory principles, is an ideal impossible in practice, and it is well to recognize this fact explicitly. That the pattern of interpretation used in an investigation can itself be examined in reflection, and thus be "clarified," disposes of the danger of a "predicament."

Philosophers have become so accustomed to regarding the analysis of experience as falling to them that they for the most part fail to inquire wherein their procedure differs from that of the psychologist and social scientist. It must be possible to draw the line clearly between them, or else philosophy must surrender any claim to independence, or even partial independence. Take prejudices on the social level, for example. The logician's interest in exposing the errors in reasoning can be readily distinguished from that of the psychologist. As for the epistemologist, his *attitude,* his *method,* and the character of the *evidence* will distinguish his interest, which is specialized. This is clearly expressed in the literature of phenomenology, which is, in its best sense, a descriptive theory of knowledge. The attitude is one of "universal questioning," with logic and naturalistic psychology "suspended" at first, so that there is a minimum in assumptions. These considerations are not incompatible with Lewis's position, as quoted above. They underlie his position, and call attention to the need for a more explicit and thoroughgoing methodological study of the "conditions of experience" that are due to the activity of the mind, or to the contributions of the mind. The descriptive procedure that has been indicated can only be one phase of philosophic inquiry; but it does play a necessary part in the analysis of experience.

Lewis distinguishes two elements in knowledge: the concept, which is the product of the activity of thought; and the sensuously given, which is independent of such activity. His analysis is a "logical" one which involves ideal conditions never met in experience. To that extent it is non-empirical. There is always a mixture of the two factors—which Lewis recognizes, of course—and he is interested in "cognitive experience," in which the immediate senuous data are given to the mind, and a form, construction, or interpretation is present as a result of the activity of thought. This distinction is sound as far as it goes. But lacking in Lewis's analysis is a detailed descriptive account of how the mind actually performs its "constructive" activities. Elaborate descriptive-philosophical as well as psychological studies are called for. It is necessary to point out the truth of the causal-genetic view, as to the conditions underlying the activities of the mind—the dependence of the mind on nature and on society, and the way in which the mind may be said to "reflect" the world. Analysis in the theory of knowledge can only suffer because of detachment from such basic facts. This is shown, for example, when Lewis holds the "given" to be "ineffable," to be that which remains untouched and unaltered, however it is construed by thought.[7] The term "given" may be used in this ideal, limiting sense for purposes of analysis. It names a limiting, conditioning element in experience, abstracting from the interpretation of the mind. But there is also the more inclusive sense of givenness, according to which the world of experience as a whole is "given"—the physical and the cultural environment, with their "deposits" of meaning. The "given" in the full sense really includes the domain of nature; the society into which one is born; the language which he learns; the intellectual, moral, and religious traditions; and, fundamentally, the very likes and dislikes which one has.

It is the "thick experience of the world of things, not the thin given of immediacy," that constitutes the datum for philosophical reflection, in Lewis's view. "We do not see patches of color, but trees and houses. . . . Such initial data of object and fact set the problem in philosophy and are, in a measure, the criteria of its solution." [8].The use of the term "immediacy" to name the "thin" content of the "given" is not altogether fortunate, since the total situation and things are "first" for actual experience, as Lewis himself indicates. He points out that the "given," as he conceives it, is an abstraction, even though it is not an "unreal" abstraction; that the "given" is *in,* not before, experience; and that it is an identifiable constituent of experience.[9] He is right in defending the use of abstractions. So long as one recognizes the actual total nature of experience and avoids confusing products of analysis with real elements, it is a proper procedure to carry through an analysis from the point of view of a knower who separates his meaning-activities from that which is sensuously "given." That is one level of analysis which may be accepted as such. But it is society that is prior to the individual in a naturalistic, genetic sense, i.e., *in reality*. What is called "first" in an analysis depends upon the purpose of the analysis and the frame of reference. If it is the actual knower and his actual experience, the immediate fact is that whole objects and their relationships are there, in their natural and social setting. If it is a physical-psychological inquiry, the sensuous basis of experience is fundamental. For a phenomenological investigation, the objectively directed experiences themselves are taken to be "first." This does not mean, however, that the judgment of what is fundamentally real is arbitrary. Alternative procedures for special purposes, involving abstraction as they do, should not be taken to imply that alternative views of reality are equally justifiable.

Lewis's analysis makes it impossible to construct or constitute all the elements of experience on the basis of the mind and its contents. The basic pattern which he lays down, the dualism between "what the mind brings to experience" and "what is given in experience," bears a resemblance to the Kantian analysis. But it is advanced without the Kantian dogma of a fixed, unifying self and the categorial forms, and without the Kantian pretense to *a priori* knowledge, meaning universal and necessary knowledge. Lewis's construction is a pale shadow of Kant's enormous claims. The mind brings alternative concepts, theories, or interpretations, and a choice is made from among them, in order to make application to situations in experience. The name *a priori* for such concepts is thus hardly appropriate, in view of their modest status as possible patterns of thought, which may or may not find application in experience.

It is always desirable, in undertaking a systematic analysis of knowledge and experience, to remind oneself of their physical, organic, and social conditions. That would prevent errors from arising due to the "static" treatment of the mind—as though it were a finality, without beginning in time, and a long history. In short, such a reminder is like providing ordinate and abscissa to establish the proper locus of the discussion. Its preventive value is very important. A philosopher should not be vague or noncommittal on the basic questions of metaphysics. An analysis of experience and knowledge should not neglect to indicate the basic facts which, if recognized, would make agnosticism, skepticism, and spiritualism untenable. In other words, the epistemologist has no right to forget the place of the knower in reality, or to forget the knowledge forced upon us by ordinary experience, let alone science. The content of established knowledge is relevant to an inquiry into the nature and structure of experience. One errs in his analysis, if these facts are not made explicit. Healthymindedness is at issue.

It would be best to designate the "given" in Lewis's sense as the "sensuous given," so as to distinguish it from other "givens," such as the cultural whole of experience. The stratum of the "sensuous given" can be provided only by an analysis which introduces ideal conditions. The "empirical given" for any person consists of things, of interpreted objects; and the alleged "indubitably given" of phenomenology (or the "given" *qua* indubitable) consists of an actual experience with its object "meant," but not posited as existent.

E. *Dewey on Immediate Knowledge and the Nature of the "Given"*

As a representative of the tradition of naturalism, Dewey endeavors to hold to the truth that man the organism strives to preserve himself in a hostile environment, and to represent it unflinchingly in all its consequences. Extensive consequences are determined by it, positively as well as negatively. Inspection shows, however, that even the most resolute naturalistic inquiry which favors the use of organic categories meets with difficulties on the social level, where clear, concrete reference must be made to basic problems in terms of concepts appropriate to the social level. Precisely this point is a characteristic distinction between a cautious naturalism (an incomplete materialism, really) and a thoroughgoing materialism applied to all levels of existence.

Dewey undertakes to give an account of experience which does justice to its naturalistic character and conditions, and which at the same time recognizes the difficulties caused by the interpretations of the mind and the construction of theories. He calls attention [10] to the frequently occurring and perhaps inevitable error of the philosopher "to mix with his reports of direct experience interpretations made by previous thinkers." The tradition of empiricism is cited as a striking illustration of this danger, so that empiricism faces the objection that it is not true to experience. By experience Dewey means "something at least as wide and deep and full as all history on this earth, a history which, since history did not occur in the void, includes the earth and the physical relations of man." [11] It would be better to say "involves" instead of "includes," and to make sure that the definition of "experience" makes it clear that the natural world antedates the emergence of human experience. This would effectively avoid any suggestion of idealism. The concept of experience, as construed by Dewey in all its comprehensiveness, is intended to provide philosophy with the advantage of "the method of pointing, finding, showing." [12] "Reality" is held to include "whatever is denotatively found." "Experience" is thus a "directive" word, and it appears to be all the more useful because the unfavorable and the hateful will therewith receive the attention usually accorded to the noble and honorable. However, if "reality" is taken to include that which is "found," it must be explicitly pointed out that the field of reality is antecedent to any process of "finding," i.e., if the narrowness of positivism is to be avoided.

In his treatment of experience Dewey does not consider that *true* and *adequate* knowledge will not give a false emphasis to the intellectual elements, and do an injustice to the nonintellectual elements. With the use of the "denotative method" he proposes to go "behind the refinements and elaborations of reflective experience to the gross and compulsory things of our doings, enjoyments, and sufferings—to the things that force us to labor, that satisfy needs." [13] The recognition of such things certainly belongs to the program of the descriptive analysis of experience, beginning with the naïvely "natural" view of the world and man. The truth of the "natural" view of the world must be accepted and done justice in the reflective analysis of experience. It is concerned with temporally and causally prior facts which provide the material and the primary occasion for reflection. Dewey's admonition that we go "behind the refinements . . . of reflective experience to the . . . things" recalls Husserl's famous slogan, "Back to the things themselves." For both thinkers, direct seeing is held up as the basic method. Dewey's observation [14] that the things which a man experiences come to him clothed with meanings which originate in custom and tradition, brings to mind Husserl's discussion of "sedimented meanings," and also his apt figure of the "garment of ideas" thrown over the data of experience. But there are also differences—

above all the basic difference that the "things" to which Dewey refers are social, physical, biological, whereas Husserl's appeal is to direct experience, his best examples being in the field of logical experience. He never spoke as a naturalist. It will be sufficient at this point to mention one further difference in the analyses of the two thinkers. For Dewey, experience is history,[15] and it is a method, not a stuff. The "taking" of some objects as final is itself declared to be an episode of history. Husserl, being interested in finality, in ultimate and eternal truths, endeavors to rise above history and time in their naturalistic sense. Dewey, on the other hand, regards the "assumption that the ultimate and immediate object is timeless" as responsible for an insoluble problem. In his view, anything denoted is found to have *temporal quality* and reference.

Dewey's reflective procedure goes back "to the primitive situations of life that antecede and generate" the reflective interpretation, "so that we re-live former processes of interpretation." Thus we go "knowingly and cautiously through steps which were first taken uncritically."[16] The resemblance to Husserl's general pattern of inquiry is apparent. The "naturalistic" program for reflective analysis of Dewey seeks to probe to the "elementary building-stones of experience." But much more should be said regarding the mechanism of the procedure to be followed out. Dewey is cautious in his claims for his empirical method. One may show the way to others, so that they can see for themselves. Moreover, the findings of one person are to be rectified and extended by the findings of others. In this way cooperation for philosophical reflection resembles the cooperation seen in inquiry in the natural sciences.[17]

When Dewey speaks of experience, in the complete sense in which he means it to be understood, as the *method* of philosophy, he is doing little more than providing emphasis in a desired direction. In the main, he sketches a naturalistic genetic method which runs parallel to the "pure" genetic method proposed by Husserl. He fails, however, to point out adequately the procedure which he must use as a philosopher, and the conditions under which it must be used, *qua* philosophy. The main lines that philosophy has to take are indicated by him, as follows: "It has the task of analytic dismemberment and synthetic reconstruction of experience."[18] Surely that must include the attempt at a thoroughgoing reflective inspection of all the activities and contributions of the mind, of all the conditions that bear upon the experience of the group and the individual, the challenging of every belief and judgment with respect to its foundation in experience, and the systematic "questioning" of all items of knowledge in terms of one's own direct experience ("reflective experience," which "reactivates" the original presumed experiences)—in short, an attempt at a complete analysis of experience, in connection with the findings of the various special sciences which show the place of man (and the mind) in nature, and the mutual relationships between the mind and its environment.

The parallelism with Husserl should not be overdrawn, however, in view of the differences in dominant aims and premises and the emphasis upon testing, upon experimentalism, especially as shown in Dewey's philosophy of logic. If a subjectivist sees clearly and truly, in his descriptive analysis of experience, his findings can and must be ordered in the naturalistic account of experience. But it does not follow that all idealistic *theories* can be translated into naturalistic terms, e.g., the alleged "supertemporal" elements.

Distrusting any flight to a realm of certainty which is removed from the realities of experience, Dewey never loses sight of the "outstanding fact," "the evidence that the world of empirical things includes the uncertain, unpredictable, uncontrollable, and hazardous."[19] It is the "predicament of the inextricable mixture of stability and uncertainty" that gives rise to philosophy, and that is reflected "in all its recurrent problems and issues."[20] Even a cursory inspection of the historical problems of philosophy will convince the reader that this thesis could not be sustained. It expresses a limited truth merely, and will not apply properly to such thinkers as Hobbes, Spinoza, and Hegel. Dewey goes so far as to state that "variant philosophies may be looked at as different ways of supplying recipes for denying to the universe the character of contingency." This view of philosophy will hardly apply to the major issues of the tradition. The medieval conflict of realism and nominalism, for example, had objective historical significance for the Church and its opponents. In Dewey's view, however, "quarrels among conflicting types of philosophy are family quarrels." For many philosophical disputes that is undoubtedly true. There is indeed "warfare of the schools," and sometimes it seems as senseless as a feud that is continued by the descendants of the original combatants. But the most important historical conflicts in philosophy cannot be disposed of so easily. Thus, the words of William of Occam to the Emperor Louis, who was opposed to the Pope, may serve to indicate the historical vitality of his "terminism": "Thou defend me by the sword, and I will defend thee by the pen."

In accordance with his empirical method, Dewey recognizes "the contextual situation in which thinking occurs," and notes that "the starting-point is the actually problematic." For a naturalistic empirical philosophy, the work of thinking goes on within the same world of experienced things, and not as "a jump from the latter world into one of objects constituted once and for all by thought." [21] He is thus opposed on principle to a constitutive, transcendental idealism, with the usual fixed, supertemporal structures. When he goes on to ascribe the general, basic error involved to the imagination influenced by emotion, he is neglecting history and giving only a part of the explanation. To pair spiritualistic idealism and materialism, as he does,[22] is to commit an error of historical shortsightedness. As Dewey views them, "one doctrine finds structure in a framework of ideal forms, the other finds it in matter. They agree in supposing that structure has some superlative reality. This supposition is another form taken by preference for the stable over the precarious and uncompleted." Why there should be two rival parties over a period of so many centuries, or why they should function differently in different historical periods, is not answered in this way. The abstract opposition between the "stable" and the "precarious" is really empty until tested by actual historical examples, and defined concretely in terms of real, social forces. Insisting that incompleteness and precariousness be given footing of the same rank as the finished and the fixed, Dewey regards philosophy as concerned with the "proportioned union" of the safe and sane and the hazardous. But he does not point out just how philosophy adds to the sciences in determining the desired "proportioned union"; nor does he consider that such a union must be undertaken repeatedly and endlessly, because of the varying factors requiring unification.

Dewey is right in calling attention to the importance of the "precariousness" of the world. That is a factor of permanent importance. But so far as intellectual history is concerned, the precariousness of *social* life is far more important. It is necessary to be quite specific, and to point out what is "precarious," especially in relation to the given system of society. The facts requiring explanation are not simple, and one must be on his guard against oversimplification. Certainly some have sought, and others will seek, a philosophy of eternalism in compensation for the evils of temporal existence. But still others revel in a temporalistic view. How can that be explained on the basis of the precariousness of "the world"? Differences of temperament, or of insight, or of knowledge and ignorance play their part in individual cases. Thus it may not be possible in a given case—e.g., Parmenides—to assign a complete social-historical explanation on the basis of the available evidence. But it could well be that the philosophy of "Being," which excluded change, represented a vested interest in stability, in preserving the existing social system. This line of thought, which has been developed in great detail by historical (or dialectical) materialists, is fruitful in its bearing upon philosophical movements and thinkers.

According to a naturalistic metaphysics, reflection is itself "a natural event occurring *within* nature because of traits of the latter." [23] One underlying condition for reflection is correctly described in that way; but it is also essential to point out the social-historical conditions of reflection. It is certainly true that all types of reflection are "natural events," just as it is true that they cannot occur without the human organism. But that is not to say that one has to accept the basic assumptions and concepts of the current sciences as unquestionable in reflection. Their philosophical examination is a supplement to their scientific criticism. Those philosophers who think that they are rising "above" nature, however, exhibit incredible naïveté, surprising even if that is maintained as a mode of response to religious or vested academic interests. That reflection is itself an event in existence is a statement of simple fact. All "purely reflective" procedures and analyses of abstractions, etc., are natural events. In a very real sense, one cannot get himself, or his thinking, outside the natural order. The "questioning" of all our knowledge of the natural order as such is still a "natural" process of questioning. That fact should not be lost sight of when one adopts a special terminology to name the new attitude that is systematically adopted for "questioning" not only the natural order but all the provinces of experience, "ideal" as well as real.

F. *The Subjective Procedure of Phenomenology and Its Abuses*

The phenomenological method is designed to apply to all phases of experience. That its limitation to a subjective context restricts it from realizing this aim, and that it was an irresistible temptation to Husserl to adopt a general idealistic philosophy, is made clear by a study of the development of that philosophy. It is Edmund Husserl alone who is considered here, for his type of analysis has yielded results which command the respect of other investigators, including scientific psychologists. Like some of his predecessors in the idealistic tradition (Hegel, for example), he was able to achieve valuable results despite the restricted and ultimately repressive setting of his philosophy. The means to an end which he originally adopted—a subjective procedure for reflection—which yielded analyses of interest to psychologists and logicians, proved to be a fatal limitation to his philosophy.

As a continuator of the empirical tradition, Husserl aimed to analyze experience. The method of philosophy was declared to be descriptive, direct "seeing" being the ideal. The field for description proved to be in need of extension, even on that level, and Husserl in his early period emphatically argued for the direct observation of "general objects," discussing at length the immediate apprehension of them in his first published work, *Philosophy of Arithmetic* (1891). He was careful in this period to accord full importance and value to the various scientific methods, in keeping with his own excellent scientific training.

The original aim of phenomenology was quite different from that of Dewey, or from that of any of the philosophers deriving from the natural and social sciences. It led Husserl into the ranks of the opponents of the scientific philosophy developed at the close of the nineteenth century. As for his own conscious motivation, his primary aim was to overcome logical psychologism, or the view that logical validity can be construed in psychological terms and derived from psychological principles. In other words, an admittedly erroneous position taken by logicians who were reacting to naturalistic and empiricist influences became the target of Husserl's initial criticism, and led him first of all to a "neutral" position on the issue of idealism and realism (or materialism). The phenomenology which was first formulated in his *Logical Investigations* (1900–1901) was concerned with direct description, and was even called descriptive psychology. Some years later the "phenomenological reduction" (i.e., to "pure consciousness"—the restriction to conscious experiences and their correlates) was formulated, and it was advanced as the first prerequisite for philosophical analysis. It was intended to define the field for philosophy to begin with, and it defined the setting for a transcendental philosophy. In Husserl's exposition, there was a strong feeling of opposition to naturalistic procedures.

It is possible to construe the "reduction" in non-idealistic terms, as an auxiliary method in philosophy, thus taking Husserl literally, when he calls it "a methodological expedient," and to align it with other methods, under the general heading of "methodology." Thus it should be regarded as one type of reflection among others, with its own peculiar value for philosophical understanding. Representatives of the last stage of Husserl's development object to that, however, maintaining that the subjectivistic procedure of phenomenology is something *sui generis,* absolutely unique, different in principle from all other ("mundane") methods. Such claims could hardly promote sympathetic understanding, or even an attempt at sympathetic understanding; and they are as unnecessary as they are unwarranted. It is hardly helpful to portray Husserl after the fashion of Porphyry's treatment of Plotinus. To make phenomenology ineffable and indescribable (in "natural" terms) would be to deprive it all of scientific interest. This last phase of transcendental phenomenology has been submitted to criticism in the present writer's *The Foundation of Phenomenology.*[24] The analysis of "intentional" experience in all its types constitutes a self-contained study. The phenomenological datum for analysis is my-experiencing-the-object, whether the latter be real or fictive in character. That there should be a temptation, irresistible for some philosophers, to constitute *reality* out of the experiences is understandable, but none the less inexcusable. That has had the unfortunate result of tending to discredit phenomenology as a whole. The subtle arguments in question [25] are no better basically than Berkeley's well worn argument for subjective idealism.

The descriptive analyses of phenomenology are intended to be independent of the demonstration of reality or unreality, and independent also of all causal-genetic considerations involving "natural" time. Thus the description of the content and structure of experience shows how an experience of reality is incompatible with one of illusion, for example. It portrays the structure of each type of experience. But it does not give us a test of reality. There is no "pure phenomenological" way to reality in the sense of a being independent of the knowing of it. The analysis is concerned with the context of the knower and his objects, everything being viewed from the perspective of its being known or experienced, so that there can be no talk of being apart from knowing, from that point of view. The analysis is confined to the determination of general structures, and it does not deal with factual situations except as exemplifying such structures. They are described as they are manifested in experience, where they are found. So are all the constitutive activities of thought seen in operation, through reflection. They are studied in their "essential" types by means of reenacting and reactivating experiences such as remembrances, conceptual abstractions, and recognitions. The experiencing of evidence, of truth, of adequacy, can be contrasted with the experiencing of error, of inadequacy, etc. They are seen to rule one another out "essentially." One may be quite wrong, however, in his descriptive analysis of an "essential" structure. On this level one is no more secure against error than he is on the "naturalistic" level of scientific description, say in the description of an ant colony. Thus the vaunted superiority of "inner" over "outer" experience is seen to be unfounded. But both types are necessary.

If, as the present writer maintains, Husserl's idealism is untenable, and violates his own explicitly formulated precepts, the really challenging question that must be faced concerns the fruitfulness of the entire procedure. That every sound descriptive proposition in phenomenology can be asserted in objective terms within the framework of a naturalistic (realistic, or materialistic) philosophy has been pointed out. One does not leave nature when holding its concepts in question for the sake of analysis. It is appropriate to point out its contribution to the understanding of the structure of knowledge and experience. It contributes toward the clarification of basic concepts, as seen in the "origin-analysis" studies of negation, relation, possibility, etc.[26] No method which can contribute toward that end should be ignored. The phenomenological method is not the only way of clarifying the basic ideas. It is one way, and it adds to the understanding of their meaning and structure. The social-historical interpretation or explanation of an idea also "clarifies"; so does a simple historical account; etc. All who contribute parts of truth should realize that they can coexist. Philosophers are frequently prevented from doing so because of the standpoints they represent or the interests which determine them.

Generally speaking, it is safest to welcome any and all descriptive findings, just as it is best to allow "pure" scientists complete freedom of investigation, without continually raising the possibly myopic demand for "results." It is in place to observe that some valuable results for practice have been achieved by disregarding the question of practical results, as illustrated in modern pure mathematics. The fundamental studies of the philosopher, *qua* descriptive investigator, affect the entire structure of knowledge. They represent a necessary dimension of inquiry which may well be endless. They can never be the whole story for philosophy, but they are an important part of it. It remains the function of philosophy to call attention to neglected facts and, if necessary, to include them in its field of inquiry. That applies to the analysis of experience by means of "inner description," from which psychology has turned away, leaving it to philosophers and novelists.

The philosopher who undertakes descriptions of states of anxiety, fear of death, etc., may be making a contribution which could equally well be made by a psychologist. Such findings are to be distinguished from the philosophical standpoint with which they happen to be associated, as in the case of the "Philosophy of Existence," in terms of which certain human attitudes are construed as "basic categories." What develops is a kind of "misplaced subjectivism," in which the limited virtues of a strict subjectivism tend to be lost. The danger then arises that there may be a false weighting of human states and attitudes in the total picture of man in relationship to his world. The dogmatic use of what may be called "generic determinations" in describing man (which man? which group of men? which historical period?) is characteristic of existentialism. It is a surprising dogmatism, especially so in view of the body of scientific knowledge concerning man. In carrying through certain limited descriptive studies of a structural, "essential" type, it must not be presumed that man in his real nature is portrayed thereby, and that man is fully or adequately considered. To know the "real" man, it is necessary to have the results of historical, statistical, psychological, socio-economic, etc., studies. The descriptive analysis of the experience of dread, or of a state of anxiety, does not entitle one to characterize men in general. In other words, a clear-cut line must be drawn between the "essential" descriptive and the factual orders; and, again, between the former and the philosophy of human existence, with its basic values. Description is *per se* acceptable, if it is correctly executed. The evaluation of the systematic philosophy requires the reduction of all statements of value to statements of fact, and the appraisal of the latter in terms of the evidence. The philosopher must not be allowed to mouth statements as though he were an unrestricted oracle, and particularly by means of a language which strains at accepted usage beyond the breaking point. These remarks are dedicated to Martin Heidegger and his fellow existentialists.

Heidegger was the most influential of Husserl's students in his last period. Husserl was late in expressing opposition to the danger latent in Heidegger's work, and he even seemed to close his eyes to it at first. Heidegger's influence on his students has been tenacious, and has seemed to survive his inexcusable actions under the Nazi regime, even in the personal feelings of many of them. It cannot be denied that he has promoted obscurantism in his systematic thought. The "Philosophy of Existence" is a type of philosophy which can only alienate one for whom the canons and ideals of logic are meaningful, and especially one for whom the ideal of philosophy as a rigorous science is definitive. It is a strange myth that the "problem of existence" was never recognized before, when one considers the enormous literature devoted to the conditions bearing upon human existence, cultural as well as biological and physical, including man's efforts to know himself and his place in the world. Such a myth can be rendered plausible only by means of a cryptic statement of the concept and problem of "existence," using such seductive terms as "thrownness" and "fallenness." Such terms bespeak their theological significance and can only be misleading in a supposedly descriptive investigation, Heidegger's alleged aims notwithstanding. The monstrous linguistic medium (so painfully evident in the much ado about "nothing" in his *Was ist Metaphysik?* for example) and the perpetual fog of existentialism could only aid it in being used and perhaps misused for purposes which not even an idealistic phenomenologist could condone.

How evil the consequences of Heidegger's efforts have been can be seen in a paper by Oskar Becker, "Transzendenz und Paratranszendenz," presented at the Ninth International Congress of Philosophy.[27] A few excerpts will be of interest. "Not the *being* of the being 'man' (*des Seienden 'Mensch'*) is in question, but his *essence,* more exactly his '*essencing* essence' (*Wesendes Wesen*). And here is seen the philosophical nature of our language: we sometimes apply the expression 'essence' not only abstractly but also concretely to man.

But not to every human being; namely, not to a grown man, but to a child and a young woman. Thus we speak of a 'small essence' (*dem 'kleinen Wesen,'* the child) and of a 'charming essence' (e.g., a young girl). A man as a historical personality *has* indeed an essence (his character), but he *is* not one. The natural human being still close to naïve primitiveness is on the other hand an essence, it 'essences' (*'west'*). His existence or as we now say it more exactly: his *para-existence* is essence (*Wesen*)" (p. 103). Then Becker reassures his audience: "These are not mere words and quibbling." His proposal to inspect the "primal phenomenon" recalls a familiar precept. The use to which it is put is indicated by the following passage: "The phenomenon of birth, which is only to be grasped intuitively, determines the existence of an unbroken human being, or more exactly, the mode of existence of a human being, in so far as he is unbroken. It is here that basic experiences . . . are the old powers of blood and earth. . . . It is furthermore the blood, that apparently material but in truth to the highest degree formative and impressing force, which determines the types, the 'kinds' (*'Schläge'*) of human beings, the basic forms which are possible for human beings." (pp. 101 f.). The apparatus of "intuition" and "basic experience" is, in this context, just so much pseudo-phenomenological claptrap. Becker, who was for years a devoted student and colleague of Husserl, attached himself to Heidegger and drank deeply at the latter's fountain of linguistic jugglery. Some of his rather painful efforts in his Congress paper (*Uebersteigendheit, Unentstiegenheit,* etc.) show him to be a worthy continuator of Heidegger, one who is capable of new tricks of his own. It could be simply judged to be comical balderdash were it not connected with Nazism; for there is no accidental connection between Becker's "blood and earth" and the teachings of the Nazis. The ease with which existentialism could accommodate itself to Nazi Germany is noteworthy.

It will be pertinent to add a few comments about one more leading figure in the larger phenomenological movement. Max Scheler, who regarded himself as a "cofounder" of phenomenology (a designation never adopted by Husserl), has had an influence reaching far beyond the limits of descriptive philosophy, all the way from religious and social thought to the Nazi ideology. Much of Scheler's work could hardly survive critical inspection, but it must be reckoned with practically. He argued that naturalism neglects certain "facts" (e.g., pertaining to "spiritual" and "holy" love), and that it cannot account for them successfully by any of its theories. The strict descriptive phenomenologist will not in the least impugn the merit of naturalistic findings. But Scheler placed himself conspicuously in the ranks of those trying to hold back the tide of scientific naturalism and materialism, ranks including conservatives, and reactionaries of all shades When Scheler argues [28] that the idea of "absolute monogamy" is *never* to be derived from the naturalistic presuppositions, and that sexual love must be regarded as a kind of love which is peculiarly qualified psychically, in order to give absolute monogamy a "phenomenological foundation," one is tempted to draw a curtain of charity over the entire performance. For Scheler, "Marriages are made in heaven" has a deeper meaning in terms of essences and essential connections. Scheler's critique of naturalism proceeds assumptively and fallaciously: assumptively because he assumes as real and as unanalyzable in "naturalistic" terms such phenomena as "holy love"; and fallaciously because he gives what is presumed to be an exhaustive set of naturalistic explanations, including the Freudian approach, but fails to give the strongest explanation. He neither does justice to the explanations he cites, nor gives the best possible one.[29]

All the types of experience with which the existentialists are concerned, including types which are of interest in psychiatry, can be investigated by means of the strictly controlled phenomenological method, which is designed to take account of all regions of experience, and all attitudes, in its way. That all the conditions bearing causally and genetically upon the existence of the knower and his attitudes should also be considered, has already been set forth.

II. THE GOAL OF CERTAINTY AND TRANSCENDENTAL SUBJECTIVISM

A. The Ideal of Certainty

Exponents of the subjective tradition maintain that the procedure of pure reflection provides certainty, in contradistinction to the doubts, the "mere probability" of "natural experience." This thesis is of crucial importance for subjectivism and requires careful consideration. Two questions are involved: What are the motives for the interest in the ideal of certainty? And is the claim to certainty tenable, on the part of subjectivism?

Dewey's extensive criticism of the goal of certainty bears mainly on the first question. The first chapter of his *Quest for Certainty*[30] is significantly entitled "Escape from Peril." He suggests that man's distrust of himself has caused him to get beyond and above himself by means of "pure knowledge." Activities in the sought-for realm would not be overt, and would have no "external consequences." It is Dewey's thesis that the notions about "certainty and the fixed" flow from the separation, set up in the interest of the quest for absolute certainty, between theory and practice, knowledge and action. He charges that "in the absence of actual certainty in . . . a precarious world, men cultivated all sorts of things that would give them the *feeling* of certainty." In his view, "no mode of action . . . can give anything approaching absolute certitude"; and "since no amount of pains and care in action can ensure complete certainty, certainty in knowledge was worshipped as a substitute." In *Experience and Nature,* Dewey observes that philosophers have set out with data and principles sufficiently simple to yield what is sought, in this case absolute certainty in knowledge of things. He sees philosophy used as a substitute for religion, when the latter ceases to give men the sense of certainty and security they want. The element of truth in this thesis may readily be confirmed by the history of philosophy. But such reflections do not give the whole truth concerning the goal of certainty by any means. The appeal to the absolute reliableness of the "inner life" was a convenient way of disposing of the factors of doubt and incompleteness which make the empirical knowledge of the world more or less probable, and of supporting the position of religious faith. It is sufficient to refer to St. Augustine, and the principle of Catholic philosophy that it is possible to achieve "certitude."

It is necessary to devote more attention to the social-historical factors underlying ideas and beliefs than Dewey's analysis provides. An important perspective is opened up when one considers the role of science in economic development. Modern science, as a basic factor of the Industrial Revolution, has made "certainty" a reality in the sense of making possible the conquest of nature by man. The causal understanding of natural phenomena, the striking degree of success of scientific prediction, and the great progress in the field of social science, all argue against the rejection of "certainty" in all senses. The universal determinism of Spinoza reflects the confidence of the early period of modern development, the exuberance of scientists who first found nature to exhibit laws. With the party of science aligned against the feudal-ecclesiastical tradition, there was no motivation to plead limits to the human mind, or to experience. The situation becomes more complicated when the religious tradition, adapted to the new economic and social conditions, makes itself felt in philosophy; when more complex intellectual conditions result from the fact that the rising bourgeois class finds it desirable to restrict the program of science, to soften it by reconciling it with religious interests, and to safeguard itself against the findings of social scientists. Various modes of compromise result at different times: Hume's skepticism and ultimate doubts, and Kant's agnostic dualism in the eighteenth century, both circumscribing the validity or extent of scientific knowledge; the agnosticism of the evolutionary philosophers and of some recent scientists; the cautious temper of recent empiricism and pragmatism; the current distrust of laws and generalizations in social science.

C. I. Lewis's cautious temper of mind is seen in his defense of the thesis that all empirical knowledge is probable, never certain. Any number of perceptions may be cited as "certain"—or at least as certain as our knowledge that $2+2=4$. If one asserts that the proposition $2+2=4$ is "certain" deductively, but that one's actual judgment of it may not be infallible, the same thing would apply to empirical knowledge. Is the proposition "I am an American citizen" merely probable, i.e., less than the limiting case of certainty? Or, let us fancy a factory worker to be doubtful about the relationship between his "take-home pay" and the rising cost of living. Even if he were doubtful, on the ground that a mistake is possible in a great number of instances, his wife would clinch the argument with all the desired "certainty." There is a point beyond which one should not press his doubts—the point of adequate practical verification.

"Man's distrust of himself," which is deplored by Dewey, is hardly an explanation of the retreat to "pure knowledge." That retreat may well be, in effect, a device for safeguarding vested interests. "Certainty" need not be paired with "the fixed," or regarded as "absolute," as seen when one considers the nature of scientific progress. Obviously, different concepts of certainty are involved. It is interesting to note how apparently diverse forces cooperate in opposing a thoroughgoing scientific view of the world. The party of religion in philosophy retreated, via the idealistic tradition, to an "inner life" which provided certainty in a specially defined sense; while philosophers of various schools and tendencies made concessions to it, whether consciously or not, by arguing that science cannot provide certainty, in another sense.

"Certainty" may be construed subjectively in terms of feeling, as a kind of inner illumination; or objectively, as the upper limit of probability; or as indubitability without contradiction—the Cartesian meaning. Formal knowledge which is independent of the course of real events may be said to be "certain," in the sense that it could not be denied without contradiction. So far as our general purposes are concerned, "certain" means "certain enough," just as "clear" means "clear enough," as Whitehead once put it. The subjective meaning may be dismissed, as leading to an impasse, in which each individual is the absolute authority, so that only objective meanings can be considered. The procedure of systematic doubt as initiated by Descartes and appropriated by Husserl is intended to eliminate all possibilities of error, and thus arrive at a point, or region, of certainty. It proves to be a most revealing approach to the last stage of phenomenology, which may well be the last stronghold of idealism.

B. The Cartesian Procedure of Doubt and Its Phenomenological Use

Husserl states [31] that what is intentionally indicated in the apperceptive horizon of a perception is not possible but *certain*. That can always be said of the *present* experience. Can it be said of "inner" experience as a whole? This question is best answered in connection with the Cartesian method of doubt.

Because of its adoption by Husserl as a device for defining the field of transcendental subjectivity, special interest attaches to the Cartesian procedure. The latter is open to serious objections, as is well known. If the purpose were to ascertain how far one could proceed in doubting without contradiction, the answer would have to be, to a solipsism of the present, and hence passing, moment with the past moment already doubted as soon as one reflects upon it. The experience of doubt which occurs "now" is indubitable; but a new "now" takes its place, and the old one is "not now," which makes it dubitable. Unless absolute reliance can be placed upon memory, or an absolute mind with a fixed structure is provided, or some such principle is allowed, the Cartesian procedure is utterly fruitless. What Descartes did with his method is of historical interest merely. There is a tradition among idealists to admit that what Descartes established was a "thin truth," while maintaining that it is the "important truth" (viz., the "certainty" of the "I doubt" which cannot be doubted, or of the mind). Nietzsche's words in *Beyond Good and Evil*[32] may be recalled: "There may even be puritanical fanatics of conscience, who prefer to put their last trust in a sure nothing, rather than in an uncertain something."

On the other hand, the Cartesian method of doubt may be appropriated in quite a different way, and "doubt" be instituted as a means of inspecting the "normal and natural" assumptions of the mind. It is really the phenomenological substitute for doubt, and now means "suspension." The attempt to achieve a universal suspension of judgment or belief takes the place of the fruitless method of doubt. The general "thesis of existence" which underlies normal experience, and every element of assent or denial in cognitive experience, are placed in abeyance, in order to serve as the subject matter of reflective analysis. The suspension affects beliefs pertaining to other human beings, and oneself as a psychological subject. What is the advantage of this method? And does it provide certainty, in the sense of indubitability?

For one thing, it delimits a distinctive domain for philosophical inquiry. The detached reflective procedure, according to which every object in the world or in human society, or every item in experience and knowledge, is treated as a correlate of a particular experience of an individual experiencing being, with the "existence" judgment suspended, determines the initial stage of the reflective analysis. This stream of experience is indeed the result of a social-historical process, and it could not be inspected without the prior existence of society and a long tradition. That "naturalistic" truth must be recognized. Can the phenomenological residuum resulting from the *logical* analysis be said to be "certain"? Not in the Cartesian sense, or, rather, in the Cartesian sense rendered consistent, if one seeks to determine an endless domain in that way. Without assumptions of uniformity the latter cannot be established; and therewith is sacrificed the ideal of certainty. In other words, it appears that if certainty is to be realized, then nothing is realized; for one must be restricted to a passing now, which allows no basis for generalization and objectively valid determinations.

If one proceeds to determine the "essential" structures and laws of experience, viewed from the subjective perspective, he may claim to be able to discern, to intuit something "general" and thus to have obviated the difficulty of the passing stream of nows. But he can only do that by assuming that every general structure persists, by a principle of the conservation of "generals," analogous to the "conservation of simples" of Platonic and Leibnizian fame. Can *that* principle be made a matter of intuitive evidence? And even if it could, would not another principle of conservation be required, in order to make it continue to be valid—a principle of the conservation of conservation principles? And must not that principle in turn be established by direct vision? And so on, *ad infinitum*?

As a matter of fact, the direct discernment of general structures must be accepted as an important feature of experience. So far as certainty with respect to the occurrence of events is concerned, however, i.e., certainty of anything beyond the specious present, or the content of the "now," it appears clear that although a perception of a general structure may be termed a "general" perception, it must always be instated anew. Only the passing general perception is "certain" in the Cartesian sense. Thus, "essences" are no better off than particular sensory objects, *so far as this criterion is concerned.* While phenomenologically real (i.e., appearing in experience), the idealities (concepts, forms, relations) which are "read out of" experience are said to have a nontemporal kind of "being," [33] which is, strictly speaking, no being at all. The term "exists" is really nonsignificant for them, unless one refers to the experiences in which they are thought or meant.

To hold that the "essential" structures, which are conceptual in character, are "prior" to the real order of existence, is to commit a fundamental error of confusion. The conceptual forms are really derived; they are "ideal," in the sense that they are the results of a *process of idealization,* of identification. The events of the existent world are prior to the abstractions of the conceptual order, in the sense of temporal precedence, and also in the sense that they alone can be spoken of as "existent." It is maintained therewith that "to exist" means to have a space-time locus in terms of physical reality.

This position is not at all met by the distinction, so often referred to, between what is "first for me" and what is "first in itself." With reference to man, the physical process of becoming is "first," because man is such a late-comer in cosmic history. To argue for "logical" precedence, in the sense that structures or essences are prior to existent events, is to reify abstractions. Nothing that one can establish with regard to the logical relationships of concepts may alter the facts of the relationships in time.

Husserl has maintained (in his *Formale und transzendentale Logik*) that the law of noncontradiction is a "negative condition" of reality. That it is necessary for ordered discourse will be granted. But one cannot legislate for the facts of reality by an appeal to general principles, which are either inductive, and thus presuppose reality, or analytic, with no inherent reference to reality. The metaphysical problem in question cannot be solved by an "essential" analysis and an appeal to "essential" insight, for the required evidence is lacking, and in the nature of the case must always be lacking.

The metaphysical problem can only be treated on a naturalistic-inductive basis, and whether there is anything permanent in the world is a conclusion to be reached and not a settled fact as a point of departure. In short, the pure reflection procedure of phenomenology can only draw a metaphysics out of its procedural hat if it has already been inserted there—which is strictly forbidden by its own precepts.

Even if human beings should disappear, the determinations of the "essential" structures of perception, phantasy-experience, negation, etc., would remain valid as representing determinations of possible types of experience. They are "certain" while being experienced, and valid independently of experience. Such knowledge cannot be used as a means of compensation for those that suffer in the changing world of experience, any more than pure mathematics can be so used.

In the present discussion attention has been devoted to such examples as Husserl himself cites—conceptual forms clearly derived by a process of ideal abstraction. It is not implied therewith that reality does not exhibit general relations or patterns of order.

C. Husserl on Descartes

Husserl has taken Descartes very seriously in a historical as well as in a systematic sense, and he has repeatedly discussed his significance as a pretranscendental-phenomenological philosopher.[34] In the last publication to appear during his lifetime. "The Crisis of the European Sciences and Transcendental Phenomenology," he describes Descartes as the "primal instituting genius" of modern philosophy. He finds in the first two Meditations of Descartes a depth which it is difficult to fathom, and which Descartes himself was so little able to appreciate that he let go "the great discovery" he had in his hands. This exaggerated opinion of the importance of the Cartesian *Meditations* is obviously due to Husserl's own aims. In the complete structure of Descartes's thought, as well as with respect to his influence, his works on the principles of philosophy and methodology are surely not to be subordinated to the *Meditations*. On the contrary, they deserve a greater emphasis. The *Meditations* served their historical purpose for Descartes, allowing him to settle accounts with the traditional Church philosophy in a conciliatory manner. For us they have a different function. It is a good thing to carry through a method of doubt periodically, as a means of freeing one's mind of fixed beliefs and dogmas, and of reexamining one's own philosophy. It is also useful as a means of achieving the universal suspension of belief ("epoché") with which a philosopher must begin his meditations on a first philosophy. In Husserl's hands the procedure of "suspension" is certainly different from anything Descartes envisaged or intended.

But it must also be observed that another "dimension" of reflection must be added to the suspension (*epoché*) of Husserl. It is necessary to view the thinker "longitudinally" as well as "cross-sectionally," and to see him in his place in society and history, as responding to motives prompted by his social system. Reflection which neglects the causally determined order of culture is one-sided and empty in a most important respect. *Complete* reflective analysis thus goes beyond "pure" reflection. It does not face the hopeless problem of making application to reality, so that it is not enmeshed in a dilemma, the alternatives of which are a subjective detachment from reality, or the "constitution" of reality out of pure subjectivity. The complete method of reflection does not neglect any items of established knowledge, least of all the basic fact of man's place in nature and society.

As Husserl depicts Descartes's method, it is a requirement for philosophical knowledge that it be "absolutely founded," and that it be based on a ground of immediate and apodictic knowledge which in its evidence precludes all conceivable doubt. Furthermore, every step of "mediate" knowledge must be able to achieve such evidence. The radicalism of the Cartesian procedure requires that everything be "placed in question"—the validity of all previous sciences, as well as the prescientific and extrascientific "life-world"—and this is the historical beginning of a "radical critique of objective knowledge." The role of the Descartes-who-anticipates-Husserl is thus a clearly defined one, even if the historical Descartes was much more modest and far less thoroughgoing in his endeavor. With the fervor of Meister Eckhart, Husserl describes the original Cartesian motive in the following words: "through the hell of a quasi-skeptical *epoché,* to penetrate to the entrance to heaven of an absolute rational philosophy, and to build that up systematically." [35] The ego that performs the suspension or "epoché" is not included in the latter's scope. Here one finds the sought-for apodictic ground, which absolutely excludes every possible doubt, for a universal doubt would annul itself.

As Husserl views the procedure, "the" world is transformed into a mere "phenomenon," into my "ideae." "Here we have an absolutely apodictic sphere of being, under the title of 'ego,' and merely the one axiomatic proposition '*Ego* cogito' or 'sum cogitans.' " Husserl adds another "remarkable" result: Through the *epoché* (i.e., "method of doubt" regarded as a "suspension" of judgment) I have reached that *sphere of being* which on principle precedes everything that can conceivably be for me as its absolute, apodictic presupposition. Or, as maintained by Descartes: I, the performing ego of the *epoché,* am alone absolutely indubitable. All scientific, "mediate" foundations must therefore be led back to a single absolute, primal evidence. Husserl seems to forget, in his complete feeling of assurance, that there is no *real* "sphere of being" discovered by or for Descartes, but rather an Archimedean point of reference for philosophy, with respect to its "evidence." It is fundamentally a device for universal questioning, for descriptive analysis, and for possible philosophical construction. Evidently what the present writer sees in the *epoché* is not identical with what Husserl sees. The present writer's understanding of it makes it to be a different kind of procedure, devoid of pretense and dogma, and with a firm intention of preventing idealistic metaphysical capital from being made out of it. Any aid in making possible the delineation of a universal field for descriptive analysis is to be greeted. The *epoché* itself will not make all experience and knowledge the subject of investigation, but it does contribute toward that end, in its peculiar way. The suspension of all belief and judgment distinguishes it as a *philosophical* field for investigation. The philosophical inquiry overlaps the regions chosen by the special sciences, but it does so in its own way. It does not presume to go into the fields of the special sciences, but orders them and their basic concepts and principles within the total framework of phlosophy.

For Husserl, the ego is not a residuum of the world, but rather "the absolutely apodictic positing, which is only possible through the *epoché*," through the "bracketing" of the entire "validity of the world." Descartes's admission of the soul, for example, is therefore subject to criticism. Although he is credited with beginning "a completely new kind of philosophizing which seeks its foundation in the subjective," Husserl criticizes him for not seeing that the ego, as it is discovered in the *epoché* as being for itself, is not "an" ego that can have other egos outside itself. Descartes evidently did not see that all such distinctions as I and you, inner and outer, first "constitute" themselves in the "absolute ego." As judged from Husserl's perspective, Descartes did not see "the great problems—to 'ask back' systematically from the world as a 'phenomenon' in the ego, in which really exhibitable immanent contributions of the ego the world has first received its being-sense." It is quite certain that Descartes would not have been able to understand this criticism during his lifetime, and probably not for an additional century and a half. Has "the world" really received its "being-sense" in that way? Or is it as viewed *phenomenologically* that one *considers* it in that way? The shifting to metaphysical language and, in general, the use of pictorial, assumptive expressions are revealing of Husserl's actual intentions. The Cartesian "radicalism or freedom from presuppositions," which was intended to lead genuine scientific knowledge back to the final sources of validity and thus to ground them absolutely, was held to require a carefully defined subjective procedure, which meant going back to the knowing ego "in its immanence." That is, in other words, the "transcendental sphere."

D. *The Transcendental Dimension and the Treatment of History*

"Transcendental" is one of the most objectionable tradition-laden terms. Use of it in the context of a descriptive philosophy of experience permits exploitation of its original reference to purely reflective knowledge-experience for purposes of idealistic metaphysics. Husserl uses "transcendental" in a very wide sense, to name the motive of "asking back" or retrospective inquiry concerning the "ultimate source" of all cognitive functions, of all self-reflection of the knower. There will clearly be differences of view on the nature of the alleged "ultimate source"—for example, among continuators of the Holbach-Feuerbachian, or dialectical materialist, type of philosophy and among representatives of the natural and social sciences. From Husserl's point of view, such thinkers are "naïve" and dogmatic, and are really not philosophers at all. Unfortunately for him, however, he is not at liberty to remake the history of philosophy, however freely he may operate in interpreting it with respect to his own aims and deciding motives.

The meaning of "transcendentalism" in the present context is clarified by contrasting it with "objectivism." As Husserl states it, objectivism operates on the ground of a world that is self-evidently given through experience and asks about its "objective truth," about that which it is in itself. For transcendentalism, however, the "being-sense" of the pregiven life-world is a *subjective structure,* is the "contribution" of an experiencing, prescientific life. As for the "objectively true world" of science, that is a structure of a higher level. Transcendentalism maintains that only a radical, retrospective inquiry to *the* subjectivity which ultimately brings about all world-validity, to the nature of the contributions of reason, can make the objective truth "understandable" and reach the final "being-sense" of the world. Hence it is not the being of the world in its unquestionable obviousness that is "first in itself." That which is "first in itself" is *subjectivity,* which "pregives" the world. Expressed in this way, with the world itself and not the "world-meaning" "pregiven," the thesis of transcendentalism is a sheer dogma, which is characteristic of the writings of Husserl's last period. The methodological reasons for the subjective frame[36] are long forgotten, and Husserl has come to believe that an actual process of meaning-giving, etc., is at work, amounting to *creation*. Husserl is careful to point out the danger that this subjectivity be construed as man, or as a psychological subjectivity. His error is on a different level, and is so far-reaching that it involves a reinterpretation of the entire philosophical tradition.

The central problem of Husserl's "radical transcendental subjectivism" is formulated as one which concerns the relationship of the ego and its conscious life to the world of which the ego is conscious, and whose true being the ego knows in its own cognitive structures.[37] The evidence of the method of positive science is not held to be deceptive, nor are its contributions held to be merely apparent ones. His point is that this evidence itself is made to be a problem, that the method of objective science is based upon an unquestioned "deeply concealed subjective ground." The "philosophical illumination" first shows the true sense of the contributions of positive science, as well as the true "being-sense" of the objective world, to be transcendental-subjective in character.[38] The "concealed" dimension of the transcendental is held to be really brought to view. The realm of experience that is "opened up" in its infinitude becomes a field for "a methodological philosophy of work," and that is intended to provide the ground on which all conceivable philosophical and scientific problems of the past are to be put and to be decided.[39] The pretense of this contention is so unwarranted that it seems doubtful that Husserl could have realized concretely what he was asserting. Even if one could allow him the possibility in principle of handling all past philosophical problems in his way, it is preposterous to boast of a method for deciding all scientific problems. That could only be done by shutting one's eyes to them, or by dissolving them in intuition, which phenomenology as a descriptive method cannot do. Husserl had lived alone too much, had practiced his unchallenged monologue too long, and had combed over his self-consciousness to such an extent, that to him the term "everything" came to mean only the set of correlates of his consciousness.

The treatment of history—intellectual and general—carries the basic pattern of the discussion to its final consequences. The history of philosophy, ever since the appearance of the theory of knowledge and the serious attempts at a transcendental philosophy, is portrayed by Husserl as a history of mighty tensions between objectivistic and transcendental philosophy. Why that is so prominent in intellectual history, he does not venture to explain; nor would one expect that it could be done on this level of analysis. In the form of the issue of materialism *vs.* spiritualism this "inner split in philosophical development" has long been familiar. Husserl does not specify and apparently does not recognize the issues involved by the traditional opposition he portrays; the actors in the drama are nameless. He does not apply a historical method in the usual sense, his aim being to make comprehensible the "teleology" in the historical becoming of philosophy and to "clarify" ourselves as its carriers. That is not to view the process "from without," as though the temporal stream in which we ourselves have become were "a merely external, causal succession," but "from within." [40] He is interested in a critical understanding of "the total unity of history—of *our* history." We have our function "as heirs and co-carriers of the will-direction going through it," and we owe that to a "primal instituting which is at once a post-instituting and transformation of the Greek primal instituting." In this is found to lie the "teleological" beginning and the true birth of the European spirit in general. It would be difficult to say less about history and to miss its real nature more than Husserl has done here. He had long ago lost contact with concrete historical facts. True, he mentioned such facts as Torquemada and the Inquisition in his last period; but, for his philosophical purposes, he had forgotten the real facts of history, which are also sordid, and which make impossible the carrying-through of a "teleological" point of view of this kind. One need not, however, go to the sweat and blood of history to make a demurrer. By attending to the history of philosophy itself, any claim to the alleged unity of aspiration can be broken down. The conflict between objectivism and transcendentalism is, to be sure, a conspicuous one. But the issue is defined in terms of Husserl's own philosophizing. That interpretation goes on within the frame of a subjective inquiry. The "elucidation of history by a retrospective inquiry concerning the primal instituting of the aims which bind future generations in so far as they live in their sedimented forms, but can always be awakened and criticized in a new liveliness"—that kind of inquiry is the self-reflection of the philosopher about his aims and his relations to his spiritual predecessors. The point is, again to make alive, in their "concealed" historical sense, the sedimented concepts which are the basis of his private and nonhistorical work. Toward that end one must free oneself from all prejudices (prejudgments), including one's own "self-evidences," recognizing that prejudices are elements of unclearness deriving from a traditional sedimentation. A "historical reflection" of this kind is thus a self-reflection (a "deepest" self-reflection) designed to give a self-understanding of one's aims.

If there is a historical origin, a "primal instituting," then it appears to Husserl (and this is not proved) that there is also, essentially, a "final instituting." The spirit of the inquiry requires that there be complete clarity concerning the truth, by a method for which every step is apodictic. Philosophy thus becomes an "infinite task." The present discussion shows how Husserl has derived from post-Kantian idealism as well as from Descartes.

But Husserl insists on turning away from the "self-interpretations" of the historical philosophers. Because of his carefully defined subjective procedure, he feels that he is superior to his predecessors, in being so reliable in his own self-inspection. (N.B.: Husserl never "inspected" himself with respect to his actual economic, social, and political place in German society, either under the monarchy, to which he later looked back with regret at its passing, or under the Weimar republic. To the extent to which such "meanings" should have entered even his pure reflective consciousness, the self-inspection of the latter was empty.) Only in the "final outcome" (or "final instituting") is the aim revealed, only from that point can the unity of all philosophies and philosophers be revealed, and an illumination be gained, in which one understands the past thinkers as they never could have understood themselves.[41] Whether Husserl considered in detail the amazing proposal to "unify" Catholics, materialists, and "whatnotists," is doubtful. Not that a unified theory of intellectual history is impossible: it is indeed possible to account for the development of ideas in relationship to the various conditioning factors of history—social, economic, scientific, religious, etc.—by a well integrated logical theory, in which due "weight" is given to the various factors. Notable contributions toward such a theory have been made in the literature of historical materialism. The situation is quite different for the subjective point of view, however, and even the most liberal use of suspension and "bracketing" of judgments of real events cannot achieve the desired unity. The causal-genetic explanation of intellectual history endeavors to account for conflicts, and not to render them unreal, or merely mistaken, whereas the subjective demand for unity misses the actual historical significance of the conflicts. It appears that Husserl removes his view from any possible refutation by what purport to be facts. The peculiar truth of such a "teleological view of history," he states, can never be decisively refuted by the citation of documentary "self-witnessing" of earlier philosophers; for it is shown alone in the evidence of a critical total view, which displays a meaningful final harmony behind the "historical facts" of documented philosophies and their "apparent oppositions."

This view of history not only promises to be sterile but threatens to be dangerous, in the "wrong" hands, just as the misuse of the concept of "eidetic (essential) intuition" led to bizarre results of a mystical kind. At its best, it shows all past thinkers as leading toward or away from the "clarity" which Husserl sets up as *his* ideal of reflection. With Husserl as the "final institutor," who can deny him the right to interpret his predecessors in a way they never could have achieved?

Even if it were a successful venture, within well defined limits, the aim of "self-understanding" as portrayed in the "Crisis" essay could not be defended as the sole aim of philosophical reflection. The "pure" analysis provided by the subjective method must be justified by its value for the solution of theoretical and practical problems, including practical social problems. "Pure" reflective analysis has been found to be useful, especially in the philosophy of logic. But there are also shortcomings and dangers, if one forgets the real place of the knower in nature. Only when used in cooperation with other logical methods, and with the special sciences, can such dangers be obviated. For practical social problems, however, the subjective procedure is completely nugatory. A philosopher who refuses or neglects to take account of the pressing practical problems of his day (the well known ones—capital and labor, imperialism and war, etc.) is guilty of the cardinal error of making his reflection "empty" in a most important respect. He may believe that he is grand and noble in his flight from reality, in his absorption in an honorific realm of pure ideas, removed "in principle" from the "lowly" world about us. But that action may be construed as a renunciation of the obligations one has toward society as well as himself. The neglect of practical problems may also take the form of vagueness or generality of language, even from a professedly naturalistic point of view. To discuss a philosophical theory of value and define justice without explicit reference to property relations is surely to commit the error of "emptiness."

Whether one becomes an active participant in social and political movements or not, it is evident that, *qua* philosopher, one cannot afford to disregard the actual content of social experience. One's conceptual work will not suffer thereby; one will not cease to be a philosopher in so doing. Quite the contrary is the case. Instead of avoiding all social problems and becoming a "pure" specialist, and instead of tacitly falling in line with a "safe," conservative tradition, he becomes a philosopher most worthy of the name, one who sees in philosophy a mode of response to important problems in all fields of experience, social as well as physical and purely conceptual.

References

[1] *Dialectics of Nature* (New York, 1940), p. 172.

[2] The dependence of being upon being known is the basic dogma. For the critique of idealism, cf. R. B. Perry, *Present Philosophical Tendencies* (New York, 1912), for his formulation of the "ego-centric predicament"; and Lenin, *Materialism and Empirio-Criticism* (New York, 1927).

[3] A. N. Whitehead, *The Concept of Nature* (Cambridge, England, 1920), chap. iii.

[4] Cf. E. Husserl, *Erfahrung und Urteil* (Prague, 1939), for a detailed descriptive analysis of such contributions. This little-known treatise merits the careful study of all students of philosophy. In it Husserl undertakes to do what Kant failed to do—to show the actual part played by perception and the understanding in the process of experience. Accepting his descriptive findings in no way commits one to his systematic idealism.

[5] Cf. H. Bergson, *Creative Evolution* (New York, 1911). Bergson's logical shortcomings were effectively exposed by contemporary critics, including Santayana and Perry; and Whitehead has shown how a constructive answer can be given to the criticism of intellectual devices. Their improvement, and not the abandonment of the intellect, is called for. For a recent French criticism of Bergson, see Politzer, *Le Bergsonisme: Une Mystification philosophique* (Paris, 1947).

[6] C. I. Lewis, *Mind and the World-Order* (New York, 1929), p. 36.

[7] *Ibid.*, p. 53.

[8] *Ibid.*, p. 54.

[9] *Ibid.*, pp. 54, 66.

[10] *Experience and Nature* (Chicago, 1925), pp. 3 f.

[11] *Ibid.*, p. 8.

[12] *Ibid.*, p. 11.

[13] *Ibid.*, p. 16.

[14] *Ibid.*, p. 26.
[15] *Ibid.*, pp. 29 f.
[16] *Ibid.*, p. 31.
[17] *Ibid.*, p. 35.
[18] *Ibid.*, p. 40.
[19] *Ibid.*, p. 42.
[20] *Ibid.*, pp. 45 f.
[21] *Ibid.*, p. 68.
[22] *Ibid.*, p. 72.
[23] *Ibid.*, p. 68.

[24] Further discussions by the present writer which indicate his version of phenomenology are provided by three papers in *Philosophy and Phenomenological Research:* "The Significance of Phenomenology for the Americas" (Vol. IV, No. 2), "Remarks about the Phenomenological Program" (Vol. VI, No. 1), and "Modes of Reflection" (Vol. VIII, No. 4).

[25] Cf. Husserl's *Formale und transzendentale Logik* (Halle, 1929), e.g., especially the argument for idealism, pp. 205 ff. Husserl's exploitation of his method for idealistic purposes is shown by his conclusion: "There is no conceivable place where the life of consciousness could be pierced and we could come to a transcendence, which could have another meaning than that of an intentional unity appearing in the subjectivity of consciousness."

[26] Cf. Husserl, *Erfahrung und Urteil,* pp. 94 ff.

[27] *Travaux du IXe Congrès International de Philosophie* (Paris, 1937), Vol. VIII, pp. 97–104.

[28] Scheler, *Wesen und Formen der Sympathie,* (1st ed., Bonn, 1923), p. 87.

[29] Scheler's role as an ideological precursor of the Nazis is pointed out by V. J. McGill in his paper, "Scheler's Theory of Sympathy and Love," in *Philosophy and Phenomenological Research,* Vol. II, No. 3 (Mar., 1942).

[30] New York, 1929.

[31] *Erfahrung und Urteil,* p. 105.

[32] *Beyond Good and Evil* (New York, 1923), pp. 14 f.

[33] Cf. Husserl, *Erfahrung und Urteil,* pp. 309 ff.

[34] Cf. Husserl, *Méditations Cartésiennes* (Paris, 1931), and "Die Krisis der europäischen Wissenschaften und die transzendentale Phänomenologie," *Philosophia,* Vol. I (1936), pp. 77–176.

[35] *Op. cit.*, p. 152.

[36] It is worth noting in this connection that the principle of the "primacy of the self," or of subjectivity, is taken over by the existentialists. Cf. Sartre, *Existentialism* (New York, 1947), where it appears "as though shot out of a pistol"—unheralded, unjustified, unclarified.

[37] *Op. cit.*, p. 173.

[38] *Ibid.*, p. 175.

[39] *Ibid.*, pp. 175 f.

[40] *Ibid.*, pp. 146 ff.

[41] *Ibid.*, p. 148.

INDEX

B

I

M

Q

R

S

T

U

V